Instructor's Solutions Manual

A Problem Solving Approach to Mathematics

for Elementary School Teachers

Sixth Edition

BILLSTEIN LIBESKIND LOTT

Louis L. Levy

Edward Fritz

Northland Pioneer College

ADDISON-WESLEY

An imprint of Addison Wesley Longman, Inc.

Reading, Massachusetts • Menlo Park, California • New York • Harlow, England
Don Mills, Ontario • Sydney • Mexico City • Madrid • Amsterdam

Reproduced by Addison-Wesley from camera-ready copy supplied by the authors.

ISBN 0-201-44082-2

1 2 3 4 5 6 7 8 9 10 CRS 99989796

CONTENTS

CHAPTER 1 - TOOLS FOR PROBLEM SOLVING

On-going Assessment 1-1

1. (a) Each figure in the sequence adds one box each to the top and bottom rows. Next would be:

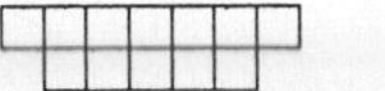

(b) Each figure in the sequence adds one upright and one inverted triangle. Next would be:

(c) Each figure in the sequence adds one box to the base and one triangle to each row; adds one row. Next would be:

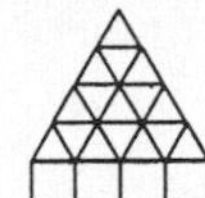

(d) In a clockwise direction, the shaded area moves to a new position separated from the original by one open space, then two open spaces, then by three, etc. The separation in each successive step increases by one unit; next would be:

2. (a) Terms that continue a possible pattern are 11, 13, 15, … . This is an arithmetic sequence because we obtain each successive term from the previous term by the addition of the integer 2.

(b) Terms that continue a possible pattern are 250, 300, 350, … . This is an arithmetic sequence because we obtain each successive term from the previous term by the addition of the integer 50.

(c) Terms that continue a possible pattern are 96, 192, 384, … . This is a geometric sequence because we obtain each successive term from the previous term by multiplying by the integer 2.

(d) Terms that continue a possible pattern are 1,000,000, 10,000,000, 100,000,000, … . This is a geometric sequence because we obtain each successive term from the previous term by multiplying by the integer 10.

(e) Terms that continue a possible pattern are 33, 37, 41, … . This is an arithmetic sequence because we obtain each successive term from the previous term by the addition of the integer 4.

(f) Terms that continue a possible pattern are 216, 343, 512, … . We obtain each successive term by taking the third power of the number of the term in the sequence (i.e., the 6th term in the sequence is $6^3 = 216$). This sequence is neither arithmetic nor geometric.

3. In these problems, let a_n represent the nth term in a sequence and let d represent the common difference between terms in an arithmetic sequence or r represent the common ratio between terms in a geometric sequence. In an arithmetic sequence, $a_n = a_1 + (n - 1)d$; in a geometric sequence $a_n = a_1 r^{n-1}$. Thus:

(a) Arithmetic sequence; $a_1 = 1$ and $d = 2$:

(*i*) $a_{100} = 1 + (100 - 1) \cdot 2 = 1 + 99 \cdot 2 = 199$

(*ii*) $a_n = 1 + (n - 1) \cdot 2 = 1 + 2n - 2 = 2n - 1$

3. (b) Arithmetic sequence; $a_1 = 0$ and $d = 50$:

   (*i*) $a_{100} = 0 + (100 - 1) \cdot 50 = 99 \cdot 50 = 4950$

   (*ii*) $a_n = 0 + (n - 1) \cdot 50 = 50n - 50$ or $50(n - 1)$

   (c) Geometric sequence; $a_1 = 3$ and $r = 2$:

   (*i*) $a_{100} = 3 \cdot 2^{100-1} = 3 \cdot 2^{99}$ (*ii*) $a_n = 3 \cdot 2^{n-1}$

   (d) Geometric sequence; $a_1 = 10$ and $r = 10$:

   (*i*) $a_{100} = 10 \cdot 10^{100-1} = 10^{100}$ (*ii*) $a_n = 10 \cdot 10^{n-1} = 10^n$

   (e) Arithmetic sequence; $a_1 = 9$ and $d = 4$:

   (*i*) $a_{100} = 9 + (100 - 1) \cdot 4 = 9 + 99 \cdot 4 = 405$

   (*ii*) $a_n = 9 + (n - 1) \cdot 4 = 9 + 4n - 4 = 4n + 5$

   (f) Neither arithmetic nor geometric; each term is the 3rd power of n:

   (*i*) $a_{100} = 100^3 = 1{,}000{,}000$ (*ii*) $a_n = n^3$

4. 2, 7, 12, … . Each term is the 5th number on a clock face (clockwise) from the preceding term.

5. (a) Answers may vary:

   (*i*) The sum of the first *n* odd numbers is n^2; that is, $1 + 3 + 5 + \cdots + a_n = n^2$

   (*ii*) Square the average of the first and last terms; e.g., $1 + 3 + 5 + 7 = \left(\frac{1+7}{2}\right)^2 = 4^2$

   (b) This is the arithmetic sequence of problem 3.(a), where $a_n = 2n - 1$.
   Thus $35 = 2n - 1 \Rightarrow 36 = 2n \Rightarrow n = 18$. That is, 35 is the 18th term.
   Therefore $1 + 3 + 5 + 7 + \cdots + 35 = 18^2 = 324$

6. 10 white circles (one before each of the black groups) and $1 + 2 + 3 + 4 + \cdots 10 = 55$ black circles

7. The pattern in each is the difference 8 between successive elements on the right diagonal and the difference 6 between successive elements on the left diagonal.

(a)

Su	M	T	W	Th	F	Sa
		1				
			9			12
	14			17		
					25	

(b)

Su	M	T	W	Th	F	Sa
			2			
					18	
	21					

8. (a) In each step, one more row and column of dots is added to the preceeding figure. The next three terms are thus 5 rows by 6 columns = 30 dots, 6 rows by 7 columns = 42 dots, and 7 rows by 8 columns = 56 dots.

   (b) The 100th term would have 100 rows and 101 columns, or $100 \cdot 101 = 10{,}100$ dots.

8. (c) The *n*th term has $n \cdot (n + 1)$ dots, or $n^2 + n$.

9. (a) Note that 5 toothpicks are added to form each succeeding hexagon. We thus have an arithmetic sequence with $a_1 = 6$ and $d = 5$, so $a_{10} = 6 + (10 - 1) \cdot 5 = 6 + 9 \cdot 5 = 51$ toothpicks.

   (b) *n* hexagons would require $6 + (n - 1) \cdot 5 = 6 + 5n - 5 = 5n + 1$ toothpicks

10. (a) The number of squares in each windmill form an arithmetic sequence with 1st term 5 and difference between terms 4. The number of squares required to build the 10th windmill is thus $5 + (10 - 1) \cdot 4$, or $5 + 9 \cdot 4 = 41$ squares.

   (b) *n* windmills would require $5 + (n - 1) \cdot 4 = 5 + 4n - 4 = 4n + 1$ squares

11. (a) Looking at the 3rd figure, we have $5 + 3 + 1 = 9$ triangles. The 4th figure would then have $7 + 5 + 3 + 1 = 16$ triangles. An alternative to simply adding 7, 5, 3, and 1 together is to note that $7 + 1 = 8$ and $5 + 3 = 8$. There are $\frac{4}{2} = 2$ of these sums, and $\frac{4}{2}(8) = 16$. Now see that the 100th figure would have $100 + 99 = 199$ triangles in the base, $99 + 98 = 197$ triangles in the second row, and so on until the 100th row where there would be 1 triangle. $199 + 1 = 200$; $197 + 3 = 200$; etc. and so the sum of each pair is 200 and there are $\frac{100}{2} = 50$ of these pairs. $50 \cdot 200 = 10{,}000 \Rightarrow 10{,}000$ triangles in the 100th figure.

   (b) The number of triangles in the *n*th figure is $\frac{n}{2}$(number of triangles in base + 1). The number of triangles in the base is $n + (n - 1)$, or $2n - 1$. $(2n - 1) + 1 = 2n$. Then $\frac{n}{2}(2n) = n^2 \Rightarrow n^2$ triangles in the *n*th figure.

12. (a) Each cube adds 4 squares to the preceeding figure, or 6, 10, 14, 18, 22, 26, 30, 34, 38, 42 squares. Thus there are 42 squares to be painted in the 10th figure.

   (b) This is an arithmetic sequence with first term 6 and difference 4. The *n*th term is thus: $6 + (n - 1)4$, or $4n + 2$.

13. Ten years at 50 students per year increase gives a total of 500 new students, which added to the current enrollment gives 1200 students. Alternatively, we have an arithmetic sequence with 1st term 700 and difference 50, so the 11th term (enrollment currently plus ten more years) is $700 + (11 - 1)50 = 1200$.

14. If we make a table:

Day	Amount of Water Remaining
1	$15{,}360 \cdot \frac{1}{2} = 7680$ liters
2	$7680 \cdot \frac{1}{2} = 3840$ liters
⋮	⋮
9	$60 \cdot \frac{1}{2} = 30$ liters
10	$30 \cdot \frac{1}{2} = 15$ liters

So there will be 15 liters of water left in the tank after 10 days.

Alternatively, note that we have a geometric sequence with 1st term 7680 and ratio of $\frac{1}{2}$. We know that the *n*th term of a geometric sequence with 1st term a and ratio r is ar^{n-1}. Thus the 10th term would be $7680(\frac{1}{2})^9 = 15$ liters.

15. We can analyze this problem as follows:

<u>Cost per foot</u>

1st 10 feet	10.00 + 0(0.50)
2nd 10 feet — 10.00 + 0.50, or	10.00 + 1(0.50)
3rd 10 feet — 10.00 + 0.50 + 0.50, or	10.00 + 2(0.50)
4th 10 feet — 10.00 + 0.50 + 0.50 + 0.50, or	10.00 + 3(0.50)
⋮	⋮
10th 10 feet — 10.00 + 0.50 + 0.50 + ⋯, or	10.00 + 9(0.50)

<u>Cost for each 10-foot section</u>

1st	$10.00 \cdot 10.00 = 100.00$
2nd	$10.00 \cdot 10.50 = 105.00$
3rd	$10.00 \cdot 11.00 = 110.00$
4th	$10.00 \cdot 11.50 = 115.00$
⋮	⋮
10th	$10.00 \cdot 14.50 = 145.00$

Adding the cost of each 10-foot section gives a total cost of $1225.00.

16. (a) The employee's monthly pay is $1200 the 1st month, $1220 the 2nd month, $1240 the 3rd month, and so on. This is an arithmetic sequence with 1st term 1200 and difference of 20. At the end of 24 months, therefore, the worker's monthly salary will be 1200 + (24 - 1)20 = $1660.

(b) After 6 months, the employee will have earned 1200 + 1220 + 1240 + 1260 + 1280 + 1300 = $7500.

(c) Using the general expression for the *n*th term of an arithmetic sequence, where the *n*th term is 3240, we have:

$3240 = 1200 + (n - 1)20$
$3240 = 1180 + 20n$
$20n = 2060$, or $n = 103$. The employee's monthly salary will be $3240 after 103 months.

17. This is an arithmetic sequence with 1st term 1 and difference 2. The 10th term, representing the 10th stop, is thus $1 + (10 - 1)2 = 19$ people.

18. Using the general expression for the *n*th term of an arithmetic sequence with 1st term 24,000 and 9th term 31,680, we have:

$31{,}680 = 24{,}000 + (9 - 1)d$
$31{,}680 = 24{,}000 + 8d$
$7680 = 8d$, or $d = 960$, the amount by which Joe's income increased each year. To find the year in which his income was $45,120, we then have:
$45{,}120 = 24{,}000 + (n - 1)960$
$45{,}120 = 23{,}040 + 960n$
$960n = 22080$, or $n = 23$. Joe's income was $45,120 in his 23rd year.

19. (a) If the 1st difference of the sequence increases by 2 for each term, then the 5 first differences between the 1st 6 terms of the original sequence are 2, 4, 6, 8, 10. If the 1st term of the original sequence is 3, then the 1st 6 terms are 3, 5, 9, 15, 23, 33.

(b) If the 1st term is a, then $a + (a + 2) = 10$, or $a = 4$. Thus the 1st 6 terms of the original sequence are 4, 6, 10, 16, 24, 34.

(c) If the 5th term is 35, then:

The 6th term is $35 + 10 = 45$
The 4th term is $35 - 8 = 27$
The 3rd term is $27 - 6 = 21$
The 2nd term is $21 - 4 = 17$
The 1st term is $17 - 2 = 15$. Thus the sequence is 15, 17, 21, 27, 35, 45.

20. (a) Look for the differences:

5 6 14 32 64 115 191

1 8 18 32 51 76

7 10 14 19 25

3 4 5 6

1 1 1

It can now be seen that the 3rd difference is an arithmetic sequence with fixed difference 1. Thus the 6th term in the 2nd difference row is 25 + 7 = 32; the 7th term in the 1st difference row is 76 + 32 = 108; and the 8th term in the original sequence is 191 + 108 = 299. Using the same reasoning, we find the next three terms in the original sequence to be 299, 447, 644.

(b) Look for the differences:

0 2 6 12 20 30 42

2 4 6 8 10 12

2 2 2 2 2

The 1st difference is an arithmetic sequence with fixed difference 2. Thus the 7th term in the 1st difference row is 12 + 2 = 14; the 8th term in the original sequence is 42 + 14 = 56. Using the same reasoning, the next three terms in the original sequence are 56, 72, 90.

(c) Look for the differences:

10 8 3 0 4 20 53

$^{-}2$ $^{-}5$ $^{-}3$ 4 16 33

$^{-}3$ 2 7 12 17

5 5 5 5

The second difference is an arithmetic sequence with fixed difference 5. Thus the 6th term in the 2nd difference row is 17 + 5 = 22; the 7th term in the 1st difference row is 33 + 22 = 55; and the 8th term in the original sequence is 53 + 55 = 108. Using the same reasoning, the next three terms in the original sequence are 108, 190, 304.

21. (a) Using the general expression for the nth term of an arithmetic sequence with 1st term 51, nth term 151, and difference 1, we have:

$151 = 51 + (n - 1)1$

$151 = 50 + n$

$101 = n$, so there are 101 terms in the sequence.

(b) Using the general expression for the nth term of a geometric sequence with 1st term 1, nth term 2^{60}, and ratio 2, we have:

$2^{60} = 1(2)^{n-1}$

$2^{60} = 2^{n-1}$

Since the bases, 2, are the same, then:

$60 = n - 1$, and $n = 61$. There are 61 terms in the sequence.

(c) Using the general expression for the nth term of an arithmetic sequence with 1st term 10, nth term 2000, and difference 10, we have:

$2000 = 10 + (n - 1)10$

$2000 = 10n$

$200 = n$, so there are 200 terms in the sequence.

(d) Using the general expression for the nth term of an arithmetic sequence with 1st term 9, nth term 353, and difference 4, we have:

$353 = 9 + (n - 1)4 \Rightarrow 353 = 5 + 4n \Rightarrow 348 = 4n$

$87 = n$, so there are 87 terms in the sequence.

21. (e) Using the general expression for the *n*th term of a geometric sequence with 1st term 1, *n*th term 1024, and ratio 2, we have:
$1024 = 1(2)^{n-1}$
$2^{10} = 2^{n-1} \Rightarrow n - 1 = 10$ and $n = 11$. There are 11 terms in the sequence.

22. (a) 1st term: $(1)^2 + 2 = 3$
2nd term: $(2)^2 + 2 = 6$
3rd term: $(3)^2 + 2 = 11$
4th term: $(4)^2 + 2 = 18$
5th term: $(5)^2 + 2 = 27$

(b) 1st term: $5(1) - 1 = 4$
2nd term: $5(2) - 1 = 9$
3rd term: $5(3) - 1 = 14$
4th term: $5(4) - 1 = 19$
5th term: $5(5) - 1 = 24$

(c) 1st term: $10^{(1)} - 1 = 9$
2nd term: $10^{(2)} - 1 = 99$
3rd term: $10^{(3)} - 1 = 999$
4th term: $10^{(4)} - 1 = 9999$
5th term: $10^{(5)} - 1 = 99999$

(d) 1st term: $3(1) + 2 = 5$
2nd term: $3(2) + 2 = 8$
3rd term: $3(3) + 2 = 11$
4th term: $3(4) + 2 = 14$
5th term: $3(5) + 2 = 17$

23. (a) 1, 1, 2, 3, 5, 8, 13, 21, 34, 55, 89, and 144

(b) Yes. The sum of the first four terms is one less than the 6th term; likewise the sum of the first five terms is one less than the 7th term and the sum of the first six terms is one less the the 8th term.

(c) The sum of the first 10 terms is the 12th term minus 1, or $144 - 1 = 143$

(d) The sum of the first n terms is the $(n + 2)th$ term minus 1

24. (a) 2, 4, 6, 10, 16, 26, 42, 68, 110, 178, 288, 466, ...

(b) The sum of the first three terms is 4 less than the fifth; the sum of the first four terms is 4 less than the sixth; the sum of the first five terms is 4 less than the seventh; etc.

(c) The sum of the first 10 terms is the 12th term minus 4, or $466 - 4 = 462$

(d) The sum of the first *n* terms equals the $(n + 2)th$ term $- 4$.

25. The *n*th term of the arithmetic sequence is $300 + (n - 1)200 = 200n + 100$.
We find the *n*th term of the geometric sequence to be $2(2)^{n-1} = 2^n$.

Now construct a table such as:

n	2^n	200n + 100
1	2	300
2	4	500
3	8	700
⋮	⋮	⋮
11	2028	2300
12	4056	2500

We find that with the 12th term the geometric sequence is larger.

26. (a) Given that the scissors are small enough and sharp enough, an infinite number of pieces may be obtained.

26. (b) We start with 1 piece of paper. Cutting it into five pieces gives us 5. Taking one of the pieces and cutting it into fives pieces again gives us 4 + 5 = 9 pieces. Continuing this process, we have an arithmetic sequence: 1, 5, 9, 13, … . Thus the number of pieces after the *n*th experiment would be $1 + (n - 1)4 = 4n - 3$

27. Using the expression for a geometric sequence with 1st term 32 and 5th term 512, we have:
$512 = 32r^{5-1} \Rightarrow r^4 = \frac{512}{32} \Rightarrow r = \sqrt[4]{16} \Rightarrow r = 2$
Thus $a = 32 \cdot 2 = 64$; $b = 64 \cdot 2 = 128$; and $c = 128 \cdot 2 = 256$

28. Letter the boxes A through K. B and C must sum to 9 to make A + B + C = 15. Then D must be 6 so that B + C + D = 15. Similarly, G must be 6. Since I is 4, H must be 5 so that G + H + I = 15. The pattern 6, 5, 4, 6, 5, 4, … now becomes apparent, and the numbers are:

6	5	4	6	5	4	6	5	4	6	5

On-going Assessment 1-2

1. (a) Adding "front and back" terms (1 + 99, 2 + 98, …) gives 49 pairs which add to 100, plus the single middle term 50. The sum is thus $49 \cdot 100 + 50 = 4950$.

   (b) The technique is the same as for (a). There will always be a single middle term whose value is the average of the 1st and last, or $\frac{1+n}{2}$. The number of pairs may be obtained by dividing n by 2 and rounding down, or $\frac{n}{2} - \frac{1}{2}$. The pairs will all add to n + 1. Thus the sum is $(\frac{n}{2} - \frac{1}{2})(n + 1) + \frac{1+n}{2} = \frac{n}{2}(n + 1)$

   (c) 251,001. To find the number of terms in any arithmetic sequence, subtract the 1st term from the last, divide by the common difference, and add 1 (because both ends must be accounted for). There are thus $\frac{1001-1}{2} + 1 = 501$ terms. The sum is $\frac{501}{2}$(first term + last term) $= \frac{501}{2}(1 + 1001) = 251{,}001$

2. The last cut always makes <u>two</u> equal pieces. Thus there will always be one less cut than the desired number of pieces.

   (a) 4 cuts (b) 5 cuts

   (c) n – 1 cuts

3. For all teams to play each other once, each of the 8 teams would play 7 others, and $8 \cdot 7 = 56$ games. But when Team A plays Team B, Team B is also playing Team A; so $56 \div 2 = 28$ games for all to play once. Then 28 games $\cdot$ 4 times = 112 total games.

4. A systematic list would be a good approach here, where each row represents the number of each package size to make a dozen cookies. There are 12 rows, so there are 12 different ways to buy a dozen cookies.

6-cookie packages	2-cookie packages	single-cookie packages
2	0	0
1	3	0
1	2	2
1	1	4
1	0	6
0	6	0
0	5	2
0	4	4
0	3	6
0	2	8
0	1	10
0	0	12

5. It is 200 miles – 120 miles = 80 miles from Butte to Bozeman. The rest stop between Butte and Bozeman would be 40 miles from each, or 40 miles past Butte. Thus the rest stop would be 120 miles + 40 miles = 160 miles from Missoula.

6. Bubba is last; Cory must be between Alababa and Dandy; Dandy is faster than Cory. Listing from fastest to slowest, we then have the finishing order of: Dandy, Cory, Alababa, and Bubba.

7. They have been reading for 9 days, since 72 pages for Frankie ÷ 8 pages per day = 9 days. Thus Johnny is on 5 pages per day · 9 days = page 45.

8. There are 13 squares of 1 unit each; 4 squares of 4 units each; and 1 square of 9 units. There are a total of 18 squares.

9. The maximum amount is $1.19, composed of:
   - 1 half-dollar
   - 1 quarter
   - 4 dimes
   - 0 nickels
   - 4 pennies

   Any other combination would result in less money; e.g., including a nickel would allow only one dime to keep from having change for a quarter.

10. 12 ways. Make a table as follows and note the pattern:

$5	$10	$20
0	1	2
2	0	2
0	3	1
2	2	1
4	1	1
6	0	1

$5	$10	$20
0	5	0
2	4	0
4	3	0
6	2	0
8	1	0
10	0	0

11. 12. There are four choices for the 1st digit, then three for the 2nd (since one has already been used), two for the 3rd digit, and one final digit to finish the number. This gives $4 \cdot 3 \cdot 2 \cdot 1 = 24$ numbers, but the two nines are indistinguishable so 24 must be divided by 2, giving 12.

12. Let B be the number of boys and D be the number of dogs. Since dogs and boys each have one head, while boys have 2 feet and dogs 4, we can form the equations:

$$B + D = 22$$
$$2B + 4D = 68.$$

Solving this system of equations, we find we have 10 boys and 12 dogs.

13. Let R be the cost of the ruler and C be the cost of the compass. We can then form the equations:

$$R + C = 4.00$$
$$C = R + 0.90$$

To solve, we substitute the cost of the compass, $R + 0.90$, into the first equation:

$$R + (R + 0.90) = 4.00$$
$$2R + 0.90 = 4.00$$
$$2R = 3.10$$

$R = 1.55$, so the cost of the ruler is \$1.55, and

$$C = 1.55 + 0.90$$

$C = 2.45$, so the cost of the compass is \$2.45.

14. The cat makes one foot progress each day except for the last day when it will not slide back (because it will be out of the well). So in 15 days it will climb 15 feet; on the 16th day it will climb 3 more feet and be out of the well.

15. (a) 29 (existing),42, 55, 68, 81, 94, 107, 120, 133, 146, 159, 172, 185, 198, 211 (existing)

(b) There are 14 "spaces" between the 15 houses and a spread of $211 - 29 = 182$ to be covered. Thus each space must be $182 \div 14 = 13$. The difference could also be found by using the general expression for an arithmetic sequence, where the *n*th term is $a_1 + (n - 1)d$. Let $a_{15} = 211$, $a_1 = 29$, and $n = 15$.

16. (*i*) The number of squares to be painted in the 1st solid is 6; in the 2nd, 14; in the 3rd, 24; in the 4th, 36; etc. The number of <u>additional</u> squares to be painted in each succeeding solid is thus $14 - 6 = 8$, $24 - 14 = 10$, $36 - 24 = 12$; or 8, 10, 12, 14, … . This is an arithmetic sequence with 1st term 8 and difference 2. From the 1st to the 100th solid, there are 99 terms in the sequence. The number of additional squares from the 99th to the 100th solid is therefore $8 + (99 - 1)2 = 204$.
The total number of additional squares, from the 1st to the 100th, is $\frac{99}{2}(8 + 204) = 10{,}494$. Finally, 6 squares to be painted in the 1st solid plus 10,494 = 10,500 squares.

(*ii*) Generalizing from (*i*), the *n*th solid will require $n^2 + 5n$ squares to be painted.

17. (a) 11 coins. He must have 5 pennies to make an even \$1.00. The minimum number of coins would have as many quarters as possible, or 3 quarters. The remaining \$0.20 must consist of at least one dime and one nickel; the only possibility is one dime and two nickels. Thus the minimum coins are 5 pennies, 2 nickels, 1 dime, and 3 quarters.

(b) 63 coins. The maximum number of coins is achieved by having as many pennies as possible. It is a requirement to have 1 quarter, 1 dime, and 1 nickel = \$0.40, so there may then be 60 pennies.

18. The perimeter of a rectangle is twice the length plus twice the width, or $P = 2L + 2W$. If the length is 80 feet more than the width, then $L = 80 + W$. The perimeter is 1080 feet, or:

$$2(80 + W) + 2W = 1080.$$

Solving, we find $W = 230$ feet, and L then is $230 + 80$ or 310 feet.

19. Adding the numbers gives 99. This tells you that each row, diagonal, and column must add to $99 \div 3 = 33$.
Write 33 as a sum of the numbers in all possible ways:
$19 + 11 + 3$
$19 + 9 + 5$
$17 + 13 + 3$
$17 + 11 + 5$
$17 + 9 + 7$
$15 + 13 + 5$
$15 + 11 + 7$
$13 + 11 + 9$

Summarize the pattern:

Number	3	5	7	9	11	13	15	17	19
Nr. sums containing number	2	3	2	3	4	3	2	3	2

Thus 11 must be in the center of the square and 5, 9, 13, and 17 must be in the corners. One solution is:

17	7	9
3	11	19
13	15	5

20. Each of the 20 people shook hands with 17 others after dinner. Multiplying, $20 \cdot 17 = 340$. This counts each handshake twice, however (i.e., Mary was one of the 17 Joe shook with and Joe was one of the 17 Mary shook with). Thus there were $340 \div 2 = 170$ handshakes.

21. Yes. She can use the $8\frac{1}{2}$-inch side twice to get 17 inches and then use the 11-inch side to get back to 6 inches.

22. (a) There are $\frac{1020-2}{2} + 1 = 510$ terms. There are then $\frac{510}{2} = 255$ pairs which add to $2 + 1020 = 1022 \Rightarrow$ the sum is $255 \cdot 1022 = 260{,}610$

(b) There are $\frac{1001-1}{5} + 1 = 201$ terms $\Rightarrow$ the sum is $\frac{201}{2}(1 + 1001) = 100{,}701$

(c) There are $\frac{403-3}{4} + 1 = 101$ terms $\Rightarrow$ the sum is $\frac{101}{2}(3 + 403) = 20{,}503$

23. (a) 204. Counting $1 \times 1, 2 \times 2, 3 \times 3, \ldots$ squares gives 8^2 1×1 squares, 7^2 2×2 squares (i.e., for 2×2 squares there are 7 pairs of consecutive squares in each column and row, or $7 \cdot 7$ 2×2 squares), 6^2 3×3 squares, ... , etc. The total is $8^2 + 7^2 + 6^2 + 5^2 + 4^2 + 3^2 + 2^2 + 1 = 204$ squares.

(b) No. The number of different squares is more than doubled;
$16^2 + 15^2 + 14^2 + \cdots + 3^2 + 2^2 + 1 = 1496$ squares

24. (a) If both numbers were less than or equal to 9, then their product would be less than $9 \times 9 = 81$, which is not greater than 82.

(b) Same as (a); 81 is not greater than 81.

On-going Assessment 1-2; Review Problems

36. (a) 21, 24, 27, ... (adding 3 to each term to obtain the subsequent term)

(b) 243, 2, 729, 2, ... (mutliplying every other term by 3 with 2's in between)

37. The nth term is $22 + (n - 1)10 = 10n + 12$

38. There are $\frac{83-3}{4} + 1 = 21$ terms
Alternatively, use the expression for the *n*th term of an arithmetic sequence:
$83 = 3 + (n - 1)4 \Rightarrow n = 21$

39. $\frac{21}{2}(3 + 83) = 903$

40. (a) The sum of the digits in each product is always 9
The tens digit in the answer is always one less than the number that is multiplied by 9
Checking: $7 \times 9 = 63$; $8 \times 9 = 72$; $9 \times 9 = 81$

(b) Answers may vary, but the pattern can be used as a check to see whether the product of a digit and 9 is remembered correctly

On-going Assessment 1-3

1. (a) The largest 3- and 2-digit numbers are the 700's and 50's or the 500's and 70's. Using the calculator to try various combinations, we find [5][4][1] [×] [7][2] = 38,952, which is the greatest possible product. For the largest quotient, we want the smallest divisor, or 12, and the largest dividend, or 754. We thus find that [7][5][4] [÷] [1][2] = $62.8\overline{3}$, which is the greatest possible quotient.

(b) The least possible product is [2][5][7] [×] [1][4]. The least possible quotient is [1][2][4] [÷] [7][5].

2. (a) $\$10 \cdot 365$ days = \$3650

(b) $\$120 \cdot 52$ weeks = \$6240 (this plan yields the greatest amount of money.)

(c) $\$0.25 \cdot 24$ hours per day $\cdot$ 365 days = \$2190

(d) $\$0.01 \cdot 60$ minutes $\cdot$ 24 hours $\cdot$ 365 days = \$5256

3. Vera bought items costing \$3.99 + \$5.87 + \$6.47 = \$16.33.

4. Try 7: $7 \cdot 259 = 1813$; $1813 \cdot 429 = 777777$. Try 9: $9 \cdot 259 = 2331$; $2331 \cdot 429 = 999999$.
This works because $259 \cdot 429 = 111111$, and any single-digit number multiplied by 111111 gives a corresponding series of that number.

5. There is a difference of 7 between each term of the sequence. Enter [7] [+] [K] in your calculator; then enter [1] to place a 1 in the display. Now count the number of times [=] must be depressed to arrive at 113 in the display. You will find that there are 17 terms in the sequence.

6. [.] [2] [×] [2] [2] [EE] [9] [=] gives 4.4×10^9 ounces of catsup needed.
[÷] [1] [6] [=] gives 2.75×10^8 (or 275,000,000) catsup bottles.

7. Try multiplying 5,230,010 by the natural numbers until your result exceeds eight digits (because most calculators have an eight-digit display). You will find that $5{,}230{,}010 \cdot 19$ has eight digits; $5{,}230{,}010 \cdot 20$ has nine digits. $5{,}230{,}010 \cdot 20$ and all larger multipliers must therefore be displayed in scientific notation.

8. Answers may vary. Some options will depend on the calculator being used; some possible solutions include:

(a) (*i*) Add 500 + 256 + 160 + 23

8. (a) (*ii*) If you have a fraction key, multiply $155 \cdot \frac{1}{31}$. If not, subtract 31 over and over until you obtain a remainder less than 31. Keep track of the number of times you subtract. This number is your quotient; the remainder will be whatever is left over.

   (b) Answers may very; one way is $90 - 16 - 1$

9. (a) [6] [×] [7] [+] [8]

   (b) This determination will depend on your calculator:

   (*i*) Some inexpensive calculators do not use algebraic logic; that is, they perform operations in the order in which they are entered rather than according to order of operations (multiplication before addition, etc). On one of these, [6] [×] [2] [+] [6] [0] [÷] [3] will give 24.

   (*ii*) On a scientific calculator, using proper order of operations, [6] [-] [2] [+] [6] [0] [÷] [3] will give 24.

10. (*i*) Divide 1430 by 24; the remainder represents those left over. $1430 \div 24 = 59.58\overline{3}$, representing 59 full boxes plus $0.58\overline{3}$ box. $0.58\overline{3} \cdot 24 = 14$, so there will be 14 balls left over. (To retain the repeating decimal on your calculator, subtract 59 from $59.58\overline{3}$)

    (*ii*) Another option would be to use your fraction key to enter $\frac{1430}{24}$; depressing the key gives $59\frac{7}{12}$. Then $\frac{7}{12}$ of 24 is 14 balls left over.

    (*iii*) For integer key usage, refer to your calculator instructions. Operation varies by manufacturer.

11. \$10 per minute · 60 minutes per hour · 24 hours per day · 365 days per year = \$5,256,000

12. Answers may vary, depending on your calculator. Using the constant feature (k) is easiest. On a number of calculators, depressing an operator (×, ÷, +, −) twice in succession will perform that operation each time [=] is used. For example, [3] [+] [+] [7] will start with 7 and add 3 each time [=] is depressed.

    (a) [5] [+] [+] [5] [=] [=] [=] ⋯ (b) [2] [×] [×] [2] [=] [=] [=] ⋯

13. Let n be the number for which we are looking. Then $\left(\frac{n}{25} - 18\right)37 = 259$. Solving, we have:

    $\frac{n}{25} - 18 = 7$

    $\frac{n}{25} = 25$, and $n = 625$.

14. $10! = 3{,}628{,}800$.

15. (a) For example:

    $11 \cdot 99 = 1089$
    $37 \cdot 99 = 3663$
    $54 \cdot 99 = 5346$

    The 1st and 3rd digits add to 9; the 2nd and 4th digits also add to 9.

    (b) For example:

    $11 \cdot 999 = 10989$
    $23 \cdot 999 = 22977$
    $46 \cdot 999 = 45954$

    The middle digit is always 9; the sum of the 1st and 4th digits is 9; the sum of the 2nd and 5th digits is also 9.

16. Divide the display on the calculator by 10

17. (a) $1 + 2 + 2^2 + 2^3 + 2^4 + 2^5 = 2^6 - 1$, since:

$$\begin{aligned}(1 + 2 + 2^2 + 2^3 + 2^4) + 2^5 &= 2^5 - 1 + 2^5 \\ &= (2^5 + 2^5) - 1 \\ &= 2 \cdot 2^5 - 1 \\ &= 2^6 - 1\end{aligned}$$

(b) The sum in the *n*th row of the pattern is $2^n - 1$

(c) If n = 15, then $2^n - 1 = 2^{15} - 1 = 32{,}768 - 1 = 32{,}767$ which checks

18. (*i*) 334,956 (using a calculator)

(*ii*) 5202 [anything times 1 returns the original number (that is, 1 is the multiplicative identity element)]

(*iii*) 335,166 (using a calculator)

(*iv*) 334,956 (same as (*i*), since multiplication is commutative)

(*v*) 0 (anything times 0 returns 0)

(*vi*) 335,166 (same as (*iii*), using the commutative property)

(*vii*) 334,956 (same as (*i*). $542 \times 600 + 542 \times 18 = 542 \times (600 + 18) = 542 \times 618$, using the distributive property of multiplication over addition)

19. (*i*) 1000 (add the 1 from 501 to 499, giving 500 + 500 = 1000)

(*ii*) 249,999 [from your previous algebra, remember that $(x - 1)(x + 1) = x^2 - 1$. Then $499 \times 501 = (500 - 1)(500 + 1) = 250{,}000 - 1 = 249{,}999$]

(*iii*) 2 (B is 2 larger than A)

(*iv*) 249,999 (same as (*ii*), using the commutative property)

(*v*) 49,900 [to multiply a number by 100, add two zeros to that number (in general, multipliction of any natural number by 10^n, where *n* is a natural number, results in annexing n zeros to the number)]

(*vi*) 249,999 [same as (*ii*) and (*iv*). $A \times 500 + A = A \times 500 + A \times 1 = A \times (500 + 1)$, which is $A \times B$]

(*vii*) 0 (0 divided by anything returns 0)

(*viii*) 0 (0 times anything returns 0)

On-going Assessment 1-3; Review Problems

26. (a) . . . , 35, 42, 49, . . .

(b) . . . , 1, 16, 1, 20, . . .

27. This is an arithmetic sequence with first term 12 and difference 20 $\Rightarrow$ the nth term is:
$12 + (n - 1)20 = 12 + 20n - 20 = 20n - 8$

28. This is arithmetic with first term 6, nth term 86, and difference 4
$\Rightarrow 86 = 6 + (n - 1)4 \Rightarrow n = 21$, so there are 21 terms in the sequence

29. There are nine ways of making change:

Pennies	Nickels	Dimes
1	4	0
1	2	1
1	0	2
6	3	0
6	1	1
11	2	0
11	0	1
16	1	0
21	0	0

Chapter 1 Review

1. (a) 15, 21, 28 (add 1 to the difference each time between terms; e.g., 10 + 5, 15 + 6, . . .)

   (b) 32, 27, 22 (subtract 5 from each term to obtain the subsequent term)

   (c) 400, 200, 100 (each term is half the previous term)

   (d) 21, 34, 55 (each term is the sum of the previous two terms - this is the Fibonacci sequence)

   (e) 17, 20, 23 (add 3 to each term to obtain the subsequent term)

   (f) 256, 1024, 4096 (multiply each term by 4 to obtain the subsequent term)

   (g) 16, 20, 24 (add 4 to each term to obtain the subsequent term)

   (h) 125, 216, 343 (each term is the 3rd power of the counting numbers - 1^3, 2^3, 3^3, etc.)

2. (a) Neither (b) Arithmetic

   (c) Geometric (d) Neither

   (e) Arithmetic (f) Geometric

   (g) Arithmetic (h) Neither

3. (a) The nth term is $5 + (n - 1)3 = 3n + 2$

   (b) The nth term is n^3 (third powers of the counting numbers)

   (c) The nth term is 3^n (each term is the nth power of 3)

4. (a) $3(1) + 2 = 5$
$3(2) + 2 = 8$
$3(3) + 2 = 11$
$3(4) + 2 = 14$
$3(5) + 2 = 17$

(b) $1^2 + 1 = 2$
$2^2 + 2 = 6$
$3^2 + 3 = 12$
$4^2 + 4 = 20$
$5^2 + 5 = 30$

(c) $4(1) - 1 = 3$
$4(2) - 1 = 7$
$4(3) - 1 = 11$
$4(4) - 1 = 15$
$4(5) - 1 = 19$

5. (a) There are $\frac{200-2}{2} + 1 = 100$ terms. The sum is $\frac{100}{2}(2 + 200) = 10{,}100$.

(b) There are $\frac{151-51}{1} + 1 = 101$ terms. The sum is $\frac{101}{2}(51 + 151) = 10{,}201$.

6. (a) To obtain the nth term, add the units digit of n to the end of the previous term:
…, 1234, 12345, 123456, 12345678, … .

(b) 1234567890. The last digit of the nth term matches the last digit of the number n.

7. Given row 1, all rows, columns, and diagonals must add to 34. First complete those with one missing, then two, etc., to work through the square:

16	3	2	13
5	10	11	8
9	6	7	12
4	15	14	1

8. 89 years. Remember that dates skip from 1 BC to 1 AD.

9. 10 days. On the 9th day it reaches as high as 19 cm before sliding back to 18 cm. On the 10th day it climbs out before sliding back.

10. 26 people. The 10 middle tables will hold 2 each and the 2 end tables will hold 3 each.

11. If S is the cost of the shirt and T is the cost of the tie, then:
$S + T = 9.50$
$S = T + 5.50$
$(T + 5.50) + T = 9.50$
$2T + 5.50 = 9.50$
$2T = 4.00 \Rightarrow T = 2.00$, or the cost of the tie is \$2.00

12. 21 posts. $100 \div 5 = 20$ plus 1 because both ends must be counted.

13. 128 matches. The rounds proceed as follows:
64 matches - 1 bye
32 matches - 1 bye
16 matches - 1 bye
8 matches - 1 bye
4 matches - 1 bye
2 matches - 1 bye
1 match - 1 bye
<u>1 match</u>
128 matches

14. 3, 5, 9, 11, 13, since 19,305 is not divisible by 7.

15. 44,000,000 turns:

    1 mile = 5280 feet

    $5280 \div 6 = 880$ turns to travel 1 mile

    (880 turns per mile)(50,000 miles) = 44,000,000.

16. 20 students. There are 9 students between 7 and 17 (8 to 16). There must be 9 between them in both directions, since they are direct opposites. Thus $9 + 9 + 2 = 20$.

17. 3 large + (3 large)(2 medium in each) + ($3 \cdot 2$ medium)(5 small in each)

    3 large + 6 medium + 30 small = 39 boxes.

18. | Pointing up | Pointing down |
    |---|---|
    | 1×1: $1+2+3+4+5$ | 1×1: $1+2+3+4$ |
    | 2×2: $1+2+3+4$ | 2×2: $1+2$ |
    | 3×3: $1+2+3$ | Total: 13 |
    | 4×4: $1+2$ | |
    | 5×5: 1 | |
    | Total: 35 | |

    There are $35 + 13 = 48$ triangles in the figure.

19. 9 hours. Since the return trip took 4 hours at 20 kph, the distance between homes is $4 \cdot 20 = 80$ km. Then (80 km uphill) $\div$ (16 kph uphill) = 5 hours to Larry's. The total trip was 5 hours + 4 hours = 9 hours.

20. The perimeter, P, of a rectangle is twice the length plus twice the width, or $P = 2W + 2L$. If the length, L, is $2W + 4$, then:

    $2W + 2(2W + 4) = 68$

    $2W + 4W + 8 = 68$

    $6W = 60$

    $W = 10$, so the width is 10 feet

    $L = 2W + 4$

    $L = 2 \cdot 10 + 4 = 24$, so the length is 24 feet.

21. Extend the pattern of doubling the number of ants each day. This is a geometric sequence with first term 1500, last (or nth) term 100,000, and ratio 2. Thus we have:

    $100{,}000 = 1500 \cdot 2^{n-1} \;\Rightarrow\; 66\tfrac{2}{3} = 2^{n-1}$.

    Since $2^7 > 66\frac{2}{3}$, we find that $n - 1 > 7$, or $n > 8$. That is, the ant farm will be full by the 8th day.

22. The best strategy would be one of guessing and checking.

    First guess: Ten 3's and two 5's $\Rightarrow$ $10 \cdot 3 + 2 \cdot 5 = 40$ ... close but too low

    Second guess: Nine 3's and three 5's $\Rightarrow$ $9 \cdot 3 + 3 \cdot 5 = 42$ ... closer but still too low

    Third guess: Eight 3's and four 5's $\Rightarrow$ $8 \cdot 3 + 4 \cdot 5 = 44$

    They must have answered four 5-point questions

23. Pick a fruit from the APPLES AND ORANGES box. You know the box labeled A and O is really either APPLES or ORANGES; whichever fruit you pick will tell you which box. For example, if you reached in and pulled out an apple, the A + O box is really A. The box labeled O is not oranges, so it must really be A and O. The remaining box, therefore, must be O. Similar reasoning would allow you to label the boxes if you had extracted an orange first.

    If you try picking first from either A or O, the remaining boxes could be either of two choices. For example, if you pick an orange, the box could have been either A or A and O, and you cannot tell which. Thus you cannot label the boxes if you follow this path.

CHAPTER 2 - SETS, FUNCTIONS, AND LOGIC

1. (a) {m, a, t, h, e, i, c, s} or {x | x is a letter in the word *mathematics*}

   (b) {x | x is a a state in the continental United States}

   (c) {21, 22, 23, 24, ... } or {x | x is a natural number and x > 20} or {x | x $\in$ N and x > 20}

   (d) {Alaska, California, Hawaii, Oregon, Washington} or {x | x is a state in the United States that borders the Pacific Ocean}

2. (a) B = {x, y, z, w} (b) $\{1, 2\} \subset \{1, 2, 3, 4\}$

   (c) $0 \notin \emptyset$ (d) $\{0\} \neq \emptyset$

3. (a) Yes ({1, 2, 3, 4, 5} $\sim$ {m, n, o, p, q})

   (b) No ({m, a, t, h} $\not\sim$ {f, u, n})

   (c) Yes ({a, b, c, d, e, f, ... , m} $\sim$ {1, 2, 3, 4, 5, 6, ... , 13})

   (d) No ({x | x is a letter in the word *mathematics*} $\not\sim$ {1, 2, 3, 4, ... , 13}. Note that there are only eight unduplicated letters in the word *mathematics*.)

   (e) No ({○, △} $\not\sim$ {2})

4. (a) 120. The 1st element of the 1st set can be paired with any of the five in the 2nd set, leaving four possible pairings for the 2nd element, three for the 3rd, two for the 4th, and one for the 5th. There are thus $5 \cdot 4 \cdot 3 \cdot 2 \cdot 1 = 24$ possible one-to-one correspondences.

   (b) There are $6 \cdot 5 \cdot 4 \cdot 3 \cdot 2 \cdot 1 = 720$ possible one-to-one correspondences

   (c) There are $n \cdot (n - 1) \cdot (n - 2) \cdot \cdots \cdot 2 \cdot 1 = n!$ possible one-to-one correspondences

5. (a) If x must correspond to 5, then y may correspond to any of the four remaining elements of {1, 2, 3, 4, 5}, z may correspond to any of the three remaining, etc.
   $\Rightarrow$ there would be $1 \cdot 4 \cdot 3 \cdot 2 \cdot 1 = 24$ one-to-one correspondences

   (b) There would be $1 \cdot 1 \cdot 3 \cdot 2 \cdot 1 = 6$ one-to-one correspondences

   (c) The set {x, y, z} could correspond with the set {1, 3, 5} in $3 \cdot 2 \cdot 1 = 6$ ways
   The set {u, z} could correspond with the set {2, 4} in $2 \cdot 1 = 2$ ways
   $\Rightarrow$ there would then be $6 \cdot 2 = 12$ one-to-one correspondences

6. A, C, and D are equal; note that the order of the elements is immaterial. E and H are equal; they are both the null set.

7. (a) Use the arithmetic sequence expression $a_n = a_1 + (n - 1)d$, where $a_n = 1001$, $a_1 = 1$, and $d = 2$:
   $1001 = 1 + (n - 1) \cdot 2 \Rightarrow 1001 = 1 + 2n - 2 \Rightarrow n = 501$
   So the cardinal number of the set {1, 3, 5, ... , 1001} is 501

7. (b) Use the geometric sequence expression $a_n = a_1r^{n-1}$, where $a_n = 1024$, $a_1 = 1$, and $r = 2$:
$1024 = 1 \cdot 2^{n-1} \Rightarrow 2^{10} = 2^{n-1} \Rightarrow n - 1 = 10 \Rightarrow n = 11$
So the cardinal number of the set $\{1, 2, 4, 8, 16, \ldots, 1024\}$ is 11

(c) $k = 1, 2, 3, \ldots, 100 \Rightarrow$ cardinal number = 100

(d) This set has three elements, each of which is a set $\Rightarrow$ cardinal number = 3

(e) $\left\{i+j \mid i \in \{1, 2, 3\} \text{ and } j \in \{1, 2, 3\}\right\} = \{(1 + 1), (1 + 2), (1 + 3), (2 + 1), \ldots, (3 + 3)\}$
which has only five distinguishable elements, 2, 3, 4, 5, and 6 $\Rightarrow$ cardinal number = 5

8. $\overline{A} = \{x \mid x$ is a college student who does not have a straight-A average$\}$

9. (a) 7 elements (a proper subset must have at least one less element than the set)

(b) 1 element (B, to be a proper subset, would have no elements; $\Rightarrow$ it would be the null set)

10. (a) $n(D) = 5$ (b) $C = D$

11. (a) $\in$ (b) $\notin$

(c) $\notin$ ($\{1\}$ is a set, while 1 and 2 are elements)

(d) $\notin$ (the empty set has no elements)

(e) $\notin$ ($\{1, 2\}$ is a subset of $\{1, 2\}$, not an element)

12. (a) $\not\subseteq$ (3 is not a set and thus cannot be a subset)

(b) $\not\subseteq$ (0 is not a set and thus cannot be a subset of $\emptyset$, the null set)

(c) $\subseteq$ ($\{1\}$ is actually a proper subset of $\{1,2\}$)

(d) $\subseteq$ (e) $\subseteq$

13. No ($A \not\subseteq B$ does not imply that $B \subseteq A$; A and B may have no elements in common)

14. (a) True

(b) False (A could equal B; then A would be a subset but not a proper subset of B)

(c) True

(d) False (A could be any of the proper subsets of B, thus not equal to B)

15. (a) Let $A = \{a, b\}$ and let $B = \{a, b, c, d\}$. Then $A \subset B$ and since $n(A) = 2$ and $n(B) = 4 \Rightarrow 2 < 4$

(b) $\{1, 2, 3\} \subset \{1, 2, 3, \cdots, 100\}$ and since $n\{1, 2, 3\} = 3$ and $n(1, 2, 3, \ldots, 100\} = 100 \Rightarrow 3 < 100$

(c) $\{\,\} \subset \{1, 2, 3\}$ and since $n\{\,\} = 0$ and $n\{1, 2, 3\} = 3 \Rightarrow 0 < 3$

16. (a) There are $2^6 = 64$ subsets of A $\Rightarrow$ there are $2^6 - 1 = 63$ proper subsets (the subset equal to A is not a proper subset of A)

(b) B has $2^n - 1$ proper subsets.

17. There would be $7 \cdot 6 \cdot 5 = 210$ possible subcommittees

On-going Assessment 2-2

1. (a) $A \cap B = \{t, i, e\}$; $B \cap A = \{t, i, e\} \Rightarrow$ the sets are equal
(In other words, $A \cap B = \{x \mid x \in A \text{ and } x \in B\} = B \cap A \Rightarrow$ the sets are equal)

(b) $A \cup B = \{l, i, t, e\} = B \cup A \Rightarrow$ the sets are equal

(c) $B \cup C = \{t, i, e, q, u\}$; $A \cup (B \cup C) = \{l, i, t, e, q, u\}$
$A \cup B = \{l, i, t, e\}$; $(A \cup B) \cup C = \{l, i, t, e, q, u\} \Rightarrow$ the sets are equal

(d) $A \cup \emptyset = \{l, i, t, e\} = A \Rightarrow$ the sets are equal

(e) $A \cup A = A = A \cup \emptyset \Rightarrow$ the sets are equal

(f) $A \cap A = A$; $A \cap \emptyset = \emptyset \Rightarrow$ the sets are not equal

2. (a) True

(b) False ($A = \{1, 2\}$; $B = \{2, 3\} \Rightarrow A - B = \{1\}$; $B - A = \{3\}$)

(c) True

(d) False ($U = \{1, 2\}$; $A = \{1\}$, $B = \{2\} \Rightarrow \overline{A \cap B} = \{1, 2\}$; $\overline{A} \cap \overline{B} = \emptyset$)

(e) True

(f) False (let $A = \{1, 2\}$ and $B = \{2, 3, 4\} \Rightarrow (A \cup B) - A = \{1, 2, 3, 4\} - \{1, 2\} = \{3, 4\} \neq A$)

(g) False (let $A = \{1, 2\}$ and $B = \{2, 3\} \Rightarrow (A - B) \cup A = \{1\} \cup \{1, 2\} = \{1, 2\}$;
$(A - B) \cup (B - A) = \{1\} \cup \{3\} = \{1, 3\}$)

3. (a) If $B \subseteq A$, all elements of B must also be elements of A $\Rightarrow A \cap B = B$

(b) $B \subseteq A$ implies that A is either equal to or larger than B $\Rightarrow A \cup B = A$

4. (a)

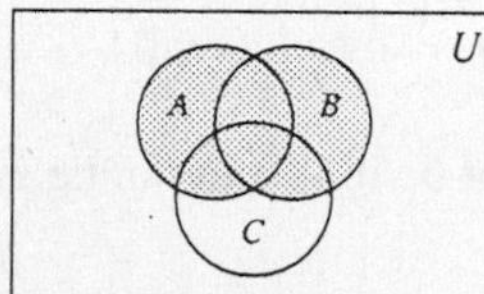

(b)

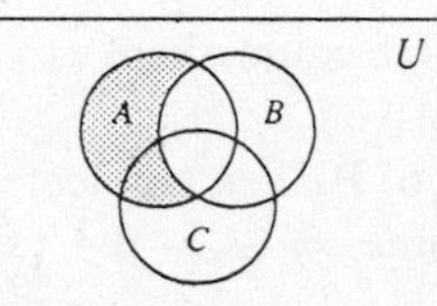

(c)

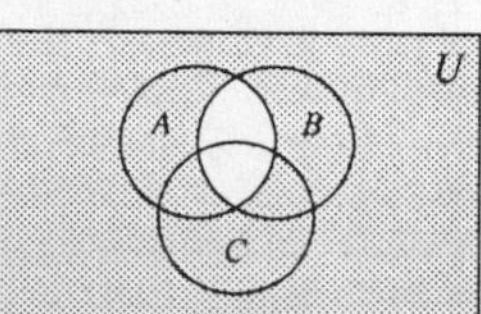

(d)

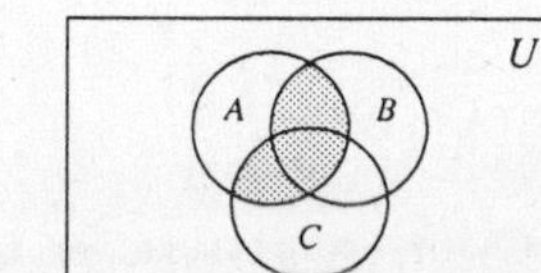

4. (e) 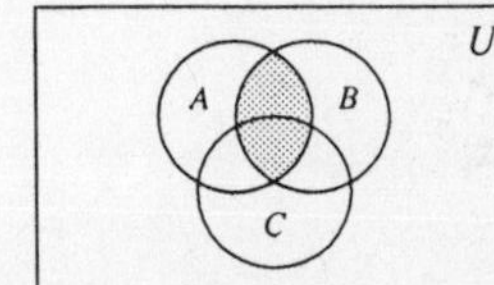

(f) 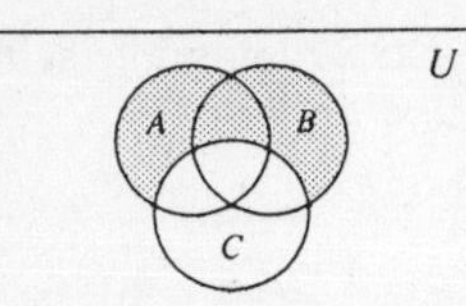

(g) 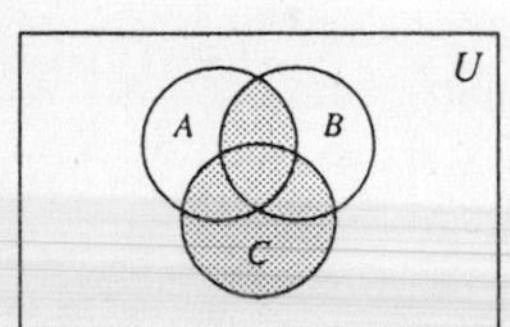

(h) 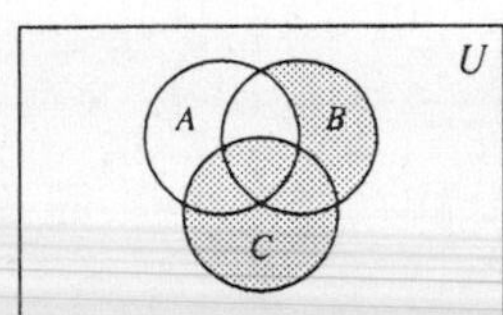

5. (a) $\overline{S}$ is the set of all elements in U that are not in S $\Rightarrow$ $S \cup \overline{S} = U$

(b) $S \cup U = \{x \mid x \in S \text{ or } x \in U\} = U$ (i.e., S can add nothing more to the whole universe)

(c) $\emptyset \cup S = \{x \mid x \in \emptyset \text{ or } x \in S\} = S$ (i.e., $\emptyset$ has nothing to add to S)

(d) If U is the universe, the complement of U can have no elements $\Rightarrow$ $\overline{U} = \emptyset$.

(e) $S \cap U = \{x \mid x \in S \text{ and } x \in U\} = S$ (i.e., all elements of S must be in U)

(f) If the null set has no elements, the complement of the null set must have all elements $\Rightarrow$ $\overline{\emptyset} = U$

(g) There are no elements common to S and $\overline{S}$ $\Rightarrow$ $S \cap \overline{S} = \emptyset$

(h) There are no elements common to S and $\overline{S}$ $\Rightarrow$ $S - \overline{S} = S$

(i) $U \cap \overline{S} = \overline{S}$

(j) $\overline{S} = U - S$

(k) Since there are no elements in the null set there are none common to it and S $\Rightarrow$ $\emptyset \cap S = \emptyset$

(l) $U - S = \overline{S}$ (taking the elements of S from U leaves only $\overline{S}$)

6. (a) If $A \cap B = \emptyset$, then A and B are disjoint sets; thus anything in A is <u>not</u> in B $\Rightarrow$ $A - B = \{x \mid x \in A \text{ and } x \notin B\} = A$

(b) Since $B = U$, there can be no elements in A which are not in B $\Rightarrow$ $A - B = \emptyset$

(c) Since A and B are equal, there can be nothing in one set that is not in the other $\Rightarrow$ $A - B = \emptyset$

(d) If A is a subset of B, then all elements of A must be in B; so an element cannot be in A and not be in B at the same time $\Rightarrow$ $A - B = \{x \mid x \in A \text{ and } x \notin B\} = \emptyset$

7. (a) $B \cap \overline{A}$ or $B - A$

(b) $\overline{A \cup B}$ or $\overline{A} \cap \overline{B}$

(c) $(A \cap B) \cap \overline{C}$ or $(A \cap B) - C$

(d) $A \cap C$

(e) $(A \cap C) \cup (B \cap C)$ or $(A \cap B) \cup C$ or $C - (A \cup B)$

(f) $[(B \cup C) - A] \cup (A \cap B \cap C)$ or $[(B \cup C) \cap \overline{A}] \cup (A \cap B \cap C)$

8\. (a) (b) (c) (d)

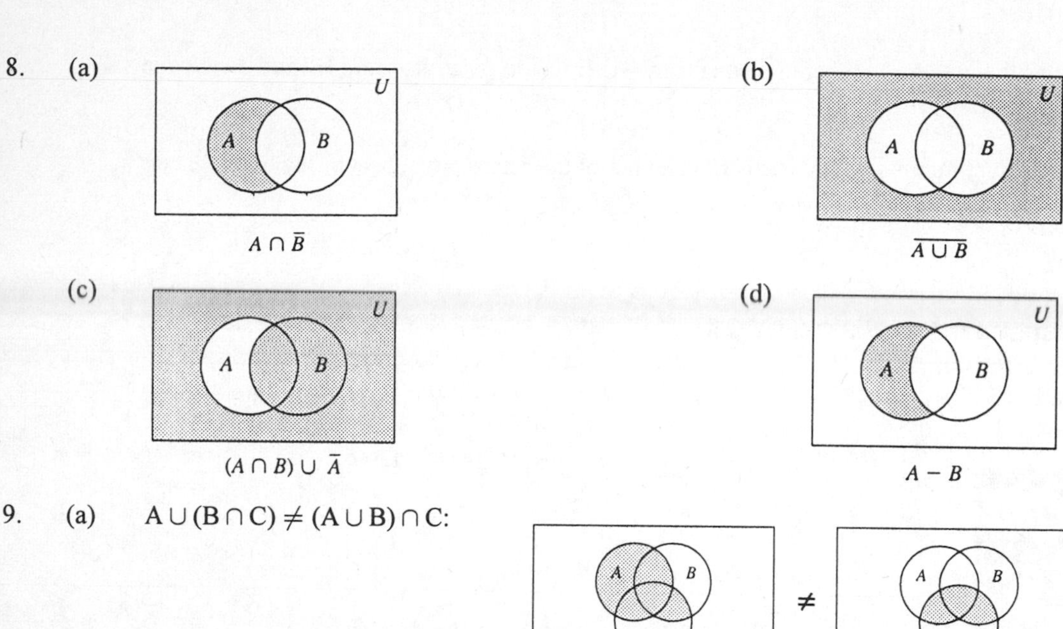

9\. (a) $A \cup (B \cap C) \neq (A \cup B) \cap C$:

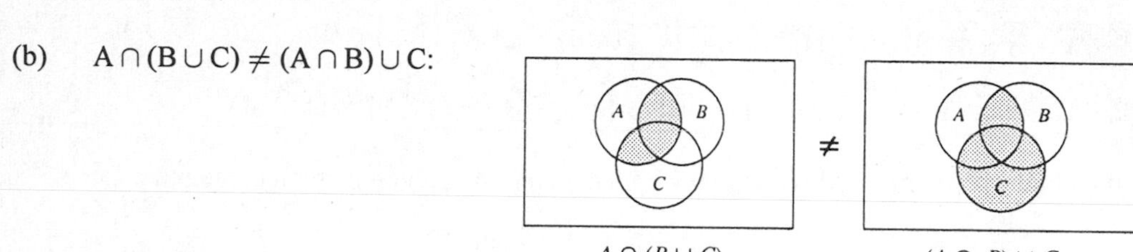

(b) $A \cap (B \cup C) \neq (A \cap B) \cup C$:

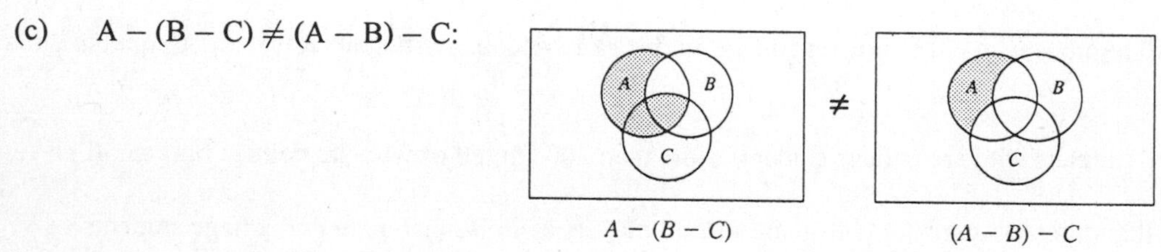

(c) $A - (B - C) \neq (A - B) - C$:

≠

$A - (B - C)$ $(A - B) - C$

10\. (a) $A \cap B \cap C \subseteq A \cap B$ (b) $A \cup B \subseteq A \cup B \cup C$

(c) $(A \cup B) \cap C \subseteq A \cup B$:

(d) Neither, in general, is a subset of the other. For example, if A and B are disjoint, then $A - B = A$ and $B - A = B$; these are also disjoint.

11\. (a) (*i*) The greatest number of elements in $A \cup B$ would occur if A and B were disjoint sets. In that case, $n(A \cup B) = n(A) + n(B) = 5$

(*ii*) The greatest number of elements in $A \cap B$ would occur if B were a subset of A. In that case, $n(A \cap B) = n(B) = 2$

(*iii*) $n(B - A) = n(B) = 2$ if the sets are disjoint

(*iv*) $n(A - B) = n(A) = 3$ if the sets are disjoint

11. (b) (*i*) As in (a), the greatest number of elements in A ∪ B would occur if A and B were disjoint sets. Then $n(A \cup B) = m + n$

(*ii*) The maximum number would occur when either of the sets was a subset of the other. Then $n(A \cap B)$ would be the smaller of m or n

(*iii*) m elements (*iv*) n elements

12. (a) (*i*) Greatest is 15 if A, B, and C are disjoint (*ii*) Least is 6 if $A \subset B \subset C$

(b) (*i*) Greatest is 4 if $A \subset B \subset C$ (*ii*) Least is 0 if A, B, and C are disjoint

13. (a) A B = A B

$\overline{A \cup B}$ $\overline{A} \cap \overline{B}$

(b) $\overline{A \cap B} = \overline{A} \cup \overline{B}$

(c) Let $U = \{1, 2, 3, 4\}$, $A = \{1, 2, 3\}$, $B = \{2, 4\}$

(*i*) $\overline{A \cup B} = \overline{\{1, 2, 3, 4\}} = \emptyset$; $\overline{A} \cap \overline{B} = \overline{\{1, 2, 3\}} \cap \overline{\{2, 4\}} = \{4\} \cap \{1, 3\} = \emptyset$

(*ii*) $\overline{A \cap B} = \overline{\{2\}} = \{1, 3, 4\}$; $\overline{A} \cup \overline{B} = \overline{\{1, 2, 3\}} \cup \overline{\{2, 4\}} = \{4\} \cup \{1, 3\} = \{1, 3, 4\}$

14. A and B are equal (they have in common everything they both contain ⇒ they must both contain the same elements)

15. (a) The set of college basketball players who are more than 200 cm tall

(b) The set of all humans who either are not college students or are college students less than or equal to 200 cm tall

(c) The set of all humans who are college students more than 200 cm tall or who are college basketball players

(d) The set of all humans who are not college basketball players and those who are not college students more than 200 cm tall

(e) The set of all non-basketball-playing college students taller than 200 cm

(f) The set of all college basketball players less than or equal to 200 cm tall

16. (a) The set of all Paxson 5th graders who are members of the band but not the choir

(b) The set of all Paxson 5th graders who are members of both the band and the choir

(c) The set of all Paxson 5th graders who are members of the choir but not the band

(d) The set of all Paxson 5th graders who are neither members of the band nor the choir

17. Use a three-set Venn diagram, labeling the sets B (for basketball), V (volleyball), and S (soccer).
Enter 2 in the region representing $B \cap V \cap S$ (i.e., there were 2 who played all three sports).
Enter 1 in the region representing $(B \cap V) - S$ (i.e., there was 1 who played basketball and volleyball, but not soccer).
Enter 1 in the region representing $(B \cap S) - V$.

17. (Continued) Enter 2 in the region representing $(V \cap S) - B$.
Enter $7 - (1 + 1 + 2) = 3$ in the region representing $B - (V \cup S)$ (i.e., of the 9 who played basketball, 1 also played volleyball, 1 also played soccer, and 2 also played both volleyball and soccer, leaving 3 who played basketball only).
Enter $9 - (1 + 2 + 2) = 4$ in the region representing $V - (B \cup S)$.
Enter $10 - (1 + 2 + 2) = 5$ in the region representing $S - (V \cup B)$.
There are then $3 + 4 + 5 + 1 + 1 + 2 + 2 = 18$ who played one or more sports.

18. From the diagram below, there were 4 members who took biology but not mathematics

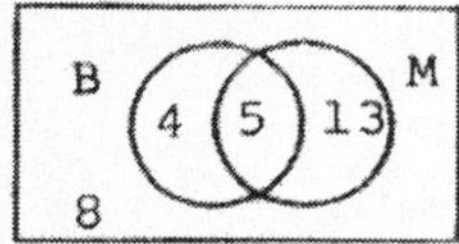

19.

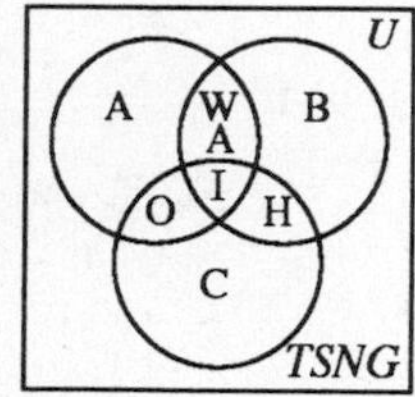

20. (a) 20 bikes (which occurs if all bikes needing new tires also need gear repairs; symbolically, if TIRES ⊂ GEARS then TIRES ∩ GEARS = 20)

(b) 10 bikes (Adding the separate repairs gives $20 + 30 = 50$. This indicates that at least 10 bikes were counted twice; i.e., needed both repairs.)

(c) 10 bikes (This occurs if the maximum number of bikes received both repairs, as in (a). All 20 that received tires were among the 30 having gear work, leaving 10 that required no service.)

21. (a) False (let $A = \{1, 2\}$ and $B = \{3, 4\}$ $\Rightarrow$ the sets are equivalent but not equal)

(b) False (let $A = B$)

(c) False [let $n(A) < n(B)$]

(d) True

(e) True (unless A and B are infinite sets; e.g., $A = \{2, 4, 6, \dots\}$ and $B = \{1, 2, 3, \dots\}$)

(f) False (let $A = \{1, 2\}$ and $B = \{4, 5, 6\}$)

22. Cowboys vs Giants, Vikings vs Packers, Redskins vs Bills, and Jets vs Steelers. All picked the Cowboys to win their game, so the opponent cannot be among any of the choices. The only team not picked was the Giants. Phyllis and Paula both picked the Steelers, so their opponent cannot be among their other choices. This leaves the Jets. Phyllis and Rashid both picked the Vikings which leaves the Packers as the only possible opponent. The Redskins and Bills are left as opponents by elimination.

23. (a) $A \times B = \{(x, a), (x, b), (x, c), (y, a), (y, b), (y, c)\}$

(b) $B \times A = \{(a, x), (a, y), (b, x), (b, y), (c, x), (c, y)\}$

(c) $B \times \emptyset = \emptyset$ (there are no elements in $\emptyset$ with which to have a cross-product)

(d) $(A \cup B) \times C = \{(x, 0), (y, 0), (a, 0), (b, 0), (c, 0)\}$

23. (e) $A \cup (B \times C) = \{x, y, (a, 0), (b, 0), (c, 0)\}$

24. (a) $C = \{a\}, D = \{b, c, d, e\}$ (b) $C = \{1, 2\}, D = \{1, 2, 3\}$

(c) $C = D = \{0, 1\}$

25. (a) $5 \cdot 4 = 20$ elements (each of the five in A are paired with each of the four in B)

(b) $m \cdot n$ elements

(c) $m \cdot n \cdot p$ elements ($A \times B$ has $m \cdot n$ elements, each of which is paired with the p elements in C)

26. (a) $3 \cdot 0 = 0$ elements (b) $1 \cdot 0 = 0$ elements

(c) $0 \cdot 0 = 0$ elements

27. If $n[(A \cup B) \times B] = 24$, then $n(A \cup B) = \frac{24}{3} = 8$. If $A \cap B = \emptyset$, then A and B are disjoint sets. Thus if $n(B) = 3$ then $n(A) = 8 - 3 = 5$.

28. Yes (this is the only situation in which $A \times B = B \times A$)

29. (a) Always true (a special case of (b) below)

(b) Always true [Let (x, y) be a member of $A \times C$. Then $X \in A \subseteq B$ and $y \in C \subseteq D \Rightarrow (x, y) \in B \times D$]

30. 30 games (equivalent to the number in the Cartesian product of the two sets of teams; i.e., $6 \cdot 5 = 30$)

31. This is equivalent to the cross product of {SLACKS}, {SHIRTS}, and {SWEATERS}. Thus the number of elements in the cross product is $n(\text{SLACKS}) \cdot n(\text{SHIRTS}) \cdot n(\text{SWEATERS}) = 4 \cdot 5 \cdot 3 = 60$, or 60 different combinations.

On-going Assessment 2-2; Review Problems

41. (a) The question is really, "how many subsets of {2, 3, 4} are there?" $\Rightarrow 2^3 = 8$ subsets not containing 1

(b) Of the $2^4 = 16$ subsets of A, there are $16 - 8$ [from (a)] $= 8$ containing 1

(c) All except $\emptyset$, {3}, {4}, {3, 4} $\Rightarrow 16 - 4 = 12$ subsets containing 1 or 2

(d) $16 - 12 = 4$ subsets containing neither 1 nor 2

(e) See (a) and (b) above

(*i*) There are $2^4 = 16$ subsets not containing the element 5

(*ii*) There are $2^5 - 16 = 32 - 16 = 16$ subsets containing the element 5

(f) Keep all subsets of A, then list each again adding the element 5 $\Rightarrow$ the number of subsets will double to 32

42. (a) $B = \{x \mid x = 2n + 2, n = 0,1,2,3,\ldots\} = \{2, 4, 6, 8, 10, \ldots\} = A$

(b) $C = \{4, 8, 12, 16, \ldots\} \Rightarrow C \not\subset A$ and $C \subset B$

43. Answers may vary

   (a) There is one-to-one correspondence between the players of two teams during a basketball game; students and desks in a full classroom; etc

   (b) There is no one-to-one correspondence between letters and keys on a telephone keypad; makes and models of cars; etc

On-going Assessment 2-3

1. Where x is the first element in each ordered pair and $f(x)$ is the second:

   (a) Double the input number

   (b) Subtract 2 from the input number

   (c) Add 6 to the input number

   (d) Square the input number and add 1

2. (a) Not a function (the element 1 is paired with both *a* and *d*)

   (b) Not a function (the element 2 is not paired with any element from the set {a, b, c, d})

   (c) A function

   (d) Not a function (1 is paired to more than one element from the set {a, b, c, d}, while 2 and 3 are not paired at all)

3. (a)

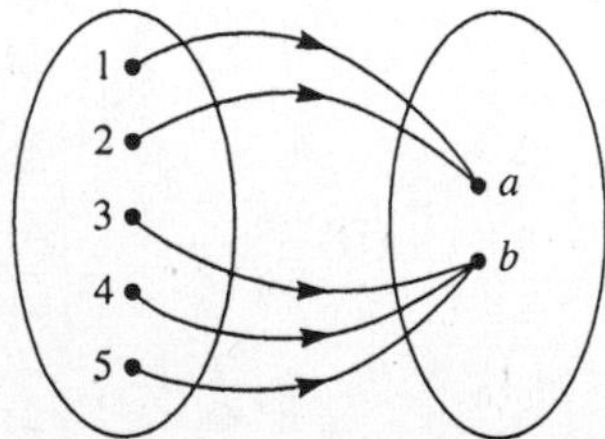

   (b) 32 (each of the five elements in the domain have two choices for a pairing, which implies $2^5 = 32$ possible functions)

4. (a)

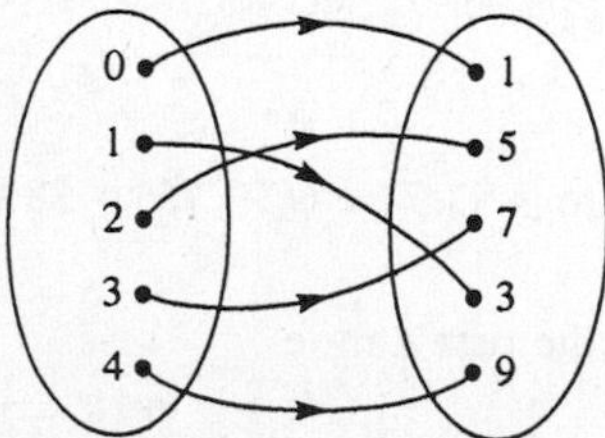

   (b) {(0, 1), (1, 3), (2, 5), (3, 7), (4, 9)}

   (c)

x	$f(x)$
0	1
1	3
2	5
3	7
4	9

   (d)

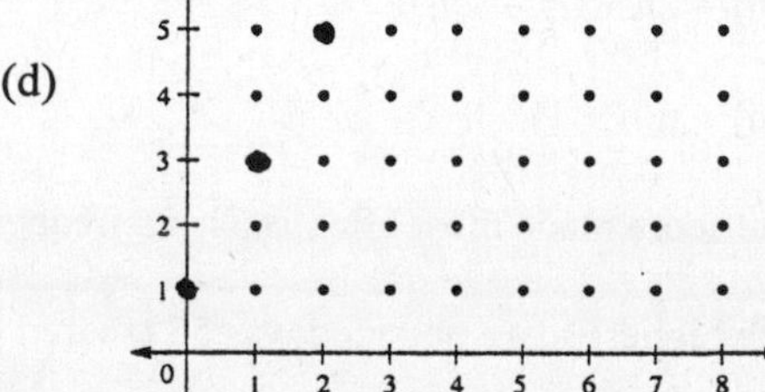

5. (a) Function: {(0,2), (1,2), (2,2), (3,2), ... }
(called a constant function)

5. (b) Function: {(0,0), (1,0), (2,0), (3,0), (4,3), (5,3), (6,3), … }

   (c) Function: {(0,x), (1,x), (2,x), … }

   (d) Not a function [contains (3,0) and (3,1)]

   (e) Function: {(0,0), (1,1), (2,2), … , (10,1), (11,2), (12,3), (13,4), … }

6. Assume 32 cents for the first ounce plus 23 cents for each additional ounce. Then:

   (a) $[32 + 23(n - 1)]$ is the cost in cents for an n-ounce letter

   (b) $[32 + 23(3 - 1)]$ ¢ = 32 + 46 = 78¢ for a 3-ounce letter

7. Note in the following graph that a child weighing exactly 30, 32, 34, … pounds uses the lower dosage at the break point

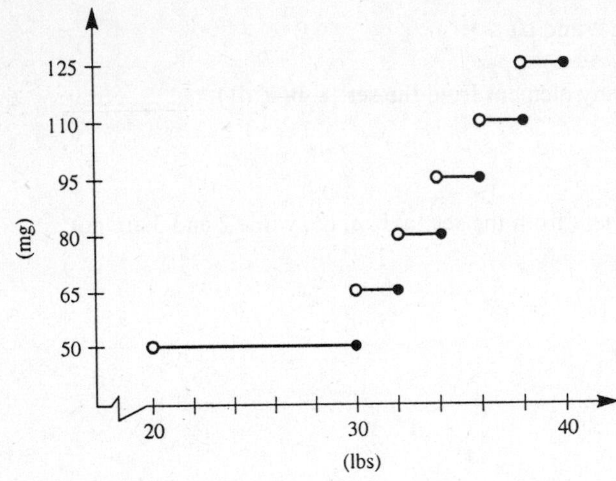

8. (a) T = 70° F ⇒ C = 70 − 40 = 30 chirps per 15 seconds = 2 chirps each second

   (b) 40 chirps per minute = 40 chirps per 60 seconds = 10 chirps per 15 seconds ⇒ 10 = T − 40 ⇒ T = 10 + 40 = 50° F

9. (a) Two miles is $\frac{1}{2}$ mile plus six $\frac{1}{4}$-mile segments ⇒ the fare is \$3.50 + 6(\$0.75) = \$8.00

   (b) \$0.75 for each $\frac{1}{4}$-mile gives \$3.00 for each mile beyond the first $\frac{1}{2}$ mile ⇒ cost (in dollars for an n-mile trip) is $3.5 + 3(n - \frac{1}{2}) = 3.5 + 3n - 1.5 = \$(3n + 2)$

10. (a) $L(n) = 2n + (n - 1)$ (b) $L(n) = n^2 + 1$

    (c) $L(n) = n(n + 1)$

11. (a) The score made most often is 51; its frequency is 7

    (b) The highest score obtained was 55 (scored by two girls)

    (c) Two girls scored 54 ⇒ two boys must score 54 to match that number

12. If the sequence is arithmetic, the relationship $a_n = a_1 + (n - 1)d$ may be used to find the general rule:

(a) f(Domain) = 5n − 2 (arithmetic) (b) f(Domain) = 3^n

(c) f(Domain) = 2n (arithmetic)

13. (a) $(g \circ f)(0) = g[f(0)] = f(0) - 5 = 7(0) - 5 = {}^{-}5$

(b) $(g \circ f)(3) = g[f(3)] = f(3) - 5 = 7(3) - 5 = 16$

(c) $(g \circ f)(10) = g[f(10)] = f(10) - 5 = 7(10) - 5 = 65$

14. (a) (*i*) 4(1) − 3 = <u>1</u>; (*ii*) 4(97) − 3 = <u>385</u>; (*iii*) 4(98) − 3 = <u>389</u>

(b) (*i*) 1^2 = <u>1</u>; (*ii*) 2^2 = <u>4</u>; (*iii*) 3^2 = <u>9</u>; (*v*) 30^2 = <u>900</u>

(c) (*i*) 1(1 + 1) = <u>2</u>; (*ii*) 3(3 + 1) = <u>12</u>; (*iii*) 50(50 + 1) = <u>2550</u>

15. (a) (*i*) $(1,7) \Rightarrow 2 \cdot 1 + 2 \cdot 7 = 16$ (*ii*) $(2,6) \Rightarrow 2 \cdot 2 + 2 \cdot 6 = 16$

(*iii*) $(6,2) \Rightarrow 2 \cdot 6 + 2 \cdot 2 = 16$ (*iv*) $(5,5) \Rightarrow 2 \cdot 5 + 2 \cdot 5 = 20$

(b) If output (or perimeter) = 20 $\Rightarrow 2\mathcal{L} + 2w = 20 \Rightarrow 2(\mathcal{L} + w) = 20 \Rightarrow \mathcal{L} + w = 10$
The possibilities are {(1,9), (2,8), (3,7), (4,6), (5,5), (6,4), (7,3), (8,2), (9,1)}

(c) Domain = $\{\mathcal{L} \times w \mid \mathcal{L} = 1, 2, 3, \ldots \text{ and } w = 1, 2, 3, \ldots\}$; Range = {4, 5, 6, ... }

16. (a) 151 cm − 150 cm = 1 cm change

(b) 154 − 152.8 = 1.2 cm between months 4 and 5

(c) We do not know her height at her birthday

17. As nearly as can be determined from the graph:

(a) 650 cars − 600 cars = 50 cars (b) Between 6:00 and 6:30

(c) No change

(d) The number of cars decreased from 700 to 600 (or by 100 cars) between 8:30 and 9:00

18. (a) C(x) = \$100 + \$40 per month = 100 + 40x (in dollars for x months)

(b&c) Graph:

Months of membership (x)	3	6	9	12	15	18	21	24
$C_1(x)$ = \$100 + \$40 · x	\$220	\$340	\$460	\$580	\$700	\$820	\$940	\$1060
$C_2(x)$ = \$300 + \$30 · x	\$390	\$480	\$570	\$660	\$750	\$840	\$930	\$1020

(d) $C_1(20) = 100 + 40 \cdot 20 = \$900$ and $C_2(20) = 300 + 30 \cdot 20 = \$900$
⇒ the second plan would be less after 20 months

19. (a) (*i*) $H(2) = 128(2) - 16(2)^2 = 192$ feet (*ii*) $H(6) = 128(6) - 16(2)^2 = 192$ feet

(*iii*) $H(3) = 128(3) - 16(3)^2 = 240$ feet (*iv*) $H(5) = 128(5) - 16(5)^2 = 240$ feet

Some of the heights correspond to the ball going up; some to the ball going down

19. (b) Plot:

t	0	1	2	3	4	5	6	7	8
$H(t) = 128t - 16t^2$	0	112	192	240	256	240	192	112	0

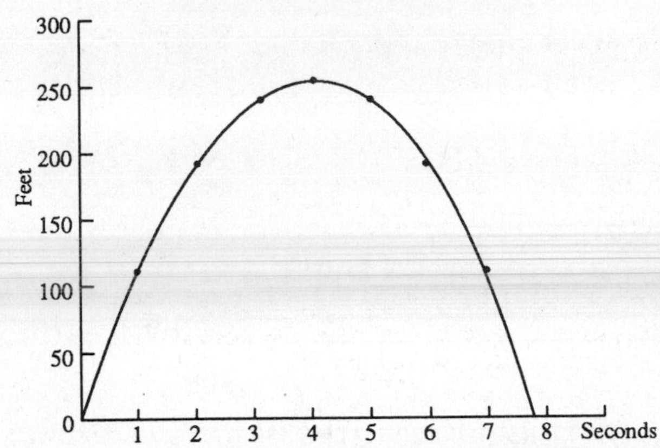

The ball will reach its highest point of 256 feet at t = 4 seconds

(c) It will hit the ground $\Rightarrow$ H = 0 at 8 seconds

(d) Domain = $\{t \mid 0 \leq t \leq 8 \text{ seconds}\}$

(e) Range = $\{H(t) \mid 0 \leq H(t) \leq 256 \text{ feet}\}$

20. (a) If x is the length of the side parallel to the river, there are (900 – x) yards in the other two sides
If the other two sides are equal, there are $\frac{900-x}{2} = 450 - \frac{1}{2}x$ yards in each
Area = length · width $\Rightarrow$ $A(x) = x \cdot \left(450 - \frac{1}{2}x\right) = \frac{1}{2}x\,(900 - x)$ square yards

(b) Graph:

x yards	0	100	200	300	400	500	600	700	800	900
A(x) yd^2	0	40,000	70,000	90,000	100,000	100,000	90,000	70,000	40,000	0

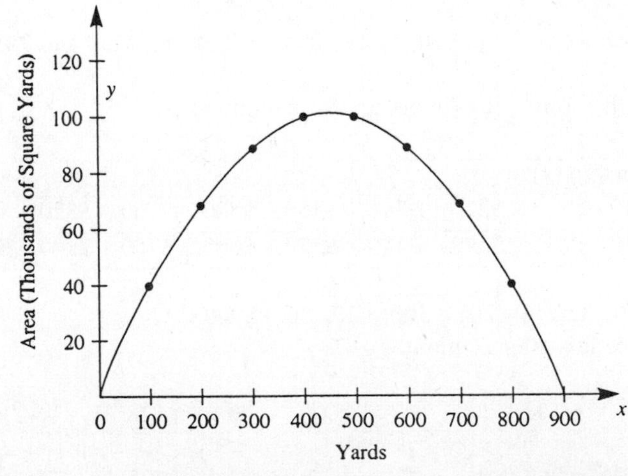

19. (c) The graph is symmetrical, with areas of 100,000 square yards when x is 400 and when x is 500
$\Rightarrow$ substitute $x = 450$ into $A(x) \Rightarrow A(450) = \frac{1}{2} \cdot 450\ 0(900 - 450) = 101{,}250$ square yards
Since the maximum area occurs when $x = 450$, the other two sides are:
$450 - \frac{1}{2}(450) = 225$
So the dimensions for which area is largest are 450 yards by 225 yards

21. (a) (*i*) 4, 12, 24, and 40 matchsticks, respectively

(*ii*) 4, 10, 22, and 38 matchsticks, respectively

(*iii*) 4, 10, 16, and 22 matchsticks, respectively

(b) (*i*) $S(n) = n(n + 1) + n(n + 1) = 2n(n + 1)$

(*ii*) Same as (a) with a corner removed $\Rightarrow$ all but the first have two less matchsticks
So: $S(n) = 4$ when $n = 1$
$S(n) = 2n(n + 1) - 2$ when $n \geq 2$

(*iii*) Note that the number of matchsticks is an arithmetic sequence [where $a_n = 4 + (n - 1) \cdot 6$]
$\Rightarrow S(n) = 6n - 2$

22. No (Every set of ordered pairs is a *relation*; a *function* is a special relation in which each member of the domain is paired with one and only one member of the range. The converse of the statement might include a relation such as $\{(2,3), (2,4)\}$ where the element 2 of the domain is paired with both 3 and 4 of the range.)

23. (a) B and J must be boys, since others are "the sister of" them but they are not "the sister of" in return
E and H are not paired, so that their gender is indeterminate. The remainder; A, C, D, F, G, and I; must be girls.

(b) {(A,B), (A,C), (A,D), (C,A), (C,B), (C,D), (D,A), (D,B), (D,C), (F,G), (G,F), (I,J)}

(c) No (A "is the sister of" three different people $\Rightarrow$ the relation is not a function)

24. (a) Function (each element of the domain is paired with one and only one element of the range)

(b) A relation but not a function (New York from the domain is paired with two elements of the range)

(c) A relation but not a function ("mother" from the domain could be paired with more than one element of the range)

(d) Function

(e) A relation but not a function (the element 1 from the domain could be paired with any odd number from the range to produce an even number)

25. (a) Yes [The set of all people has exactly one mother (assuming biological mothers only) each.
More or less than one is not possible.]

(b) No (some elements of the set of all boys do not have a brother)

26. (a) Not reflexive (a person cannot be a parent to him/herself)
Not symmetric (John can be a parent to Jane, but Jane cannot be a parent to John)
Not transitive (if John is the parent of James and James is the parent of Joseph, John is not the parent of Joseph)
Not an equivalence relation

26\. (b) Reflexive (Juan is the same age as Juan)
Symmretic (if Juan is the same age as Juanita, then Juanita is the same age as Juan)
Transitive (if Juan is the same age as Jose and Jose is the same age as Victor, Juan is the same age as Victor)
An equivalence relation (because the relation is reflexive, symmetric, and transitive)

(c) Reflexive (Jo Ann has the same last name as herself)
Symmetric (if Jo Ann has the same last name as Cheryl, then Cheryl has the same last name as Jo Ann)
Transitive (if Jo Ann has the same last name as Cheryl and Cheryl has the same last name as Penelope, then Jo Ann has the same last name as Penelope)
An equivalence relation

(d) Reflexive (Vicky is the same height as herself)
Symmetric (if Barbara is the same height as Margarita, then Margarita is the same height as Barbara)
Transitive (if Willy is the same height as Billy and Billy is the same height as Don, then Willy is the same height as Don)
An equivalence relation

(e) Not reflexive (Cindy cannot be married to herself)
Symmetric (if Arnold is married to Pam, then Pam is married to Arnold)
Not transitive (if John is married to Clara and Clara is married to James, then John is not married to James)
Not an equivalence relation

(f) Reflexive (Peter lives within 10 miles of himself)
Symmetric (if Jon lives within 10 miles of Evangeline, then Evangeline lives within 10 miles of Jon)
Not transitive (if Fred lives within 10 miles of Jim and Jim lives within 10 miles of Herb, then Fred does not necessarily live within 10 miles of Herb)
Not an equivalence relation

(g) Not reflexive (Juan cannot be older than himself)
Not symmetric (if Jose is older than Mireya then Mireya cannot be older than Jose)
Transitive (if Jean is older than Mike and Mike is older than Cybil, then Jean is older than Cybil)
Not an equivalence relation

27\. In each of the following, use the nonempty set $\{1, 2, 3\}$ as an example:

(a) Reflexive ($\{1\}$ is equal to $\{1\}$)
Symmetric (if $\{1, 2\}$ is equal to $\{2, 1\}$, then $\{2, 1\}$ is equal to $\{1, 2\}$)
Transitive (if $\{1, 2, 3\} = \{1, 3, 2\}$ and $\{1, 3, 2\} = \{2, 1, 3\}$, then $\{1, 2, 3\} = \{2, 1, 3\}$)
An equivalence relation

(b) Not reflexive ($\{1\}$ is not a proper subset of $\{1\}$)
Not symmetric (if $\{1\}$ is a proper subset of $\{1, 2\}$, then $\{1, 2\}$ is not a proper subset of $\{1\}$)
Transitive ($\{1\} \subset \{1, 2\}$ and $\{1, 2\} \subset \{1, 2, 3\}$, so $\{1\} \subset \{1, 2, 3\}$)
Not an equivalence relation

(c) Not reflexive ($\{1\}$ is not "not equal to" $\{1\}$)
Symmetric (if $\{1\}$ is not equal to $\{2\}$, then $\{2\}$ is not equal to $\{1\}$)
Not transitive (if $\{1\}$ is not equal to $\{2\}$ and $\{2\}$ is not equal to $\{1\}$, $\{1\}$ is not "not equal to" $\{1\}$)
Not an equivalence relation

27. (d) Reflexive $(n\{1,2\} = n\{1,2\})$
Symmetric (if $n\{1,2\} = n\{1,3\}$, then $n\{1,3\} = n\{1,2\}$)
Transitive (if $n\{1,2\} = n\{1,3\}$ and $n\{1,3\} = n\{2,3\}$, then $n\{1,2\} = n\{2,3\}$)
An equivalence relation

On-going Assessment 2-3; Review Problems

39. (a) $n\{2, 4, 6, 8, \ldots, 1000\} = n\{3, 6, 9, 12, 15, \ldots, 1500\} = 500 \Rightarrow$ sets are equivalent

(b) $n\{1, 4, 7, 10, 13, \ldots, 3001\} = 1001$ and $n\{1, 2, 3, 4, \ldots, 1000\} = 1000 \Rightarrow$ not equivalent

(c) The function $f(x) = x + 1$ establishes a one-to-one correspondence between the two sets (with the first set as domain) $\Rightarrow$ the sets are equivalent

(d) $n(S) = n(W)$ (that is, there is one-to-one correspondence) $\Rightarrow$ sets are equivalent

40. (a) True $[A - (B \cup C) = A \cap \overline{B \cup C} = A \cap (\overline{B} \cap \overline{C}) = A \cap \overline{B} \cap \overline{C} = (A \cap \overline{B}) \cap (A \cap \overline{C}) = (A - B) \cap (A - C)]$

(b) True $[A \subseteq A \cup B = B]$

(c) True $[\overline{A} \cup \overline{B} = \overline{A \cap B} = \overline{\emptyset} = U]$

(d) False (let $A = \{1, 2\}$, $B = \{4\}$, and $C = \{1, 2, 3\}$)

41. (a) $3 \cdot 2 \cdot 1 = 6$ (b) $3 \cdot 3 = 9$

42. (a) False [B and C could be subsets of A (let $A = \{1, 2\}$, $B = \{1\}$, $C = \{2\}$)]

(b) False (let $A = \{1, 2\}$, $B = \{2, 3\}$, $C = \{2, 4\}$)

(c) False (let $A = \{1, 2\}$, $B = \{4\}$, $C = \{2, 3\}$)

(d) False (let $A = \{1\}$ and $B = \{2\}$ ... then $A \times \emptyset = 0$ and $B \times \emptyset = 0$ but $A \neq B$)

(e) True (there are no elements in either set so no ordered pairs exist)

43. A two-thirds majority requires four, five, or six senators for a winning coalition
There are 15 unique sets of four senators, 6 sets of five senators, and 1 set of six senators, for 22 winning coalitions

44. (a) 2200 (all 2200 that saw The Lion King may have also seen Apollo 13)

(b) 500 [there were 1700 people (4800 – 3100) that did not see The Lion King; if all these went to see Apollo 13 then only 500 people (2200 – 1700) saw both movies]

45. Answers may vary

(a) Two possibilities are $\{x \mid x \text{ is an even number greater than } 12\}$ and $\{x \mid x = 2n, n \in N \text{ and } n > 6\}$

(b) Two possibilities are $\{x \mid x \text{ is a natural number less than } 14\}$ and $\{x \mid x < 14, x \in N\}$

46. (a) $\overline{B} = \{a, d\} \Rightarrow A \cup \overline{B} = \{a, b, c\} \cup \{a, d\} = \{a, b, c, d\} = U$

(b) $A \cap B = \{b, c\} \Rightarrow \overline{A \cap B} = \{a, d\}$

46. (c) $A \cap \emptyset = \emptyset$ (d) $B \cap C = \{b, c\} \cap \{d\} = \emptyset$

(e) $B - A = \{x \mid x \in B \text{ and } x \notin A\} = \{b, c\} \cap \{d\} \Rightarrow B - A = \emptyset$

On-going Assessment 2-4

1. (a) False statement (a statement is a sentence that is either true or false, but not both)

(b) Not a statement

(c) False statement

(d) Not a statement (i.e., it can be either true or false)

(e) Not a statement.

(f) Not a statement (truth cannot be determined without knowing the value of x)

(g) True statement

(h) Not a statement (could be either true or false depending upon the value of x)

(i) Not a statement (this is a paradox; if it is true, it must be false, but then it isn't true . . . .)

(j) Not a statement

2. (a) There exists at least one natural number x such that $x + 8 = 11$

(b) For all natural numbers x, $x + 0 = x$

(c) There exists at least one natural number x such that $x^2 = 4$

(d) There exists no natural number x such that $x + 1 = x + 2$

(e) For all natural numbers x, $x + 3 = 3 + x$

(f) There exists at least one natural number x such that $3 \cdot (x + 2) = 12$

(g) For all natural numbers x, $5x + 4x = 9x$

3. (a) For all natural numbers x, $x + 8 = 11$

(b) There is no natural number x such that $x + 0 = x$

(c) For all natural numbers x, $x^2 = 4$

(d) There exists a natural number x such that $x + 1 = x + 2$

(e) There is no natural number x such that $x + 3 = 3 + x$

(f) For every natural number x, $3 \cdot (x + 2) = 12$

(g) There is no natural number x such that $5x + 4x = 9x$

4. (a) The book does not have 500 pages (b) Six is greater than or equal to eight

(c) $3 \cdot 5 \neq 15$ (d) No people have blond hair

(e) No dogs have four legs (f) All cats have nine lives

(g) There exists a square that is not a rectangle (h) All rectangles are squares

5. (a)

p	$\sim p$	$\sim(\sim p)$
T	F	T
F	T	F

(b)

p	$\sim p$	$p \vee \sim p$	$p \wedge \sim p$
T	F	T	F
F	T	T	F

(c) Yes (d) No

6. (a) $q \wedge r$ (b) $r \vee \sim q$

(c) $\sim(q \wedge r)$ (d) $\sim q$

7. (a) False (true if and only if both p and q are true)

(b) True (false if both p and q are false; true otherwise)

(c) True (negation of p) (d) False

(e) False [analgous to -(-x) = x] (f) True (both $\sim p$ and q are true)

(g) False (both are false) (h) False ($p \vee q$ is true)

(i) False ($\sim p \wedge q$ is true) (j) False

8. (a) False (b) False

(c) True (d) True

(e) False (f) True

(g) False (h) True

(i) True (j) True

9. (a)

p	q	$\sim p$	$\sim q$	$\sim p \vee \sim q$	$\sim(p \vee q)$
T	T	F	F	F	F
T	F	F	T	T	F
F	T	T	F	T	F
F	F	T	T	T	T

Since the truth table for $\sim p \vee \sim q$ is not the same as for $\sim(p \vee q)$, the statements are not logically equivalent.

9. (b)

p	q	$\sim p$	$\sim q$	$p \vee q$	$\sim (p \vee q)$	$\sim p \wedge \sim q$
T	T	F	F	T	F	F
T	F	F	T	T	F	F
F	T	T	F	T	F	F
F	F	T	T	F	T	T

Since the truth table for $\sim (p \vee q)$ is the same as for $\sim p \wedge \sim q$, the statements are logically equivalent.

(c)

p	q	$\sim p$	$\sim q$	$p \wedge q$	$\sim (p \wedge q)$	$\sim p \wedge \sim q$
T	T	F	F	T	F	F
T	F	F	T	F	T	F
F	T	T	F	F	T	F
F	F	T	T	F	T	T

Since the truth table for $\sim (p \wedge q)$ is not the same as for $\sim p \wedge \sim q$, the statements are not logically equivalent.

(d)

p	q	$\sim p$	$\sim q$	$p \wedge q$	$\sim (p \wedge q)$	$\sim p \vee \sim q$
T	T	F	F	T	F	F
T	F	F	T	F	T	T
F	T	T	F	F	T	T
F	F	T	T	F	T	T

Since the truth table for $\sim (p \wedge q)$ is the same as for $\sim p \vee \sim q$, the statements are logically equivalent.

10.

p	q	$\sim p$	$\sim q$	$\sim p \vee q$
T	T	F	F	T
T	F	F	T	F
F	T	T	F	T
F	F	T	T	T

11. (a) This statement is equivalent to $\sim (W \wedge J)$; DeMorgan's equivalent is $\sim W \vee \sim J \Rightarrow$ either today is not Wednesday or this is not the month of June

(b) This statement is equivalent to $\sim (B \wedge T)$; DeMorgan's equivalent is $\sim B \vee \sim T \Rightarrow$ yesterday I either didn't eat breakfast or I didn't watch television

(c) This statement is equivalent to $\sim R \vee \sim J$; DeMorgan's equivalent is $\sim (R \wedge J) \Rightarrow$ it is not true that it is both raining and the month is July

12. (a) $p \rightarrow q$ (b) $\sim p \rightarrow q$

(c) $p \rightarrow \sim q$ (d) $p \rightarrow q$

(e) $\sim q \rightarrow \sim p$ (f) $p \leftrightarrow q$

13. (a) Converse: If you are good in sports, then you eat Meaties
Inverse: If you do not eat Meaties, then you are not good in sports
Contrapositive: If you are not good in sports, then you do not eat Meaties

13. (b) Converse: If you do not like mathematics, then you do not like this book
Inverse: If you like this book, then you like mathematics
Contrapositive: If you like mathematics, then you like this book

(c) Converse: If you have cavities, then you do not use Ultra Brush toothpaste
Inverse: If you use Ultra Brush toothpaste, then you do not have cavities
Contrapositive: If you do not have cavities, then you use Ultra Brush toothpaste

(d) Converse: If your grades are high, then you are good at logic
Inverse: If you are not good at logic, then your grades are not high
Contrapositive: If your grades are not high, then you are not good at logic

14. No (if it does not rain, then Iris can either go to the movies or not without making her statement false)

15. Let p = "every digit of a number is 6" and q = "the number is divisible by 3"

(a) ⇒ Not logically equivalent

p	q	$p \rightarrow q$	$\sim p$	$\sim q$	$\sim p \rightarrow \sim q$
T	T	T	F	F	T
T	F	F	F	T	T
F	T	T	T	F	F
F	F	T	T	T	T

(b) ⇒ Logically equivalent

p	q	$p \rightarrow q$	$\sim q$	$\sim p$	$\sim q \rightarrow \sim p$
T	T	T	F	F	T
T	F	F	T	F	F
F	T	T	F	T	T
F	F	T	T	T	T

(c) ⇒ Not logically equivalent

p	q	$p \rightarrow q$	$q \rightarrow p$
T	T	T	T
T	F	F	T
F	T	T	F
F	F	T	F

16. Contrapositive is logically equivalent: "If a number is not a multiple of 4, then it is not a multiple of 8"

17. (a) Valid (use the chain rule: Hypatia was a woman → all women are mortal → Hypatia was mortal)

(b) Valid (all squares are quadrilaterals → all quadrilaterals are polygons → all squares are polygons)

(c) Valid (some teachers are rich $\wedge$ all teachers are intelligent → some intelligent people are rich)

(d) Invalid (there is no statement "sophomores, juniors, and seniors do not take mathematics")

18. (a) Let p = Helen is a college student
q = All college students are poor
Then we have $p \rightarrow q$, or if Helen is a college student she is poor
p is true, she is a college student
So q is true, Helen is poor

(b) Let p = Some freshmen like math
q = All who like math are intelligent
Then $p \rightarrow q$, or some freshmen are intelligent

18. (c) Let p = I study for the final
q = I pass the course
r = I look for a teaching job
Then $p \rightarrow q$, if I study for the final I pass the course
$q \rightarrow r$, if I pass the course I look for a teaching job
$p \rightarrow r$, if I study for the final I will look for a teaching job

(d) Let p = Equilateral triangle
q = Isosceles triangle
Then $p \rightarrow q$
$\sim p \rightarrow \sim q$, or, there may exist triangles that are not equilateral

19. (a) If a figure is a square, then it is a rectangle

(b) If a number is an integer, then it is a rational number

(c) If a figure has exactly three sides, then it may be a triangle

(d) If it rains, then it is cloudy

Chapter 2 Review

1. {x | x is a letter of the Greek alphabet}

2. {m, a, t, h}, {m, a, t}, {m, a, h}, {m, t, h}, {a, t, h}, {m, a}, {m, t}, {m, h}, {a, t}, {a, h}, {t. h}, {m}, {a}, {t}, {h}, { }

3. (a) A person younger than 30 living in Montana

(b) A person 30 or older living in Montana who owns a pickup

(c) A person living in Montana

(d) A person living in Montana who does not own a pickup

(e) A person living in Montana who is younger than 30 or does not own a pickup

(f) A person living in Montana who is 30 or older and does not own a pickup

4. (a) $\{r, a, v, e\} \cup \{a, r, e\} = \{r, a, v, e\} = A$

(b) $\{l, i, n, e\} \cap \{s, a, l, e\} = \{l, e\}$

(c) {u, n, i, v, r}

(d) $\{r, a, v, e\} \cap \{u, n, i, v, r\} = \{r, v\}$

(e) $\overline{\{a, r, e\} \cup \{l, i, n, e\}} = \{u, v, s\}$

(f) {a, l, e}

(g) {i, n}

(h) {e}

(i) $\overline{C} = \{u, v, r, s, a\} \Rightarrow n(\overline{C}) = 5$

(j) 16 (each of the four elements in C can be paired with each of the four in D $\Rightarrow 4 \cdot 4 = 16$ in $C \times D$)

5. (a) A ∩ (B ∪ C):

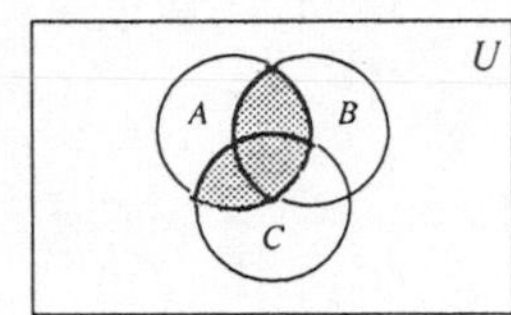

(b) $\overline{A \cup B} \cap C$:

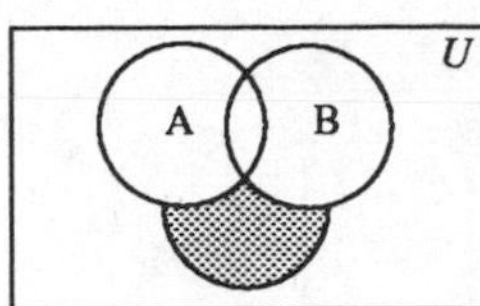

6. 5040, assuming that all 7 letters are distinct. (Consider seven "slots" in which to put the letters; there are 7 letters which could go in the 1st slot, then 6 left which could go in the 2nd slot, and so on. The number of possible words is then $7 \cdot 6 \cdot 5 \cdot 4 \cdot 3 \cdot 2 \cdot 1 = 7! = 5040$.)

7. (a) Answers may vary. One possible correspondence is t ↔ e, h ↔ n, and e ↔ d.

   (b) $3 \cdot 2 \cdot 1 = 6$ one-to-one correspondences are possible

8. A ∩ (B ∪ C) ≠ (A ∩ B) ∪ C

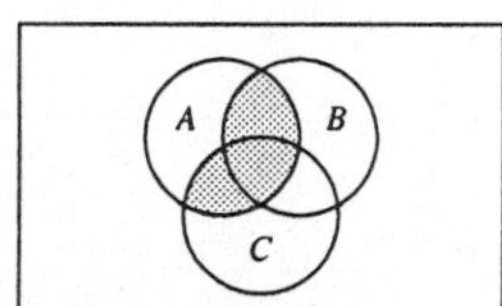

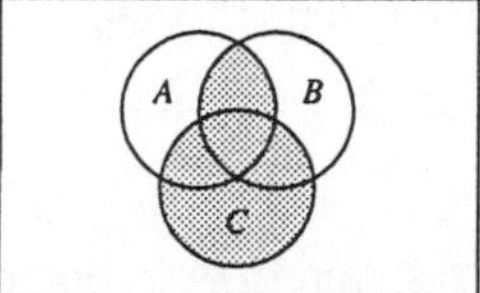

9. (a) B ∪ (A ∩ C) (b) B − C

10. (a) False (sets A and B could be disjoint)

    (b) False (the empty set is not a proper subset of itself)

    (c) False (A ~ B only requires the same number of elements - not necessarily the same elements)

    (d) False (the set is in one-to-one correspondence with the set of natural numbers ⇒ it increases without limit)

    (e) False (infinite sets are equivalent to proper subsets of themselves)

    (f) False (let A = {1, 2, 3, 4, ...) and let B = {1})

    (g) True

    (h) False (the sets may be be disjoint but not empty)

11. (a) 17, if P = Q (b) 34, if P and Q are disjoint

    (c) 0, if P and Q are disjoint (d) 17, if P = Q

12. 7 [*n*(Crew) + *n*(Swimming) + *n*(Soccer) = 57. The two lettering in all three sports are counted 3 times, so subtract 2 twice, giving 53. *n*(Awards) = 46, thus 53 - 46 = 7 were counted twice; i.e., 7 lettered in exactly two sports.]

13. Answers may vary. The first question might be, "Is the state or province one of the 48 contiguous states in the U.S.?" If the answer is yes, the second question could be, "Does its name begin with a vowel?" The third question could then be, "Is it ________________?" If the answer to the first question is no, the second question could be, "Is it in Canada?", and the third question could again be, "Is it ________________?"

14. Use the following Venn diagram, placing values in appropriate areas starting with the fact that 3 students liked all three subjects:

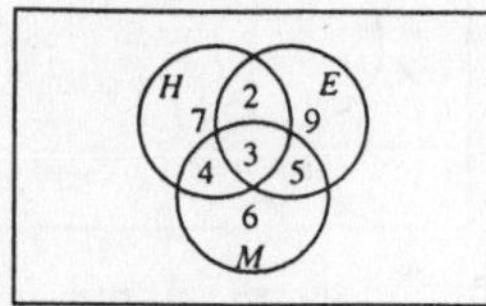

(a) 36 students were in the survey

(b) 6 students liked only mathematics

(c) 5 students liked English and mathematics but not history

15. (a) Yes

(b) No (*a* and *b* both correspond to two components of the range)

(c) Yes

16. (a) Pair each post office with the zip code it serves

(b) Let A be the set of all addresses in the 5th set of states, B the set of all addresses in the 98th geographic region in A, and C the set of all addresses in the first local delivery area in B. Let x be my address $\Rightarrow x \in A \cap B \cap C$.

17. (a) $\{3, 4, 5, 6\}$ (b) $\{14, 29, 44, 59\}$

(c) $\{0, 1, 4, 9, 16\}$ (d) $\{5, 9, 15\}$

18. (a) (*i*) Not a function if any students have double majors

(*ii*) Otherwise, a function $\Rightarrow$ range is all majors with active students

(b) A function $\Rightarrow$ range will be the number of pages in each of the various books

(c) A function $\Rightarrow$ range is all even natural numbers ≥ 6

(d) A function $\Rightarrow$ range is $\{0, 1\}$

(e) A function $\Rightarrow$ range is $\mathcal{N}$

19. (a) $C(x) = 200 + 55(x - 1)$, in dollars for x months

(b) Graph:

x	1	2	3	4	5	6	7	8	9	10	11	12
C(x)	200	255	310	365	420	475	530	585	640	695	750	805

19. (b)

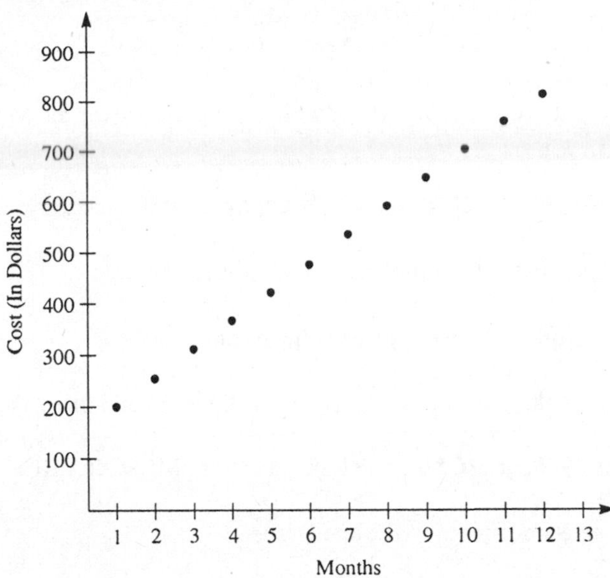

(c) The cost will exceed \$600 beginning with the 9th month

(d) Determine when $C(x) = 200 + 55(x - 1) = 6000$:

$55x - 55 = 5800$

$55x = 5855 \Rightarrow x = 106.5$

Or the cost will exceed \$6000 after the 107th month

20. (a) Yes (b) Yes

(c) No (unless the value of x is determined) (d) Yes

21. (a) No women smoke (b) $3 + 5 \neq 8$

(c) Some heavy metal rock is not loud (d) Beethoven wrote some non-classical music

22. Converse: If someone will faint, we are having a rock concert
Inverse: If we do not have a rock concert, no one will faint
Contrapositive: If no one will faint, we are not having a rock concert

23. (a) Joe Czernyu loves Mom and apple pie

(b) The structure of the Statue of Liberty will eventually rust

(c) Albertina will pass Math 100 (she had two options; since she did not fulfill one, she must do the other).

24. Let f = fair-skinned; s = sunburned; d = went to the dance; w = parents ask why.

Then $f \rightarrow s$

$s \rightarrow \sim d$

$\sim d \rightarrow w$

The final argument is $\sim w \rightarrow \sim f$, which is valid. (Consider the contrapositives of the first three arguments from bottom to top.)

CHAPTER 3 - NUMERATION SYSTEMS FOR THE AGES

On-going Assessment 3-1

1. (a) $\overline{\overline{\text{M}}}$CDXXIV (the double bar over the M represents 1000 · 1000 · 1000, while a single bar over the M would represent only 1000 · 1000)

   (b) 46,032 (the 4 in 46,032 represents 40,000, while the 4 in 4632 represents 4000)

   (c) < ▼▼ [< in the first number =10, in the second = 10 · 60 (because of the space)]

   (d) 𓆼 ∩ | (𓆼 has a place value of 1000, while 9 has a place value of only 100)

   (e) [Mayan symbols] ([Mayan symbols] represents three groups of 20 plus zero 1's; [Mayan symbols] means three 5's and three 1's, or 15)

2. (a) MCMXLIX represents 1949; thus one more is 1950, or MCML; one less is 1948, or MCMXLVIII

   (b) $\overline{\text{M}}$I represents 1000 · 1000 + 1, or 1,000,001; thus one more is $\overline{\text{M}}$II; one less is $\overline{\text{M}}$

   (c) CMXCIX is 999; one more is M; one less is CMXCVIII

   (d) << <▼ is 20 · 60 + 11 = 1211; thus one more is 1212, or << <▼▼ ; one less is 1210, or << <

   (e) 𓆼99 is 1200; one more is 1201, or 𓆼99| ; one less is 1199, or 𓆼9∩∩∩∩∩∩∩∩∩|||||||||

   (f) [Mayan symbols] is 7 · 20 + 13 · 1 = 153, thus one more is 154, or [Mayan symbols] ; one less is 152, or [Mayan symbols]

3. MCMXXII is 1000 + 900 + 20 + 2, or the year 1922

4. (a) CXXI (b) XLII

   (c) LXXXIX (d) $\overline{\text{V}}$CCLXXXII

5. (a) ∩∩∩∩∩|| (b) 9|||

   (c) [Egyptian symbol] ||| (d) ∩∩∩|||||||||

6.

	Arabic	Babylonian	Egyptian	Roman	Mayan
(a)	72	▼ <▼▼	∩∩∩∩∩∩∩||	LXXII	[Mayan symbols]
(b)	602	< ▼▼	999999||	DCII	[Mayan symbols]
(c)	1223	<< <<▼▼	𓆼99∩∩|||	MCCXXIII	[Mayan symbols]

7. (a) Hundreds (from the decimal point left: units → tens → hundreds)

   (b) Tens (units → tens)

   (c) Thousands (units → tens → hundreds → thousands)

   (d) Hundred thousands (units → tens → hundreds → thousands → ten thousands → hundred thousands)

8. (a) $3{,}000{,}000 + 4{,}000 + 5 = 3{,}004{,}005$

   (b) $20{,}000 + 1 = 20{,}001$

   (c) $3000 + 500 + 60 = 3560$

   (d) $9{,}000{,}000 + 90 + 9 = 9{,}000{,}099$

9. (a) $(3 \cdot 25) + (2 \cdot 5) + (1 \cdot 1) = 86$

   (b) $(1 \cdot 8) + (0 \cdot 4) + (1 \cdot 2) + (1 \cdot 1) = 11$

10. The number could be either 811 or 910. Either satisfies the conditions that the hundreds digit must be 8 or 9, the tens digit must be odd, and the sum of the digits must equal 10.

11. (a) Remember that place values represent powers of 2; i.e.,
    $1 = 1 \cdot 2^0$
    $10 = 1 \cdot 2^1 + 0 \cdot 2^0$
    $100 = 1 \cdot 2^2 + 0 \cdot 2^1 + 0 \cdot 2^0$, etc. Thus the first 15 counting numbers are:
    $(1, 10, 11, 100, 101, 110, 111, 1000, 1001, 1010, 1011, 1100, 1101, 1110, \text{and } 1111)_{two}$

    (b) $(1, 2, 10, 11, 12, 20, 21, 22, 100, 101, 102, 110, 111, 112, 120)_{three}$

    (c) $(1, 2, 3, 10, 11, 12, 13, 20, 21, 22, 23, 30, 31, 32, 33)_{four}$

    (d) $(1, 2, 3, 4, 5, 6, 7, 10, 11, 12, 13, 14, 15, 16, 17)_{eight}$

12. One digit is needed for each of the units; 20 digits (including zero) would be needed in base 20

13. $2032_{four} = (2 \cdot 10^3 + 0 \cdot 10^2 + 3 \cdot 10 + 2)_{four}$ or $2 \cdot 4^3 + 0 \cdot 4^2 + 3 \cdot 4 + 2$

14. (a) 1 is the largest units digit; thus the largest three-digit number is 111_{two}

    (b) 555_{six} (c) 999_{ten}

    (d) EEE_{twelve}

15. (a) $EE0_{twelve} = 11 \cdot 12^2 + 11 \cdot 12 + 0$
    Thus $(EE0 - 1)_{twelve} = 11 \cdot 12^2 + 10 \cdot 12 + 11 = ETE_{twelve}$, and
    $(EE0 + 1)_{twelve} = 11 \cdot 12^2 + 11 \cdot 12 + 1 = EE1_{twelve}$

    (b) $(100000 - 1)_{two} = 11111_{two}$; $(100000 + 1)_{two} = 100001_{two}$

    (c) $(555 - 1)_{six} = 554_{six}$; $(555 + 1)_{six} = 1000_{six}$

    (d) $(100 - 1)_{seven} = 66_{seven}$; $(100 + 1)_{seven} = 101_{seven}$

15. (e) $(1000-1)_{five} = 444_{five}$; $(1000+1)_{five} = 1001_{five}$

(f) $(110-1)_{two} = 101_{two}$; $(110+1)_{two} = 111_{two}$

16. (a) There is no numeral 4 in base four (the numerals are 0, 1, 2, and 3)

(b) There are no numerals 6 or 7 in base five

(c) There is no numeral T in base three

17. (a) Place values in base 5 are $5^4 = 625$, $5^3 = 125$, $5^2 = 25$, $5^1 = 5$, and 1. The largest needed here is 125 $\Rightarrow$

$125 \mid 432 \mid 3$, -375	There are 3 groups of 125 in 432, with remainder 57
$25 \mid 57 \mid 2$, -50	There are 2 groups of 25 in 57, with remainder 7
$5 \mid 7 \mid 1$, -5	There is 1 group of 5 in 7, with remainder 2
$1 \mid 2 \mid 2$, -2, 0	There are 2 groups of 1 in 2, with remainder 0

Thus $432 = 3212_{five}$

(b) There is 1 group of 1728 (or 12^3) in 1963, with remainder 235
There is 1 group of 144 in 235, with remainder 91
There are 7 groups of 12 in 91, with remainder 7
There are 7 groups of 1 in 7, with remainder 0
Thus $1963 = 1177_{twelve}$

(c) There is 1 group of 256 (or 4^4) in 404, with remainder 148
There are 2 groups of 64 in 148, with remainder 20
There is 1 group of 16 in 20, with remainder 4
There is 1 group of 4 in 4, with remainder 0
There are 0 groups of 1 in 0, with remainder 0
Thus $404 = 12110_{four}$

(d) There is 1 group of 32 (or 2^5) in 37, with remainder 5
There are 0 groups of 16 in 5, with remainder 5
There are 0 groups of 8 in 5, with remainder 5
There is 1 group of 4 in 5, with remainder 1
There are 0 groups of 2 in 1, with remainder 1
There is 1 group of 1 in 1, with remainder 0
Thus $32 = 100101_{two}$

(e) $4 \cdot 10^4 + 3 \cdot 10^2 = 40300$
There is 1 group of 20736 (or 12^4) in 40300, with remainder 19564
There are 11 groups of 1728 in 19564, with remainder 556
There are 3 groups of 144 in 556, with remainder 124
There are 10 groups of 12 in 124, with remainder 4
There are 4 groups of 1 in 4, with remainder 0
Thus $40300 = 1E3T4_{twelve}$

18. $42_{eight} = 4 \cdot 8 + 2 = 34$
There is 1 group of 32 in 34, with remainder 2
There are 0 groups of 16 in 2, with remainder 2
There are 0 groups of 8 in 2, with remainder 2
There are 0 groups of 4 in 2, with remainder 2
There is 1 group of 2 in 2, with remainder 0
There are 0 groups of 1 in 0, with remainder 0
Thus $42_{eight} = 34 = 100010_{two}$

19. (a) $432_{five} = 4 \cdot 5^2 + 3 \cdot 5 + 2 = 100 + 15 + 2 = 117$

(b) $101101_{two} = 1 \cdot 2^5 + 1 \cdot 2^3 + 1 \cdot 2^2 + 1 = 32 + 8 + 4 + 1 = 45$

(c) $92E_{twelve} = 9 \cdot 12^2 + 2 \cdot 12 + 11 = 1296 + 24 + 11 = 1331$

(d) $TOE_{twelve} = 10 \cdot 12^2 + 11 = 1440 + 11 = 1451$

(e) $111_{twelve} = 1 \cdot 12^2 + 1 \cdot 12 + 1 = 144 + 12 + 1 = 157$

(f) $346_{seven} = 3 \cdot 7^2 + 4 \cdot 7 + 6 = 181$

20. $2 \cdot 25¢ + 4 \cdot 5¢ + 2 \cdot 1¢ = 72¢$; this is $2 \cdot 5^2 + 4 \cdot 5 + 2 = 242_{five} \Rightarrow$ the fortune is 242_{five} ¢

21. To give the fewest number of prizes, the dollar amount of each must be maximized. Thus $900 =
1 prize at $625 with $275 left over
2 prizes at $125 with $25 left over
1 prize at $25 with nothing left over; thus no $5 or $1 prizes awarded
Notice that 900 has been converted to base five, or 12100_{five}

22. $97¢ = 342_{five}$ ¢ $\Rightarrow$ 3 quarters, 4 nickels, and 2 pennies

23. (a) There are 8 groups of 7 days (1 week), with 2 days left over, so 58 days = 8 weeks and 2 days

(b) There are 4 groups of 12 months (1 year), with 6 months left over, so 54 months = 4 years and 6 months

(c) There is 1 group of 24 hours (1 day), with 5 hours left over, so 29 hours = 1 day and 5 hours

(d) There are 5 groups of 12 (5 feet), with 8 inches left over, so 68 inches = 5 feet 8 inches

24. $\text{Pencils}_{twelve} = 11 \cdot 12^2 + 6 \cdot 12 + 6 = E66_{twelve}$; $\text{Pencils}_{ten} = 11 \cdot 144 + 6 \cdot 12 + 6 = 1662$

25. (a) There are 6 groups of 7 in 44 $\Rightarrow$ b = 6

(b) Subtracting 5 groups of 144 from 734 leaves 14; there is 1 group of 12 in 14 $\Rightarrow$ b = 1

(c) There must be 2 groups of b in 23, with remainder 5; thus $2b + 5 = 23 \Rightarrow 2b = 18 \Rightarrow b = 9$
Thus $23_{ten} = 25_{nine}$

26. (a) The minimum number of coins totaling 117 pennies is 4 quarters, 3 nickels, and 2 pennies

(b) 2 quarters = 50 pennies; 4 nickels = 20 pennies $\Rightarrow$ she would have 50 + 20 + 3 = 73 pennies

27. (*i*) 5's, 50's, 500's, and 5000's are depicted above the bar. 1's, 10's, 100's, and 1000's are below the bar. Thus there are $1 \cdot 5000$, $1 \cdot 500$, $3 \cdot 100$, $1 \cdot 50$, $1 \cdot 5$, and $3 \cdot 1$ depicted for a total of 5857.

    (*ii*) The number 4869 could be depicted as follows:

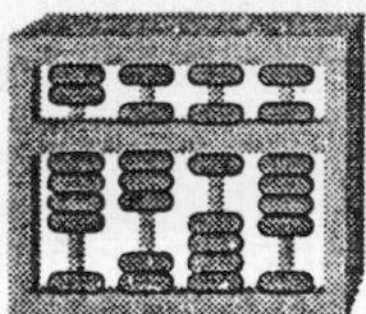

28. On most calculators enter [9] [×] [×] [9] and then depress the [=] key six times $\Rightarrow$ $9^7 = 4{,}782{,}969$

29. (a) If your calculator has an eight-digit display, the largest possible number using these keys only once would be 98,765,432

    (b) 12,345,678

    (c) 99,999,999

    (d) 11,111,111

30. (a) We need to subtract a number with a 2 in the thousands place and a 2 in the tens place, or 2020 $\Rightarrow$ 32,420 – 2020 = 30,400

    (b) 67,357 – 50 = 67,307

On-going Assessment 3-2

1. (a) 5 is less than 7 if and only if there exists a natural number k such that $5 + k = 7$. In this case, $k = 2$ (a natural number).

   (b) 6 is greater than 3 if and only if there exists a natural number k such that $3 + k = 6 \Rightarrow k = 3$

2. No (If $k = 0$, we would have $k = 0 + k$, implying $k > k$)

3. Suppose A and B were not disjoint; let A = {1, 2, 3} and B = {3, 4, 5}. Then A ∪ B = {1, 2, 3, 4, 5} and $n(A \cup B) = 5$. But $n(A) + n(B) = 3 + 3 = 6$; thus sets must be disjoint to define addition.

4. (a) Closed

   (b) Closed

   (c) Closed

   (d) Not closed ($3 + 7 \notin \{3, 5, 7\}$)

   (e) Closed

5. Answers may vary; one example would be:

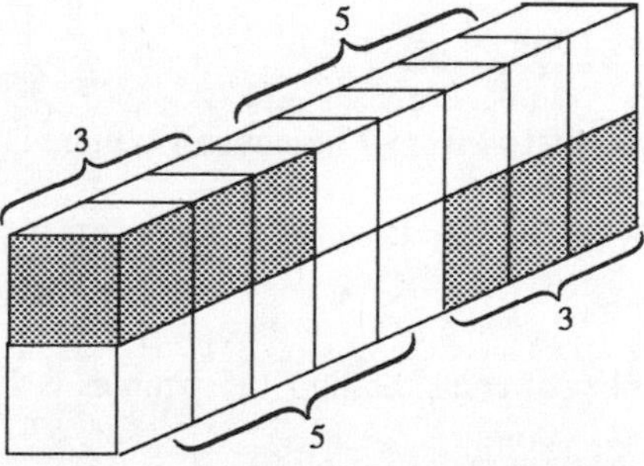

6. (a) $x = 119 + 213$

   (b) $213 = x + 119$

   (c) $213 = 119 + x$

7. (a) Commutative property of addition (b) Associative property of addition

   (c) Commutative property of addition [i.e., $(6 + 3) = (3 + 6)$]

8. (a) $3280 < 3802, 3820, \text{ or } 8023 < 8032$

   (b) $2803 < 2830, 3028, 3082, 3208, 3280, \text{ or } 3802 < 3820$

9. (a) Each term is found by adding 5 to the previous term $\Rightarrow$ the next three are $28 + 5 = \underline{33}$, $33 + 5 = \underline{38}$, and $38 + 5 = \underline{43}$

   (b) Each term is found by subtracting 7 from the previous term $\Rightarrow$ the next three are $63 - 7 = \underline{56}$, $56 - 7 = \underline{49}$, and $49 - 7 = \underline{42}$

10. (a) 9 (a number greater than 9 would have two digits)

    (b) 8 (if A were larger, C must be larger than 9)

    (c) 3 ($A + B$ must be 1 and 2; no smaller single digit numbers are available)

    (d) 6 or 8 (A and B must be 2 and 4 or 2 and 6)

    (e) 5 ($A + B = C$ and C is 5 more than A $\Rightarrow$ $A + 5 = C$)

    (f) 4 or 8 (B could be 1 and A then must be 3; or B could be 2 and then A must be 6)

    (g) 9 (B must be 2 and A must be 7)

11. (a) $C = 1$ (addition of no two different single-digit numbers will result in a sum greater than 17)

    (b) No ($C = 1$) (c) A can be 8 or 9

    (d) D can only be 2

12. Note that even rows sum to 0, while odd rows sum to 1. Since row 50 is even, its sum is 0.

13. (a) The total of 6, 7, and 2 in the right column is 15. Then 8 must be added to 1 and 6 in the top row to give 15; 3 must be added to 5 and 7 in the middle row to give 15; etc. Thus:

8	1	6
3	5	7
4	9	2

    (b) 10, 14, and 18 in the middle column sum to 42. Then 15 must be added to 17 and 10 in the top row to give 42; etc. Thus:

17	10	15
12	14	16
13	18	11

14. (a) Assign letters to each of the blanks, as follows:

a	b
c	d

14. (a) We can then write equations: $a + b = 11$; $a + c = 12$; and $b + c = 7$.
Solving this system of equations, we find: $a = 8$, $b = 3$, and $c = 4$. Substituting these values for a, b, and c, then d must equal 12, and so our squares are:

8	3
4	12

(b) Not necessarily (the systems of equations must have whole-number solutions)

15. (a) Answers may vary; for example:

1	2
3	5
4	6

(b) Yes, for example:

1	3
2	5
4	6

or

1	4
2	5
3	6

16. (a) 28 dominos (7 doubles plus $7 \cdot 6 \div 2$ others)

(b) The sum of the dots is the same, whether adding from left to right or from right to left

17. If Millie and Samantha both start with \$0, then Millie's savings will be \$3, \$6, \$9, ... and Samantha's will be \$5, \$10, \$15, ... After five months Millie will have \$15 and Samantha will have \$25. (Or: Samantha saves \$2 more than Millie each month, so it will take $10 \div 2 = 5$ months)

18. Look for a pattern:
2 nails on each axis → 1 intersection
3 nails on each axis → 3 intersections → 2 new ones
4 nails on each axis → 6 intersections → 3 new ones
5 nails on each axis → 10 intersections → 4 new ones
⋮
6 nails → 15 intersections
7 nails → 21 intersections
8 nails → 28 intersections
9 nails → 36 intersections
10 nails → 45 intersections

19. (a) [7] [×] [10] [=] (70)

(b) [9] [×] [1000] [=] (9000)

(c) [11] [×] [100] [=] (1100)

(d) [56] [×] [10] [=] (560)

(e) [347] [×] [10] [=] (3470)

20. Calculators may vary; some systems are shown below:

(a) Enter **1** + + **1** = = = ... = = (100 times)

(b) Enter **2** + + **2** = = = ... = = (50 times)

(c) Enter **5** + + **5** = = = ... = = (20 times)

21. Calculators may vary; some systems are shown below:

(a) Enter $^{-}$**1** + + **27** = = = ... = = (27 times)

(b) Enter $^{-}$**3** + + **27** = = = = = = = = =

(c) Enter $^{-}$**9** + + **27** = = =

22. Calculators may vary; one example is: **2 + + 2 = = ⋯ = =** (thirteen times) returns 26

23. The number of guests on successive rings is 1, 3, 5, ... $\Rightarrow$ the arithmetic sequence $1 + 2 + 3 + \cdots$
Using the methods of chapter 1:

$$\text{20th term} = \text{1st term} + (\text{number of terms} - 1) \cdot \text{constant difference} = 1 + (20 - 1)2 = 39$$

$$\text{Sum of terms} = \frac{\text{number of terms}}{2} \cdot (\text{1st term} + \text{last term}) = \frac{20}{2}(1 + 39) = 400$$

So there were 400 guests

24. (a) $\boxed{\text{Kent}} < \boxed{\text{Mischa}} < \boxed{\text{Sally}} < \boxed{\text{Vera}}$
Kent is shortest; Vera is tallest

(b) Answers may vary, as long as the player's heights increase in the order Kent < Mischa < Sally < Vera

On-going Assessment 3-2; Review Problems

37. (a) Subtracting 1 from 10 (or X), we have CMLIX

(b) Subtracting 1 from 9 (or IX), we have XXXVIII

38. There are fewer symbols to remember, place value is used, and after 300 B.C. there was a symbol for 0

39. $5286 = 5 \cdot 10^3 + 2 \cdot 10^2 + 8 \cdot 10^1 + 6 \cdot 1$

On-going Assessment 3-3

1. 5 tickets × \$2 + 5 tickets × \$5 = \$10 + \$25 = \$35

2. (a) $3 \cdot \boxed{5} = 15$ (b) $18 = 6 + 3 \cdot \boxed{4}$

(c) $\boxed{x} \cdot (5 + 6) = \boxed{x} \cdot 5 + \boxed{x} \cdot 6$, where x may be any whole number

3. The sets must be disjoint (if A = {1, 2}, B = {2, 3}, and C = {3, 4}, then:
$A \cup B \cup C = \{1, 2, 3, 4\}$ and $n(A \cup B \cup C) = 4$, implying falsely that $3 \cdot 2 = 4$)

4. Let set A contain 2 elements. Let set B be the empty set. Since there are no elements in B, there are no ordered pairs in the Cartesian product $\Rightarrow 2 \cdot 0 = n(A \times B) = 0$.

5. (a) Closed ($0 \cdot 0 = 0$, $0 \cdot 1 = 0$, $1 \cdot 0 = 0$, and $1 \cdot 1 = 1$ are all products contained in {0, 1})

(b) Closed ($0 \cdot 0 = 0$, and $0 \in \{0\}$)

(c) Closed (the product of any two even numbers is also an even number)

(d) Closed (the product of any two odd numbers is also an odd number)

(e) Closed (if we multiply any two terms in the sequence, we will still have an arithmetic sequence with 1st term 1 and difference 3)

(f) No ($2 \cdot 2 = 4 \notin \{0, 1, 2\}$)

6. (a) No $(2 + 3 = 5)$

(b) Yes (there will be no products with unit digit equal to 5)

(c) (*i*) No $(2 + 4 = 6)$ (*ii*) No $(2 \cdot 3 = 6)$

7. (a) Given $(a + b)(c + d)$ and applying the distributive property twice, we have:
$$a(c + d) + b(c + d) = ac + ad + bc + bd$$

(b) $3 \cdot x + 3 \cdot y + 3 \cdot 5 = 3x + 3y + 15$ (c) $\square \cdot \triangle + \square \cdot \circ$

(d) $x(x + y + z) + y(x + y + z) = xx + xy + xz + yx + yy + yz = xx + xy + xy + xz + yy + yz$
$= x^2 + 2xy + xz + y^2 + yz$

8. (a) $(4 + 3) \times 2 = 14$

(b) $(9 \div 3) + 1 = 4$ (parentheses unnecessary)

(c) $(5 + 4 + 9) \div 3 = 6$

(d) $(3 + 6 - 2) \div 1 = 7$ or $3 + 6 - 2 \div 1 = 7$

9. $a(b + c + d) = a[(b + c) + d] = a(b + c) + ad = ab + ac + ad$

10. (a) $18 \div 3 = \boxed{6}$ (b) $\boxed{0} \div 76 = 0$

(c) $28 \div \boxed{4} = 7$

11. (a)

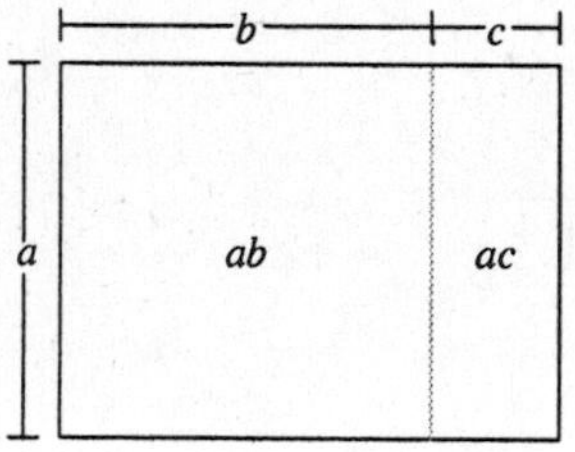

a (b + c) = ab + ac

(b)

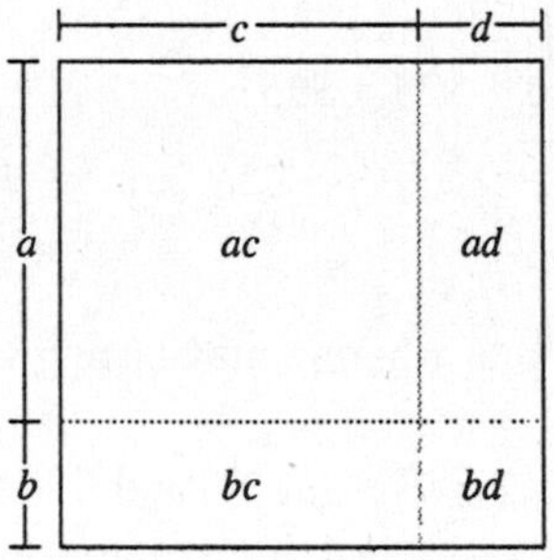

(a + b)(c + d) = ac + ad + bc + bd

12. (a) $40 = 8 \cdot 5$ (b) $326 = 2 \cdot x$

(c) $48 = x \cdot 16$ (d) $x = 5 \cdot 17$

13. (*i*) The original number is returned. (*ii*) Yes.

(*iii*) If n is the original number: $\frac{2n+2}{2} - 1 = \frac{2(n+1)}{2} - 1 = n + 1 - 1 = n$

14. (a) $2 \div 1 \neq 1 \div 2$ (b) $(8 \div 4) \div 2 \neq 8 \div (4 \div 2)$

(c) $8 \div (2 + 2) \neq (8 \div 2) + (8 \div 2)$ (d) $3 \div 4 \notin W$

15. \$160 $\div$ 5 months = \$32 per month

16. (*i*) 17 sandwiches $\div$ 7 people = 2 whole sandwiches for each person

16. (*ii*) $17 - 2 \cdot 7 = 3$ sandwiches left over

17. (a) (1,36), (2,18), (3, 12), (4, 9), (6, 6), (9, 4), (12, 3), (18, 2), (36, 1)

(b)

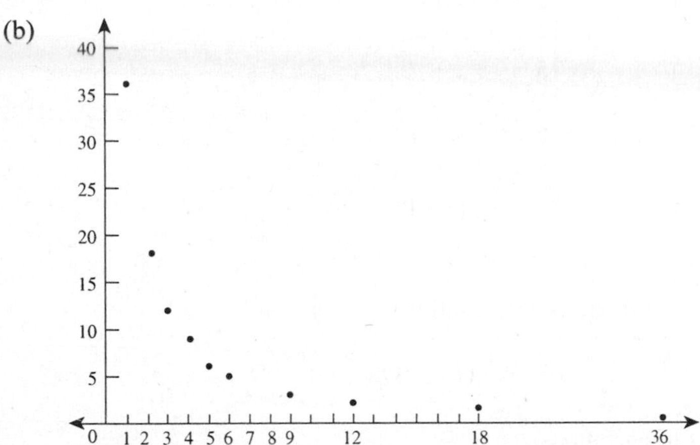

(c) The pattern formed by adding all pairs of whole numbers having a sum of 36 would be a straight line

18. Answers may vary; one possibility is:

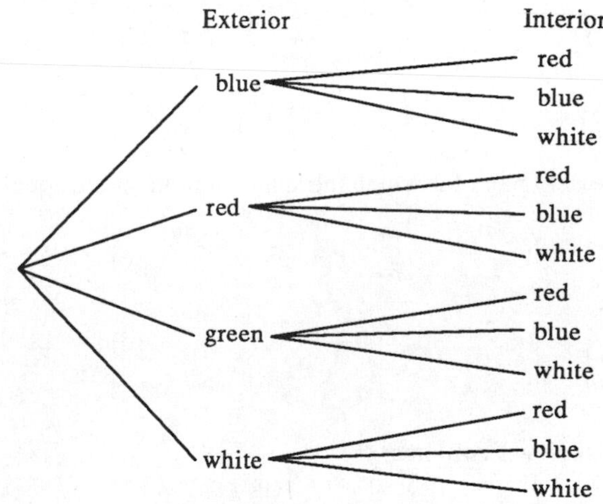

19. Tony has 6 ways to continue after each of the 5 ways to the park $\Rightarrow$ total number of choices is $5 \cdot 6 = 30$

20. 8 teams $\times$ 9 players per team = 72 players $\Rightarrow$ 72 players $\div$ 6 players per team = 12 teams

21. (a) $28 \div 5 = 5.6 \rightarrow 5 \times 5 = 25 \rightarrow 28 - 25 = 3$ (the remainder)

(b) $32 \div 10 = 3.2 \rightarrow 10 \times 3 = 30 \rightarrow 32 - 30 = 2$ (the remainder)

(c) $29 \div 3 = 9.\overline{6} \rightarrow 3 \times 9 = 27 \rightarrow 29 - 27 = 2$ (the remainder)

(d) $41 \div 7 = 5.\overline{857142} \rightarrow 7 \times 5 = 35 \rightarrow 41 - 35 = 6$ (the remainder)

(e) $49{,}382 \div 14 = 3527.\overline{285714} \rightarrow 14 \times 3527 = 49{,}378 \rightarrow 49{,}382 - 49{,}378 = 4$ (the remainder)

22. Answers may vary; for example (after $1 = 9 - 7 - 1$ and $2 = 1 \cdot 9 - 7$):

(a)
$3 = 1 + 9 - 7$
$4 = 1^7 + \sqrt{9}$
$5 = 7 - \sqrt{9} + 1$
$6 = 7 - 1^9$
$7 = 7 \times 1^9$
$8 = 7 + 1^9$
$9 = 1^7 \times 9$
$10 = 1^7 + 9$
$11 = 7 + 1 + \sqrt{9}$
$12 = 19 - 7$
$13 = 91 \div 7$
$14 = 7(\sqrt{9} - 1)$
$15 = 7 + 9 - 1$
$16 = (7 + 9) \times 1$
$17 = 7 + 9 + 1$
$18 = \sqrt{9}\,(7 - 1)$
$20 = 7\sqrt{9} - 1$

(b) $(4 \cdot 4 \cdot 4 - 4 - 4 - 4) \div 4$ and $4 \div 4 + 4 + 4 + 4$ are two possibilities

(c) $22 + 2$

(d) $111 - 11$

23. Choice (a) is correct (it illustrates the proper order of operations)

24. (a) Subtract 18

(b) Divide 54 by 9

(c) Add 11 to 48

(d) Add 8

25. No $\left(\frac{x}{x} \neq 1 \text{ when } x = 0\right)$

26. Yes (if $x = 0$ or $x = 1$)

27. (0, 0) and (2, 2) are the only pairs for which the sum and product are equal

28. (a) $\frac{A}{\pi}$

(b) $\frac{f}{3}$

(c) 60h

(d) $\frac{d}{7}$

On-going Assessment 3-3; Review Problems

39. Egyptian: ∩∩∩∩∩∩∩|||||
Roman: LXXV
Babylonian: ▼ <▼▼▼▼▼

40. Points representing these pairs are in a straight line

41. Addition: $5, 5 + 5, 5 + 5 + 5, 5 + 5 + 5 + 5, \cdots$
Multiplication: $5 \cdot 1, 5 \cdot 2, 5 \cdot 3, 5 \cdot 4, \cdots$

42. $35{,}206 = 3 \cdot 10^4 + 5 \cdot 10^3 + 2 \cdot 10^2 + 0 \cdot 10^1 + 6 \cdot 1$

43. $\{1, 2\}$ $(1 + 2 = 3 \notin \{1, 2\})$

44. Subtraction is not commutative (for example, $3 - 2 \neq 2 - 3$)

45.

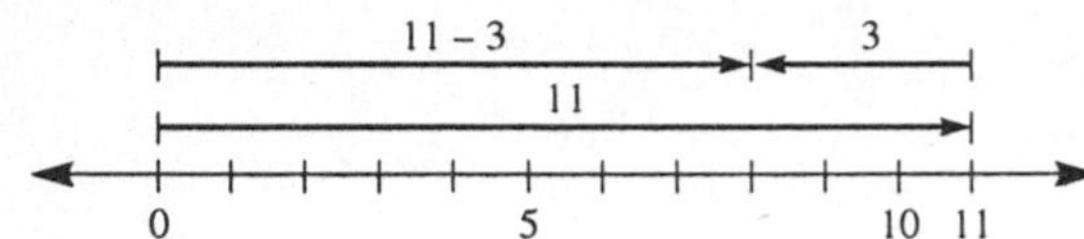

On-going Assessment 3-4

1. (a)
$$\begin{array}{r} 9\ 8\ 1 \\ +\ 4\ 2\ 1 \\ \hline 1\ 4\ 0\ 2 \end{array}$$

(b)
$$\begin{array}{r} 2\ 0\ 2\ 5 \\ 1\ 1\ 9\ 6 \\ +\ 3\ 1\ 4\ 8 \\ \hline 6\ 3\ 6\ 9 \end{array}$$

(c)
$$\begin{array}{r} 1\ 0\ 6\ 9 \\ 2\ 0\ 9\ 4 \\ 9\ 5\ 4\ 6 \\ 9\ 0\ 0\ 3 \\ +\ 7\ 0\ 6\ 4 \\ \hline 2\ 8\ 7\ 7\ 6 \end{array}$$

(d)
$$\begin{array}{r} 2\ 9\ 1 \\ 4\ 5\ 1 \\ +\ 5\ 8\ 4 \\ \hline 1\ 3\ 2\ 6 \end{array}$$

2. (a)
$$\begin{array}{r} 8\ 7\ 6\ 9\ 3 \\ -\ 4\ 6\ 4\ 1\ 4 \\ \hline 4\ 1\ 2\ 7\ 9 \end{array}$$

(b)
$$\begin{array}{r} 8\ 1\ 3\ 5 \\ -\ 4\ 6\ 8\ 2 \\ \hline 3\ 4\ 5\ 3 \end{array}$$

(c)
$$\begin{array}{r} 3\ 8\ 3 \\ -\ 1\ 5\ 9 \\ \hline 2\ 2\ 4 \end{array}$$

(d)
$$\begin{array}{r} 1\ 3\ 2\ 9\ 6 \\ -\ \ 8\ 3\ 0\ 9 \\ \hline 4\ 9\ 8\ 7 \end{array}$$

3. (a)
$$\begin{array}{r} \boxed{7}\boxed{6}\boxed{2} \\ +\ \boxed{8}\boxed{5}\boxed{3} \\ \hline 1\ 6\ 1\ 5 \end{array}$$

(b)
$$\begin{array}{r} \boxed{2}\boxed{6}\boxed{7} \\ +\ \boxed{3}\boxed{5}\boxed{8} \\ \hline 6\ 2\ 5 \end{array}$$

4. (a)
$$\begin{array}{r} \boxed{8}\boxed{7}\boxed{6} \\ -\ \boxed{2}\boxed{3}\boxed{5} \\ \hline 6\ 4\ 1 \end{array}$$

(b)
$$\begin{array}{r} \boxed{6}\boxed{2}\boxed{3} \\ -\ \boxed{5}\boxed{8}\boxed{7} \\ \hline 3\ 6 \end{array}$$

5. 125 + 137 + 238 = 500 books were added ⇒ 15,282 + 500 = 15,782 books at year's end

6. (a) Each term of the sequence is found by adding 5 to the preceding term ⇒ the next three are: 29 + 5 = 34; 34 + 5 = 39; 39 + 5 = 44

   (b) Each term of the sequence is found by subtracting 3 from the preceding term ⇒ the next three are: 85 – 3 = 82; 82 – 3 = 79; 79 – 3 = 76

7. Maria spends 25¢ + 15¢ + 17¢ = 57¢ ⇒ 87¢ – 57¢ = 30¢ is left over

8. By dinner time Tom had consumed 90 + 120 + 119 + 185 + 110 + 570 = 1194 calories. Subtracting from 1500: 1500 – 1194 = 306. Tom may have steak or salad, but not both.

9. Wally's income was $150 + $54 + $260 = $464. His expenses were $22 + $60 + $15 + $58 + $185 = $340. Wally's savings were $464 – $340 = $124.

10.
$$\begin{array}{r} \boxed{3}\,\boxed{4}\,\boxed{2}\,\boxed{8} \\ +\ \boxed{5}\,\boxed{6}\,\boxed{3}\,\boxed{1} \\ \hline 9\ \ 0\ \ 5\ \ 9 \end{array}$$

11. (a) (*i*) Clustering can be used when a group of numbers cluster around a common value. In case (*i*), the numbers are at wide variance, so clustering would not be a good strategy.

(*ii*) These numbers cluster around 500, so the strategy would be a good one.

(b) (*i*) Case (*i*): Total value of lead digits is 1000 + 2000 = 3000. 64 + 445 is about 500. 474 + 467 is about 900. The estimate is about 3000 + 500 + 900 = 4400. (The exact sum is 4450)

Case (*ii*): Total value of lead digits is 400 + 400 + 500 + 500 + 500 = 2300. 83 + 28 is about 100. 75 + 30 is about 100. 3 may be disregarded. The estimate is about 2300 + 100 + 100 = 2500. (The exact sum is 2519)

(*ii*) Case (*i*): 64 + 2445 is about 2500. 1467 + 474 is about 1900. The estimate is about 2500 + 1900 = 4400.

Case (*ii*): 503 is about 500. 528 + 475 is about 1000. 530 + 483 is about 1000. The estimate is about 500 + 1000 + 1000 = 2500.

(*iii*) Case (*i*): 474 rounds to 500; 1467 rounds to 1500; 64 rounds to 100; 2445 rounds to 2400. The estimate is 500 + 1500 + 100 + 2400 = 4500.

Case (*ii*): 483 rounds to 500; 475 rounds to 500; 530 rounds to 500; 503 rounds to 500; 528 rounds to 500. The estimate is $5 \cdot 500 = 2500$.

12. Her estimate is too high [38 + 74 is about 100; 92 + 17 is about 100. If we add 100 + 100 + 130, we get an estimate of about 330 (the exact sum is 351).]

13. (a) 2 years is 104 weeks; 4 months is about 16 weeks; 9 days is about 1 week ⇒ Lewis and Clark spent about 104 weeks + 16 weeks + 1 week = 121 weeks in the Northwest

(b) 1126 days ÷ 365 days per year is slightly over 3 years

(c) There are 365 days per year × 24 hours per day × 60 minutes per hour × 60 seconds per minute = 31,536,000 seconds per year ⇒ if you are age 20, you have lived 630,720,000 seconds

(d) There are 365 days per year × 24 hours per day × 60 minutes per hour = 525,600 minutes per year. If your average pulse is 72, your heart will beat 72 × 525,600 = 37,843,200 times per year.

14.

Hawks	15	32	40	33	120
Elks	20	25	47	39	131

15. (a) (*i*)
$$\begin{array}{r} 6\ 8\ 7 \\ +\ 5\ 4\ 9 \\ \hline 1\ 6 \\ 1\ 2\ \ \\ 1\ 1\ \ \ \ \\ \hline 1\ 2\ 3\ 6 \end{array}$$

(*ii*)
$$\begin{array}{r} 3\ 5\ 9 \\ +\ 6\ 7\ 3 \\ \hline 1\ 2 \\ 1\ 2\ \ \\ 9\ \ \ \ \\ \hline 1\ 0\ 3\ 2 \end{array}$$

(b) Placing partial sums under their addends maintains place value (the process would have to be adapted if more than two numbers were added)

16. (a) A tens digit was not carried when the sum of the units digits was more than 9

    (b) Partial sums are not in the correct place value position

    (c) The units minuend is subtracted from the subtrahend

    (d) 1 tens value should have been borrowed from the 5 in the minuend's ten position

17. 75 minutes + 18 minutes + 45 seconds + 30 seconds = 93 minutes + 75 seconds
= 93 minutes + 1 minute + 15 seconds = 94 minutes + 15 seconds = 1 hour + 34 minutes + 15 seconds
So George's meal required 1 hour 34 minutes 15 seconds cooking time.

18. (a)
```
  1
  43
+ 23
 121five
```
(b)
```
  42
- 23
  20five
```
(c)
```
  1 1
  4 3 2
+   2 3
1 0 1 0five
```
(d)
```
  3 12
  42
- 2 3
  1 4five
```
(e)
```
  1
  1 1 0
+   1 1
1 0 0 1two
```
(f)
```
  1 1
  1Ø 1Ø 10
1 Ø Ø Ø 1
-   1 1 1
  1 0 1 0two
```

19. (*i*) Addition:

+	0	1	2	3	4	5	6	7
0	0	1	2	3	4	5	6	7
1	1	2	3	4	5	6	7	10
2	2	3	4	5	6	7	11	12
3	3	4	5	6	7	10	11	12
4	4	5	6	7	10	11	12	13
5	5	6	7	10	11	12	13	14
6	6	7	10	11	12	13	14	15
7	7	10	11	12	13	14	15	16

Base Eight

(*ii*) Multiplication:

×	0	1	2	3	4	5	6	7
0	0	0	0	0	0	0	0	0
1	0	1	2	3	4	5	6	7
2	0	2	4	6	10	12	14	16
3	0	3	6	11	14	17	22	25
4	0	4	10	14	20	24	30	34
5	0	5	12	17	24	31	36	43
6	0	6	14	22	30	36	44	52
7	0	7	16	25	34	43	52	61

Base Eight

20. (a)

1	1	
3 hours	36 minutes	58 seconds
+ 5 hours	56 minutes	27 seconds
9 hours	33 minutes	25 seconds

(b)

	95	
4	35	98
5 hours	36 minutes	38 seconds
− 3 hours	56 minutes	58 seconds
1 hour	39 minutes	40 seconds

21. (a) Since 2 cups is 1 pint and 2 pints is 1 quart, we are essentially operating in base 2:

1	1		
1 quart	1 pint	1 cup	
+	1 pint	1 cup	
2 quarts	1 pint	0 cups	(or 1 half-gallon, 0 quarts, 1 pint, 0 cups)

(b) Again, we are essentially in base 2; we must borrow 2 pints from 1 quart in order to subtract 1 pint:

	2	
1 quart		1 cup
-	1 pint	1 cup
	1 pint	0 cups

(c) Since there are 4 cups in 1 quart and 4 quarts in 1 gallon, we are essentially in base 4:

	6		
0	2	5	
1 gallon	3 quarts	1 cup	
-	4 quarts	2 cups	
	2 quarts	3 cups	(or 2 quarts, 1 pint, 1 cup)

22. 20 friends × 2 cups each = 40 cups needed. There are 2 cups per pint × 2 pints per quart × 4 quarts per gallon, or 16 cups per gallon. 40 cups needed ÷ 16 cups per gallon = 2.5 gallons; she would have to buy 3 gallons to have enough.

23. (a) (*i*) 93 + 39 = 132; 132 + 231 = 363, which is a palindrome

(*ii*) 588 + 885 = 1473; 1473 + 3741 = 5214; 5214 + 4125 = 9339, which is a palindrome

(*iii*) 2003 + 3002 = 5005, which is a palindrome

(b) Answers may vary; 89 or 97 are examples

24. We want to work around 700 + 300, since that sum is the closest to the 1111 for which we are trying:

```
   0 0 0
   7 7 0
   0 0 0
   3 3 0
 + 0 1 1
 -------
 1 1 1 1
```

25. Trial and error (preferably with a calculator) will yield 8 + 8 + 8 + 88 + 888 = 1000. The starting point would be 888, since that is close to but not over 1000; the other values come with the remaining five 8's.

26. (a)

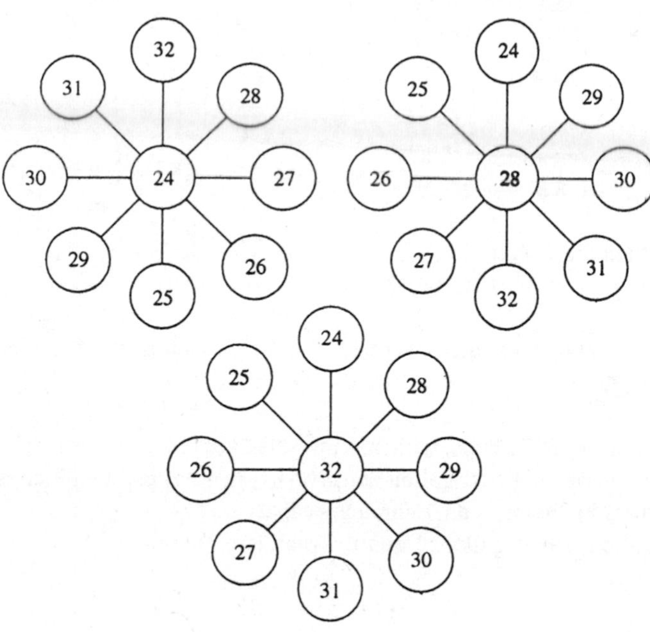

(b) Three (24, 28, or 32)

27. It appears that the second number was being doubled: 8 + 6 + 6 = 20; 5 + 4 + 4 = 13; 15 − 3 − 3 = 9

28. (a) Each sums to 34

(b) The sum is 34

(c) The sum is 34

(d) Yes [all rows, columns, and diagonals still contain four numbers; adding 11 to each adds 44 to all sums and they are still equal (to 78)]

(e) Yes [this subtracts 44 from all sums and they are still equal (to ⁻10)]

29. (a)

$$\begin{array}{rrrr} & {}^{1}4 & {}^{1}3 & 2 \\ & 9_4 & 7_1 & 6 \\ + \; {}^{1}1 & 4 & 1 & 8_6 \\ \hline 2 & 8 & 2 & 6 \end{array}$$

(b)

$$\begin{array}{rrr} & {}^{3} & \\ & 3_1 & 2 \\ & 1 & 3_0 \\ & 2 & 2 \\ & 4_3 & 3_0 \\ & 2_0 & 3 \\ + & 1 & 2_0 \\ \hline 3 & 1 & 0_{five} \end{array}$$

30. (a)

		15	
	3	3	18
	4 gross	4 dozen	6 ones
−		5 dozen	9 ones
	3 gross	10 dozen	9 ones

(b)

	1	1	
	2 gross	9 dozen	7 ones
+	3 gross	5 dozen	9 ones
	6 gross	3 dozen	4 ones

31. (a) If each student receives 1 cup, then there were:
1 pint = 2 cups
1 quart = 2 pints = 4 cups
1 gallon = 4 quarts = 8 pints = 16 cups $\Rightarrow$ there were $2 + 4 + 16 = 22$ cups, or 22 students

(b) 31 students = 31 cups
There is 1 group of 16 (or 1 gallon) in 31 cups, with 15 cups left over
There are 3 groups of 4 (or 3 quarts, or 1 half-gallon and 1 quart) in 15 cups, with 3 cups left over
There is 1 group of 2 (or 1 pint) in 3 cups, with 1 cup left over
$\Rightarrow$ it was necessary to buy 1 gallon, 1 half-gallon, 1 quart, 1 pint, and 1 cup

32. (a) $3 \cdot 20 + 10 = 70$ (b) $4 \cdot 20 + 7 = 87$

33. There is no numeral 5 in base five

34. (a)

$$\begin{array}{rrrr} & 2 & 3 & 0 \\ - & & 2 & 2 \\ \hline & 2 & 0 & 3_{five} \end{array}$$

(b)

$$\begin{array}{rrrrrr} & 2 & 0 & 0 & 1 & 0 \\ - & & 2 & 0 & 2 & 2 \\ \hline & 1 & 0 & 2 & 1 & 1_{three} \end{array}$$

On-going Assessment 3-4; Review Problems

44. If our proposed plan for a metric system is to use base 10 as a foundation, then each time the decimal point is moved it will convert to a different unit

45. $5280 = 5 \cdot 10^3 + 2 \cdot 10^2 + 8 \cdot 10^1 + 0 \cdot 1$

46. Answers may vary: $3 + (4 + 5) = (3 + 4) + 5 \Rightarrow 3 + 9 = 7 + 5$ is one example

47.

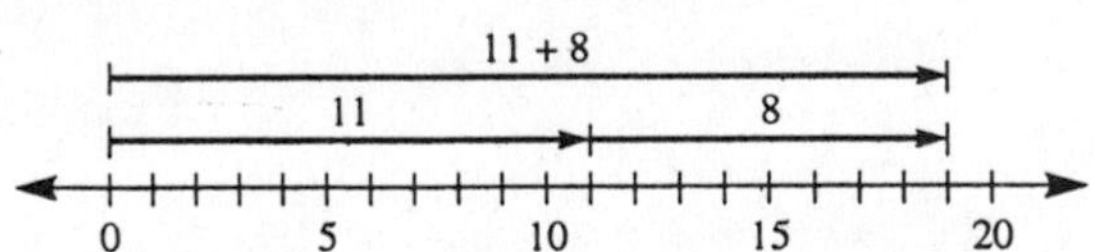

48. $\overline{\text{M}}$ indicates $1000 \cdot 1000 \Rightarrow \overline{\text{M}}\text{CDX} = 1{,}000{,}410$

49. (a) $ax + a = a(x + 1)$ (b) $3(x + y) + a(x + y) = (3 + a)(x + y)$

50. 5 shirts with each of 3 pants is $5 \times 3 = 15$ combinations

On-going Assessment 3-5

1. (a) $728 \times 94 = 68{,}432$ (b) $306 \times 24 = 7344$

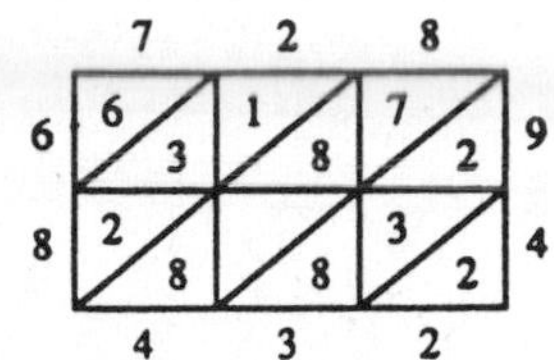

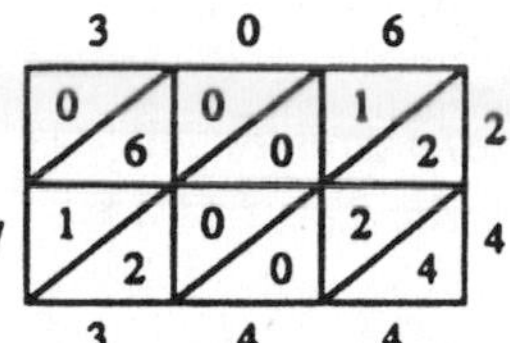

2. Diagonals separate place values as placement does in the conventional algorithm

3. (a) Start with multiplication of 4 _ 6 by 3. The _ must be 2, since we have carried 1 from $3 \cdot 6$, and only $3 \cdot 2 + 1 = 7$. Similar reasoning gives:

$$\begin{array}{r} 4\ 2\ 6 \\ \times \quad 7\ 8\ 3 \\ \hline 1\ 2\ 7\ 8 \\ 3\ 4\ 0\ 8\ \\ 2\ 9\ 8\ 2\ \ \\ \hline 3\ 3\ 3\ 5\ 5\ 8 \end{array}$$

(b)

$$\begin{array}{r} 3\ 2\ 7 \\ \times \quad 9\ 4\ 1 \\ \hline 3\ 2\ 7 \\ 1\ 3\ 0\ 8\ \\ 2\ 9\ 4\ 3\ \ \\ \hline 3\ 0\ 7\ 7\ 0\ 7 \end{array}$$

4. (a) Answers may vary. Assume one shower, six toilet flushes, three face/hand washings, five drinks, two teeth brushings, three dish washes, and two cookings (we'll have cold cereal for breakfast). Then $1 \cdot 75 + 6 \cdot 22 + 3 \cdot 7 + 5 \cdot 1 + 2 \cdot 1 + 3 \cdot 30 + 2 \cdot 18 = 361$ liters.

(b) The hypothetical person in (a) uses more water than average

(c) About $215{,}000{,}000 \cdot 200$ liters per day each $= 43{,}000{,}000{,}000$ liters per day

5. (a) There are $7 + 12 = 19$ factors of 5 $\Rightarrow$ $5^7 \cdot 5^{12} = 5^{7+12} = 5^{19}$

(b) $6^{10} \cdot 6^2 \cdot 6^3 = 6^{10+2+3} = 6^{15}$ (c) $10^{296} \cdot 10^{17} = 10^{296+17} = 10^{313}$

(d) $2^7 \cdot 10^5 \cdot 5^7 = 2^7 \cdot 5^7 \cdot 10^5 = (2 \cdot 5)^7 \cdot 10^5 = 10^7 \cdot 10^5 = 10^{7+5} = 10^{12}$

6. (a) 2^{100} is greater $(2^{80} + 2^{80} = 2^{80}(1 + 1) = 2 \cdot 2^{80} = 2^{81})$

(b) 2^{102} is greatest $(2^{101} = 2 \cdot 2^{100};\ 3 \cdot 2^{100} = 3 \cdot 2^{100};$ and $2^{102} = 2^2 \cdot 2^{100})$

7. (a)

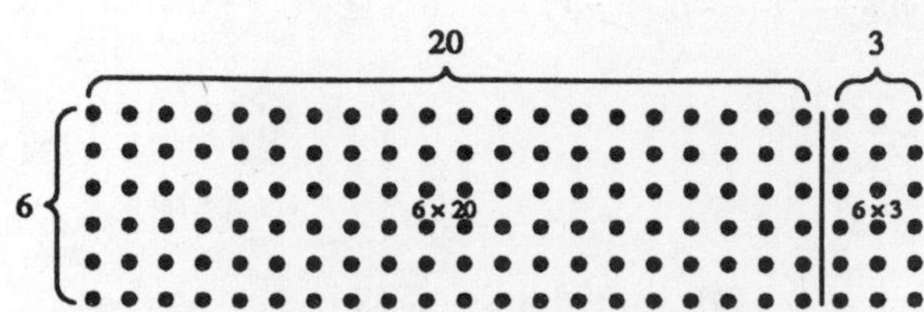

$6 \cdot 23 = 6 \cdot (20 + 3) = (6 \cdot 20) + (6 \cdot 3) = 138$

(b)

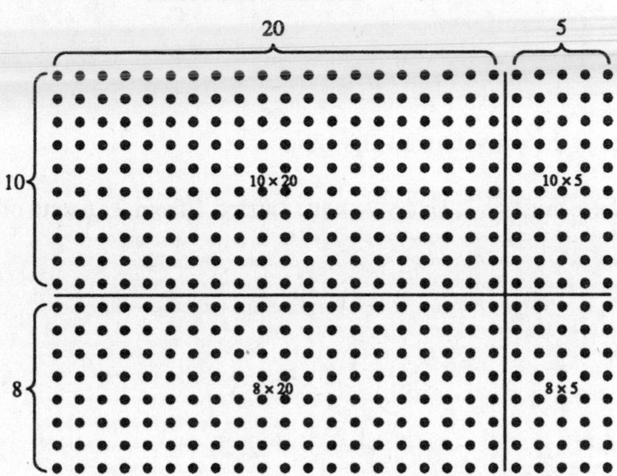

$18 \cdot 25 = (20 + 5) \cdot (10 + 8) = (20 \cdot 10) + (20 \cdot 8) + (5 \cdot 10) + (5 \cdot 8) = 450$

8. (a)

$$\begin{array}{r} 476 \\ \times\ 293 \\ \hline 1428 \\ 4284 \\ 952 \\ \hline 139468 \end{array}$$

(b) Placement still indicates place value

(c)

$$\begin{array}{rl} 363 & \\ \times\ 84 & \\ \hline 2904 & (8 \cdot 363) \\ 1452 & (4 \cdot 363) \\ \hline 30492 & \end{array}$$

9.

$$\begin{array}{lrcr} \rightarrow & 17 & \times & 63 \\ & 8 & & 126 \\ & 4 & & 252 \\ & 2 & & 504 \\ \rightarrow & 1 & & 1008 \end{array}$$

and $63 + 1008 = 1071$

10. (a) $300 \div 14 = 21$ with a remainder of 6. We can discard the remainder, since we are looking only for a whole number. Thus $14 \cdot 21 = 294 < 300 \Rightarrow n = 21$.

10. (b) $7459 \div 21 = 355$ with a remainder of 4. Thus $21 \cdot 355 = 7455 < 7459 \Rightarrow n = 355$.

(c) $2134 \div 7 = 304$ with remainder of 6. Thus $7 \cdot 304 = 2128 < 2134 \Rightarrow n = 304$.

(d) $79{,}485 \div 483 = 164$ with a remainder of 273. Thus $483 \cdot 164 = 79{,}212 < 79{,}485 \Rightarrow n = 164$.

11. (a) $300 \div 14 = 21$ plus a remainder. To find a number greater than 300, round up to 22; i.e., $21 \cdot 14$ is the greatest multiple less than 300, while $22 \cdot 14$ is the least multiple greater than 300 $\Rightarrow n = 22$.

(b) $4369 \div 23 = 189$ plus a remainder $\Rightarrow n = 190$

(c) $782 \div 183 = 6$ plus a remainder $\Rightarrow n = 7$

(d) $8654 \div 222 = 38$ plus a remainder $\Rightarrow n = 39$

12. (a) $15 \cdot 12 = (10 + 5) \cdot 12 = (10 \cdot 12) + (5 \cdot 12) = 120 + 60 = 180$

(b) $14 \cdot 102 = 14 \cdot (100 + 2) = (14 \cdot 100) + (14 \cdot 2) = 1400 + 28 = 1428$

(c) $30 \cdot 99 = 30 \cdot (100 - 1) = (30 \cdot 100) - (30 \cdot 1) = 3000 - 30 = 2970$

13. Use division to reverse multiplication and subtraction to reverse addition. We thus find:
Row 1: $a \cdot 56 = 3752 \Rightarrow 3752 \div 56 = a \Rightarrow a = 67$
Row 2: $32 + b = 110 \Rightarrow b = 110 - 32 \Rightarrow b = 78$
Row 3: We can write equations (*i*) $a + b = 33$ or $a = 33 - b$ (*ii*) $a \cdot b = 270$
Substituting (*i*) into (*ii*) gives: $(33 - b) \cdot b = 270 \Rightarrow b = 18$
Substituting $b = 18$ into (*i*) gives: $a = 15$

a	b	a · b	a + b
67	56	3752	123
32	78	2496	110
15	18	270	33

14. (a) $3 \cdot 444 = 1332$ calories

(b) Jane: $2 \cdot 462 = 924$ calories
Carolyn: $3 \cdot 198 = 594$ calories
Jane burned $924 - 594 = 330$ calories more

(c) Lyle: $3 \cdot 708 = 2124$ calories
Maurice: $5 \cdot 444 = 2220$ calories
Maurice burned $2220 - 2124 = 96$ calories more

15. 2 hours · 666 calories per hour = 1332 calories per day expended in swimming
$1500 - 1332 = 168$ calories per day increased intake
$168 \cdot 14 = 2352$ excess calories consumed in the 14 days $\Rightarrow$ $2352 < 3500$ so he gained less than 1 pound

16. \$24 per thousand · 30 thousands = \$720 total annual premiums $\Rightarrow$ \$720 ÷ 12 months = \$60 per month

17. (a) (*i*) Repeated Subtraction

```
8 | 6 2 3
    5 6 0     7 0  eights
      6 3
      5 6       7  eights
        7     7 7  remainder 7
```

(*ii*) Familiar

```
        7 7   remainder 7
8 | 6 2 3
    5 6
      6 3
      5 6
        7
```

(b) (*i*) Repeated Subtraction

```
3 6 | 2 9 8
      2 8 8     8  36's
        1 0     8  remainder 10
```

(*ii*) Familiar

```
              8   remainder 10
3 6 | 2 9 8
      2 8 8
        1 0
```

(c) (*i*) Repeated Subtraction

```
3 9 1 | 4 0 0 1
        3 9 1 0     10   391's
            9 1     10   remainder 91
```

(*ii*) Familiar

```
              1 0   remainder 91
3 9 1 | 4 0 0 1
        3 9 1
          9 1
```

18. (a) $3\overline{)876}$

(b) $8\overline{)367}$

19. (a) \$450 per month × 24 months = \$10,800; \$10,800 + \$1500 = \$12,300 total price if paid monthly
⇒ the monthly payment option is the more expensive

(b) \$12,300 – \$8600 = \$3700 more expensive if paid monthly

20. 64 × 1024 = 65,536 bits

21. Reverse the operation: 300 ÷ 10 = 30 ⇒ 30 ÷ 10 = 3 (the correct answer)

22. Income: 245 cars × \$2 per car = \$490 from washing cars + \$490 in school matching funds = \$980
Expenses: 350 miles × \$0.72 per mile = \$252 bus rent
2 nights × 20 members × \$5 per night = \$200 dorm fees
20 members × \$28 per member = \$560 meals
Total expenses = \$1012
Total expected expenses are greater than income ⇒ the band has not yet raised enough money
\$1012 – \$980 = \$32 still needed; at \$2 per car plus \$2 matching from the school ⇒ \$32 ÷ \$4 = 8 more cars to wash

23. When given an input, perform operations as noted on the function machines. When given an output, reverse the operations. For example:
Input 4: 4 + 5 = 9; 9 × 4 = 36; 36 – 6 = 30; 30 ÷ 2 = 15
Output 19: 19 × 2 = 38; 38 + 6 = 44; 44 ÷ 4 = 11; 11 – 5 = 6

Input	Output
2	11
4	15
0	7
6	19
12	31

24. (a) Choose 3, 6, and 7 ⇒ possible numbers are 36, 37, 63, 67, 73, and 76

24. (b) Sum = 352 (c) Sum = 16

(d) $353 \div 16 = 22$

(e) Numbers may vary. One set is 4, 5, and 9, from which 45, 49, 54, 59, 94, and 95 may be formed. Sum of the two-digit numbers is 396; sum of the one-digit numbers is 18. $396 \div 18 = 22$.

(f) Yes. Let the numbers be represented by a, b, and c. Then the possible two-digit numbers are:
$10a + b$, $10a + c$, $10b + c$, $10b + a$, $10c + a$, and $10c + b$.
Their sum is: $a(10 + 10 + 1 + 1) + b(10 + 10 + 1 + 1) + c(10 + 10 + 1 + 1)$
$= 22a + 22b + 22c = 22(a + b + c)$. Dividing by $(a + b + c)$ always gives 22.

25. (a) Examples may vary; one such is: $36 \cdot 84 = 3024$; $63 \cdot 48 = 3024$

(b) $(10a + b)(10c + d) = (10b + a)(10d + c) \Rightarrow 100ac + 10bc + 10ad + bd = 100bd + 10ad + 10bc + ac$
$\Rightarrow 99ac = 99bd \Rightarrow ac = bd$

26. Molly reads at the rate of 160 pages $\div$ 4 hours = 40 pages per hour $\Rightarrow$ she will finish the book in $200 \div 40 = 5$ hours
Karly reads at the rate of 100 pages $\div$ 4 hours = 25 pages per hour $\Rightarrow$ she will finish the book in $200 \div 25 = 8$ hours
It will take Karly $8 - 5 = 3$ hours more than for Molly

27. Sami's exact collections are \$12 per month $\times$ 38 customers = \$456, so her estimate is high; she probably multiplied 15×40 for her \$600 guess. She would have had a closer estimate if she'd rounded 12 to 10 and 38 to 40, or $10 \cdot 40 = \$400$.

28. (a) Digits were not carried; place value was not observed

(b) 5 was multiplied by 6 to get 30; the 3 was carried; but then 3 was multiplied by the carried 3 instead of 6 again

(c) 4 was multiplied by 6 and 2 was carried; then 6 and 3 were added instead of being multiplied

(d) When 1 was brought down, the quotient of 0 was not recorded

29. Mira needs \$980 – \$356 = \$624 more $\Rightarrow$ saving \$30 per week will require \$624 $\div$ \$30 = 20.8, or about 21 weeks

30. 1672 students $\div$ 29 students per bus = 57.7 buses $\Rightarrow$ 58 buses will be needed, but not all will be full

31. Jerry used $40 \text{ L} - 4 \text{ L} = 36 \text{ L} \Rightarrow \frac{396\ km}{36\ liters} = 11$ km/L

32. The two digits of the number are repeated in the product; e.g., $25 \cdot 101 = 2525$. If we let the two digits be designated by a and b, then:

```
    1 0 1
  ×   a b
  -------
    b 0 b
  a 0 a
  -------
  a b a b
```

Note that no partial products are greater than 9, so no carrying is involved

33. (a) (*i*) She saves (\$200 + \$80 + \$20 + \$100) – \$330 = \$70

(*ii*) She saves (\$25 + \$0 + \$5 + \$10) – \$30 = \$10

(b) \$330 cost to buy $\div$ \$30 cost per trip to rent = 11 trips to break even $\Rightarrow$ she will save on the 12th trip and beyond

34. (a)
```
    1
   3 2
 ×   4
 2 3 3five
```

(b)
```
     4five R 1five
  4⟌3 2
    3 1
      1
```

(c)
```
     4 3
 ×   2 3
   2 3 4
 1 4 1
 2 1 4 4five
```

(d)
```
     3 1five
  3⟌1 4 3
    1 4
      0 3
      0 3
        0
```

(e) $13_{eight} \cdot 5_{eight} = 67_{eight}$

(f) $67_{eight} \div 4_{eight} = 15_{eight}$ with remainder 3_{eight}

(g) $10010_{two} \div 11_{two} = 110_{two}$

(h) $10110_{two} \cdot 101_{two} = 1101110_{two}$

35. (a) In the units column 3 + 8 = 12 with the 2 brought down and the 1 carried ⇒ base nine $[(3 + 8)_{nine} = 12_{nine}]$

(b) In the units column it was necessary to borrow to subtract; since 6 − 3 = 3 a 4 must have been borrowed ⇒ base four $[(4 + 2)_{four} - 3_{four} = 3_{four}]$

(c) In the units column 2 · 3 = 10 ⇒ base 6 (or one 6 and zero 1's)

(d) Any base greater than or equal to 2

36. (a) $323_{five} \cdot 42_{five} = 30221_{five}$:

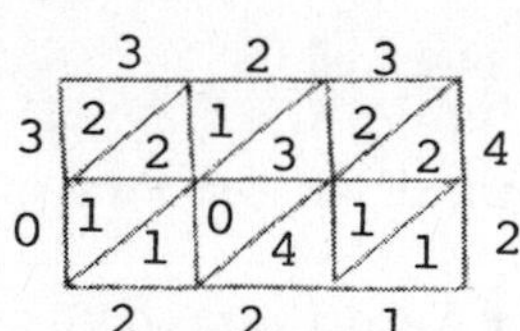

(b) $32_a = 23_b \Rightarrow 3a + 2 = 2b + 3 \Rightarrow b = \frac{3a-1}{2}$ ⇒ the smallest value of a (a > 1) for b to be whole is a = 3 ⇒ a = 3 and b = 4 ⇒ $32_{three} = 23_{four}$

37. (a) For the greatest product, we need the largest multiplicands which can be formed using the four numbers. 8 × 763 is greater than 7 × 863 because 8 × 700 = 7 × 800, but 8 × 63 is greater than 7 × 63.

```
 [7][6][3]
 ×     [8]
```

(b) For the least product, we need the smallest multiplicands which can be formed using the four numbers. 3 × 678 is smaller than 6 × 378 because 3 × 600 = 6 × 300, but 3 × 78 is smaller than 6 × 78.

```
 [6][7][8]
 ×     [3]
```

38. (a)
```
   7 6 2
 ×   8 3
```

(b)
```
   3 7 8
 ×   2 6
```

39. 700 pounds per cow × 4 Quarter Pounders per pound = 2800 Quarter Pounders per cow.
21,000,000,000 Quarter Pounders ÷ 2800 Quarter Pounders = 7,500,000 cows

40. (a)
```
     3 7
 ×   4 3
   1 1 1
 1 4 8 0
 1 5 9 1
```

(b)
```
     9 3
 ×   3 6
   5 5 8
 2 7 9 0
 3 3 4 8
```

40. (c)

```
    1 3
 9)1 2 3
   9
   3 3
   2 7
     6
```

41. (a) $1 \times 1 = 1$
$11 \times 11 = 121$
$111 \times 111 = 12321$
$1111 \times 1111 = 1234321$
For n 1's in each of the two factors, the product "counts up" to n, then back down to 1
$\Rightarrow$ without multiplying, the next product should be 123454321

(b) $99 \times 99 = 9801$
$999 \times 999 = 998001$
$9999 \times 9999 = 99980001$
For n 9's in each of the two factors, the product appears, in order, as $(n - 1)$ 9's, one 8, $(n - 1)$ 1's, and one 0
$\Rightarrow$ without multiplying, the next product should be 9999800001

(c) The pattern continues for (b) but not for (a), which fails when $n > 9$ ones

42. \$1 per second × 60 seconds = \$60 per minute
\$60 per minute × 60 minutes = \$3600 per hour
\$3600 per hour × 24 hours = \$86,400 per day
\$86,400 per day × 7 days = \$604,800 per week
\$86,400 per day × 30 days = \$2,592,000 per month (assuming a 30-day month)
\$86,400 per day × 365 days = \$31,536,000 per year (assuming a non-leap year)
\$31,536,000 × 20 = \$630,720,000 in 20 years (plus \$86,400 for each leap year)

43. The number 625,000 is midway between 250,000 and 1,000,000. If you ask, "Is the number less than 625,000?", the yes or no answer gives you a new range. By continually narrowing the range in this manner, you will find that a minimum of 19 questions is needed.

44. (a) (*i*) $27 \times 198 = 5346$ (*ii*) $48 \times 159 = 7632$

(*iii*) $39 \times 186 = 7254$

(b) (*i*) $1963 \times 4 = 7852$ (*ii*) $483 \times 12 = 5796$

(*iii*) $297 \times 18 = 5346$

(c) 1 (if 1 is the units digit of one factor, the units digit of the other factor will be repeated in the product)

On-going Assessment 3-5; Review Questions

53. 999999∩∩∩∩∩∩||||

54. 300,260

55. Numbers may vary; one example is: $5 + 0 = 5 = 0 + 5$

56. (a) $x(a + b + 2)$ (b) $(3 + x)(a + b)$

57. 59,260 miles − 52,281 miles = 6,979 miles traveled

58. There were 192 people + 215 people + 317 people = 724 people at the conference

Chapter 3 Review

1. (a) $\overline{\text{CD}}\text{XLIV} = 1000 \cdot \text{CD} + \text{XLIV} = 1000 \cdot 400 + 40 + 4 = 400{,}044$

   (b) $432_{five} = 4 \cdot 5^2 + 3 \cdot 5 + 2 = 117$

   (c) $ET0_{twelve} = 11 \cdot 12^2 + 10 \cdot 12 + 0 = 1704$

   (d) $1011_{two} = 1 \cdot 2^3 + 0 \cdot 2^2 + 1 \cdot 2 + 1 = 11$

   (e) $4136_{seven} = 4 \cdot 7^3 + 1 \cdot 7^2 + 3 \cdot 7 + 6 = 1448$

2. (a) CMXCIX

   (b) ∩∩∩∩∩∩∩∩|||||||

   (c) $\overset{\bullet}{\bullet\bullet\bullet}$

   (d) 2 groups of 125 + 3 groups of 25 + 4 groups of 5 + 1 = 2341_{five}

   (e) 1 group of 16 + 1 group of 8 + 0 groups of four + 1 group of 2 + 1 = 11011_{two}

3. (a) $3^{4+7+6} = 3^{17}$

   (b) $2^{10+11} = 2^{21}$

   (c) $3^4(1+2) = 3^4 \cdot 3 = 3^5$

   (d) $2^{80}(1+3) = 2^{80} \cdot 2^2 = 2^{82}$

4. (a) Distributive property of multiplication over addition

   (b) Commutative property of addition

   (c) Identity property of multiplication

   (d) Distributive property of multiplication over addition

   (e) Commutative property of multiplication

   (f) Associative property of multiplication

5. (a) $3 < 13$ if and only if there exists a number k such that $3 + k < 13$. If $k < 10$, then $3 + k < 13$ $\Rightarrow 3 < 13$.

   (b) $12 > 9$ if and only if there exists a number k such that $12 - k > 9$. If $k < 3$, then $12 - k > 9$ $\Rightarrow 12 > 9$

6. $$\begin{aligned} 1000 \cdot 483 &= 10^3(4 \cdot 10^2 + 8 \cdot 10 + 3) \\ &= 4 \cdot 10^5 + 8 \cdot 10^4 + 3 \cdot 10^3 \\ &= 4 \cdot 10^5 + 8 \cdot 10^4 + 3 \cdot 10^3 + 0 \cdot 10^2 + 0 \cdot 10^1 + 0 \cdot 1 \\ &= 483{,}000 \end{aligned}$$

7. Scratch

$$\begin{array}{rrrr} & {}^1 & & \\ & 3 & 1 & 6 \\ & 7_1 & 1 & 2 \\ + & & \not{9}_1 & 1 \\ \hline 1 & 1 & 1 & 9 \end{array}$$

Traditional

$$\begin{array}{rrrr} & {}^1 & & \\ & 3 & 1 & 6 \\ & 7 & 1 & 2 \\ + & & 9 & 1 \\ \hline 1 & 1 & 1 & 9 \end{array}$$

8. Traditional

```
    6 1 3
 ×    9 8
  4 9 0 4
5 5 1 7
6 0 0 7 4
```

Lattice

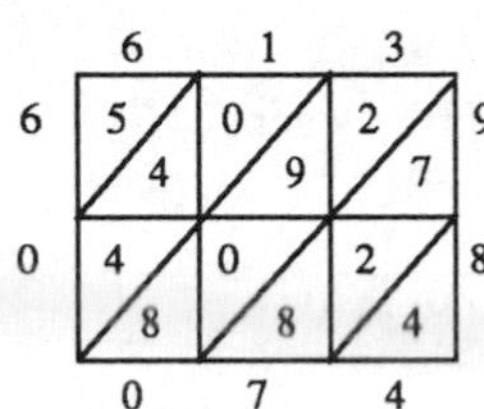

9. (a) Repeated Subtraction

```
9 1 2 | 4 8 0 3
        4 5 6 0    5 - 912's
          2 4 3    5 - 912's   ⇒ 5, remainder 243
```

Conventional

```
                5
9 1 2 | 4 8 0 3
        4 5 6 0
          2 4 3    ⇒ 5, remainder 243
```

(b) Repeated Subtraction

```
1 1 | 1 0 1 1
        9 9 0    90 - 11's
          2 1
          1 1     1 - 11
          1 0    91 - 11's   ⇒ 91, remainder 10
```

Conventional

```
          9 1
1 1 | 1 0 1 1
        9 9
          2 1
          1 1
          1 0    ⇒ 91, remainder 10
```

(c) Repeated Subtraction

```
2 3 | 3 3 1 2
      2 3 0 0    (100 - 23's)five
      1 0 1 2
      1 0 1 0    (20 - 23's)five
            2    (120 - 23's)five   ⇒ 120five, remainder 2five
```

Conventional

```
        1 2 0five
2 3 | 3 3 1 2
      2 3
      1 0 1
      1 0 1
          0 2    ⇒ 120five, remainder 2five
```

9. (d) Repeated Subtraction

```
1 1 | 1 0 1 1
        1 1 0      (10 elevens)two
        1 0 1
          1 1      (1 eleven)two
          1 0      (11 elevens)two     ⇒ 11two, remainder 10two
```

Conventional

```
          1 1two
1 1 | 1 0 1 1
      1 1
      1 0 1
        1 1
        1 0     ⇒ 11two, remainder 10two
```

10. (a) $5 \cdot 912 + 243 = 4803$ (b) $91 \cdot 11 + 10 = 1011$

(c) $(120 \cdot 23)_{five} + 2_{five} = 3312_{five}$ (d) $(11 \cdot 11)_{two} + 10_{two} = 1011_{two}$

11. (a) Tens (b) Thousands

(c) Hundreds

12. (a) $\boxed{9 < \text{whole numbers} < 16}$ (b) $\boxed{10}$

(c) $\boxed{\text{Any whole number}}$ (d) $\boxed{\text{Whole numbers} \leq 26}$

13. (a) $(3 + 7 + 5)a = 15a$ (b) $(3 + 7 - 5)x^2 = 5x^2$

(c) $ax + bx + yx$ (d) $(3 + y)(x + 5)$

14. (a) $2 + 4 + C = 7 \Rightarrow C = 1$ (b) $D = 6$ (i.e., $1 + 2 + 3$)

(c) $D = 9$ when $A = 1$, $B = 3$, and $C = 5$ (for $A > 1$, $D > 9$)

15. \$720 – \$162 – \$158 – \$33 + \$28 = \$395 balance

16. \$320 × 6 months + \$410 × 6 months = \$4380 total earnings

17. 15,600 cans ÷ 24 cans per case = 650 cases per hour ⇒ 650 × 4 hours = 2600 cases in four hours

18. \$461,040 ÷ 120 investors = \$3842 per investor

19. 60 people × 8 ounces = 480 ounces required ⇒ 480 ÷ 12 ounces per can = 40 12-ounce cans

20. 2 slacks × 3 blouses × 2 sweaters = 12 outfits

21. Work backward from 93 using inverse operations:
Subtract 89, giving 4
Add 20, giving 24
Divide by 12, giving 2
Multiply by 13, giving 26 as the original number

22. There are 8 groups of 3 in 24 (or 2 dozen) apples $\Rightarrow$ 8 × 69¢ per group = \$5.52 on sale
    32¢ × 24 apples = \$7.68 regular price $\Rightarrow$ \$7.68 – \$5.52 = \$2.16 saved

23. \$6000 for the group (\$80 per person × 80 people = \$6400)

24. Use trial and error, or: let B be the number of bicycles and T be the number of tricycles
    $2B + 3T = 126$ wheels (*i*)
    $2B + 2T = 108$ pedals (*ii*)
    Subtracting equation (*ii*) from equation (*i*) $\Rightarrow$ T = 18 tricycles
    Substituting T = 18 into equation (*i*) $\Rightarrow$ $2B + 3(18) = 126$ $\Rightarrow$ B = 36 bicycles

25. 30 hours per week × \$5 per hour + 8 hours overtime × \$8 per hour = \$150 + \$64 = \$214 earned

26. Let q be the amount from the first question. Then we have $q + 2q + 4q + \cdots$
    This is a geometric sequence with 1st term q, ratio 2, and number of terms 5
    $\Rightarrow 6400 = q(2)^{5-1}$
    $6400 = 16q \Rightarrow q = \$400$

27. Answers will vary with student preferences, but multiplication as repeated addition would probably be more familiar to elementary students

28. Answers may vary; selling pencils by units, dozens, and gross is an example of the use of base 12

29. Answers may vary

30. Units addition would be:
    [( ] [7] [+] [5] [ )] [INT] [8] [=] yields 1 with a remainder of 4
    Carry the 1 and compute:
    [( ] [1] [+] [2] [+] [6] [ )] [INT] [8] [=] yields 1 with a remainder of 1
    The sum is 114_{eight}

CHAPTER 4 - INTEGERS AND NUMBER THEORY

1. (a) The opposite of an integer is the integer of the opposite sign $\Rightarrow$ if 2 is an integer, then the unique integer $^{-}2$ is called the opposite of 2

   (b) The opposite of a negative number is a positive number $\Rightarrow$ the opposite of $^{-}5$ is 5

   (c) The opposite of a variable is the variable with the opposite sign, just as with integers $\Rightarrow$ the opposite of m is ^{-}m

   (d) 0 is neither negative nor positive $\Rightarrow$ the opposite of 0 is 0

   (e) The opposite of ^{-}m is $^{-}(^{-}m) = m$

   (f) The opposite of (a + b) is $^{-}(a + b) = {}^{-}a + {}^{-}b$

2. (a) $^{-}(^{-}2)$ means the opposite of $^{-}2$, or 2

   (b) m (c) 0

3. (a) Absolute value is the distance on a number line between 0 and a specified number
   Distance on the number line between 0 and $^{-}5$ is 5 units $\Rightarrow$ $|^{-}5| = 5$

   (b) Remember that absolute value does not mean opposite sign $\Rightarrow$ $|10| = 10$

   (c) $^{-}|^{-}5|$ means the opposite of the absolute value of $^{-}5$ $\Rightarrow$ $^{-}|^{-}5| = {}^{-}(5) = {}^{-}5$

   (d) $^{-}|5| = {}^{-}(5) = {}^{-}5$

4. (a)

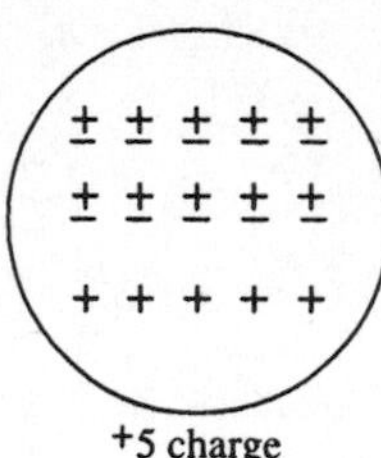

+5 charge

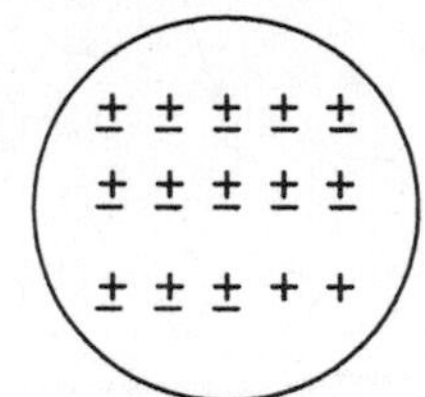

Add 3 negative charges. Net result: 2 positive charges

(b)

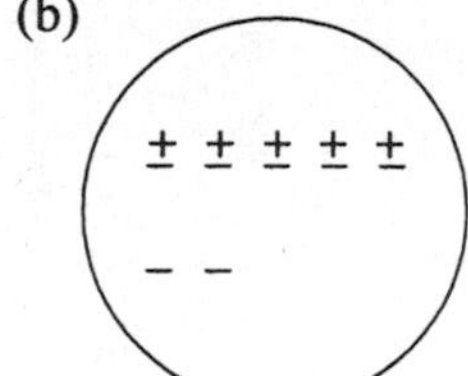

−2 charge on the field

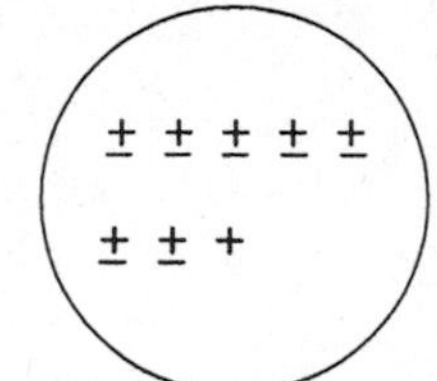

Add 3 positive charges; net result 1 positve charge

(c)

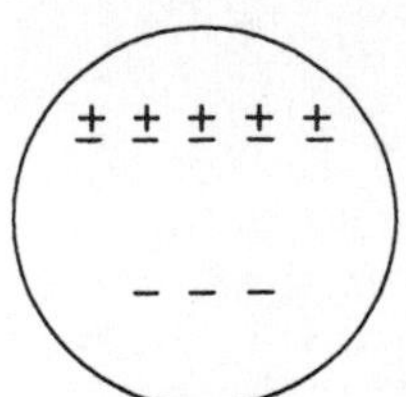

−3 charge on field

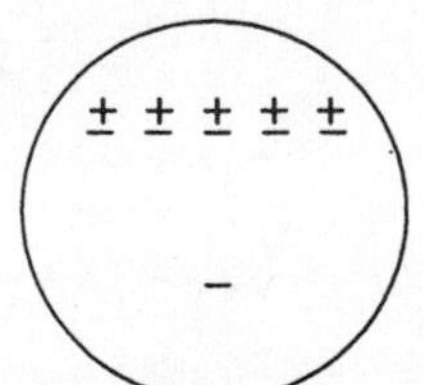

Take away 2 negative charges. Net result: 1 negative charge on the field

(d)

−3 charge on the field

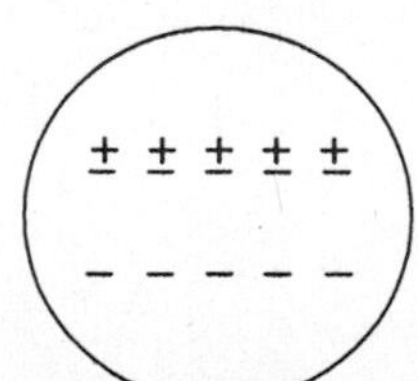

Add 2 negative charges. Net result: 5 negative charges

5. Black chips represent positive numbers; white chips represent negative numbers:

(a) Net result: 2 positive chips

(b) Net result: 1 positive chip

(c) Net result: 1 negative chip

(d) Net result: 5 negative chips

6. (a) $5 + {}^-3$, $^-3$, 5

(b) 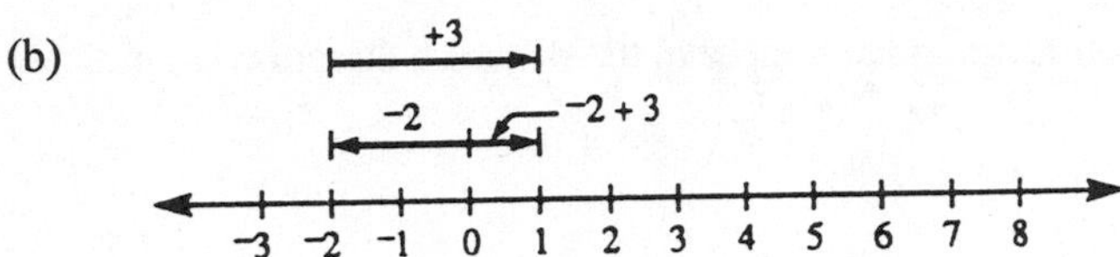

(c) 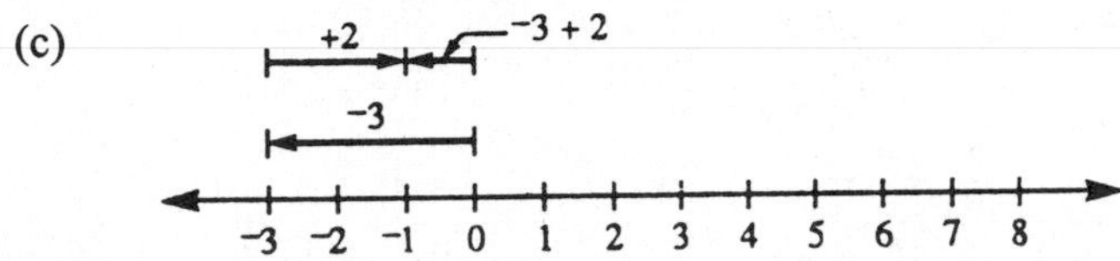

(d) 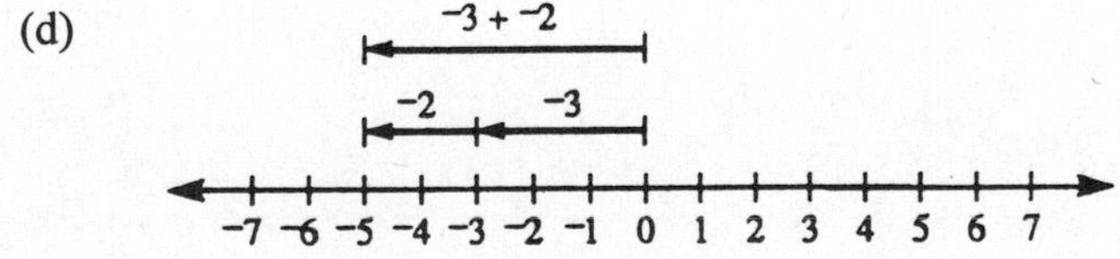

7. To add integers with unlike signs, subtract the lesser of the two absolute values from the greater. The sum of the two integers will be the difference of the absolute values with the sign of the integer having the greater absolute value.

(a) A drop in stock value is negative; an increase is positive $\Rightarrow$ a drop of 17 points followed by a gain of 10 points may be represented by $^-17 + 10$

To find the sum: Subtract the lesser of the two absolute values from the greater $\Rightarrow$ $|^-17| - |10| = 7$

Give the result the sign of the integer with the larger absolute value $\Rightarrow$ $^-7$

$^-7$ represents a net drop of 7 points

(b) $^-10°\text{ C} + 8°\text{ C} = {}^-2°\text{ C}$

(c) 5000 feet + $^-100$ feet = 4900 feet

(d) $^-\$200 + \$100 + {}^-\$50 = {}^-\$250 + \$100 = {}^-\$150$ $\Rightarrow$ \$150 drop in net worth

(e) $^-2$ yards + 7 yards + 0 yards + $^-8$ yards = $^-10$ yards + 7 yards = $^-3$ yards $\Rightarrow$ 3 yards net loss

8. (a) $^-45 + {}^-55 + {}^-165 + {}^-35 + {}^-100 + 75 + 25 + 400 = {}^-400 + 500 = 100$

(b) \$300 (beginning balance) + \$100 (net transaction result) = \$400 new balance

9. (a)

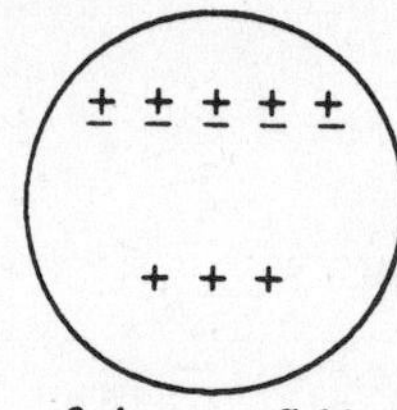

3 charge on field

Take away 2 negative charges; net result 5 positive charges on the field

(b)

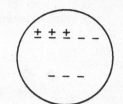

−3 charge on field

Take away 2 positive charges; net result 5 negative charges on the field

(c)

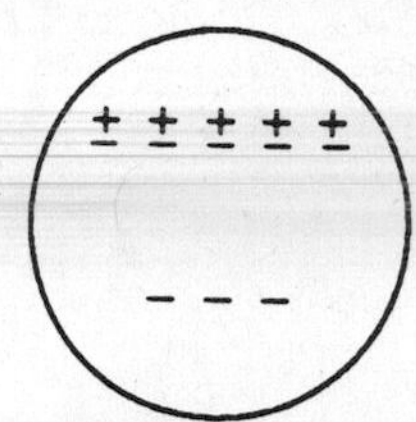

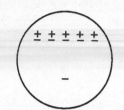

−3 charge on field

Take away 2 negative charges; net result 1 negative charge on the field

10. (a) The car starts at 0 and backs up 4 units. It then turns around and faces in the negative direction (to indicate subtraction) and backs up 1 unit (for $^-1$). Thus:

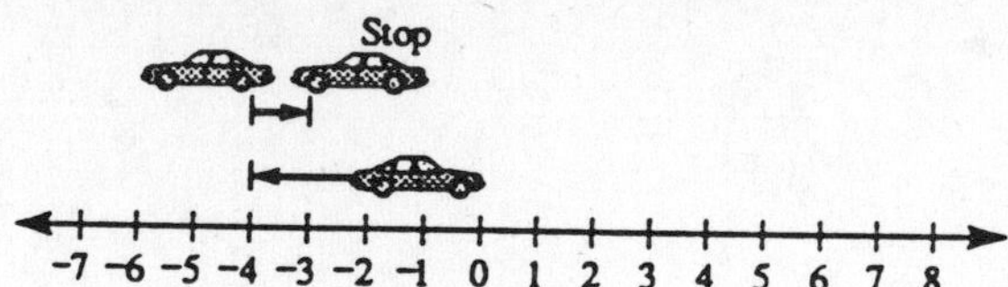

(b)

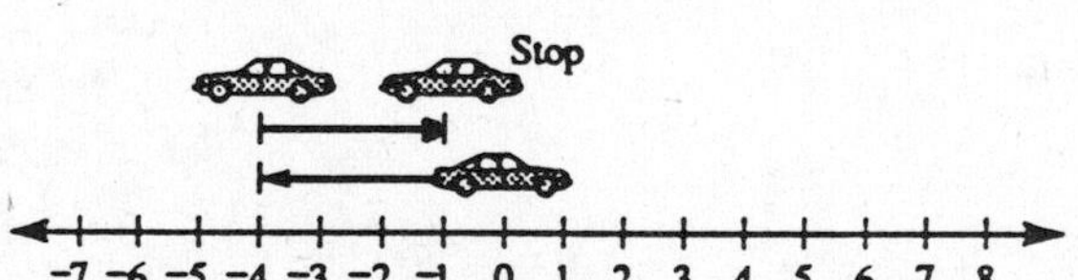

11. (a) Start with subtraction that we already know how to do:

$^-4 - 2 = {}^-6$

$^-4 - 1 = {}^-5$

$^-4 - 0 = {}^-4 \Rightarrow$ since the next value in the pattern is $^-3$

$^-4 - {}^-1 = {}^-3$

(b) $2 - 1 = 1$

$1 - 1 = 0$

$0 - 1 = {}^-1$

$^-1 - 1 = {}^-2 \Rightarrow$ since the next value in the pattern is $^-3$

$^-2 - 1 = {}^-3$

12. (a) Each term in the sequence has one more red chip than black $\Rightarrow$ the next integer = $^-1$

(b) Each term in the sequence has one more black chip than red $\Rightarrow$ the next integer = 1

(c) Each term in the sequence has three more black chips than red $\Rightarrow$ the next integer = 3

13. (a) $^-2 + (3 - 10) = {}^-2 + ({}^-7) = {}^-9$

(b) $[8 - ({}^-5)] - 10 = [8 + {}^-({}^-5)] - 10 = [8 + 5] - 10 = 13 - 10 = 3$

13. (c) $(^-2 - 7) + 10 = (^-2 + {}^-7) + 10 = (^-9) + 10 = 1$

(d) $^-2 - (7 + 10) = {}^-2 - (17) = {}^-2 + {}^-17 = {}^-19$

(e) $8 - 11 - 10 = 8 + {}^-11 + {}^-10 = {}^-3 + {}^-10 = {}^-13$

(f) $^-2 - 7 + 3 = {}^-2 + {}^-7 + 3 = {}^-9 + 3 = {}^-6$

14. (a) (*i*) $T = 55° F - 60° F$ (*ii*) $T = 55° F + {}^-60° F$

(*iii*) $T = {}^-5° F$

(b) (*i*) Balance = \$200 – \$220 (*ii*) Balance = \$200 + $^-$\$220

(*iii*) Balance = $^-$\$20

15. Subtract to find how far off she was ⇒ $12 - {}^-21 = 33$ (21 is negative since the team lost by 21)
She misjudged by 33 points

16. (a) Jack's total was $17 + {}^-8 + {}^-9 + 14 + 45 = 59$ points

(b) The new temperature is $^-247° C + {}^-11° C + {}^-11° C = {}^-269° C$

(c) The temperature variation is $98° F - {}^-94° F = 192° F$

17. $5 + {}^-10 + 8 + {}^-2 + 3 + {}^-1 + {}^-1 = {}^-5 + 8 + {}^-2 + 3 + {}^-1 + {}^-1 = 3 + {}^-2 + 3 + {}^-1 + {}^-1 = 1 + 3 + {}^-1 + {}^-1 = 4 + {}^-1 + {}^-1 = 3 + {}^-1 = 2$

OR

$5 + {}^-10 + 8 + {}^-2 + 3 + {}^-1 + {}^-1 = (5 + 8 + 3) + (^-10 + {}^-2 + {}^-1 + {}^-1) = 16 + {}^-14 = 2$
⇒ Dolores's stock rose by 2 points

18. $^-2 + {}^-4 + 3 + 0 + {}^-2 + {}^-3 + 1 + 3 = {}^-4$ ⇒ Jim lost 4 pounds

19. (a) 10W-30 or 10W-40 (b) 5W-30

(c) 5W-30, 10W-30, or 10W-40 (d) None of the oils shown

(e) 10W-30 or 10W-40

20. (a) $3 - (2 - 4x) = 3 + {}^-(2 + {}^-4x) = 3 + (^-2 + 4x) = 3 + {}^-2 + 4x = 1 + 4x$

(b) $x - (^-x - y) = x + {}^-(^-x + {}^-y) = x + x + y = 2x + y$

(c) $4x - 2 - 3x = (4x - 3x) - 2 = x - 2$

21. (a) If x is negative, then its opposite, ^-x, is $^-(^-x)$, which is positive ⇒ all negative integers

(b) All positive integers (c) $^-x - 1 > 0 \Rightarrow {}^-x > 1 \Rightarrow x < {}^-1$

(d) $|x| = 2$ ⇒ any x which is 2 units away from 0 on the number line ⇒ $x = 2$ or $x = {}^-2$

(e) $^-|x| = 2 \Rightarrow |x| = {}^-2$ ⇒ there are no values of x which make this true

(f) All integers except 0 (g) There are no values of x which make this true

22. 1492 – 2275 = $^-783$ ⇒ Rome was founded in 784 B.C. since there is no year "0"
(Hint: Try this using numbers such as 3 years earlier than 2 A.D. 2 – 3 = $^-1$, but 3 years earlier is 2 B.C., not 1 B.C.)

23. (a) $W \cup I = I$ (since $W \subset I$) (b) $W \cap I = W$

(c) $I^+ \cup I^- = I - \{0\}$ (since 0 is neither positive nor negative)

(d) $I^+ \cap I^- = \emptyset$ (the empty set) (e) $W - I = \emptyset$

(f) $I - W = I^-$ (g) $W - I^+ = \{0\}$

(h) $W - I^- = W$ (since W and I^- are disjoint) (i) $I \cap I = I$

24. Adding all numbers gives $^-9$; dividing by 3 tells us each row, column, and diagonal must total $^-3$
Possible solutions are

8	$^-7$	$^-4$
$^-13$	$^-1$	11
2	5	$^-10$

or

2	$^-13$	8
5	$^-1$	$^-7$
$^-10$	11	$^-4$

25. One possible solution is

	3	5	
7	1	8	2
	4	6	

other answers are possible

26. Given $f(x) = {}^-x - 1$:

(a) $f(^-1) = {}^-(^-1) - 1 = 0$ (b) $f(100) = {}^-(100) - 1 = {}^-101$

(c) $f(^-2) = {}^-(^-2) - 1 = 1$ (d) $3 = {}^-x - 1 \Rightarrow 4 = {}^-x \Rightarrow x = {}^-4$

27. Given $f(x) = |1 - x|$:

(a) $f(10) = |1 - (10)| = |^-9| = 9$ (b) $f(^-1) = |1 - (^-1)| = |2| = 2$

(c) If f(x) = 1, the value inside the absolute value symbol must be either 1 or $^-1$

⇒ (*i*) $1 - x = 1$, $^-x = 0$, $x = 0$ (*ii*) $1 - x = {}^-1$, $^-x = {}^-2$, $x = 2$

(d) Because f(x) is an absolute value, it can be only positive or 0 ⇒ range is all integers ≥ 0

28. (a) Range is all nonnegative integers

(b) (*i*) x is a positive integer ⇒ $|5| = 5$ (*ii*) x is a negative integer ⇒ $|^-5| = {}^-(^-5) = 5$

(*iii*) x is 0 ⇒ $|0| = 0$ (*iv*) $^-|^-7| = {}^-[^-(^-7)] = {}^-[7] = {}^-7$

29. For problems such as this, subtract the smaller integer from the larger, then:
(*i*) Add 1 if the ends are to be included
(*ii*) Subtract 1 if neither end is to be included; e.g., 3 – 2 = 1, but there are no integers between them

(a) (100 – 10) – 1 = 89 integers (b) ($^-10$ – $^-30$) – 1 = 19 integers

(c) (10 – $^-1$) – 1 = 19 integers (d) (y – x) – 1 integers

30. (*i*) Greatest: $a - (b - c) - d = 6 - (5 - 4) - {}^-3 = 8$ (*ii*) Least: $a - b - (b - c) = 6 - 5 - (4 - {}^-3) = {}^-6$

31. (a) ${}^-3 - 0 = {}^-3 \Rightarrow$ difference $= {}^-3$; next two terms are ${}^-12$, ${}^-15$

(b) $3 - 7 = {}^-4 \Rightarrow$ difference $= {}^-4$; next two terms are ${}^-9$, ${}^-13$

(c) $x - (x + y) = {}^-y \Rightarrow$ difference $= {}^-y$; next two terms are $x - 2y$, $x - 3y$

(d) $(1 - x) - (1 - 3x) = 1 - x - 1 + 3x = 2x \Rightarrow$ difference $= 2x$; next two terms are $1 + 3x$, $1 + 5x$

32. (a) Rearranging the terms to allow canceling gives: ${}^-20 + 20 + {}^-19 + 19 + {}^-18 + 18 + \cdots + 0 \Rightarrow$ sum $= 0$

(b) Canceling terms from 50 to ${}^-50$ leaves $100 + 99 + \cdots + 52 + 51$
Use techniques from Chapter 1:
$a_n = a_1 + (n - 1)d \Rightarrow 51 = 100 + (n - 1) \cdot {}^-1 \Rightarrow 51 = 100 - n + 1 \Rightarrow n = 50$ terms
$S_n = \frac{n}{2}(a_1 + a_n) \Rightarrow S_{50} = \frac{50}{2}(100 + 51) = 25 \cdot 151 \Rightarrow S_{50} = 3775$
The sum of the sequence is 3775

(c) Canceling terms from 6 to ${}^-6$ leaves $100 + 98 + \cdots + 10 + 8$
$a_n = a_1 + (n - 1)d \Rightarrow 8 = 100 + (n - 1) \cdot {}^-2 \Rightarrow 8 = 100 - 2n + 2 \Rightarrow n = 47$ terms
$S_n = \frac{n}{2}(a_1 + a_n) \Rightarrow S_{47} = \frac{47}{2}(100 + 8) = 47 \cdot 54 \Rightarrow S_{47} = 2538$
The sum of the sequence is 2538

33. $b - a = b + ({}^-a) = {}^-a + b = {}^-a - ({}^-b) = {}^-(a - b) \Rightarrow$ the terms are opposites

34. (a) True (b) True

(c) True (d) True

(e) False (let $x = {}^-2 \Rightarrow |({}^-2)^3| = |{}^-8| = 8 \neq ({}^-2)^3 = {}^-8$) (f) True

35. (*i*) The larger gear has $\frac{56}{14} = 4$ times as many teeth as the smaller. Each time 14 teeth of the larger gear come by, the smaller will complete one full rotation $\Rightarrow$ if the larger gear rotates 7 times per minute, the smaller gear will rotate $4 \cdot 7 = 28$ times per minute.

(*ii*) The smaller gear will rotate in the direction opposite to that of the larger

36. (a) ${}^-14$ (b) ${}^-24$

(c) 2 (d) 5

37. (a) Enter: [1] [2] [+/-] [+] [6] [+/-] [=] to yield ${}^-18$

(b) Enter: [7] [+/-] [+] [9] [9] [+/-] [=] to yield ${}^-106$

(c) Enter: [1] [2] [+/-] [+] [6] [=] to yield ${}^-6$

(d) Enter: [2] [7] [+] [5] [+/-] [=] to yield 22

(e) Enter: [3] [+] [1] [4] [+/-] [=] to yield ${}^-11$

(f) Enter: [7] [+/-] [–] [9] [+/-] [=] to yield 2

37. (g) Enter: [1] [2] [+/-] [−] [6] [=] to return $^{-}18$

(h) Enter: [1] [6] [−] [7] [+/-] [=] to return 23

38. (a) Estimate: $343 + {}^{-}42 - 402 \doteq 300 - 400 = {}^{-}100$ (actual is $^{-}101$)

(b) Estimate: $^{-}1992 + 3005 - 497 \doteq {}^{-}2000 + 3000 - 500 = 500$ (actual is 516)

(c) Estimate: $992 - {}^{-}10003 - 101 \doteq 1000 + 10000 - 100 = 10900$ (actual is 10894)

(d) Estimate: $^{-}301 - {}^{-}1303 + 4993 \doteq {}^{-}300 + 1300 + 5000 = 6000$ (actual is 5995)

On-going Assessment 4-2

1. $3 \cdot {}^{-}1 = {}^{-}1 + {}^{-}1 + {}^{-}1 = {}^{-}3$
$2 \cdot {}^{-}1 = {}^{-}1 + {}^{-}1 = {}^{-}2$
$1 \cdot {}^{-}1 = {}^{-}1$
$0 \cdot {}^{-}1 = 0 \Rightarrow$ continuing the pattern of a product increasing by 1 each time:
$^{-}1 \cdot {}^{-}1 = 1$

2. 

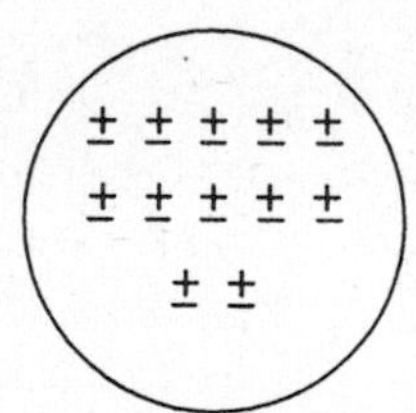

0 charge

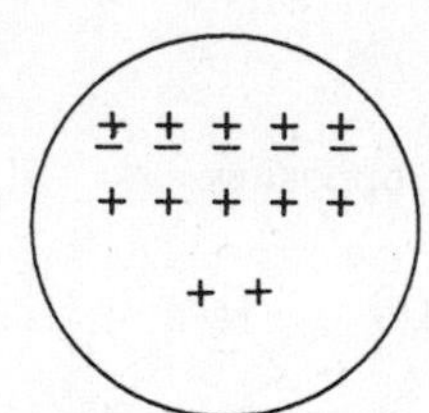

Take away four of two negative charges; net result is eight positive charges.

3. The car goes west twice, each time by four units $\Rightarrow$ it will stop at $^{-}8$:

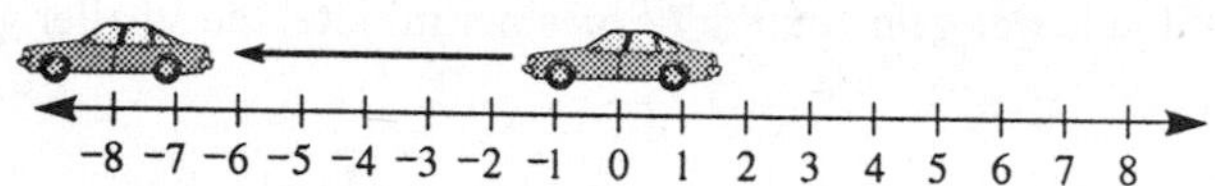

4. (a) $4 \cdot {}^{-}20 = {}^{-}80 \Rightarrow$ the number of students will decrease by 80 over the next four years

(b) $^{-}4 \cdot {}^{-}20 = 80 \Rightarrow$ there were 80 more students four years ago

(c) $n \cdot {}^{-}20 = {}^{-}20n$ (d) $^{-}n \cdot {}^{-}20 = 20n$

5. (a) $^{-}40 = 5 \cdot {}^{-}8 \Rightarrow {}^{-}40 \div {}^{-}8 = 5$ (b) $143 = {}^{-}11 \cdot {}^{-}13 \Rightarrow 143 \div {}^{-}11 = {}^{-}13$

(c) $^{-}143 = 13 \cdot {}^{-}11 \Rightarrow {}^{-}143 \div 13 = {}^{-}11$ (d) $0 = {}^{-}5 \cdot 0 \Rightarrow 0 \div {}^{-}5 = 0$

(e) $^{-}5 \neq 0 \cdot$ any integer $\Rightarrow {}^{-}5 \div 0$ is not defined

(f) $0 \neq 0 \cdot$ any unique integer $\Rightarrow 0 \div 0$ is not defined

6. (a) $({}^{-}10 \div {}^{-}2)({}^{-}2) = 5 \cdot {}^{-}2 = {}^{-}10$ (b) $({}^{-}40 \div 8)8 = {}^{-}5 \cdot 8 = {}^{-}40$

6. (a) $({}^{-}10 \div {}^{-}2)({}^{-}2) = 5 \cdot {}^{-}2 = {}^{-}10$ (b) $({}^{-}40 \div 8)8 = {}^{-}5 \cdot 8 = {}^{-}40$

(c) $(a \div b)b = a$ for any integers a and b, $b \neq 0$ (d) $({}^{-}10 \cdot 5) \div 5 = {}^{-}50 \div 5 = {}^{-}10$

(e) $(a \cdot b) \div b = a$ for any integers a and b, $b \neq 0$ (f) $({}^{-}8 \div {}^{-}2)({}^{-}8) = 4 \cdot {}^{-}8 = {}^{-}32$

(g) $({}^{-}6 + {}^{-}14) \div 4 = {}^{-}20 \div 4 = {}^{-}5$ (h) $({}^{-}8 + 8) \div 8 = 0 \div 8 = 0$

(i) ${}^{-}8 \div ({}^{-}8 + 8) = {}^{-}8 \div 0 \Rightarrow$ quotient undefined (j) $({}^{-}23 - {}^{-}7) \div 4 = {}^{-}16 \div 4 = {}^{-}4$

(k) $({}^{-}6 + 6) \div ({}^{-}2 + 2) = 0 \div 0 \Rightarrow$ quotient undefined (l) ${}^{-}13 \div ({}^{-}1) = 13$

(m) $({}^{-}36 \div 12) \div 3 = {}^{-}3 \div 3 = {}^{-}1$ (n) $|{}^{-}24| \div (3 - 15) = 24 \div {}^{-}12 = {}^{-}2$

7. (a) $32°\ C + (30 \cdot {}^{-}3)°\ C = 32 + {}^{-}90 = {}^{-}58°\ C$ (b) $0°\ C + ({}^{-}25 \cdot {}^{-}4)°\ C = 0 + 100 = 100°\ C$

(c) ${}^{-}20°\ C + ({}^{-}30 \cdot {}^{-}4)°\ C = {}^{-}20 + 120 = 100°\ C$ (d) $25°\ C + ({}^{-}20 \cdot 3)°\ C = 25 + {}^{-}60 = {}^{-}35°\ C$

(e) $0°\ C + ({}^{-}m \cdot {}^{-}d)°\ C = 0 + md = md°\ C$

(f) $20°\ C + ({}^{-}m \cdot d)°\ C = 20 + {}^{-}md = (20 - md)°\ C$

8. (a) $4 \cdot {}^{-}11 = {}^{-}44$, or 44 yards lost

(b) ${}^{-}66 \div 11 = {}^{-}6$, or 66 yards lost over 11 plays means an average of 6 yards per play lost

9. ${}^{-}12{,}000 \cdot 7 = {}^{-}84{,}000$, or 12,000 acres per year lost for 7 years is 84,000 acres lost

10. The distributive property is that $a(b + c) = ab + ac$

(a) ${}^{-}1({}^{-}5 + {}^{-}2) = {}^{-}1 \cdot {}^{-}5 + {}^{-}1 \cdot {}^{-}2 = 5 + 2 = 7 \Leftrightarrow {}^{-}1({}^{-}5 + {}^{-}2) = {}^{-}1 \cdot {}^{-}7 = 7$

(b) ${}^{-}3({}^{-}3 + 2) = {}^{-}3 \cdot {}^{-}3 + {}^{-}3 \cdot 2 = 9 + {}^{-}6 = 3 \Leftrightarrow {}^{-}3({}^{-}3 + 2) = {}^{-}3 \cdot {}^{-}1 = 3$

(c) ${}^{-}5(2 + {}^{-}6) = {}^{-}5 \cdot 2 + {}^{-}5 \cdot {}^{-}6 = {}^{-}10 + 30 = 20 \Leftrightarrow {}^{-}5(2 + {}^{-}6) = {}^{-}5 \cdot {}^{-}4 = 20$

11. (a) $({}^{-}2)^3 = {}^{-}2 \cdot {}^{-}2 \cdot {}^{-}2 = {}^{-}8$ (b) $({}^{-}2)^4 = ({}^{-}2 \cdot {}^{-}2) \cdot ({}^{-}2 \cdot {}^{-}2) = 4 \cdot 4 = 16$

(c) $({}^{-}10)^5 \div ({}^{-}10)^2 = {}^{-}100{,}000 \div 100 = {}^{-}1000$ (d) $({}^{-}3)^5 \div ({}^{-}3) = {}^{-}243 \div {}^{-}3 = 81$

(e) $({}^{-}1)^{10} = 1$ (note that negative numbers taken to an even power give positive products)

(f) $({}^{-}1)^{15} = {}^{-}1$ (note that negative numbers taken to an odd power give negative products)

(g) $({}^{-}1)^{50} = 1$ (h) $({}^{-}1)^{151} = {}^{-}1$

12. (a) ${}^{-}2 + 3 \cdot 5 - 1 = {}^{-}2 + 15 - 1 = 12$

(b) $10 - 3 \cdot 7 - 4({}^{-}2) + 3 = 10 - 21 - {}^{-}8 + 3 = (10 + 8 + 3) - 21 = 0$

(c) $10 - 3 - 12 = 7 - 12 = {}^{-}5$ (d) $10 - (3 - 12) = 10 - {}^{-}9 = 19$

(e) $({}^{-}3)^2 = {}^{-}3 \cdot {}^{-}3 = 9$ (f) ${}^{-}3^2 = {}^{-}(3 \cdot 3) = {}^{-}9$

12. (g) $^-5^2 + 3(^-2)^2 = {}^-25 + 3 \cdot 4 = {}^-25 + 12 = {}^-13$ (h) $^-2^3 = {}^-(2 \cdot 2 \cdot 2) = {}^-8$

(i) $(^-2)^5 = {}^-2 \cdot {}^-2 \cdot {}^-2 \cdot {}^-2 \cdot {}^-2 = {}^-32$ (j) $^-2^4 = {}^-(2 \cdot 2 \cdot 2 \cdot 2) = {}^-16$

13. (a) Always negative (x^2 is always positive $\Rightarrow$ its opposite is negative)

(b) Always positive (multiplication of either two positive or two negative integers is always positive)

(c) Always positive

(d) Positive when x is negative; negative when x is positive (i.e., the opposite of x^3)

(e) Positive when x is negative (the opposite of a negative integer is positive)
Negative when x is positive (the opposite of a positive integer is negative, and the product of three negative integers is negative)

(f) Always negative

(g) Always positive (the product of four negative numbers is positive)

(h) Always positive

(i) Positive when x is positive; negative when x is negative

(j) Positive when x is negative; negative when x is positive (i.e., opposites)

14. (b) and (c); (d) and (e); (g) and (h)

15. (a) Commutative property of multiplication (b) Closure property of addition

(c) Associative property of multiplication (d) Distributive property of multiplication over addition

16. (a) $(^-x)(^-y) = xy$ (b) $^-2x(^-y) = 2xy$

(c) $^-(x + y) + x + y = {}^-x + {}^-y + x + y = 0$ (d) $^-1 \cdot x = {}^-x$

(e) $x - 2(^-y) = x - {}^-2y = x + 2y$ (f) $a - (a - b) = a + {}^-a - {}^-b = b$

(g) $y - (y - x) = y + {}^-y - {}^-x = x$ (h) $^-(x - y) + x = {}^-x - {}^-y + x = y$

17. (a) $^-3x = 6 \Rightarrow x = \frac{6}{^-3} = {}^-2$ (b) $^-3x = {}^-6 \Rightarrow x = \frac{^-6}{^-3} = 2$

(c) $^-2x = 0 \Rightarrow x = \frac{0}{^-2} = 0$ (d) $5x = {}^-30 \Rightarrow x = \frac{^-30}{5} = {}^-6$

(e) $x \div 3 = {}^-12 \Rightarrow x = 3 \cdot {}^-12 = {}^-36$ (f) $x \div {}^-3 = {}^-2 \Rightarrow x = {}^-3 \cdot {}^-2 = 6$

(g) $x \div {}^-x = {}^-1 \Rightarrow x = {}^-x \cdot {}^-1 = x \ (x \neq 0)$ (h) $0 \div x = 0 \Rightarrow 0 = x \cdot 0 = 0 \ (x \neq 0)$

(i) $x \div 0 = 1 \Rightarrow$ no solution possible (division by 0 is undefined)

(j) $x^2 = 9 \Rightarrow (^-3)^2 = 9$ or $(3)^2 = 9 \Rightarrow x = {}^-3$ or $x = 3$

17. (k) $x^2 = {}^{-}9 \Rightarrow$ no solution possible (x^2 is always positive)

(l) ${}^{-}x \div {}^{-}x = 1 \Rightarrow x = x \ (x \neq 0)$

(m) ${}^{-}x^2$ is negative $\Rightarrow$ x may be any integer except 0 (0 is neither positive nor negative)

(n) ${}^{-}(1 - x) = x - 1 \Rightarrow {}^{-}1 - {}^{-}x = x - 1 \Rightarrow$ x may be any integer

(o) $x - 3x = {}^{-}2x \Rightarrow {}^{-}2x = {}^{-}2x \Rightarrow$ x may be any integer

18. (a) ${}^{-}2(x - 1) = {}^{-}2x - {}^{-}2 = {}^{-}2x + 2$

(b) ${}^{-}2(x - y) = {}^{-}2x - {}^{-}2y = {}^{-}2x + 2y$

(c) $x(x - y) = x^2 - xy$

(d) ${}^{-}x(x - y) = {}^{-}x^2 - {}^{-}xy = {}^{-}x^2 + xy$

(e) ${}^{-}2(x + y - z) = {}^{-}2x + {}^{-}2y - {}^{-}2z = {}^{-}2x - 2y + 2z$

(f) ${}^{-}x(x - y - 3) = {}^{-}x^2 - {}^{-}xy - {}^{-}3x = {}^{-}x^2 + xy + 3x$

(g) $({}^{-}5 - x)(5 + x) = {}^{-}5(5 + x) + {}^{-}x(5 + x) = {}^{-}25 + {}^{-}5x + {}^{-}5x + {}^{-}x^2 = {}^{-}25 - 10x - x^2$

(h) $(x - y - 1)(x + y + 1) = [x - (y + 1)][x + (y + 1)] = x^2 - (y + 1)^2 = x^2 - [y(y + 1) + 1(y + 1)]$
$= x^2 - (y^2 + y + y + 1) = x^2 - y^2 - 2y - 1$

(i) $({}^{-}x^2 + 2)(x^2 - 1) = {}^{-}x^2(x^2 - 1) + 2(x^2 - 1) = {}^{-}x^4 - {}^{-}x^2 + 2x^2 - 2 = {}^{-}x^4 + 3x^2 - 2$

19. The difference-of-squares formula is: $(a + b)(a - b) = a^2 - b^2$

(a) $52 \cdot 48 = (50 + 2)(50 - 2) = 50^2 - 2^2 = 2500 - 4 = 2496$

(b) $(5 - 100)(5 + 100) = 5^2 - 100^2 = 25 - 10{,}000 = {}^{-}9975$

(c) $({}^{-}x - y)({}^{-}x + y) = ({}^{-}x)^2 - y^2 = x^2 - y^2$

(d) $(2 + 3x)(2 - 3x) = 2^2 - (3x)^2 = 4 - 9x^2$

(e) $(x - 1)(1 + x) = (x - 1)(x + 1) = x^2 - 1^2 = x^2 - 1$

(f) $213^2 - 13^2 = 45{,}369 - 169 = 45{,}200$

20. (a) $3x + 5x = x(3 + 5) = 8x$

(b) $ax + 2x = x(a + 2)$

(c) $xy + x = x \cdot y + x \cdot 1 = x(y + 1)$

(d) $ax - 2x = x(a - 2)$

(e) $x^2 + xy = x \cdot x + x \cdot y = x(x + y)$

(f) $3x - 4x + 7x = x(3 - 4 + 7) = 6x$

(g) $3xy + 2x - xz = x(3y + 2 - z)$

(h) $3x^2 + xy - x = x(3x + y - 1)$

(i) $abc + ab - a = a(bc + b - 1) = a[b(c + 1) - 1]$

(j) $(a + b)(c + 1) - (a + b) = (a + b) \cdot (c + 1) - (a + b) \cdot 1 = (a + b)[(c + 1) - 1] = (a + b)[c] = c(a + b)$

(k) $16 - a^2 = 4^2 - a^2 = (4 + a)(4 - a)$

(l) $x^2 - 9y^2 = x^2 - (3y)^2 = (x + 3y)(x - 3y)$

(m) $4x^2 - 25y^2 = (2x)^2 - (5y)^2 = (2x + 5y)(2x - 5y)$

(n) $(x^2 - y^2) + y + y = (x + y)(x - y) + (x + y) = (x + y)[(x - y) + 1] = (x + y)(x - y + 1)$

21. (a) $(a - b)^2 = (a - b)(a - b) = a(a - b) + {}^{-}b(a - b) = a^2 - ab - ab - {}^{-}b^2 = a^2 - 2ab + b^2$

(b) (*i*) $98^2 = (100 - 2)^2 = 100^2 - 2 \cdot 100 \cdot 2 + 2^2 = 10{,}000 - 400 + 4 = 9604$

21. (b) (*ii*) $99^2 = (100 - 1)^2 = 100^2 - 2 \cdot 100 \cdot 1 + 1^2 = 10{,}000 - 200 + 1 = 9801$

(*iii*) $997^2 = (1000 - 3)^2 = 1000^2 - 2 \cdot 1000 \cdot 3 + 3^2 = 1{,}000{,}000 - 6000 + 9 = 994{,}009$

22. (a) False $(x^2 \cdot {}^-x < 0)$ (b) True

(c) True (d) True

23. (a) The sums are always 9 times the middle number

(b) Let m be the middle number ⇒ the following array:

m − 8	m − 7	m − 6
m − 1	m	m + 1
m + 6	m + 7	m + 8

The sum of these numbers is 9m, which is 9 times the middle number

24. (a) Arithmetic sequence; difference is 3 ⇒ $a_n = {}^-10 + (n - 1)3 = {}^-10 + 3n - 3 = 3n - 13$
The next two terms are 8 and 11

(b) Arithmetic sequence; difference is $^-3$ ⇒ $a_n = 10 + (n - 1) \cdot {}^-3 = 10 - 3n + 3 = 13 - 3n$
The next two terms are $^-8$ and $^-11$

(c) Geometric sequence; ratio is 2 ⇒ $a_n = {}^-2 \cdot 2^{n-1} = {}^-2^n$
The next two terms are $^-128$ and $^-256$

(d) Geometric sequence; ratio is $^-2$ ⇒ $a_n = {}^-2 \cdot {}^-2^{n-1} = ({}^-2)^n$
The next two terms are $^-128$ and 256

(e) Geometric sequence; ratio is $^-2$ ⇒ $a_n = 2 \cdot ({}^-2)^{n-1} = {}^-({}^-2)^n$
The next two terms are 2^7 and $^-2^8$

25. $S_n = \frac{n}{2}(a_1 + a_n)$ is the sum of an arithmetic sequence of n terms with first term a_1 and last term a_n

(a) $a_{100} = 3(100) - 13 = 287 \Rightarrow S_{100} = \frac{100}{2}({}^-10 + 287) = 50 \cdot 277 = 13{,}850$

(b) $a_{100} = 13 - 3(100) = {}^-287 \Rightarrow S_{100} = \frac{100}{2}(10 + {}^-287) = 50 \cdot {}^-277 = {}^-13{,}850$
(Since all corresponding terms are the opposites of the terms in (a), the sum should be the opposite of the sum in (a), which is in fact the case)

26. (a) $a_1 = 1^2 - 10 = {}^-9$
$a_2 = 2^2 - 10 = {}^-6$
$a_3 = 3^2 - 10 = {}^-1$
$a_4 = 4^2 - 10 = 6$
$a_5 = 5^2 - 10 = 15$

(b) $a_1 = {}^-5 \cdot 1 + 3 = {}^-2$
$a_2 = {}^-5 \cdot 2 + 3 = {}^-7$
$a_3 = {}^-5 \cdot 3 + 3 = {}^-12$
$a_4 = {}^-5 \cdot 4 + 3 = {}^-17$
$a_5 = {}^-5 \cdot 5 + 3 = {}^-22$

(c) $a_1 = ({}^-2)^1 - 1 = {}^-3$
$a_2 = ({}^-2)^2 - 1 = 3$
$a_3 = ({}^-2)^3 - 1 = {}^-9$
$a_4 = ({}^-2)^4 - 1 = 15$
$a_5 = ({}^-2)^5 - 1 = {}^-33$

(d) $a_1 = ({}^-2)^1 + 2^1 = 0$
$a_2 = ({}^-2)^2 + 2^2 = 8$
$a_3 = ({}^-2)^3 + 2^3 = 0$
$a_4 = ({}^-2)^4 + 2^4 = 32$
$a_5 = ({}^-2)^5 + 2^5 = 0$

26. (e) $a_1 = 1^2({}^-1)^1 = {}^-1$
$a_2 = 2^2({}^-1)^2 = 4$
$a_3 = 3^2({}^-1)^3 = {}^-9$
$a_4 = 4^2({}^-1)^4 = 16$
$a_5 = 5^2({}^-1)^5 = {}^-25$

(f) $a_1 = {}^-1({}^-2)^1 = 2$
$a_2 = {}^-2({}^-2)^2 = {}^-8$
$a_3 = {}^-3({}^-2)^3 = 24$
$a_4 = {}^-4({}^-2)^4 = {}^-64$
$a_5 = {}^-5({}^-2)^5 = 160$

(g) $a_1 = |10 - 1| = 9$
$a_2 = |10 - 2| = 8$
$a_3 = |10 - 3| = 7$
$a_4 = |10 - 4| = 6$
$a_5 = |10 - 5| = 5$

(h) $a_1 = [1 + ({}^-1)^1] \cdot 2^1 = 0$
$a_2 = [1 + ({}^-1)^2] \cdot 2^2 = 8$
$a_3 = [1 + ({}^-1)^3] \cdot 2^3 = 0$
$a_4 = [1 + ({}^-1)^4] \cdot 2^4 = 32$
$a_5 = [1 + ({}^-1)^5] \cdot 2^5 = 0$

27. $a_4 = {}^-8 \Rightarrow {}^-8 = a_1 + (4 - 1)d$ AND $a_{101} = {}^-493 \Rightarrow {}^-493 = a_1 + (101 - 1)d$ ... which leads to:
$a_1 + 3d = {}^-8$, or $a_1 = {}^-8 - 3d$ (*i*)
$a_1 + 100d = {}^-493$ (*ii*)
Substituting equation (*i*) into equation (*ii*):
$({}^-8 - 3d) + 100d = {}^-493 \Rightarrow {}^-8 + 97d = {}^-493 \Rightarrow 97d = {}^-485 \Rightarrow d = {}^-5$
Substituting $d = {}^-5$ into equation (*i*):
$a_1 = {}^-8 - 3 \cdot ({}^-5) = {}^-8 + 15 = 7$
So the first two terms are 7 and 2

28. (a) Consider $({}^-a)b + ab = ({}^-a + a)b = 0 \cdot b = 0 \Rightarrow ({}^-a)b$ is the additive inverse of ab. Since the additive inverse is unique, and the additive inverse of ab is ${}^-ab$, then $({}^-a)b$ must equal ${}^-ab$.

(b) Consider $({}^-a)({}^-b) + {}^-(ab) = ({}^-a)({}^-b) + ({}^-a)b = {}^-a({}^-b + b) = {}^-a \cdot 0 = 0$. This implies that $({}^-a)({}^-b)$ is the additive inverse of ${}^-(ab)$, or that $({}^-a)({}^-b) = ab$ by uniqueness.

29. (a) Enter: [2] [7] [+/-] [×] [3] [=] to obtain ${}^-81$

(b) Enter: [4] [6] [+/-] [×] [4] [+/-] [=] to obtain 184

(c) Enter: [2] [6] [+/-] [÷] [1] [3] [=] to obtain ${}^-2$

(d) Enter: [2] [6] [+/-] [÷] [1] [3] [+/-] [=] to obtain 2

On-going Assessment 4-2; Review Problems

40. The car goes backward 8 units, then backward 5 more units, for a total of 13 backward, or ${}^-13$:

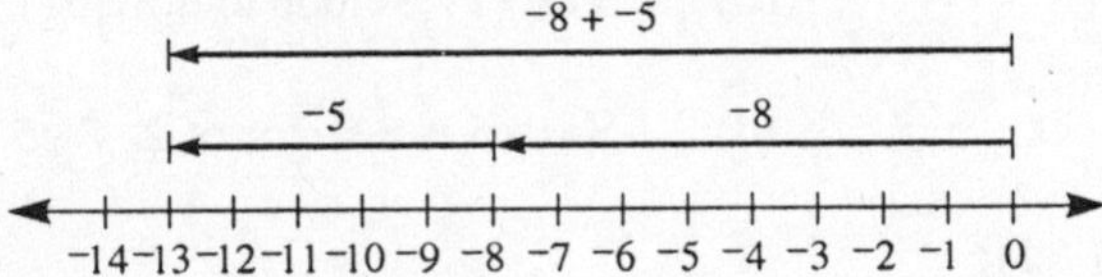

41. (a) The opposite of ${}^-5$ is 5

(b) The opposite of 7 is ${}^-7$

(c) The opposite of 0 is 0 (0 is neither positive nor negative)

42. (a) $|{}^-14| = 14$

(b) $|{}^-14| + 7 = 14 + 7 = 21$

42. (c) $8 - |^{-}12| = 8 - 12 = {}^{-}4$ (d) $|11| + |^{-}11| = 11 + 11 = 22$

43. Total weight was $(100 + 4) + (100 - 3) + (100 + 5) + (100 - 6) = 400$ pounds

On-going Assessment 4-3

1. (a) True $(30 = 5 \cdot 6)$ (b) True $(30 \div 6 = 5)$

   (c) True $(2|30$ and $3|30$, so $6|30)$ (d) True $(30 \div 6 = 5)$

   (e) True $(6 \cdot 5 = 30)$ (f) False (6 is a factor of 30, not a multiple of 30)

2. (a) Yes (The question is really, "Does $9|1379$?" Using the divisibility test for 9, $9\nmid(1 + 3 + 7 + 9)$, so $9\nmid 1379 \Rightarrow$ there will be a remainder; i.e., a group of less than 9 players.)

   (b) No (this amounts to, "Does $11\nmid 43{,}682$?" $11\nmid[(4 + 6 + 2) - (3 + 8)]$, so $11\nmid 43{,}682$)

   (c) Yes $[9|261$ because $9|(2 + 6 + 2)]$

   (d) No ($6\nmid\$242{,}600$ because $2|\$242{,}600$ but $3\nmid\$242{,}600$)

   (e) Yes ($3|\$7812$ and $4|\$7812$ so $12|\$7812$)

3. Use tests: (*i*) $2|n$ if the units digit is divisible by 2 (*ii*) $3|n$ if the sum of the digits is divisible by 3
   (*iii*) $4|n$ if the last two digits are divisible by 4 (*iv*) $5|n$ if the units digit is 0 or 5
   (*v*) $6|n$ if $2|n$ and $3|n$ (*vi*) $8|n$ if the last three digits are divisible by 8
   (*vii*) $9|n$ if the sum of the digits is divisible by 9 (*viii*) $10|n$ if the units digit is 0
   (*ix*) $11|n$ if the sum of the digits in places that are even powers of 10 minus the sum of the digits in the places that are odd powers of 10 is divisible by 11

   These tests give results as follows:

	2	3	4	5	6	8	9	10	11
(a) 746,988	Yes	Yes	Yes	No	Yes	No	No	No	Yes
(b) 81,342	Yes	Yes	No	No	Yes	No	Yes	No	No
(c) 15,810	Yes	Yes	No	Yes	Yes	No	No	Yes	No
(d) 4,201,012	Yes	No	Yes	No	No	No	No	No	No
(e) 1001	No	No	No	No	No	No	No	No	Yes
(f) 10,001	No	No	No	No	No	No	No	No	No

4. (a) No $(17|34{,}000$ but $17\nmid 15)$ (b) Yes $(17|34{,}000$ and $17|51)$

   (c) No $(19|19{,}000$ but $19\nmid 31)$ (d) Yes (5 is a factor of $2 \cdot 3 \cdot 5 \cdot 7$)

   (e) No $\{5 \mid (2 \cdot 3 \cdot 5 \cdot 7)$ so $5 \nmid [(2 \cdot 3 \cdot 5 \cdot 7) + 1]\}$

5. (a) Theorem 4-1 (b) Theorem 4-2(b)

   (c) None (in fact, $4|1300$) (d) Theorem 4-2(b) (consider a + b a single integer)

   (e) Theorem 4-1

6. (a) True

   (b) False (the <u>sum</u> being divisible does not force every digit to be)

   (c) False (e.g., 12)

   (d) True

   (e) True

   (f) False (e.g., 20; the difference between (e) and (f) is that 2 and 3 have no common factors while 2 and 4 do)

   (g) True

7. (a) Always

   (b) Sometimes (e.g., 360)

   (c) Never

   (d) Always

   (e) Always

   (f) Sometimes (e.g., 24)

   (g) Always

8. (a) $16|n$ if $16|$(last four digits of n). Notice the pattern of divisibility by 2, 4, and 8.

   (b) $25|n$ if $25|$(last two digits of n); that is, if n ends in 00, 25, 50, or 75

9. 85,041. The number must be divisible by 9 and 11; if we write it as 85ab1
   $\Rightarrow 9|(8+5+a+b+1)$ and $11|[(8+a+1)-(5+b)]$
   $9|(14+a+b)$ and $11|(4+a-b)$. So $a+b=4$ or 13 and $a - b = {}^-4$ or 7.
   $\Rightarrow a+b=4$ and $a-b={}^-4$ or 7
   Solving, and using trial and error, we find $a=0$ and $b=4$

10. (a) 7

    (b) 7

    (c) 6

11. (a) Any digit 0-9 (the units digit of 527,4□2 is divisible by 2)

    (b) $3|(5+2+7+4+\square+2) \Rightarrow 3|(20+\square) \Rightarrow \square = 1, 4,$ or 7

    (c) $4|\square 2 \Rightarrow \square = 1, 3, 5, 7,$ or 9

    (d) $9|(5+2+7+4+\square+2) \Rightarrow 9|(20+\square) \Rightarrow \square = 7$

    (e) $11|[(2+4+2)-(5+7+\square)] \Rightarrow 11|({}^-4-\square) \Rightarrow \square = 7$

12. The number of notepads sold must be between 16 (if the price was close to \$2) and 31 (if the price was close to \$1). 17 notepads at \$1.85 each would total \$31.45.

13. 19¢ ($209 = 11 \cdot 19$ (both prime numbers); for whole cent pricing 11¢ and 19¢ are the only possibilities, and the candy bars must cost more than 12¢)

14. (a) Yes ($4|76$)

    (b) No ($4\nmid 86$)

    (c) Yes ($4|100$ and $400|2000$)

    (d) Yes ($4|24$)

15. (a) 1, 2, 4, 5, 8, 11

15. (b) 1 touchdown and 11 field goals or 4 touchdowns and 4 field goals (consider 0 touchdowns - $3 \nmid 40$, impossible; 2 touchdowns - $3 \nmid (40 - 14)$, impossible; etc.)

(c) 5 field goals (6 touchdowns · 7 points each = 42 points; 57 − 42 = 15 ⇒ 15 ÷ 3 = 5 field goals)

16.

n	Remainder when n ÷ 9	Sum of n's digits	Remainder when sum ÷ 9
(a) 31	4	4	4
(b) 143	8	8	8
(c) 345	3	12	3
(d) 2987	8	26	8
(e) 7652	2	20	2

(f) The remainder when n is divided by 9 is the same as the remainder when the sum of the digits of n is divided by 9

17. (Notation: R1 + R3 = R4 would mean remainders of 1 + 3 sum to a remainder of 4)

(a) R4 + R1 + R2 = R7 (i. e., sum of the individual remainders)
Sum of numbers = 16,945 → R7

(b) R6 + R6 + R8 = R20 → R2
Sum = 10,208 → R2

(c) R8 + R7 + R4 + R2 = R21 → R3
Sum = 13,458 → R3

(d) Yes. 29 + 42 + 3 + 11 = 85
R2 + R6 + R3 + R2 → R4; sum = 85 → R4
(Examples may vary)

(e) 1003 → R4; 46 → R1. 1003 − 46 = 957 → R3 = R4 − R1

(f) 345 → R3; 56 → R2. 345 · 56 = 19,320 → R6 = R3 · R2

(g) No (the division may not have an integer quotient, in which case the test fails)

18. (a) False (consider d = 7, a = 10, b = 4 ⇒ $7 \mid (10 + 4)$ but $7 \nmid 10$ and $7 \nmid 4$)

(b) False (substitute "or" for "and" in (a))

(c) False ($4 \mid 60$ but $4 \nmid 6$ or $4 \nmid 10$)

(d) True

(e) True

(f) True

(g) False (if a = 5 and b = $^-5$ then $a \mid b$ and $b \mid a$ but $a \neq b$)

(h) True

(i) False ($3 \nmid 5$ and $3 \nmid 7$ but $3 \mid (5 + 7)$)

(j) False ($4 \mid 10^2$ but $4 \nmid 10$)

(k) False ($4 \nmid 6$ but $4 \mid 6^2$)

(l) True

19. $a \mid b$ implies a · m = b for some integer m. $b \mid c$ implies b · n = c for some integer n. Substituting a · m for b, we have (a · m) · n = c, or a · (m · n) = c ⇒ $a \mid c$.

20. Prove: If $d|a$ and $d\nmid ab$, then $d\nmid(a + b)$.
$d|a$ implies $a = md$; $d\nmid b$ implies $b = nd + r$, $0 < r < d$. Then $a + b = md + nd + r = (m + n)d + r$; so $(a + b) \div d = [(m + n)d + r] \div d = m + n + \frac{r}{d}$. Since $0 < r < d$, $\frac{r}{d}$ is not an integer $\Rightarrow$ $m + n + \frac{r}{d}$ is not an integer $\Rightarrow$ $d\nmid(a + b)$.

21. Any five-digit number *abcde* may be written $a \cdot 10^4 + b \cdot 10^3 + c \cdot 10^2 + d \cdot 10 + e$, but this is equivalent to $a(9999 + 1) + b(999 + 1) + c(99 + 1) + d(9 + 1) + e$. Distributing and grouping yields $(9999a + 999b + 99c + 9d) + (a + b + c + d + e)$. The first group is divisible by 9, implying that the entire sum (equal to the five-digit number) is divisible by 9 if and only if the second group is divisible by 9; i.e., if the sum of the digits is divisible by 9.

22. (a) The two numbers with reversed digits will differ by 9

    (b) The numbers will always differ by 18

    (c) Any two-digit number's value may be represented as $10t + u$ (10 times the tens digit plus the units digit). With digits reversed, the value becomes $10u + t$. Taking the difference gives $10t + u - (10u + t) = 9t - 9u = 9(t - u)$, a multiple of 9.

    (d) The difference of the two numbers is a multiple of 9

23. $3|6{,}868{,}395$ [because $3|$(sum of digits)] and $5|6{,}868{,}395$ (because last digit is 5) $\Rightarrow$ $15|6{,}868{,}395$

On-going Assessment 4-4

1. (a) Prime (fails divisibility test for primes to 11; no need to test for primes > 11 because $13^2 > 149$)

   (b) Not prime $(13 \cdot 71 = 923)$

   (c) Prime [fails divisibility test for primes up to 19 $(23^2 > 433)$]

   (d) Prime

   (e) Prime

   (f) Not prime $(3|(8 + 9 + 7)$ so $3|897)$

2. 73 [$73^2 < 5669$, but $79^2 > 5669$ (73 is prime and 79 is the next largest prime)]

3. (a)

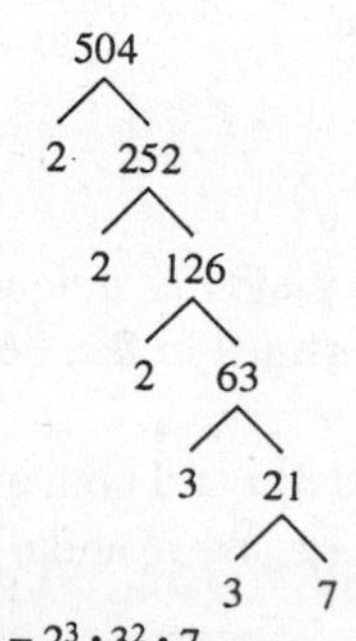

   (b)

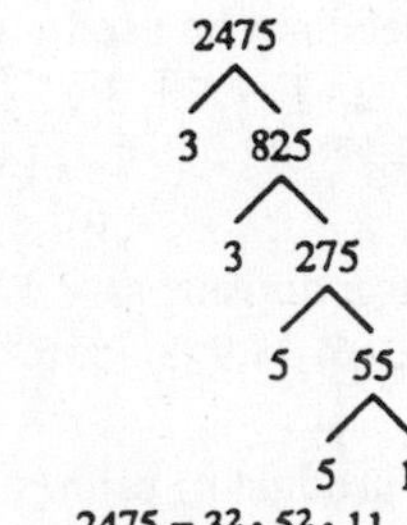

3. (c)

11250
2 5625
3 1875
3 625
5 125
5 25
5 5

$11250 = 2 \cdot 3^2 \cdot 5^4$

4. (a) The missing numbers are 210, 105, and 21 (from top to bottom)

   (b) We know the prime factorization of the top number is $2 \cdot 3 \cdot 7 \cdot 5 = 210$

5. The three smallest primes are 2, 3, and 5 $\Rightarrow$ the least number divisible by three different primes is $2 \cdot 3 \cdot 5 = 30$

6. (a) All pairs of divisors of 48 would be possible arrays: 1×48, 2×24, 3×16, or 4×12

   (b) Since 47 is prime, the only possibility would be 1×47

7. Yes (177 flotillas of 1 ship, 1 of 177 ships, 3 of 59 ships, or 59 of 3 ships)

8. (a) Prime factorization of $435 = 3 \cdot 5 \cdot 29$ $\Rightarrow$ committees can have these numbers of members or products thereof $\Rightarrow$ possibilities are 3, 5, 15, or 29 members

   (b) 145 three-member committees ($435 \div 3$), 87 five-member committees, 29 fifteen-member committees, or 15 twenty nine-member committees

9. This problem is asking for the divisors of each number. It is assumed here that a single row is a "degenerate rectangle"

   (a) 1, 2, 3, 4, 6, 9, 12, 18, or 36 rows

   (b) 1, 2, 4, 7, 14, or 28 rows

   (c) 1 or 17 rows

   (d) 1, 2, 3, 4, 6, 8, 9, 12, 16, 18, 24, 36, 48, 72, or 144 rows

10. Each number from 1 to 12 need not be used - we must only have divisors of each number:
    that is; $\{1, 2, 3, 2^2, 5, 2 \cdot 3, 7, 2^3, 3^2, 2 \cdot 5, 11, 2^2 \cdot 3\}$
    $\Rightarrow$ least common multiple $= 2^3 \cdot 3^2 \cdot 5 \cdot 7 \cdot 11 = 27{,}720$

11. 90 (If 9 is a divisor, then 3 is a divisor, as is 1. All possible groupings of these divisors yields 12 unique divisors ($1, 2, 3, 5, 9, 2 \cdot 3, 2 \cdot 5, 2 \cdot 9, 3 \cdot 5, 5 \cdot 9, 2 \cdot 3 \cdot 5, 2 \cdot 5 \cdot 9$), so the locker number must in fact be $2 \cdot 5 \cdot 9 = 90$.)

12. (a) 6 can be written as a product of primes in only one way; i.e., $2 \cdot 3$. Since $2|n$ and $3|n$ and both are prime, they must be included in the unique factorization $\Rightarrow$ $(2 \cdot 3)(p_1 \cdot p_2 \cdot \cdots \cdot p_m) = n$, and $6|n$.

    (b) Yes ($a|n \Rightarrow n = ra$. $b|n \Rightarrow n = sb$. Then $n^2 = (ra)(sb) = (rs)(ab) \Rightarrow$ since $ab|(rs)(ab)$ then $ab|n^2$.)

13. 9409 (Any number with an odd number of factors must be a perfect square. For exactly three factors, the factors must be of the form 1, p, p^2, where p is a prime. Find the largest two-digit prime and square it; i.e., $97^2 = 9409$.)

14. Use the following procedure:
   (*i*) Write the natural numbers from 1 to 200.
   (*ii*) Circle 2 because 2 is prime.
   (*iii*) Cross out multiples of 2; they are not prime.
   (*iv*) Circle 3 because 3 is prime.
   (*v*) Cross out multiples of 3 that have not already been crossed out.
   (*vi*) Circle 5, 7, 11, and 13; cross out their multiples that have not already been crossed out. (We can stop after 13 because 13 is the largest prime whose square is less than 200.)
   (*vii*) All the numbers remaining in the list and not crossed out are prime. You should end with the following:
   2, 3, 5, 7, 11, 13, 17, 19, 23, 29, 31, 37, 41, 43, 47, 53, 59, 61, 67, 71, 73, 79, 83, 89, 97, 101, 103, 107, 109, 113, 127, 131, 137, 139, 149, 151, 157, 163, 167, 173, 179, 181, 191, 193, 197, 199.

15. There is no analytic method - one must work through the list of primes. The twin primes are thus: 3 and 5, 5 and 7, 11 and 13, 17 and 19, 29 and 31, 41 and 43, 59 and 61, 71 and 73, 101 and 103, 107 and 109, 137 and 139, 149 and 151, 179 and 181, 191 and 193, and 197 and 199.

16. (a) Any natural number that is a multiple of 41 (i.e., 41, 82, 123, ...) will yield a composite number divisible by 41 when substituted into $n^2 - n + 41$. For example, if n = 82, $41 | (82^2 - 82 + 41 = 6683)$

   (b) Let n = 41a, where $a \in N \Rightarrow n^2 - n + 41 = (41a)^2 - 41a + 41 = 41(41a^2 - a + 1)$

17. Every number would have its "usual" factorization $1 \cdot (p_1 \cdot p_2 \cdot \cdots \cdot p_n)$, along with infinitely many other such factorizations because $1^n = 1$; n may be any natural number.

18. All other factors of 42: 1, 2, 3, 6, 7, 14, 21

19. No (5^z has factors of only 5; there are no factors of 5 in $2^x \cdot 3^y$)

20. (a) 0, 4, 6, 8 (all would cause divisibility by 2 at some point; 2 would allow a superprime in the leftmost position only)

   (b) 1 and 9 (9 is composite; 1 is not prime by definition)

   (c) 23, 29, 31, 37, 53, 59, 71, 73, and 79

   (d) Answers may vary; 233, 239, and 373 are three examples

21. Any number with 3, 6, 9, ... one's will be divisible by 3 $\Rightarrow$ they are composite

22. All odd terms are composite [3(odd *n*) + 1 = even number $\Rightarrow$ divisibility by 2]

23. The details of the proof are as follows: If any prime *q* in the set {2, 3, 5, ... , p} divides N, then $q | (2 \cdot 3 \cdot 5 \cdot \cdots \cdot p)$. Because $q \nmid 1$, by Theorem 5-1(b) $q \nmid (2 \cdot 3 \cdot 5 \cdot \cdots \cdot p + 1)$; that is, $q \nmid N$.

24. $2N = 2^6 \cdot 3^5 \cdot 5^4 \cdot 7^3 \cdot 11^7 \Rightarrow N = 2^5 \cdot 3^5 \cdot 5^4 \cdot 7^3 \cdot 11^7 = (2 \cdot 3 \cdot 5 \cdot 7 \cdot 11)(2^4 \cdot 3^4 \cdot 5^3 \cdot 7^2 \cdot 11^6)$
   $\Rightarrow (2 \cdot 3 \cdot 5 \cdot 7 \cdot 11)$ is a factor of N

25. Yes $[(3^2 \cdot 2^4) \cdot (3^2 \cdot 2^3) = 3^4 \cdot 2^7]$

26. (a) Divisible by 3, 5, 7, 11, and 13 $\Rightarrow$ composite

   (b) $(3 \cdot 4 \cdot 5 \cdot 6 \cdot 7 \cdot 8) + 2 = 2[(3 \cdot 2 \cdot 5 \cdot 6 \cdot 7 \cdot 8) + 1] \Rightarrow$ composite

   (c) $(3 \cdot 5 \cdot 7 \cdot 11 \cdot 13) + 5 = 5[(3 \cdot 1 \cdot 7 \cdot 11 \cdot 13) + 1] \Rightarrow$ composite

26. (d) $10! + 7 = 7[(10 \cdot 9 \cdot 8 \cdot 1 \cdot 6 \cdot 5 \cdot 4 \cdot 3 \cdot 2 \cdot 1) + 1] \Rightarrow$ composite

(e) $10! + k$ can be factored as in (d), depending on the value of k $(2 \leq k \leq 10) \Rightarrow$ composite

27. (*i*) $2^3 \cdot 3^2 \cdot 25^3$ is not a prime factorization because 25 is not prime

(*ii*) $25^3 = (5^2)^3 = 5^6 \Rightarrow$ prime factorization $= 2^3 \cdot 3^2 \cdot 5^6$

On-going Assessment 4-4; Review Problems

41. (a) False $[11 \nmid (1 + 9) - 8]$

(b) True $(13 \cdot 77 = 1001)$

(c) True [Theorem 5-2(b)]

(d) True (this is a divisibility test for 77)

42. (a) Divisors are 2, 3, 6 (b) Divisors are 2, 3, 5, 6, 9, 10

43. If $12|n$ then $n = 12b$ for some integer b $\Rightarrow n = 3 \cdot (4b) \Rightarrow 3|n$

44. Only among eight people; each would get \$422 $(8|3376$ but $7 \nmid 3376)$

On-going Assessment 4-5

1. (a) (*i*) $D_{18} = \{1, 2, 3, 6, 9, 18\}$ and $D_{10} = \{1, 2, 5, 10\} \Rightarrow GCD(18, 10) = 2$

(*ii*) $M_{18} = \{18, 36, 54, 72, 90, \ldots\}$ and $M_{10} = \{10, 20, 30, \ldots, 90, \ldots\} \Rightarrow LCM(18, 10) = 90$

(b) (*i*) $D_{24} = \{1, 2, 4, 6, 8, 12, 24\}$ and $D_{36} = \{1, 2, 3, 4, 6, 9, 12, 18, 36\} \Rightarrow GCD(24, 36) = 12$

(*ii*) $M_{24} = \{24, 48, 72, 96, \ldots\}$ and $M_{36} = \{36, 72, 108, \ldots\} \Rightarrow LCM(24, 36) = 72$

(c) (*i*) $D_8 = \{1, 2, 4, 8\}$, $D_{24} = \{1, 2, 3, 4, 6, 8, 12, 24\}$, and $D_{52} = \{1, 2, 4, 13, 26, 52\} \Rightarrow GCD(8, 24, 52) = 4$

(*ii*) $M_8 = \{8, 16, 24, \ldots, 312, \ldots\}$, $M_{24} = \{24, 48, 72, \ldots, 312, \ldots\}$,
and $M_{52} = \{52, 104, 156, \ldots, 312, \ldots\} \Rightarrow LCM(8, 24, 52) = 312$

2. (a) $132 = 2 \cdot 2 \cdot 3 \cdot 11$ and $504 = 2 \cdot 2 \cdot 2 \cdot 3 \cdot 3 \cdot 7$
$\Rightarrow GCD(132, 504) = 2 \cdot 2 \cdot 3 = 12$ and $LCM(132, 504) = 2^3 \cdot 3^2 \cdot 7 \cdot 11 = 5544$

(b) $65 = 5 \cdot 13$ and $1690 = 2 \cdot 5 \cdot 13 \cdot 13$
$\Rightarrow GCD(65, 1690) = 5 \cdot 13 = 65$ and $LCM(65, 1690) = 2 \cdot 5 \cdot 13^2 = 1690$

(c) $900 = 2 \cdot 2 \cdot 3 \cdot 3 \cdot 5 \cdot 5$; $96 = 2 \cdot 2 \cdot 2 \cdot 2 \cdot 2 \cdot 3$; $630 = 2 \cdot 3 \cdot 3 \cdot 5 \cdot 7$
$\Rightarrow GCD(900, 96, 630) = 2 \cdot 3 = 6$ and $LCM(900, 96, 630) = 2^5 \cdot 3^2 \cdot 5^2 \cdot 7 = 50{,}400$

(d) $108 = 2 \cdot 2 \cdot 3 \cdot 3 \cdot 3$ and $360 = 2 \cdot 2 \cdot 2 \cdot 3 \cdot 3 \cdot 5$
$\Rightarrow GCD(108, 360) = 2 \cdot 2 \cdot 3 \cdot 3 = 36$ and $LCM(108, 360) = 2^3 \cdot 3^3 \cdot 5 = 1080$

2. (e) $63 = 3 \cdot 3 \cdot 7$ and $149 = 3 \cdot 7 \cdot 7$
$\Rightarrow$ GCD(63, 149) $= 3 \cdot 7 = 21$ and LCM(63, 149) $= 3^2 \cdot 7^2 = 441$

(f) $625 = 5 \cdot 5 \cdot 5 \cdot 5$; $750 = 2 \cdot 3 \cdot 5 \cdot 5 \cdot 5$; $1000 = 2 \cdot 2 \cdot 2 \cdot 5 \cdot 5 \cdot 5$
$\Rightarrow$ GCD(625, 750, 1000) $= 5 \cdot 5 \cdot 5 = 125$ and LCM(625, 750, 1000) $= 2^3 \cdot 3 \cdot 5^4 = 15{,}000$

3. (a) GCD(2904, 220) = GCD(220,64) because 2924 ÷ 220 → R64
= GCD(64, 28) because 220 ÷ 64 → R28
= GCD(28,8) because 64 ÷ 28 → R8
= GCD(8,4) because 28 ÷ 8 → R4
= GCD(4,0) because 8 ÷ 4 → 0
= 4

3. (b) GCD(14595, 10856) = GCD(10856, 3739) because 14595 ÷ 10856 → R3739
= GCD(3739, 3378) because 10856 ÷ 3739 → R3378
= GCD(3378, 361) because 3739 ÷ 3378 → R361
= GCD(361, 129) because 3378 ÷ 361 → R129
= GCD(129, 103) because 361 ÷ 129 → R103
= GCD(103, 26) because 129 ÷ 103 → R26
= GCD(26, 25) because 103 ÷ 26 → R25
= GCD(25, 1) because 26 ÷ 25 → R1
= GCD(1, 0) because 25 ÷ 1 → R0
= 1

(c) GCD(123152, 122368) = GCD(122368, 784) because 123152 ÷ 122368 → R784
= GCD(784, 64) because 122368 ÷ 784 → R64
= GCD(64, 16) because 784 ÷ 64 → R16
= GCD(16, 0) because 64 ÷ 16 → R0
= 16

4. (a) 72 (b) 1440

(c) 630

5. (a) GCD(2924, 220) · LCM(2924, 220) = 2924 · 220
4 · LCM(2924, 220) = 643,280
LCM(2924, 220) = 643,280 ÷ 4 = 160,820

(b) GCD(14595, 10856) · LCM(14595, 10856) = 14595 · 10856
1 · LCM(14595, 10856) = 158,443,320
LCM(14595, 10856) = 158,443,320

(c) GCD(123152, 122368) · LCM(123152, 122368) = 123,152 · 122,368
16 · LCM(123152, 122368) = 123,152 · 122,368
LCM(123152, 122368) = 123,152 · 122,368 ÷ 16 = 941,866,496

6. GCD(6, 10) = 2 and LCM(6, 10) = 30

7. (a) The real question is "What is LCM(15, 40, 60)?", since this is when the alarms will coincide.
LCM(15, 40, 60) = 120, or 120 minutes = 2 hours later, at 8:00 AM.

(b) No (this would be equivalent to changing locations of clocks A and B in the room)

8. GCD(9, 12) = 3 and LCM(2, 3) = 6 $\Rightarrow$ since the number is odd, it must be 5

9. (a) \$60 [the smallest number divisible by 1 through 6 is needed; i.e., LCM(1, 2, 3, 4, 5, 6) = 60]

   (b) $60 \div 5 =$ \$12 each

   (c) \$12 in \$2 bills is 6 bills $\Rightarrow$ 5 winners at 6 bills each is 30 bills

10. GCD(120, 144) = 24 coins per stack

11. 24 nights (the question is really "What is the LCM(8, 6)?" LCM(8, 6) = $2^3 \cdot 3 = 24$)

12. 15 cookies [LCM(24, 45) = 360; i.e., \$3.60 worth of cookies was sold. \$3.60 at 24¢ each is 15 cookies.]

13. 2:30 A.M. [LCM(90, 75) = 450 minutes = $7\frac{1}{2}$ hours. $7\frac{1}{2}$ hours later than 7:00 P.M. is 2:30 A.M.]

14. 36 minutes [LCM(12, 18) = 36]

15. (a) LCM(a, b) = ab (*a* and *b* have no common factors)

    (b) GCD(a, a) = a and LCM(a, a) = a (*a* has all factors in common with *a*)

    (c) GCD(a^2, a) = a and LCM(a^2, a) = a^2

    (d) GCD(a, b) = a and LCM(a, b) = b

    (e) GCD(a, b) = 1 and LCM(a, b) = ab (*a* and *b* have no factors in common)

    (f) $a|b$ (if GCD(a, b) = a, then *a* must divide both *a* and *b*)

    (g) $b|a$ (if LCM(a, b) = a, then $b \cdot n = a$ (where *n* can be any integer) $\Rightarrow$ $a \div b = n$, or $b|a$)

16. (a) True (if both *a* and *b* are even, then GCD(a, b) ≥ 2)

    (b) True (GCD(a, b) = 2 $\Rightarrow$ $2|a$ and $2|b$)

    (c) False (GCD could be any larger multiple of two; e.g., GCD(8, 20) = 4)

    (d) False (for $a \neq b$, LCM > GCD)

    (e) True (Theorem 5-9)

    (f) True (if GCD(a, b) > a, it could not divide a)

    (g) True (if LCM(a, b) < a, it could not be a multiple)

17. GCD(120, 75) = GCD(75, 45) = GCD(45, 30) = GCD(30, 15) = GCD(15, 0) $\Rightarrow$ GCD(120, 75) = 15
    GCD(105, 15) = GCD(15, 0) $\Rightarrow$ GCD(105, 15) = 15
    Thus GCD(120, 75, 105) = 15

18. (a) 2 is the only prime factor of 4, and $2 \nmid 97{,}219{,}988{,}751$

    (b) 11 is its own only prime factor and $11 \nmid 181{,}345{,}913$ since $11 \nmid (1 + 1 + 4 + 9 + 3) - (8 + 3 + 5 + 1)$

19. LCM(5, 20) = 20 and LCM(6, 20) = 60 $\Rightarrow$ a person who called 20th would receive both tickets first

20. LCM(12, 16) = 48 $\Rightarrow$ Jackie would spend \$48 on each (four tapes and three CD's)

21. Larry will use the club for $\frac{360}{2} = 180$ days during the membership period
Mary will use the club for $\frac{360}{3} = 120$ days during the membership period
LCM(2, 3) = 6 $\Rightarrow$ Larry and Mary will use the club together for $\frac{360}{6} = 60$ days during the membership period
Larry will use the club alone for 180 – 60 = 120 days
Mary will use the club alone for 120 – 60 = 60 days
The club will be used for 120 days (Larry alone) + 60 days (Mary alone) + 60 days (both Larry and Mary) = 240 days
Neither will use the club for 360 – 240 = 120 days

22. LCM(30, 15, 20) = 60 $\Rightarrow$ 2 packages of plates, 4 of cups, and 3 of napkins will give 60 of each

23. LCM(48, 28) = 336 $\Rightarrow$ gear 2 must make 336 ÷ 28 = 12 revolutions to line up the arrows

24. LCM(40, 24, 60) = 120 $\Rightarrow$ gear 1 must make 120 ÷ 40 = 3 revolutions; gear 2 must make 120 ÷ 24 = 5 revolutions; and gear 3 must make 120 ÷ 60 = 2 revolutions before the arrows are realigned

25. (a)

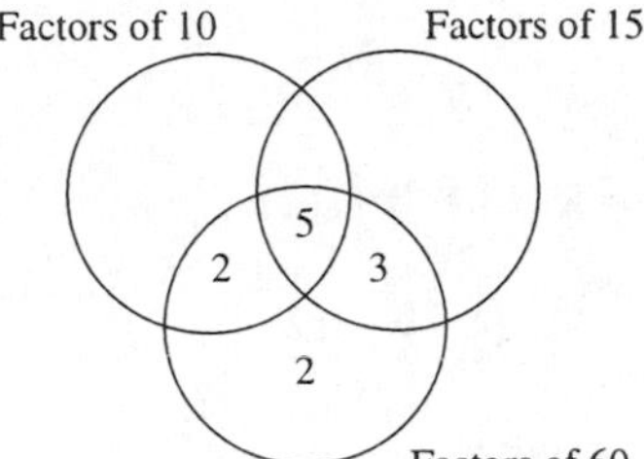

(b)

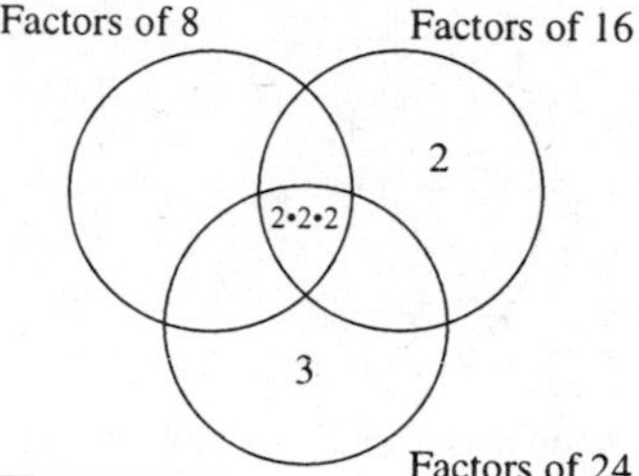

26. $p^2 = p \cdot p$, where p is prime $\Rightarrow$ the factors of p^2 are 1, p, and p^2

27. GCD(25, x) = 1 $\Rightarrow$ x can have no factors in common with 25, so x cannot have a factor of 5
The solution set is thus {1, 2, 3, 4, 6, 7, 8, 9, 11, 12, 13, 14, 16, 17, 18, 19, 21, 22, 23, 24}

28. The various requirements eliminate numbers one by one:
"between 62 and 72" eliminates 61;
"composite" eliminates 67;
"sum of digits prime" eliminates 63;
"has more than four factors" eliminates 65 (which has exactly four factors);
leaves 70 (which has eight factors - 1, 2, 5, 7, 10, 14, 35, 70)

On-going Assessment 4-5; Review Problems

35. $1{,}000{,}000 = 10^6 = 2^6 \cdot 5^6$ $\Rightarrow$ if a 2 is paired with a 5 in any factor a 0 results
No 0's as digits $\Rightarrow$ 2^6 and 5^6 must be separate factors
$\Rightarrow$ $x = 2^6 = 64$; $y = 5^6 = 15{,}625$

36. (a) Let the number be 83a51. Then 8 + 3 + a + 5 + 1 = 17 + a must be a multiple of 3. If a is a single digit, the only possibilities for 17 + a to be a multiple of 3 are 1, 4, or 7 $\Rightarrow$ n = 83,151, 83,451, or 83,751.

(b) Let the number be 8a691. Then (1 + 6 + 8) – (a + 9) = 6 – a must be a multiple of 11. The only possibility, if a is a single digit, is 6 – a = 0 and a = 6 $\Rightarrow$ n = 86,691.

(c) 10306 ÷ 23 = 448.09 $\Rightarrow$ 103_6 > 23 · 448. The 2nd factor must end in 2 to produce a 6 in the units position $\Rightarrow$ 23 · 452 = 103$\underline{9}$6

37. No $[3|(3+1+1+1) \Rightarrow 3|3111]$

38. Answers may vary. $2 \cdot 3 \cdot 5 \cdot 7 \cdot 11 \cdot 13 = 30{,}030$ is one.

39. The question is really "What is LCM(2, 3, 4, ... , 11)?"
Their factors are $\{2, 3, 2^2, 5, 2 \cdot 3, 7, 2^3, 3^2, 2 \cdot 5, 11\} \Rightarrow \text{LCM} = 2^3 \cdot 3^2 \cdot 5 \cdot 7 \cdot 11 = 27{,}720$

40. 43 (the next prime squared (47^2) is greater than 2089)

On-going Assessment 4-6

1. 8:00 A.M. + 6 hours is equivalent to $8 \oplus 6 = 2$ on a 12-hour clock $\Rightarrow$ she should take her next dose at 2:00 P.M.

2. $7 \oplus 7 = 2 \Rightarrow$ she will arrive at 2:00 P.M

3. (a) $7 \oplus 3 = 3$ $(7 + 8 - 12)$
   (b) $4 \oplus 10 = 2$ $(4 + 10 - 12)$
   (c) $3 \ominus 9 = 6$ $(3 - 9 + 12)$
   (d) $4 \ominus 8 = 8$ $(4 - 8 + 12)$
   (e) $3 \otimes 9 = 3$ $(3 \cdot 9 - 2 \cdot 12)$
   (f) $4 \otimes 4 = 4$ $(4 \cdot 4 - 12)$
   (g) Not possible [$1 \oslash 3 = y$ (where $\oslash$ denotes clock division) implies $1 = 3 \otimes y$
   But $3 \otimes n \equiv$ either 0, 3, 6, or 9 $\Rightarrow 3 \otimes y \neq 1$]
   (h) 10 ($2 \oslash 5 = y$ implies $2 = 5 \otimes y$. Checking numbers 1, 2, 3, ... , 11, 12 finds $y = 10$)

4. (a) $3 \oplus 4 = 2$ $(3 + 4 - 5)$
   (b) $3 \oplus 3 = 1$
   (c) $3 \oplus 4 = 2$
   (d) $1 \otimes 4 = 4$
   (e) $3 \otimes 4 = 2$ $(3 \cdot 4 - 2 \cdot 5)$
   (f) $4 \otimes 4 = 1$
   (g) $3 \oslash 4 = 2$ $(3 \oslash 4 = n \Rightarrow 3 = 4 \otimes n$ and $n = 2)$
   (h) $1 \oslash 4 = 4$

5. (a)

$\oplus$	1	2	3	4	5	6	7
1	2	3	4	5	6	7	1
2	3	4	5	6	7	1	2
3	4	5	6	7	1	2	3
4	5	6	7	1	2	3	4
5	6	7	1	2	3	4	5
6	7	1	2	3	4	5	6
7	1	2	3	4	5	6	7

   (b) (*i*) Defining subtraction in terms of addition, $5 \ominus 6 = x$ if $5 = 6 \oplus x$. Thus we can follow down the 6 column to find 5 as the answer. This occurs in row 6 $\Rightarrow 5 \ominus 6 = 6$.

   (*ii*) $2 \ominus 5 = x$ if $2 = 5 \oplus x$. Follow down the 5 column to 2, which is on row 4 $\Rightarrow 2 \ominus 5 = 4$.

   (c) See (b)(*i*) above. If it is defined in terms of addition, subtraction can always be performed on any hour clock.

6. (a)

⊗	1	2	3	4	5	6	7
1	1	2	3	4	5	6	7
2	2	4	6	1	3	5	7
3	3	6	2	5	1	4	7
4	4	1	5	2	6	3	7
5	5	3	1	6	4	2	7
6	6	5	4	3	2	1	7
7	7	7	7	7	7	7	7

(b) (*i*) Defining division in terms of multiplication, $3 \oslash 5 = x$ (where $\oslash$ denotes clock division) if $3 = 5 \otimes x$. Follow down the 5 column to locate the answer of 3. This occurs in row 2 $\Rightarrow$ $3 \oslash 5 = 2$.

(*ii*) $4 \oslash 6 = x$ if $4 = 6 \otimes x$. Follow down the 6 column to 4, which is on row 3 $\Rightarrow$ $4 \oslash 6 = 3$.

(c) Division by numbers other than 7 (1 through 6) is always possible since 1 to 6 is found in all columns (and rows) except the 7th.

7. (a) 10 $(10 \oplus 2 = 0)$ (b) 9 $(9 \oplus 3 = 0)$

(c) 7 $({}^-2 + {}^-3 = {}^-5 \Rightarrow {}^-5 + 12 = 7)$ (d) 7 $({}^-5 + 12 = 7)$

(e) 1 $({}^-2 + 12 = 10$ and ${}^-3 + 12 = 9 \Rightarrow 10 \ominus 9 = 1)$

(f) 6 (the product of two negative numbers is still positive in clock arithmetic)

8. Adding or subtracting multiples of 7 will give dates which fall on the same day of the week.

(a) 2, 9, 16, 30 (23 – 21; 23 – 14; 23 – 7; 23 + 7)

(b) 3, 10, 17, 24, 31 (Tuesday the 2nd $\Rightarrow$ Wednesday the 3rd; then add 7's)

(c) Wednesday. Since next year is a leap year, it has 366 days. Converting to mod 7, $366 \equiv 52 \cdot 7 + 2 \equiv 2 \pmod 7$ $\Rightarrow$ September 3 will be 52 weeks and 2 days later

9. (a) $29 = 5 \cdot 5 + 4 \Rightarrow 29 \equiv 4 \pmod 5$

(b) $3498 = 3 \cdot 1166 + 0 \Rightarrow 3498 \equiv 0 \pmod 3$

(c) $3498 = 11 \cdot 318 + 0 \Rightarrow 3498 \equiv 0 \pmod{11}$

(d) Adding a multiple of 10 will yield an equivalent number (mod 10); i.e., ${}^-23 \pmod{10} \equiv ({}^-22 + 30) \pmod{10} \equiv 7 \pmod{10}$

10. (a) $8|(81 - 1)$ (b) $10|(81 - 1)$

(c) $13|(1000 - {}^-1)$ (d) $10^1 \equiv 1 \pmod 9 \Rightarrow 10^{84} \equiv 1^{84} \pmod 9$

(e) $10^2 \equiv 1 \pmod{11} \Rightarrow (10^2)^{50} \equiv 1^{50} \pmod{11}$

(f) $100|(937 - 37)$

11. $a \equiv 0 \pmod m \Rightarrow a = km + 0 \Rightarrow m|a$ since $m|km$
Likewise, $m|a \Rightarrow a = km + 0 \equiv 0 \pmod m$

12. (a) $8|24 \Rightarrow 24 \div 8$ with remainder $= 0 \Rightarrow 24 \equiv 0 \pmod 8$

(b) $^-90 \equiv 0 \pmod 3$

(c) $n|n \Rightarrow n \div n$ with remainder $= 0 \Rightarrow n \equiv 0 \pmod n$

13. (a) $x = 2n\ (n \in I) \Rightarrow x \equiv 0 \pmod 2$

(b) $x = 2n + 1\ (n \in I) \Rightarrow x \equiv 1 \pmod 2$

(c) $x = 5n + 3\ (n \in I) \Rightarrow x \equiv 3 \pmod 5$

14. (a) $5^2 = 25 \equiv 1 \pmod 6 \Rightarrow 5^{100} = (5^2)^{50} \equiv (1)^{50} \pmod 6 \equiv 1 \pmod 6$
$\Rightarrow 5^{100}$ has remainder 1 when divided by 6

(b) $5^2 = 25 \equiv 1 \pmod 6 \Rightarrow 5^{101} = 5^1 \cdot (5^2)^{50} \equiv 5 \cdot (1)^{50} \pmod 6 \equiv 5 \pmod 6$
The remainder is 5

(c) $10^2 = 100 \equiv 1 \pmod{11} \Rightarrow 10^{99} = 10 \cdot (10^{98}) = 10 \cdot (10^2)^{49} \equiv 10 \cdot (1)^{49} \pmod{11} \equiv 10 \pmod{11}$
The remainder is 10

(d) $10^2 \equiv 1 \pmod{11} \Rightarrow 10^{100} = (10^2)^{50} \equiv (1)^{50} \pmod{11} \equiv 1 \pmod{11}$
The remainder is 1

15. Thanksgiving is always on a Thursday, so November 29 is a Thursday. December 1 is thus on the following Saturday. The subsequent Saturdays fall on December 8, 15, 22, and 29 (differing by a multiple of 7). Since Christmas is always December 25, it will fall three days after Saturday, December 22, or on a Tuesday.

16. There are 365 days in the year, and $365 \equiv 1 \pmod 7$. Thus 365 days after July 4 will be 52 weeks and 1 day later, or Wednesday.

17. $N = a_k \cdot 10^k + a_{k-1} \cdot 10^{k-1} + \cdots + a_2 \cdot 10^2 + a_1 \cdot 10^1 + a_0$ and $4|N$ if and only if $4|(a_1 \cdot 10^1 + a_0)$
$100 \equiv 0 \pmod 4 \Rightarrow N = 100(a_k \cdot 10^{k-2} + a_{k-1} \cdot 10^{k-3} + \cdots + a_2) + a_1 \cdot 10^1 + a_0 \equiv a_1 \cdot 10^1 + a_0 \pmod 4$
$\Rightarrow 4|N$ if and only if $4|(a_1 \cdot 10^1 + a_0)$

18. Answers may vary; for example: $2 \cdot 11 \equiv 1 \cdot 11 \pmod{11}$ but $2 \not\equiv 1 \pmod{11}$

Chapter 4 Review

1. (a) $^-3$

(b) a

(c) 0

(d) $^-x - y$

(e) $x - y$

(f) $(^-2)^5 = {}^-32 \Rightarrow$ additive inverse is 32

(g) $^-2^5 = {}^-32 \Rightarrow$ additive inverse is 32

2. (a) $(^-2 + {}^-8) + 3 = {}^-10 + 3 = {}^-7$

(b) $^-2 - (^-5) + 5 = 3 + 5 = 8$

(c) $^-3(^-2) + 2 = 6 + 2 = 8$

(d) $^-3(^-5 + 5) = {}^-3(0) = 0$

(e) $^-40 \div {}^-5 = 8$

(f) $(^-25 \div 5)(^-3) = (^-5)(^-3) = 15$

3. (a) ${}^{-}x + 3 = 0 \Rightarrow {}^{-}x = {}^{-}3 \Rightarrow x = 3$ (b) ${}^{-}2x = 10 \Rightarrow x = \frac{10}{{}^{-}2} = {}^{-}5$

(c) $0 \div ({}^{-}x) = 0 \Rightarrow$ Any integer except 0 (d) ${}^{-}x \div 0 = {}^{-}1 \Rightarrow$ No integer solution

(e) $3x - 1 = {}^{-}124 \Rightarrow 3x = {}^{-}123 \Rightarrow x = \frac{{}^{-}123}{3} = {}^{-}41$ (f) ${}^{-}2x + 3x = x \Rightarrow x = x \Rightarrow$ Any integer

4. $2 \cdot {}^{-}3 = {}^{-}6$
$1 \cdot {}^{-}3 = {}^{-}3$
$0 \cdot {}^{-}3 = 0$ and if the pattern of an increase of 3 with each multiplication continues:
${}^{-}1 \cdot {}^{-}3 = 3$
${}^{-}2 \cdot {}^{-}3 = 6$

5. (a) $10 - 5 = 5$ (b) $1 - {}^{-}2 = 3$

6. (a)
$$\begin{aligned}(x - y)(x + y) &= (x - y)x + (x - y)y \\ &= x^2 - yx + xy - y^2 \\ &= x^{2-xy+xy-y^2} \\ &= x^2 - y^2\end{aligned}$$

(b) $({}^{-}2 - x)({}^{-}2 + x) = ({}^{-}2)^2 - x^2 = 4 - x^2$

7. (a) ${}^{-}1x = {}^{-}x$ (b) $({}^{-}1)(x - y) = {}^{-}x - {}^{-}y = {}^{-}x + y = y - x$

(c) $2x - (1 - x) = 2x - 1 - {}^{-}x = 3x - 1$ (d) $({}^{-}x)^2 + x^2 = x^2 + x^2 = 2x^2$

(e) $({}^{-}x)^3 + x^3 = {}^{-}x^3 + x^3 = 0$

(f) $({}^{-}3 - x)(3 + x) = ({}^{-}3 - x)3 + ({}^{-}3 - x)x = {}^{-}9 - 3x - 3x - x^2 = {}^{-}9 - 6x - x^2$

8. (a) $x - 3x = {}^{-}2x$ (b) $x^2 + x = x(x + 1)$

(c) $x^2 - 36 = x^2 - 6^2 = (x + 6)(x - 6)$

(d) $81y^6 - 16x^4 = (9y^3)^2 - (4x^2)^2 = (9y^3 + 4x^2)(9y^3 - 4x^2)$

(e) $5 + 5x = 5(1 + x)$

(f) $(x - y)(x + 1) - (x - y) = (x - y)[(x + 1) - 1] = (x - y)x$

9. (a) False ($|x|$ is not positive when $x = 0$) (b) False (when x and y are of opposite signs)

(c) False (if $b < 0$) (d) True

(e) False $[({}^{-}a)({}^{-}b) = ab]$

10. Answers may vary:

(a) $2 \div 1 \neq 1 \div 2$ (b) $3 - (4 - 5) \neq (3 - 4) - 5$

(c) $1 \div 2 \notin I$ (d) $8 \div (4 - 2) \neq 8 \div 4 - 8 \div 2$

11. $T = {}^{-}16°\,C + 9°\,C = {}^{-}7°\,C$

12. Let x be the number of 2-kg packages $\Rightarrow$ $150 - x$ is the number of 1-kg packages
Total weight is: $2x + 1(150 - x) = 265 \Rightarrow 2x + 150 - x = 265 \Rightarrow x = 115$ and $150 - x = 35$
There are 115 2-kg packages and 35 1-kg packages

13. (a) False $(4 \mid 8)$ (b) False $(4 \mid 0)$
(c) True (d) False (test works only when the two numbers have no common factors)
(e) False (e.g., 9)

14. (a) False $(7 \mid 14$ and $7 \nmid 2$, but $7 \mid (14 \cdot 2)$ (b) False $(3 \nmid (6 + 1)$ but $3 \mid 6)$
(c) True (d) True
(e) True (f) False $[4 \nmid 6$ and $4 \nmid 10$, but $4 \mid (6 \cdot 10)]$

15. (a) $m = 83{,}160$
$2 \mid 0$ so $2 \mid m$
$3 \mid (8 + 3 + 1 + 6 + 0)$ so $3 \mid m$
$4 \mid 60$ so $4 \mid m$
$5 \mid 0$ so $5 \mid m$
$2 \mid m$ and $3 \mid m$ so $6 \mid m$
$8 \mid 160$ so $8 \mid m$
$9 \mid (8 + 3 + 1 + 6 + 0)$ so $9 \mid m$
$11 \mid [(0 + 1 + 8) - (6 + 3)]$ so $11 \mid m$

(b) $n = 83{,}193$
$2 \nmid 3$ so $2 \nmid n$
$3 \mid (8 + 3 + 1 + 9 + 3)$ so $3 \mid n$
$4 \nmid 93$ so $4 \nmid n$
$5 \nmid 3$ so $5 \nmid n$
$2 \nmid n$ so $6 \nmid n$
$8 \nmid 193$ so $8 \nmid n$
$9 \nmid (8 + 3 + 1 + 9 + 3)$ so $9 \nmid n$
$11 \mid [(3 + 1 + 8) - (9+3)]$ so $11 \mid n$

16. 10,007 is prime $\Rightarrow$ $17 \nmid 10{,}007$ and $17 \mid 17$ $\Rightarrow$ $17 \nmid (10{,}007+17)$

17. (a) Write the number as 87a4.
$2 \mid 4$ so $2 \mid 87a4$
If $3 \mid 87a4 \Rightarrow 3 \mid (8 + 7 + a + 4 = 19 + a) \Rightarrow 21, 24$, or 27
Thus $6 \mid 87a4$ if $a = 2, 5$, or 8

(b) Write the number as 4a856. To be divisible by 24, it must be divisible by 3 and 8.
$3 \mid 4a856$ if $3 \mid (4 + a + 8 + 5 + 6 = 23 + a) \Rightarrow 24, 27$, and $30 \Rightarrow a = 1, 4$, or 7
$8 \mid 4a856$ since $8 \mid 856$
So $24 \mid 4a856$ if $a = 1, 4$, or 7

(c) Write the number as 87ab4. $29 \mid 87{,}000 \Rightarrow 29 \mid ab4$
The only number to return 4 in the units position when multiplied by 9 is 6
$\Rightarrow$ The possibilities are $6 \cdot 29$, $16 \cdot 29$, etc., until the product of $x \cdot 29 > 999$
$6 \cdot 29 = 174$; $16 \cdot 29 = 464$; $26 \cdot 29 = 754$; $36 \cdot 29 > 999$
$\Rightarrow ab = 17, 46$, or 75

18. (a) Composite $(11 \mid 143)$ (b) Prime

19. The number must be divisible by 3 and 8 $\Rightarrow$ $3 \mid 4152$ and $8 \mid 4152$, so $24 \mid 4152$

20. (a) $24 = 2^3 \cdot 3$ and $52 = 2^2 \cdot 13 \Rightarrow \text{GCD}(24, 52) = 4$

(b) $\text{GCD}(5767, 4453) = \text{GCD}(4453, 1314) = \text{GCD}(1314, 511) = \text{GCD}(511, 292) = \text{GCD}(292, 219) = 73$

21. (a) $\text{LCM} = 2^4 \cdot 5^3 \cdot 7^4 \cdot 13 \cdot 29$

21. (b) GCD(279, 278) = GCD(278, 1) = 1 $\Rightarrow$ no common factors
Thus LCD(279, 278) $\cdot$ 1 = 279 $\cdot$ 278 = 77,562

22. 16 [To obtain *k* divisors , raise any prime to the ($k - 1$)st power. Here $2^{5-1} = 16$.
(Divisors are $2^0, 2^1, 2^2, 2^3, 2^4$)]

23. 1, 2, 3, 4, 6, 8, 9, 12, 16, 18, 24, 36, 48, 72, 144.

24. (a) $2^2 \cdot 43$ (b) $2^5 \cdot 3^2$

(c) $2^2 \cdot 5 \cdot 13$ (d) $3 \cdot 37$

25. This will happen on all common multiples of 3 and 5. The first time will be $3 \cdot 5 = 15$ minutes.

26. 31¢ [The price must divide 3193¢ (notice that $31|3100$ and $31|93$)]

27. LCM(45, 30) = 90 minutes $\Rightarrow$ 8:00 A.M. + 90 minutes = 9:30 A.M.

28. GCD(a, b) $\cdot$ LCM(a, b) = ab $\Rightarrow$ because GCD(a, b) = 1, then LCM(a, b) = ab

29. One month of 365 days; five months of 73 days; 365 months of 1 day; 73 months of 5 days

30. 5 packages (There are 15 children; the candy will come out evenly for LCM(15, 12) = 60.
60 candies ÷ 12 candies per package = 5 packages.)

31. $n = a \cdot 10^2 + b \cdot 10 + c$
$= a(99 + 1) + b(9 + 1) + c$
$= 99a + 9b + (a + a + c)$
Since $9|99a$ and $9|9b$, $9|[99a + 9b + (a + b + c)]$ if and only if $9|(a + b + c)$

32. (a) $7^2 \equiv 1 \pmod{16} \Rightarrow 7^{100} = (7^2)^{50} \equiv (1)^{50} \pmod{16} \equiv 1 \pmod{16}$
The remainder is 1

(b) $7^2 \equiv 15 \pmod{17} \Rightarrow 7^{100} = (7^2)^{50} \equiv (15)^{50} \pmod{17}$
$15^2 \equiv 4 \pmod{17} \Rightarrow 15^{50} = (15^2)^{25} \equiv 4^{25} \pmod{17}$
$4^5 \equiv 4 \pmod{17} \Rightarrow 4^{25} = (4^5)^5 \equiv 4^5 \pmod{17} \equiv 4 \pmod{17}$
The remainder is 4

(c) Find a power of 13 for which $13^x \equiv 1 \pmod{10}$
$13^4 \equiv 1 \pmod{10} \Rightarrow 13^{1937} = 13^{1+1936} = 13^1 \cdot (13^{1936}) = 13 \cdot [(13^4)^{484}] \equiv 13(1)^{484} \pmod{10}$
$\equiv 13 \pmod{10} \equiv 3 \pmod{10}$
The remainder is 3

33. Friday (Days of the week here are mod 8. $30 \equiv 6 \pmod{8} \Rightarrow$ the 30th would be the 6th day of the week, counting Sunday as the 1st day since it begins the month.)

34. Mod 360 (there are 360° in a full circle)

CHAPTER 5 - RATIONAL NUMBERS AS FRACTIONS

On-going Assessment 5-1

1. (a) The solution to $8x = 7$ is $\frac{7}{8}$

   (b) Joe ate 7 of the 8 apple slices

   (c) The ratio of boys to girls in this math class is 7 to 8 (also written 7:8)

2. (a) $\frac{1}{6}$ (b) $\frac{1}{4}$

   (c) $\frac{2}{6} = \frac{1}{3}$ (d) $\frac{7}{12}$

   (e) $\frac{5}{16}$ (f) $\frac{2}{16} = \frac{1}{8}$

3. The diagrams illustrate the fundamental law of fractions; i.e., the value of a fraction does not change if its numerator and denominator are multiplied by the same nonzero number.

   (a) Two of the three parts are shaded $\Rightarrow \frac{2}{3}$

   (b) Four of the six parts are shaded $\Rightarrow \frac{4}{6} = \frac{2}{3}$

   (c) Six of the nine parts are shaded $\Rightarrow \frac{6}{9} = \frac{2}{3}$

   (d) Eight of the twelve parts are shaded $\Rightarrow \frac{8}{12} = \frac{2}{3}$

4. (a)

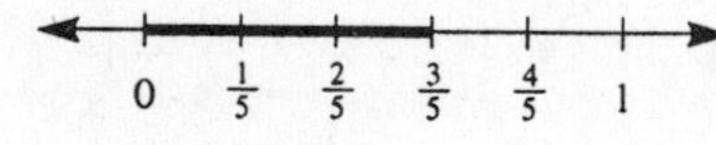

   (b)

   (c)

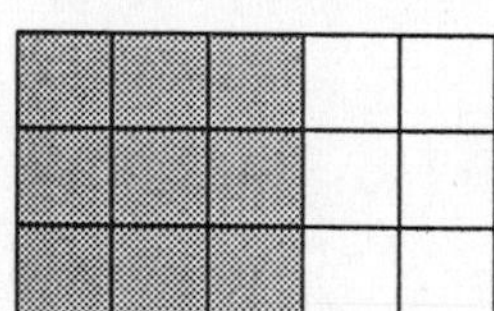

   (d)

   (e)

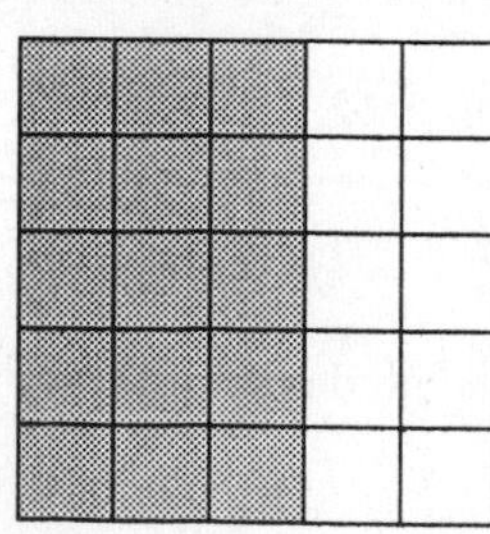

   (f)

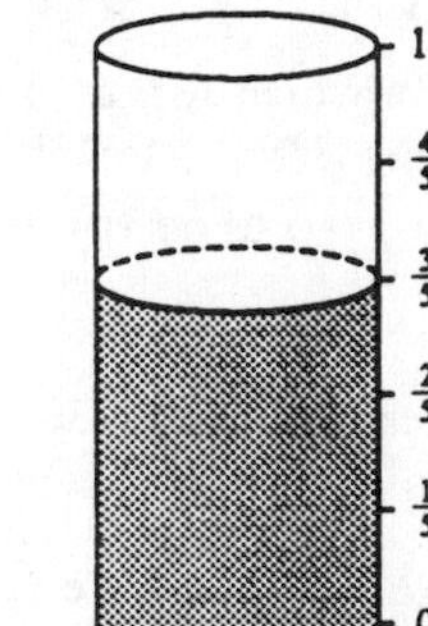

5. (a) $\frac{\text{Dots in circle}}{\text{Total dots}} = \frac{9}{24} = \frac{3}{8}$ (b) $\frac{\text{Dots in rectangle}}{\text{Total dots}} = \frac{12}{24} = \frac{1}{2}$

5. (c) $\frac{\text{Dots in intersection}}{\text{Total dots}} = \frac{4}{24} = \frac{1}{6}$ (d) $\frac{\text{Dots in rectangle} - \text{circle}}{\text{Total dots}} = \frac{8}{24} = \frac{1}{3}$

6. Answers may vary. Some possibilities are:

(a) $\frac{4}{18}, \frac{6}{27}, \frac{10}{45}$ (b) $\frac{^-4}{10}, \frac{^-20}{50}, \frac{^-24}{60}$

(c) $\frac{0}{6}, \frac{0}{9}, \frac{0}{12}$ (d) $\frac{3a}{6}, \frac{5a}{10}, \frac{8a}{16}$

7. (a) $\frac{156}{93} = \frac{3 \cdot 52}{3 \cdot 31} = \frac{52}{31}$ (b) $\frac{27}{45} = \frac{9 \cdot 3}{9 \cdot 5} = \frac{3}{5}$

(c) $\frac{^-65}{91} = \frac{^-5 \cdot 13}{7 \cdot 13} = \frac{^-5}{7}$ (d) $\frac{0}{68} = \frac{0}{1}$

(e) $\frac{84^2}{91^2} = \frac{(7 \cdot 12)^2}{(7 \cdot 13)^2} = \frac{7^2 \cdot 12^2}{7^2 \cdot 13^2} = \frac{12^2}{13^2} = \frac{144}{169}$

(f) $\frac{662}{703}$ is already in its simplest form (there are no factors common to both numerator and denominator)

8. Impossible to determine. Because $\frac{20}{25} = \frac{24}{30} = \frac{4}{5}$, the same fraction of students passed in each class, but the actual scores in one class could have been higher than in the other.

9. (a) Undefined (division by 0 is undefined) (b) Undefined (division by 0 is undefined)

(c) 0 ($\frac{0}{5} = 0$ because $0 \cdot 5 = 0$)

(d) Cannot be simplified (2 and a have no common factors other than 1 $\Rightarrow$ $\frac{2+a}{a}$ cannot be simplified)

(e) Cannot be simplified $\left(\frac{15+x}{3x}\right.$ is not the same as $\left.\frac{15 \cdot x}{3x} = \frac{15x}{3x} = 5\right)$

(f) $\frac{2}{3}$ $\left(\frac{2^6 + 2^5}{2^4 + 2^7} = \frac{2^5(2^1 + 1)}{2^4(1 + 2^3)} = \frac{2^5(3)}{2^4(9)} = \frac{32 \cdot 3}{16 \cdot 9} = \frac{2 \cdot 16 \cdot 3}{16 \cdot 3 \cdot 3} = \frac{2}{3}\right)$

(g) $\frac{5}{3}$ $\left(\frac{2^{100} + 2^{98}}{2^{100} - 2^{98}} = \frac{2^{98}(2^2 + 1)}{2^{98}(2^2 - 1)} = \frac{2^{98} \cdot 5}{2^{98} \cdot 3} = \frac{5}{3}\right)$

10. (a) $\frac{x}{x} = 1$ (b) $\frac{14x^2y}{63xy^2} = \frac{7 \cdot 2 \cdot x \cdot x \cdot y}{7 \cdot 9 \cdot x \cdot y \cdot y} = \frac{2x}{9y}$

(c) $\frac{a^2 + ab}{a + b} = \frac{a(a + b)}{a + b} = \frac{a}{1}$

(d) $\frac{a^3 + 1}{a^3 b}$ cannot be simplified (there are no factors common to both the numerator and denominator)

(e) $\frac{a}{3a + ab} = \frac{a}{a(3 + b)} = \frac{1}{3 + b}$ (f) $\frac{a}{3a + b}$ cannot be simplified

11. (a) $\frac{375}{1000} = \frac{125 \cdot 3}{125 \cdot 8} = \frac{3}{8} \Rightarrow$ equal -OR- $375 \cdot 8 = 3 \cdot 1000 \Rightarrow$ equal

(b) $\frac{18}{54} = \frac{18}{3 \cdot 18} = \frac{1}{3}$ and $\frac{23}{69} = \frac{23}{3 \cdot 23} = \frac{1}{3} \Rightarrow$ equal -OR- $18 \cdot 69 = 23 \cdot 54 \Rightarrow$ equal

(c) $\frac{600}{1000} = \frac{6 \cdot 100}{10 \cdot 100} = \frac{6}{10} \Rightarrow$ equal -OR- $600 \cdot 10 = 6 \cdot 1000 \Rightarrow$ equal

(d) $\frac{17}{27}$ is in its simplest form and $\frac{25}{45} = \frac{5 \cdot 5}{5 \cdot 9} = \frac{5}{9} \Rightarrow$ not equal -OR- $17 \cdot 45 \neq 25 \cdot 27 \Rightarrow$ not equal

12. (a) $16 = 2^4$; $18 = 2 \cdot 3^2 \Rightarrow$ LCM(16, 18) $= 2^4 \cdot 3^2 = 144$
$\frac{10}{16} = \frac{10 \cdot 9}{16 \cdot 9} = \frac{90}{144}$ and $\frac{12}{18} = \frac{12 \cdot 8}{18 \cdot 8} = \frac{96}{144} \Rightarrow$ not equal

(b) $12 = 2^2 \cdot 3$; $154 = 2 \cdot 7 \cdot 11 \Rightarrow$ LCM(12, 154) $= 2^2 \cdot 3 \cdot 7 \cdot 11 = 924$
$\frac{3}{12} = \frac{3 \cdot 77}{12 \cdot 77} = \frac{231}{924}$ and $\frac{41}{154} = \frac{41 \cdot 6}{154 \cdot 6} = \frac{246}{924} \Rightarrow$ not equal

(c) $\frac{3}{^-12} = \frac{^-3}{12} = \frac{^-3 \cdot 12}{12 \cdot 12} = \frac{^-36}{144} \Rightarrow$ equal

(d) $86 = 2 \cdot 43$; $215 = 5 \cdot 43 \Rightarrow$ LCM(86, 215) $= 2 \cdot 5 \cdot 43 = 430$
$\frac{^-21}{86} = \frac{^-21 \cdot 5}{86 \cdot 5} = \frac{^-105}{430}$ and $\frac{^-51}{215} = \frac{^-51 \cdot 2}{215 \cdot 2} = \frac{^-102}{430} \Rightarrow$ not equal

13. Yes ($\frac{3}{8} = \frac{3 \cdot 4}{8 \cdot 4} = \frac{12}{32} > \frac{11}{32} \Rightarrow$ the board is thick enough. Shaving off $\frac{1}{32}$ will bring it to the required thickness)

14. The shaded area takes in 3 of the 4 columns and 6 of the 8 small rectangles. Since the area in each case is the same, $\frac{3}{4}$ must equal $\frac{6}{8}$. See illustration:

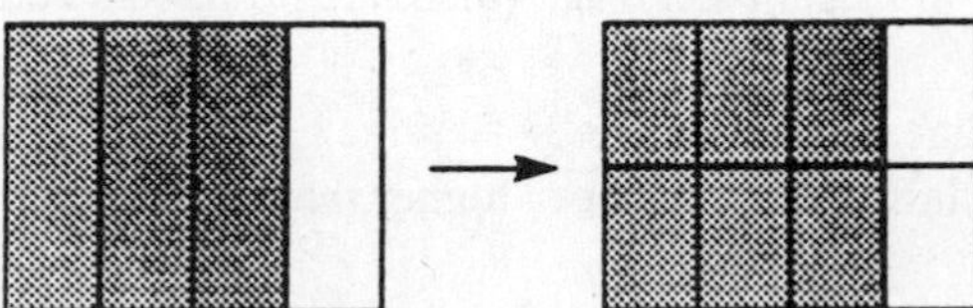

15. To obtain equivalent fractions, multiply numerator and denominator by the same number. All fractions equivalent to $\frac{3}{4}$ will then be of the form $\frac{3x}{4x}$. To satisfy the given requirement, $3x + 4x = 84$, or $x = 12$. The desired fraction is $\frac{3 \cdot 12}{4 \cdot 12} = \frac{36}{48}$.

16. Meter A has $\frac{4}{10}$ of 1 hour = 24 minutes left; meter B has $\frac{4}{10}$ of $\frac{1}{2}$ hour = $\frac{2}{10}$ of 1 hour = 21 minutes left
$\Rightarrow$ Meter A has more time by 24 minutes − 21 minutes = 3 minutes

17. Mr. Gomez had $16 - 6 = 10$ gallons left.
$\frac{10}{16} = \frac{5}{8}$ tank remained; the needle points to the 5th division of 8, as shown to the right:

18. (a) $2\frac{7}{8}$ inch (b) $2\frac{3}{8}$ inch

(c) $1\frac{3}{8}$ inch (d) $\frac{7}{8}$ inch

19. Answers may vary; $\frac{12}{21}$, $\frac{24}{42}$, and $\frac{48}{84}$ also fit the conditions

20. (a) For equal fractions $\frac{a}{b} = \frac{c}{d}$, ad = bc. With $\frac{2}{3} = \frac{x}{16}$, $2 \cdot 16 = 3 \cdot x \Rightarrow 32 = 3x \Rightarrow x = \frac{32}{3}$.

(b) $3 \cdot x = 4 \cdot (^-27) \Rightarrow 3x = {^-108} \Rightarrow x = {^-36}$

(c) $3 \cdot x^2 = x \cdot 3x \Rightarrow 3x^2 = 3x^2$ (all nonzero rational numbers are solutions)

21. (a) $ac = bc \Rightarrow a = b$ $(c \neq 0)$ (b) $b = c \neq 0$, or $a = 0$ and $b \neq 0$ and $c \neq 0$

22. (a) Not equal (b) Not equal

(c) Equal

23. (a) True (integers may be made rational with a denominator of 1)

(b) True ($I \cup W = I$ is a proper subset of Q because there exist elements of Q that are not in I; e.g., $\frac{1}{2}$)

(c) False (the elements of Q that are not in I are also not in W)

(d) False ($Q \cap I = I$)

(e) True [the intersection of rational numbers with whole numbers (i.e., numbers that are common to both sets) is the set of whole numbers, since all whole numbers are rational]

24. Bren's class ($\frac{5}{23} > \frac{6}{31}$ since $5 \cdot 31 > 6 \cdot 23$)

25. (a) $>$ $\left(\text{LCD} = 24 \Rightarrow \frac{7}{8} = \frac{21}{24} \text{ and } \frac{5}{6} = \frac{20}{24}\right)$ (b) $>$ $\left(\text{LCD} = 30 \Rightarrow 2\frac{4}{5} = 2\frac{24}{30} \text{ and } 2\frac{3}{6} = 2\frac{15}{30}\right)$

(c) $<$ $\left[\text{LCD} = 40 \Rightarrow \frac{^-7}{8} = \frac{^-35}{40} \text{ and } \frac{^-4}{5} = \frac{^-24}{40} \text{ (note that } {^-35} < {^-24})\right]$

(d) $<$ $\left(\text{LCD} = 56 \Rightarrow \frac{1}{^-7} = \frac{^-1}{7} = \frac{^-8}{56} \text{ and } \frac{1}{^-8} = \frac{^-7}{56}\right)$ (e) $=$ $\left(\frac{2}{5} = \frac{2 \cdot 2}{2 \cdot 5} = \frac{4}{10}\right)$

(f) $=$ $\left(\frac{0}{7} = 0 = \frac{0}{17}\right)$

26. (a) $\frac{11}{13}, \frac{11}{16}, \frac{11}{22}$ (when fractions have the same numerators, those with larger denominators have lesser value)

(b) $\frac{^-1}{5}, \frac{^-19}{36}, \frac{^-17}{30}$ $\left[\text{LCD} = 180 \Rightarrow \frac{^-1}{5} = \frac{^-36}{180}, \frac{^-19}{36} = \frac{^-95}{180}, \text{ and } \frac{^-17}{30} = \frac{^-102}{180} \quad ({^-36} > {^-95} > {^-102})\right]$

27. (a) A positive proper fraction is greater than its square

(b) Let $\frac{a}{b}$ be a positive proper fraction; i.e., $0 < \frac{a}{b} < 1 \Rightarrow \frac{a}{b} \cdot \frac{a}{b} < 1 \cdot \frac{a}{b} \Rightarrow \left(\frac{a}{b}\right)^2 < \frac{a}{b}$

(c) The square is greater

(d) Let $\frac{a}{b}$ be a fraction $> 1 \Rightarrow \frac{a}{b} \cdot \frac{a}{b} > 1 \cdot \frac{a}{b} \Rightarrow \left(\frac{a}{b}\right)^2 > \frac{a}{b}$

28. $\frac{a}{b} < 1 \text{ and } \frac{c}{d} > 0 \Rightarrow \frac{a}{b} \cdot \frac{c}{d} < 1 \cdot \frac{c}{d} \Rightarrow \frac{a}{b} \cdot \frac{c}{d} < \frac{c}{d}$

29. xy is greater ($x > 1 \text{ and } y > 0 \Rightarrow x \cdot y > 1 \cdot y \Rightarrow xy > y$)

30. (*i*) If the sequence is increasing, then $\frac{n}{n+1} < \frac{n+1}{n+2}$
Thus $n(n+2) < (n+1)(n+1) \Rightarrow n^2 + 2n < n^2 + 2n + 1 \Rightarrow 0 < 1$

(*ii*) Answers may vary. One example is $\frac{3}{2}, \frac{4}{3}, \frac{5}{4}, \ldots$.

31. (a) For example, there is no whole number between 2 and 3

(b) For example, there is no integer between $^-3$ and $^-2$

32. Answers may vary. One method is to convert the given fractions to equivalent fractions having larger common denominators, thus creating spaces between the two.

(a) $\frac{3}{7} = \frac{9}{21}$ and $\frac{4}{7} = \frac{12}{21} \Rightarrow$ two rational numbers between them are $\frac{10}{21}$ and $\frac{11}{21}$

32. (b) $\frac{^-7}{9} = \frac{^-28}{36}$ and $\frac{^-8}{9} = \frac{^-32}{36} \Rightarrow$ two rational umbers between them are $\frac{^-30}{36}$ and $\frac{^-31}{36}$

(c) $\frac{5}{6} = \frac{1000}{1200}$ and $\frac{83}{100} = \frac{996}{1200} \Rightarrow$ two rational numbers between them are $\frac{997}{1200}$ and $\frac{998}{1200}$

(d) $\frac{^-1}{3} = \frac{^-4}{12}$ and $\frac{3}{4} = \frac{9}{12} \Rightarrow$ two rational numbers between them are 0 and $\frac{1}{12}$

33. (a) $\frac{A}{B} = \frac{94}{94} = 1$ (b) $\frac{A}{B} = \frac{86}{86} = 1$

(c) Let x be the top circled number
The sum of the circled numbers is $x + (x + 12) + (x + 19) + (x + 31) = 4x + 62$
The sum of the interior numbers is $(x + 10) + (x + 11) + (x + 20) + (x + 21) = 4x + 62$
$\Rightarrow$ The ratio of circled to interior numbers is always 1

34.

Number of miles	12	x
Number of inches	1	38

$\Rightarrow \frac{12 \text{ miles}}{1 \text{ inch}} = \frac{x \text{ miles}}{38 \text{ inches}} \Rightarrow 12 \cdot 38 = 1 \cdot x \Rightarrow 456 \text{ miles} = x$

35. (*i*) $\frac{6 \text{ ounces}}{1 \text{ pound}} = \frac{6 \text{ ounces}}{16 \text{ ounces}} = \frac{2 \cdot 3}{2 \cdot 8} = \frac{3}{8} \Rightarrow 6 \text{ ounces} = \frac{3}{8}$ pound

(*ii*) $\frac{6 \text{ ounces}}{1 \text{ ton}} = \frac{6 \text{ ounces}}{2000 \text{ pounds}} = \frac{6 \text{ ounces}}{32{,}000 \text{ ounces}} = \frac{2 \cdot 3}{2 \cdot 16{,}000} = \frac{3}{16{,}000} \Rightarrow 6 \text{ ounces} = \frac{3}{16{,}000}$ ton

36. $\frac{4 \text{ seconds}}{90 \text{ feet}} = \frac{x \text{ seconds}}{100 \text{ yards}} = \frac{x \text{ seconds}}{300 \text{ feet}}$
So $4 \cdot 300 = 90 \cdot x \rightarrow 1200 = 90x \rightarrow x = \frac{1200}{90} = \frac{30 \cdot 40}{30 \cdot 3} = \frac{40}{3} = 13\frac{1}{3}$ seconds

On-going Assessment 5-2

1. (a) (*i*) $\frac{1}{2} + \frac{2}{3} = \frac{1 \cdot 3 + 2 \cdot 2}{2 \cdot 3} = \frac{3 + 4}{6} = \frac{7}{6}$; or

(*ii*) LCD = 6 $\Rightarrow \frac{1}{2} + \frac{2}{3} = \frac{1}{2} \cdot \frac{3}{3} + \frac{2}{3} \cdot \frac{2}{2} = \frac{3}{6} + \frac{4}{6} = \frac{7}{6}$

(b) LCD = 16 $\Rightarrow \frac{3}{16} + \frac{7}{^-8} = \frac{3}{16} - \frac{7 \cdot 2}{8 \cdot 2} = \frac{3 - 14}{16} = \frac{^-11}{16}$

(c) LCD = 12 $\Rightarrow \frac{4}{12} - \frac{2}{3} = \frac{4}{12} - \frac{2 \cdot 4}{3 \cdot 4} = \frac{4 - 8}{12} = \frac{^-4}{12} = \frac{^-1}{3}$

(d) $\frac{5}{x} + \frac{^-3}{y} = \frac{5 \cdot y - x \cdot 3}{x \cdot y} = \frac{5y - 3x}{xy}$

(e) LCD = $6x^2y^2 \Rightarrow \frac{^-3}{2x^2y} + \frac{5}{6xy^2} + \frac{7}{x^2} = \frac{^-3 \cdot 3y}{2x^2y \cdot 3y} + \frac{5 \cdot x}{6xy^2 \cdot x} + \frac{7 \cdot 6y^2}{x^2 \cdot 6y^2} = \frac{^-9y + 5x + 42y^2}{6x^2y^2}$

(f) LCD = 4xy $\Rightarrow \frac{^-3}{2x} + \frac{3}{2y} + \frac{^-1}{4xy} = \frac{^-3 \cdot 2y}{2x \cdot 2y} + \frac{3 \cdot 2x}{2y \cdot 2x} - \frac{1}{4xy} = \frac{^-6y + 6x - 1}{4xy}$

(g) $\frac{5}{6} + 2\frac{1}{8} = \frac{5}{6} + \frac{17}{8} = \frac{5 \cdot 8 + 6 \cdot 17}{6 \cdot 8} = \frac{40 + 102}{48} = \frac{142}{48} = \frac{71}{24} = 2\frac{23}{24}$

(h) LCD = $2^4 \cdot 3^4 \Rightarrow \frac{5}{2^4 \cdot 3^2} - \frac{1}{2^3 \cdot 3^4} = \frac{5 \cdot 3^2}{2^4 \cdot 3^2 \cdot 3^2} - \frac{1 \cdot 2}{2^3 \cdot 3^4 \cdot 2} = \frac{45 - 2}{2^4 \cdot 3^4} = \frac{43}{2^4 \cdot 3^4}$

(i) $^-4\frac{1}{2} - 3\frac{1}{6} = {^-4}\frac{3}{6} - 3\frac{1}{6} = {^-7}\frac{4}{6} = {^-7}\frac{2}{3}$ (or $\frac{^-23}{3}$)

2. Two methods are shown; either is acceptable.

(a) $\frac{56}{3} = \frac{3 \cdot 18 + 2}{3} = \frac{3 \cdot 18}{3} + \frac{2}{3} = 18 + \frac{2}{3} = 18\frac{2}{3}$

(b) $14 \div 5 = 2$, remainder $4 \Rightarrow 2\frac{4}{5}$

(c) $-\frac{293}{100} = {}^{-}\left(\frac{2 \cdot 100 + 93}{100}\right) = {}^{-}2\frac{93}{100}$

(d) ${}^{-}47 \div 8 = {}^{-}5$, remainder $7 \Rightarrow {}^{-}5\frac{7}{8}$

3. (a) $6\frac{3}{4} = \frac{6}{1} + \frac{3}{4} = \frac{6 \cdot 4 + 1 \cdot 3}{1 \cdot 4} = \frac{24 + 3}{4} = \frac{27}{4}$

(b) $7\frac{1}{2} = \frac{7}{1} + \frac{1}{2} = \frac{7 \cdot 2 + 1 \cdot 1}{1 \cdot 2} = \frac{15}{2}$

(c) ${}^{-}3\frac{5}{8} = {}^{-}\left(3 + \frac{5}{8}\right) = {}^{-}\left(\frac{3}{1} + \frac{5}{8}\right) = {}^{-}\left(\frac{3 \cdot 8 + 1 \cdot 5}{1 \cdot 8}\right) = \frac{{}^{-}29}{8}$

(d) ${}^{-}4\frac{2}{3} = {}^{-}\left(4 + \frac{2}{3}\right) = {}^{-}\left(\frac{4}{1} + \frac{2}{3}\right) = {}^{-}\left(\frac{4 \cdot 3 + 1 \cdot 2}{1 \cdot 3}\right) = \frac{{}^{-}14}{3}$

4. A denominator of 24 eliminates 5; 2 in the denominator would give an answer greater than 1. Trial and error thus yields: $\frac{2}{6} + \frac{5}{8} = \frac{23}{24}$

5. (a) Change 46 to 45 $\Rightarrow \frac{15}{45} = \frac{1}{3}$ (estimate is too high because the denominator is smaller than actual)

(b) Change 41 to 42 $\Rightarrow \frac{7}{42} = \frac{1}{6}$ (estimate is too low because the denominator is larger than actual)

(c) Change 62 to 60 $\Rightarrow \frac{60}{80} = \frac{3}{4}$ (estimate is too low because the numerator is smaller than actual)

(d) Change the numerator to 10 and the denominator to 20 $\Rightarrow \frac{10}{20} = \frac{1}{2}$ (estimate is too low because the numerator was increased by a greater percentage than the denominator)

6. (a) Beavers $\left(\frac{10}{19} > \frac{1}{2}\right)$

(b) Ducks $\left(\frac{10}{22} < \frac{1}{2}\right)$

(c) Bears $\left(\frac{8}{23} > \frac{1}{3}\right)$

(d) Tigers $\left(\frac{9}{28} < \frac{1}{3}\right)$

(e) Lions $\left(\frac{7}{27} > \frac{1}{4}\right)$

(f) Wildcats and Badgers $\left(\frac{6}{25} \text{ and } \frac{5}{21} < \frac{1}{4}\right)$

7. (*i*) About 0: $\frac{1}{10}, \frac{1}{100}$

(*ii*) About $\frac{1}{2}$: $\frac{4}{7}, \frac{8}{12}, \frac{1}{3}, \frac{2}{5}, \frac{3}{10}, \frac{9}{18}$

(*iii*) About 1: $\frac{7}{8}, \frac{13}{10}$

8. (a) $\frac{1}{2}$; too high $\left(\frac{19}{38} = \frac{1}{2} \text{ so } \frac{19}{39} < \frac{1}{2}\right)$

(b) 0; too low $\left(\frac{3}{197} > 0\right)$

(c) $\frac{3}{4}$; too high $\left(\frac{150}{200} = \frac{3}{4} \text{ so } \frac{150}{201} < \frac{3}{4}\right)$

(d) 1; too high $\left(\frac{8}{9} < 1\right)$

(e) 1; too low $\left(\frac{113}{110} > 1\right)$

(f) 0; too high $\left(\frac{{}^{-}2}{117} < 0\right)$

(g) $\frac{3}{4}$; too low $\left(\frac{150}{200} = \frac{3}{4} \text{ so } \frac{150}{198} > \frac{3}{4}\right)$

(h) $\frac{1}{2}$; too high $\left(\frac{1000}{2000} = \frac{1}{2} \text{ so } \frac{999}{2000} < \frac{1}{2}\right)$

9. (a) 2 (each addend is about $\frac{1}{2}$ $\Rightarrow$ the best approximation would be $4 \cdot \frac{1}{2} = 2$)

(b) $\frac{3}{4}$ ($\frac{30}{41}$ is about $\frac{3}{4}$; the other two addends are negligible compared to $\frac{3}{4}$)

(c) 0 (addends are about $\frac{1}{3} + \frac{1}{3} - \frac{2}{3} = 0$)

(d) 0 (each addend is about $\frac{1}{100}$ $\Rightarrow$ about $\frac{1-1+1-1}{100} = 0$)

10. (a) Juan needs a little more than 11 pounds of cereal. He bought about 5 pounds, 3 pounds, and 3 pounds, totalling about 11 pounds. He probably does not have enough (the exact amount he bought was $11\frac{1}{16}$ pounds).

(b) Estimating, $1\frac{3}{4} + 3\frac{1}{4} = 5$ hours. The estimate is low since $3\frac{5}{12}$ was rounded down; i.e., Jill did not make the trip in less than 5 hours.

11. Possible thought processes could be:

(a) $\frac{4}{4} - \frac{3}{4} = \frac{1}{4}$

(b) $(5 + 1) - \frac{7}{8} = 5 + \left(\frac{8}{8} - \frac{7}{8}\right) = 5\frac{1}{8}$

(c) $\left(3 + 2 + \frac{3}{8} + \frac{2}{8}\right) - 5\frac{5}{8} = 5\frac{5}{8} - 5\frac{5}{8} = 0$

(d) $\left(2 + 4 + 3 + \frac{6}{10} + \frac{1}{10} + \frac{3}{10}\right) = 9 + \frac{10}{10} = 10$

12. (a) $\frac{20}{8}$ is between 2 and 3 $\Rightarrow$ region A

(b) $\frac{36}{8}$ is between 4 and 5 $\Rightarrow$ region H

(c) $\frac{60}{16}$ is between 3 and 5 $\Rightarrow$ region T

(d) $\frac{18}{4}$ is between 4 and 5 $\Rightarrow$ region H

13. (a) $\frac{3+3}{3} \neq \frac{3}{3} + 3$

(b) $\frac{4}{2+2} \neq \frac{4}{2} + \frac{4}{2}$

(c) $\frac{ab+c}{a} \neq \frac{\cancel{a}b+c}{\cancel{a}}$

(d) $\frac{a \cdot a - b \cdot b}{a-b} \neq \frac{a \cdot \cancel{a} - b \cdot \cancel{b}}{\cancel{a} - \cancel{b}}$

(e) $\frac{a+c}{b+c} \neq \frac{a+\cancel{c}}{b+\cancel{c}}$

14. The whole student population is represented by 1. We then subtract to obtain the senior's fraction; i.e., seniors make up $1 - \frac{2}{5} - \frac{1}{4} - \frac{1}{10}$ of the class. Using a LCD of 20 $\Rightarrow$ $\frac{20}{20} - \frac{8}{20} - \frac{5}{20} - \frac{2}{20} = \frac{5}{20} = \frac{1}{4}$. Thus seniors make up $\frac{1}{4}$ of the class.

15. (a) $\frac{1}{5}$ (Japan) $-$ $\frac{1}{6}$ (Canada) $= \frac{6}{30} - \frac{5}{30} = \frac{1}{30}$

(b) $\frac{7}{20}$ (United States) $-$ $\frac{1}{4}$ (England) $= \frac{7}{20} - \frac{5}{20} = \frac{1}{10}$

(c) $\frac{7}{20}$ (1990) $-$ $\frac{1}{3}$ (1980) $= \frac{21}{60} - \frac{20}{60} = \frac{1}{60}$

(d) No (the total number of dollars might have been greater in 1980 than in 1990, but the fraction of the total dollars (i.e., $\frac{1}{10}$ versus $\frac{1}{20}$) was greater in 1990)

16. $\frac{1}{3} + 2\frac{3}{4} + 3\frac{1}{2} = \frac{4}{12} + 2\frac{9}{12} + 3\frac{6}{12} = 5\frac{19}{12} = 6\frac{7}{12}$ yards

17. He should put in $3\frac{1}{2} - \frac{3}{4} - 1 = 3\frac{2}{4} - \frac{3}{4} - \frac{4}{4} = \frac{14}{4} - \frac{3}{4} - \frac{4}{4} = \frac{7}{4}$, or $1\frac{3}{4}$ cups more

18. The amount of fabric to be used is $1\frac{7}{8} + 2\frac{3}{8} + 1\frac{2}{3} = 1\frac{21}{24} + 2\frac{9}{24} + 1\frac{16}{24} = 4\frac{46}{24} = 5\frac{22}{24}$ yards. She bought $8\frac{3}{4}$ yards, so there will be $8\frac{18}{24} - 5\frac{22}{24} = 7\frac{42}{24} - 5\frac{22}{24} = 2\frac{20}{24} = 2\frac{5}{6}$ yards left over.

19. $38\frac{1}{4} - 15\frac{3}{4} - \frac{3}{8} = 22\frac{1}{8}$ inches left after cutting

20. (a) Team 4 (collected $35\frac{3}{16} + 41\frac{1}{2} = 76\frac{11}{16}$ pounds)

(b) Collections in April were $28\frac{3}{4} + 32\frac{7}{8} + 28\frac{1}{2} + 35\frac{3}{16} = 125\frac{5}{16}$ pounds
Collections in May were $33\frac{1}{3} + 28\frac{5}{12} + 25\frac{3}{4} + 41\frac{1}{2} = 129$ pounds
The difference was $129 - 125\frac{5}{16} = 3\frac{11}{16}$ pounds

21. (a) According to this property, if two rational numbers are added, the sum should also be rational; e.g., $\frac{1}{2} + \frac{3}{4} = \frac{5}{4}$, which is a rational number.

(b) $\frac{a}{b} + \frac{c}{d}$ should equal $\frac{c}{d} + \frac{a}{b}$; e.g., $\frac{1}{4} + \frac{2}{3} = \frac{11}{12} = \frac{2}{3} + \frac{1}{4}$

(c) The associative property states that $\frac{a}{b} + \left(\frac{c}{d} + \frac{e}{f}\right) = \left(\frac{a}{b} + \frac{c}{d}\right) + \frac{e}{f}$. E.g., $\frac{1}{2} + \left(\frac{2}{3} + \frac{3}{4}\right) = \frac{23}{12} = \left(\frac{1}{2} + \frac{2}{3}\right) + \frac{3}{4}$.

22. (a) $\frac{3}{2}, \frac{7}{4}, 2$ (arithmetic; difference is $\frac{1}{4}$)

(b) $\frac{6}{7}, \frac{7}{8}, \frac{8}{9}$ (each term is $\frac{n}{n+1}$; it is not arithmetic because there is no constant difference)

(c) $\frac{17}{3}, \frac{20}{3}, \frac{23}{3}$ (arithmetic; difference is $\frac{3}{3}$)

(d) $\frac{^-5}{4}, \frac{^-7}{4}, \frac{^-9}{4}$ (arithmetic; difference is $\frac{^-1}{2}$)

23. (a) $a_n = \frac{1}{4} + (n-1)\cdot\frac{1}{4} = \frac{1}{4} + \frac{1}{4}n - \frac{1}{4} = \frac{1}{4}n$

(b) $a_n = \frac{n}{n+1}$

(c) $a_n = \frac{2}{3} + (n-1)\cdot\frac{3}{3} = \frac{2}{3} + \frac{3}{3}n - \frac{3}{3} = n - \frac{1}{3}$, or $\frac{3n-1}{3}$

(d) $a_n = \frac{5}{4} + (n-1)\cdot\frac{^-1}{2} = \frac{5}{4} - \frac{1}{2}n + \frac{1}{2} = \frac{7}{4} - \frac{1}{2}n$, or $\frac{7-2n}{4}$

24. (a) World's water usage: 436 + 147 + 93 + 123 + 186 = 985 thousand gallons per capita
United Stat es (436) + Japan (186) = 622 thousand gallons per capita
Fraction of world's water: $\frac{622}{985}$

(b) World's pesticide usage: 404 + 73 + 35 + 16 + 188 = 716 gallons per 1000 people
United States (404) + Japan (188) = 592 gallons per 1000 people
Fraction of world's pesticides: $\frac{592}{716}$

(c) France's fraction of water used: $\frac{147}{985}$; India's fraction of water used: $\frac{123}{985}$
$\Rightarrow$ France used $\frac{147}{985} - \frac{123}{985} = \frac{24}{985}$ more of the world's water than India

25. There were 13,523 thousand refugees in total

(a) Afganistan, with 4720 thousand refugees, had the greatest fraction

(b) Afganistan: $\frac{4720}{13{,}523}$; Sri Lanka: $\frac{180}{13{,}523}$ $\Rightarrow$ Sri Lanka had $\frac{4720}{13{,}523} - \frac{180}{13{,}523} = \frac{4540}{13{,}523}$ fewer

26. Let the sequence be $1, a_2, a_3, a_4, a_5, a_6, 2 \Rightarrow 2 = 1 + (7-1)d \Rightarrow 6d = 1 \Rightarrow d = \frac{1}{6}$
The sequence is $1, \frac{7}{6}, \frac{8}{6}, \frac{9}{6}, \frac{10}{6}, \frac{11}{6}, 2$

27. (a) (*i*) $f(0) = 0 + \frac{3}{4} = \frac{3}{4}$

(*ii*) $f(\frac{4}{3}) = \frac{4}{3} + \frac{3}{4} = \frac{4\cdot4+3\cdot3}{3\cdot4} = \frac{25}{12} = 2\frac{1}{12}$

27. (a) (*iii*) $f(\frac{^-3}{4}) = \frac{^-3}{4} + \frac{3}{4} = 0$

(b) (*i*) $1 = x + \frac{3}{4} \Rightarrow x = 1 - \frac{3}{4} = \frac{4}{4} - \frac{3}{4} = \frac{1}{4}$ (*ii*) $^-1 = x + \frac{3}{4} \Rightarrow x = {^-1} - \frac{3}{4} = \frac{^-4}{4} - \frac{3}{4} = \frac{^-7}{4}$

(*iii*) $\frac{1}{2} = x + \frac{3}{4} \Rightarrow x = \frac{1}{2} - \frac{3}{4} = \frac{2}{4} - \frac{3}{4} = \frac{^-1}{4}$

28. (a) $f(0) = \frac{0+2}{0-1} = \frac{2}{^-1} = {^-2}$ (b) $f(^-2) = \frac{^-2+2}{^-2-1} = \frac{0}{^-3} = 0$

(c) $f(^-5) = \frac{^-5+2}{^-5-1} = \frac{^-3}{^-6} = \frac{1}{2}$ (d) $f(5) = \frac{5+2}{5-1} = \frac{7}{4}$

29. (a) (*i*) $\frac{1}{4} + \frac{1}{3 \cdot 4} = \frac{3 \cdot 1}{3 \cdot 4} + \frac{1}{3 \cdot 4} = \frac{3}{12} + \frac{1}{12} = \frac{4}{12} = \frac{1}{3}$ (*ii*) $\frac{1}{5} + \frac{1}{4 \cdot 5} = \frac{4}{20} + \frac{1}{20} = \frac{1}{4}$

(*iii*) $\frac{1}{6} + \frac{1}{5 \cdot 6} = \frac{5}{30} + \frac{1}{30} = \frac{1}{5}$

(b) $\frac{1}{n} = \frac{1}{n+1} + \frac{1}{n(n+1)}$

(c) $\frac{1}{n+1} + \frac{1}{n(n+1)} = \frac{n}{n} \cdot \frac{1}{n+1} + \frac{1}{n(n+1)} = \frac{n+1}{n(n+1)} = \frac{1}{n}$

On-going Assessment 5-2; Review Problems

38. (a) Triangles will vary

(b) The ratio of the directed segments is always $\frac{1}{1}$

(c) For any triangle constructed with a hypotenuse along the line x = y, the ratio of directed segment lengths will always be 1

39. (a) $\frac{14}{21} = \frac{2 \cdot 7}{3 \cdot 7} = \frac{2}{3}$ (b) $\frac{117}{153} = \frac{3 \cdot 3 \cdot 13}{3 \cdot 3 \cdot 17} = \frac{13}{17}$

(c) $\frac{5^2}{7^2} = \frac{25}{49}$ (d) $\frac{a^2 + a}{1 + a} = \frac{a(a+1)}{a+1} = \frac{a}{1} = a$

(e) $\frac{a^2+1}{a+1}$ is already in simplest form.

40. (a) $\frac{a^2b^2}{b^3} = \frac{a^2 \cdot b^2}{b \cdot b^2} = \frac{a^2}{b} \Rightarrow$ equal (b) $\frac{377+1}{400+1} \neq \frac{378}{401} \Rightarrow$ not equal

(c) $\frac{0}{10} = 0$ and $\frac{0}{^-10} = 0 \Rightarrow$ equal (d) $\frac{a}{b} \neq \frac{a+1}{b+1} \Rightarrow$ not equal

41. Assuming the year is not a leap year:

(a) February, with 28 days

(b) There are 31 + 28 + 31 + 30 + 31 + 30 + 3 = 184 days before July 4 $\Rightarrow \frac{184}{365}$ (not a leap year)
Or 185 days before July 4 $\Rightarrow \frac{185}{366}$ (leap year)

(c) It is generally considered that there are $365\frac{1}{4}$ days in a year (thus the requirement for a leap year every 4th year) and $365\frac{1}{4} = \frac{1461}{4}$ as an improper fraction

42. $0 < \frac{a}{b} < \frac{c}{d} \Rightarrow 0 < \frac{1}{2} \cdot \frac{a}{b} < \frac{1}{2} \cdot \frac{c}{d} \Rightarrow 0 < \frac{a}{b} = \frac{1}{2} \cdot \frac{a}{b} + \frac{1}{2} \cdot \frac{a}{b} < \frac{1}{2} \cdot \frac{a}{b} + \frac{1}{2} \cdot \frac{c}{d} = \frac{1}{2}\left(\frac{a}{b} + \frac{c}{d}\right) < \frac{c}{d}$
Thus $0 < \frac{a}{b} < \frac{1}{2}\left(\frac{a}{b} + \frac{c}{d}\right) < \frac{c}{d}$

43. Less than (consider $\frac{a}{b}$ and $\frac{a+n}{b+n}$, where $a < b$ (because $\frac{a}{b}$ is a proper fraction) and n can be any positive number $\Rightarrow$ since $ab + an < ab + bn$ then $\frac{a}{b} < \frac{a+n}{b+n}$)

On-going Assessment 5-3

1. (a) The shaded vertical region represents $\frac{1}{3}$ of the total area. The shaded horizontal region represents $\frac{1}{4}$ of the total area. The cross-hatched region represents $\frac{1}{4}$ of $\frac{1}{3}$, or the product of the two fractions. Since one of the twelve blocks is cross-hatched, then, the product of $\frac{1}{4}$ and $\frac{1}{3}$ is $\frac{1}{12}$.

   (b) The shaded vertical region represents $\frac{3}{5}$ of the total area. The shaded horizontal region represents $\frac{2}{4}$ of the total area. The cross-hatched region represents $\frac{2}{4}$ of $\frac{3}{5}$, or the product of the two fractions. Since six of the twenty blocks are cross-hatched, then, the product of $\frac{2}{4}$ and $\frac{3}{5}$ is $\frac{6}{20}$.

2. (a)

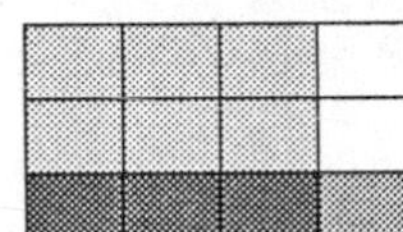

(b)

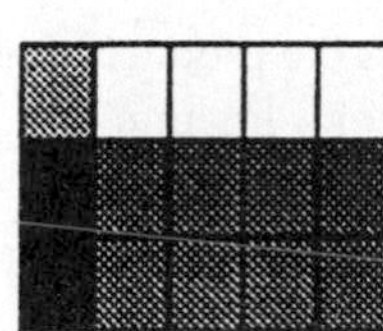

(c)

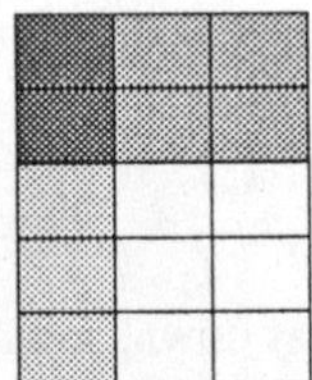

3. (a) $\frac{49}{65} \cdot \frac{26}{98} = \frac{1274}{6370} = \frac{1 \cdot 1274}{5 \cdot 1274} = \frac{1}{5}$

   (b) $\frac{a}{b} \cdot \frac{b^2}{a^2} = \frac{ab^2}{a^2b} = \frac{b \cdot ab}{a \cdot ab} = \frac{b}{a}$

   (c) $\frac{xy}{z} \cdot \frac{z^2a}{x^3y^2} = \frac{axyz^2}{x^3y^2z} = \frac{az \cdot xyz}{x^2y \cdot xyz} = \frac{az}{x^2y}$

   (d) $2\frac{1}{3} \cdot 3\frac{3}{4} = \frac{7}{3} \cdot \frac{15}{4} = \frac{105}{12} = \frac{35 \cdot 3}{4 \cdot 3} = \frac{35}{4} = 8\frac{3}{4}$

   (e) $\frac{22}{7} \cdot 4\frac{2}{3} = \frac{22}{7} \cdot \frac{14}{3} = \frac{308}{21} = \frac{44 \cdot 7}{3 \cdot 7} = \frac{44}{3} = 14\frac{2}{3}$

   (f) $\frac{{}^-5}{2} \cdot 2\frac{1}{2} = \frac{{}^-5}{2} \cdot \frac{5}{2} = \frac{{}^-25}{4} = {}^-6\frac{1}{4}$

4. (a) $4\frac{1}{2} \cdot 2\frac{1}{3} = (4 + \frac{1}{2}) \cdot (2 + \frac{1}{3}) = 4(2 + \frac{1}{3}) + \frac{1}{2}(2 + \frac{1}{3}) = 8 + \frac{4}{3} + 1 + \frac{1}{6} = 9 + \frac{8}{6} + \frac{1}{6} = 10\frac{1}{2}$

   (b) $3\frac{1}{3} \cdot 2\frac{1}{2} = (3 + \frac{1}{3}) \cdot (2 + \frac{1}{2}) = 3(2 + \frac{1}{2}) + \frac{1}{3}(2 + \frac{1}{2}) = 6 + \frac{3}{2} + \frac{2}{3} + \frac{1}{6} = 6 + \frac{9}{6} + \frac{4}{6} + \frac{1}{6} = 8\frac{1}{3}$

   (c) $248\frac{2}{5} \cdot 100\frac{1}{8} = 248(100 + \frac{1}{8}) + \frac{2}{5}(100 + \frac{1}{8}) = 24{,}800 + 31 + 40 + \frac{1}{20} = 24{,}871\frac{1}{20}$

5. (a) Inverse of $\frac{{}^-1}{3}$ is $\frac{3}{{}^-1} = {}^-3$

   (b) Inverse of $3\frac{1}{3} = \frac{10}{3}$ is $\frac{3}{10}$

   (c) Inverse of $\frac{x}{y}$ is $\frac{y}{x}$ $(x, y \neq 0)$

   (d) Inverse of ${}^-7$ is $\frac{1}{{}^-7} = \frac{{}^-1}{7}$

6. Possible thought processes are described.

(a) $3 \cdot 8 = 24$, $\frac{1}{4} \cdot 8 = 2$, and $24 + 2 = 26$

(b) $7 \cdot 4 = 28$, $\frac{1}{4} \cdot 4 = 1$, and $28 + 1 = 29$

(c) $9 \cdot 10 = 90$, $\frac{1}{5} \cdot 10 = 2$, and $90 + 2 = 92$

(d) $8 \cdot 2 = 16$, $8 \cdot \frac{1}{4} = 2$, and $16 + 2 = 18$

(e) $3 \div \frac{1}{2} = 3 \cdot \frac{2}{1} = 6$

(f) $3\frac{1}{2} \div \frac{1}{2} = 3\frac{1}{2} \cdot 2 = 7$

(g) $3 \div \frac{1}{3} = 3 \cdot 3 = 9$

(h) $4\frac{1}{2} \div 2 = 4\frac{1}{2} \cdot \frac{1}{2} \Rightarrow 4 \cdot \frac{1}{2} = 2$, $\frac{1}{2} \cdot \frac{1}{2} = \frac{1}{4}$, and $2 + \frac{1}{4} = 2\frac{1}{4}$

7. (a) 20 ($3\frac{11}{12} \cdot 5\frac{3}{100}$ is approximately $4 \cdot 5$)

(b) 16 ($2\frac{1}{10} \cdot 7\frac{7}{8}$ is approximately $2 \cdot 8$)

(c) 2 ($20\frac{2}{3} \div 9\frac{7}{8}$ is approximately $20 \div 10$)

(d) 1 ($\frac{1}{101}$ and $\frac{1}{103}$ are approximately equal)

8. (a) $6 \cdot 3 = 18$

(b) $5 \cdot 5 = 25$

(c) $21 \div 3 = 7$

(d) $12 \div 2 = 6$

9. (a) Less than 1 ($\frac{13}{14} \cdot \frac{17}{19}$ is the product of two proper fractions, thus each less than 1 $\Rightarrow$ their product is therefore less than 1, or a fraction of a fraction is less than 1)

(b) Less than 1 ($3\frac{2}{7} \div 5\frac{1}{9}$ is a number divided by a larger number $\Rightarrow$ the quotient would be less than 1)

(c) Greater than 2 ($4\frac{1}{3} \div 2\frac{3}{100}$ is a number larger than 4 divided by a number <u>very</u> slightly more than 2)

(d) Less than 4 ($16 \div 4\frac{3}{18}$ is 16 divided by more than 4)

(e) Greater than 4 ($16 \div 3\frac{8}{9}$ is 16 divided by less than 4)

10. (c), between \$6 and \$8. Estimation gives a cost of $6 \cdot 60¢ + 3 \cdot 80¢ = \$6.00$. All rounding was down, so the estimate is low.

11. If n is the number for which we are looking, then $3n - \frac{7}{18} = 2n + \frac{5}{12} \Rightarrow n = \frac{5}{12} + \frac{7}{18} = \frac{5 \cdot 18 + 12 \cdot 7}{12 \cdot 18} \Rightarrow n = \frac{29}{36}$

12. The 6000 students living in dorms are $\frac{5}{8}$ of the student population, P; i.e., $6000 = \frac{5}{8}P$ $\Rightarrow \frac{8}{5} \cdot 6000 = \frac{8}{5} \cdot \frac{5}{8}P \Rightarrow 9600 = P$

13. If F is the number of faculty members originally, then $F - \frac{1}{5}F = 320 \Rightarrow \frac{4}{5}F = 32 \Rightarrow F = \frac{5}{4} \cdot 320$ $\Rightarrow F = 400$ members originally

14. Alberto has $\frac{5}{9}$; Renatta has $\frac{1}{2} \cdot \frac{5}{9} = \frac{5}{18} \Rightarrow 1 - \frac{5}{9} - \frac{5}{18} = \frac{1}{6}$ of the stock is not owned by them

15. (a) If U is the number of uniforms to be made, then (assuming no waste) $U = 29\frac{1}{2} \div \frac{3}{4} \Rightarrow U = \frac{59}{2} \cdot \frac{4}{3}$ $\Rightarrow U = \frac{118}{3} = 39\frac{1}{3}$. Thus 39 uniforms can be made.

(b) Enough material for $\frac{1}{3}$ of a uniform will be left over. Each uniform requires $\frac{3}{4}$ yard of material; there will be $\frac{1}{3} \cdot \frac{3}{4} = \frac{1}{4}$ yard of material remaining.

16. If P is the original price, then $P - \frac{1}{4}P = 180 \Rightarrow \frac{3}{4}P = 180 \Rightarrow P = \$240$ original price

17. (a) Increasing a salary by $\frac{1}{10}$ means the salary will be $1\frac{1}{10}$, or $\frac{11}{10}$, of its previous value. With two such raises, Martha will make $(100{,}000 \cdot \frac{11}{10}) \cdot \frac{11}{10} = \$121{,}000$.

    (b) \$99,000 is $\frac{11}{10}$ of what Aaron made last year; i.e., $99{,}000 = \frac{11}{10}S$ (where S is Aaron's salary one year ago). Then, solving for S, $\frac{10}{11} \cdot 99{,}000 = \frac{10}{11} \cdot \frac{11}{10}S \Rightarrow S = \$90{,}000$.

    (c) Let S be Juanita's salary two years ago. Then $363{,}000 = \frac{11}{10}(\frac{11}{10}S)$, since two raises brought her to that value. Solving, $\frac{100}{121} \cdot 363{,}000 = \frac{100}{121} \cdot \frac{121}{100}S \Rightarrow S = \$300{,}000$.

18. Let W be the number of women who apply. Then 3W is the number of men who apply and $W + 3W = 4W$ is the total number who apply.
    So $\frac{1}{10} \cdot 4W = \frac{2}{5}W$ is the total number hired; $\frac{1}{20} \cdot 3W = \frac{3}{20}W$ is the number of men hired.
    Thus the number of women hired is $\frac{2}{5}W - \frac{3}{20}W = \frac{1}{4}W$.
    Or, $\frac{1}{4}$ of the women who apply are hired.

19. Jasmine has read $\frac{3}{4}$ of the book so she has $1 - \frac{3}{4} = \frac{1}{4}$ yet to read; i.e., 82 pages $= \frac{1}{4} \Rightarrow \frac{3}{4} = 3 \cdot 82 = 246$ pages read so far.

20. Let A be the amount of money in the account. After spending \$50 there was A – 50 left. He spent $\frac{3}{5}$ of that, or $\frac{3}{5}(A - 50)$, leaving him $\frac{2}{5}(A - 50)$. Half goes back into the bank, or $\frac{1}{2} \cdot \frac{2}{5}(A - 50) = \frac{1}{5}(A - 50)$. The other half was \$35, or $\frac{1}{5}(A - 50) = 35$. Solving, A = \$225.

21. (a) Peter: $\frac{1}{2} \cdot 60$ min. = 30 min. Paul: $\frac{5}{12} \cdot 60$ min. = 25 min. Mary: $\frac{1}{3} \cdot 60$ min. = 20 min.

    (b) Each will be back at the starting line in multiples of the time it takes for one lap; i.e., LCM(30, 25, 20) = 300 minutes, or 5 hours. Thus: Peter, 10 times; Paul, 12 times; Mary, 15 times.

22. (a) $F = \frac{9}{5} \cdot 32 + 32 = \frac{288}{5} + \frac{32 \cdot 5}{5} = \frac{448}{5} = 89\frac{3}{5}°$ F.

    (b) $^{-}40 = \frac{9}{5}C + 32 \Rightarrow {}^{-}72 = \frac{9}{5}C \Rightarrow \frac{5}{9}({}^{-}72) = \frac{5}{9} \cdot \frac{9}{5}C \Rightarrow C = {}^{-}40°$ C. (This is the only temperature where Celsius and Fahrenheit are numerically the same.)

23. Glen lost $48\frac{1}{4} - 35\frac{3}{8} = 12\frac{7}{8}$ on each share, or a total loss of $175 \cdot 12\frac{7}{8} = \$2253\frac{1}{8}$.

24. Al's marbles are halved three times in the process of Dani receiving 4 marbles; i.e., $\frac{1}{2} \cdot \frac{1}{2} \cdot \frac{1}{2} \cdot A = 4$, or $\frac{1}{8}A = 4$. Solving, A = 32 marbles (where A is the number of marbles Al had originally).

25. Not true (there are 3600 seconds in one hour; $\frac{2264}{3600} \neq 1\frac{1}{2}$)

26. There are 3600 seconds per hour; $19\frac{17}{25}$ inches per second × 3600 seconds $= \frac{492}{25} \cdot \frac{3600}{1} = 70{,}848$ inches. The centipede can travel 70,848 inches in one hour; 5904 feet in one hour; $\frac{123}{100} = 1\frac{23}{100}$ miles in one hour.

27. 13 brains × $9\frac{1}{4}$ pounds per brain $= \frac{13}{1} \cdot \frac{37}{4} = \frac{481}{4} = 120\frac{1}{4}$, or approximately 120 pounds.

28. (a) $2S = 2\left(\frac{1}{2} + \frac{1}{2^2} + \frac{1}{2^3} + \cdots + \frac{1}{2^{64}}\right) = 1 + \frac{1}{2} + \frac{1}{2^2} + \cdots + \frac{1}{2^{63}}$

    (b) $2S - S = \left(1 + \frac{1}{2} + \frac{1}{2^2} + \cdots + \frac{1}{2^{63}}\right) - \left(\frac{1}{2} + \frac{1}{2^2} + \cdots + \frac{1}{2^{64}}\right) = 1 - \frac{1}{2^{64}}$

    (c) $1 - \frac{1}{2^n}$

29. (a) From the general form of an arithmetic sequence: $a_n = a_1 + (n - 1)d$, where a_n is the *n*th term of the sequence, a_1 is the first term, n is the number of terms, and d is the common difference, we have: $2 = 1 + (100 - 1)d \Rightarrow 1 = 99d \Rightarrow d = \frac{1}{99} \Rightarrow a_{50} = 1 + (50 - 1)\frac{1}{99} = 1\frac{49}{99}$.

(b) The sum of the first 50 terms is $1 + 1\frac{1}{99} + 1\frac{2}{99} + \cdots + 1\frac{48}{99} + 1\frac{49}{99}$. Rearranging gives: $(1 + 1\frac{49}{99}) + (1\frac{1}{99} + 1\frac{48}{99}) + \cdots + (1\frac{24}{99} + 1\frac{25}{99})$, or 25 pairs, each adding to $2\frac{49}{99}$. The sum is then $25 \cdot 2\frac{49}{99} = 62\frac{37}{99}$.

30. (*i*) (a) Multiply each term by $\frac{1}{2}$ (b) $\frac{1}{32}, \frac{1}{64}$; geometric (common ratio)

(*ii*) (a) Multiply each term by $\frac{{}^-1}{2}$ (b) $\frac{{}^-1}{32}, \frac{1}{64}$; geometric

(*iii*) (a) Multiply each term by $\frac{3}{4}$ (b) $\frac{81}{256}, \frac{243}{1024}$; geometric

(*iv*) (a) General term is $\frac{n}{3^n}$ (b) $\frac{5}{3^5}, \frac{6}{3^6}$; not geometric (no common ratio)

31. (a) The square would be $n \cdot (n + 1) + (\frac{1}{2})^2$

(b) $(n + \frac{1}{2})^2 = n^2 + n + \frac{1}{4} = (n^2 + n) + \frac{1}{4} = n(n + 1) + (\frac{1}{2})^2$

32. (a) (*i*) $f(0) = \frac{3 \cdot 0 + 4}{3 \cdot 0 - 5} = \frac{{}^-4}{5}$

(*ii*) $f\left(\frac{2}{5}\right) = \frac{3 \cdot \frac{2}{5} + 4}{4 \cdot \frac{2}{5} - 5} = \frac{\frac{6}{5} + \frac{20}{5}}{\frac{8}{5} - \frac{25}{5}} = \frac{26}{5} \cdot (\frac{{}^-5}{17}) = \frac{{}^-26}{17}$

(*iii*) $f\left(\frac{{}^-2}{5}\right) = \frac{3 \cdot \frac{{}^-2}{5} + 4}{2 \cdot \frac{{}^-2}{5} - 5} = \frac{\frac{{}^-6}{5} + \frac{20}{5}}{\frac{{}^-8}{5} - \frac{25}{5}} = \frac{14}{5} \cdot (\frac{{}^-5}{33}) = \frac{{}^-14}{33}$

(b) (*i*) $\frac{3x + 4}{4x - 5} = 0$ only if $3x + 4 = 0 \Rightarrow 3x = {}^-4 \Rightarrow x = \frac{{}^-4}{3}$

(*ii*) $\frac{3x + 4}{4x - 5} = \frac{2}{5} \Rightarrow 5(3x + 4) = 2(4x - 5) \Rightarrow 15x + 20 = 8x - 10 \Rightarrow 7x = {}^-30 \Rightarrow x = \frac{{}^-30}{7}$

(*iii*) $\frac{3x + 4}{4x - 5} = \frac{{}^-1}{2} \Rightarrow 2(3x + 4) = {}^-1(4x - 5) \Rightarrow 6x + 8 = {}^-4x + 5 \Rightarrow 10x = {}^-3 \Rightarrow x = \frac{{}^-3}{10}$

(c) The value of x that makes the denominator equal 0 is not in the domain $\Rightarrow 4x - 5 = 0 \Rightarrow 4x = 5 \Rightarrow x = \frac{5}{4}$ makes the denominator 0, so $\frac{5}{4}$ is not in the domain

33. (a) (*i*) $\left(1 + \frac{1}{1}\right)\left(1 + \frac{1}{2}\right) = 2 \cdot 1\frac{1}{2} = 3$ (*ii*) $\left(1 + \frac{1}{1}\right)\left(1 + \frac{1}{2}\right)\left(1 + \frac{1}{3}\right) = 3 \cdot \left(1 + \frac{1}{3}\right) = 4$

(*iii*) $\left(1 + \frac{1}{1}\right)\left(1 + \frac{1}{2}\right)\left(1 + \frac{1}{3}\right)\left(1 + \frac{1}{4}\right) = 4 \cdot \left(1 + \frac{1}{4}\right) = 5$

(*iv*) Guess 6; $\left(1 + \frac{1}{1}\right)\left(1 + \frac{1}{2}\right)\left(1 + \frac{1}{3}\right)\left(1 + \frac{1}{4}\right)\left(1 + \frac{1}{5}\right) = 5 \cdot \left(1 + \frac{1}{5}\right) = 6$

(b) Products are 3, 4, 5, … , n + 2 $\Rightarrow$ the 100th product = 100 + 2 = 102

(c) n + 2

45. (a) $28° - {}^{-}12° = {}^{-}40°$ change in 5 minutes $\Rightarrow$ ${}^{-}8°$ per minute in the first experiment
    First experiment: 28°, 20°, 12°, ...
    Second experiment: ${}^{-}57°$, ${}^{-}60°$, ${}^{-}63°$. ...
    A spreadsheet of the two reactions will show the temperature to be equal at 17 minutes

    (b) The temperature at equality is ${}^{-}108°$ C

46. (a) $\frac{^{-}3}{16} + \frac{7}{4} = \frac{^{-}3}{16} + \frac{28}{16} = \frac{25}{16} = 1\frac{9}{16}$

    (b) $\frac{1}{6} + \frac{^{-}4}{9} + \frac{5}{3} = \frac{3}{18} + \frac{^{-}8}{18} + \frac{30}{18} = \frac{25}{18} = 1\frac{7}{18}$

    (c) $\frac{^{-}5}{2^3 \cdot 3^2} - \frac{^{-}5}{2 \cdot 3^3} = \frac{^{-}5 \cdot 3}{2^3 \cdot 3^3} - \frac{^{-}5 \cdot 2^2}{2^3 \cdot 3^3} = \frac{^{-}15}{216} + \frac{20}{216} = \frac{5}{216}$

    (d) $3\frac{4}{5} + 4\frac{5}{6} = 3\frac{24}{30} + 4\frac{25}{30} = 7\frac{49}{30} = 8\frac{19}{30}$

    (e) $5\frac{1}{6} - 3\frac{5}{8} = 5\frac{4}{24} - 3\frac{15}{24} = 4\frac{28}{24} - 3\frac{15}{24} = 1\frac{13}{24}$

    (f) ${}^{-}4\frac{1}{3} - 5\frac{5}{12} = {}^{-}4\frac{4}{12} - 5\frac{5}{12} = {}^{-}9\frac{9}{12} = {}^{-}9\frac{3}{4}$

47. The portion of students that take one of the three foreign languages is $\frac{2}{3} + \frac{1}{9} + \frac{1}{18} = \frac{5}{6}$. The portion of students not taking one of the three is then $1 - \frac{5}{6} = \frac{1}{6}$. That number of students is then $\frac{1}{6} \cdot 720 = 120$ students.

Chapter 5 Review

1. (a) 3 of 4 blocks shaded:

    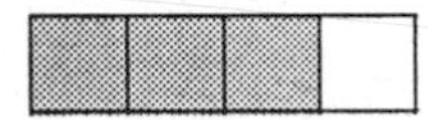

    (b) 2 of 3 blocks shaded:

    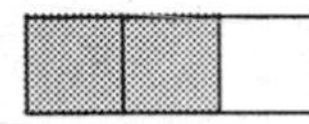

    (c) Three of four horizontal bars are shaded, meshed with two of three vertical bars. Thus six of the twelve blocks are cross-hatched $\Rightarrow \frac{3}{4} \cdot \frac{2}{3} = \frac{6}{12}$:

    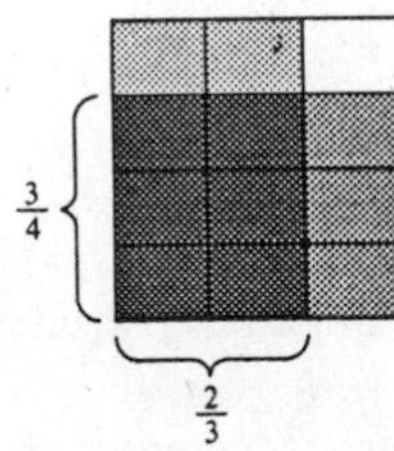

2. Answers may vary; three are $\frac{10}{12}$, $\frac{15}{18}$, and $\frac{50}{60}$

3. (a) $\frac{24}{28} = \frac{6 \cdot 4}{7 \cdot 4} = \frac{6}{7}$

    (b) $\frac{ax^2}{bx} = \frac{(ax)x}{(b)x} = \frac{ax}{b}$

    (c) $\frac{0}{1}$

    (d) $\frac{5}{9}$

    (e) $\frac{b^2 + bx}{b + x} = \frac{b(b + x)}{b + x} = \frac{b}{1}$

    (f) $\frac{2}{27}$

4. (a) $= \left(\frac{6 \cdot 20}{10 \cdot 20} = \frac{120}{200}\right)$

    (b) $> \left(\frac{^{-}3}{4} = \frac{^{-}18}{24} > \frac{^{-}5}{6} = \frac{^{-}20}{24}\right)$

    (c) $>$

    (d) $<$

5.

	Additive	Multiplicative
(a)	${}^{-}3$	$\frac{1}{3}$
(b)	${}^{-}3\frac{1}{7}$	$\frac{7}{22}$
(c)	$\frac{{}^{-}5}{6}$	$\frac{6}{5}$
(d)	$\frac{3}{4}$	$\frac{{}^{-}4}{3}$

6. ${}^{-}2\frac{1}{3}, {}^{-}1\frac{7}{8}, 0, (\frac{71}{140})^{300}, \frac{69}{140}, \frac{1}{2}, \frac{71}{140}, (\frac{74}{73})^{300}$

7. Assuming no waste, $54\frac{1}{4} \div 3\frac{1}{12} = 17\frac{22}{37}$ pieces can be cut; i.e., 17 pieces with $\frac{22}{37}$ piece $= \frac{22}{37} \cdot 3\frac{1}{12} = \frac{11}{6}$ yards left over

8. (a) 15 (approximately $\frac{30}{4} \cdot \frac{8}{4} = \frac{15}{2} \cdot 2$) (b) 15 (approximately $\frac{15}{6} \cdot 6$)

(c) 4 (approximately $\frac{1}{400} \div \frac{1}{1000}$)

9. $\frac{a}{b} \div \frac{c}{d} = x$ if and only if $\frac{a}{b} = \frac{c}{d} \cdot x \Rightarrow x = \frac{d}{c} \cdot \frac{a}{b}$ because $\frac{c}{d} \cdot \left(\frac{d}{c} \cdot \frac{a}{b}\right) = \frac{a}{b}$

10. $\frac{\text{Boys}}{\text{Girls}} = \frac{3}{5} = \frac{B}{15}$, so $5B = 45 \Rightarrow$ 9 boys are in Ms. Garcia's class

11. Answers may vary; $\frac{3}{4} = \frac{60}{80}$ and $\frac{4}{5} = \frac{64}{80} \Rightarrow \frac{61}{80}$ and $\frac{62}{80}$ are two

12. Think of $504792 \div 23$ as $504792 \cdot \frac{1}{23}$ and enter: [5] [0] [4] [7] [9] [2] [×] [2] [3] [1/x] [=]

13. Jim ate $\frac{1}{3} \cdot \frac{1}{2} = \frac{1}{6}$ of the pizza $\Rightarrow \frac{1}{6} \cdot 2000 = 333\frac{1}{3}$ calories

14. $\frac{1}{2}x = 376$ heads $\Rightarrow x = 376 \div \frac{1}{2} = 752$ times

15. $\frac{240 \text{ heads}}{1000 \text{ flips}} = \frac{6}{25}$ heads

16. It is unreasonable unless the number of games played by men and women are the same

17. The numerators of the rational numbers are integers and follow the properties of integers; the same is true of the denominators $\Rightarrow$ both the numerator and denominator of the product are integers and another property of integers may be applied to determine its sign.

18. $\frac{\frac{2}{3}}{\frac{3}{4}} = \frac{\frac{2}{3} \cdot \frac{4}{3}}{\frac{3}{4} \cdot \frac{4}{3}} = \frac{\frac{8}{9}}{1} = \frac{8}{9}$, which is the quotient of two integers

19. $\frac{2}{3}$ female $\times \frac{2}{5}$ blond $= \frac{4}{15}$ blond females.

20. The minute hand points directly at a numeral only 1 minute in each hour $\Rightarrow \frac{1}{60}$ hour

21. $\frac{{}^{-}11}{9} = \frac{{}^{-}110}{90}; \frac{{}^{-}12}{10} = \frac{{}^{-}108}{90} \Rightarrow \frac{{}^{-}12}{10} > \frac{{}^{-}11}{9}$

CHAPTER 6 - EXPONENTS AND DECIMALS

1. (a) $3^{-7} \cdot 3^{-6} = 3^{-6+{}^{-}7} = 3^{-13} = \frac{1}{3^{13}}$ (b) $3^7 \cdot 3^6 = 3^{7+6} = 3^{13}$

   (c) $5^{15} \div 5^4 = 5^{15-4} = 5^{11}$ (d) $5^{15} \div 5^{-4} = 5^{15-{}^{-}4} = 5^{19}$

   (e) $({}^{-}5)^{-2} = \frac{1}{({}^{-}5)^2} = \frac{1}{5^2}$ (f) $\frac{a^2}{a^{-3}} = a^{2-{}^{-}3} = a^{2+3} = a^5$

   (g) $\frac{a}{a^{-1}} = a^{1-{}^{-}1} = a^{1+1} = a^2$ (h) $\frac{a^{-3}}{a^{-2}} = a^{-3-{}^{-}2} = a^{-1} = \frac{1}{a}$

2. (a) $\left(\frac{1}{2}\right)^{3+7} = \left(\frac{1}{2}\right)^{10}$ (b) $\left(\frac{1}{2}\right)^{9-6} = \left(\frac{1}{2}\right)^3$

   (c) $\left(\frac{2}{3}\right)^5 \cdot \left(\left(\frac{2}{3}\right)^2\right)^2 = \left(\frac{2}{3}\right)^{5+4} = \left(\frac{2}{3}\right)^9$ (d) $\left(\frac{3}{5}\right)^{7-7} = \left(\frac{3}{5}\right)^0 = 1$

   (e) $\left(\frac{5}{3}\right)^7 \div \left(\frac{5}{3}\right)^4 = \left(\frac{5}{3}\right)^{7-4} = \left(\frac{5}{3}\right)^3$ (f) $\left(\frac{5}{6}\right)^{7\cdot 3} = \left(\frac{5}{6}\right)^{21}$

3. (a) False $[2^3 \cdot 3^2 = 8 \cdot 9 = 72 \neq (2 \cdot 3)^{3+2} = 7776]$ (b) False $[2^3 \cdot 3^2 = 72 \neq (2 \cdot 3)^{2\cdot 3} = 46{,}656]$

   (c) False $[2^3 \cdot 3^3 = (2 \cdot 3)^3 = 216 \neq (2 \cdot 3)^{2\cdot 3} = 46{,}656]$ (d) False $(a^0 = 1,\ a \neq 0)$

   (e) False $[(2+3)^2 = (2+3)(2+3) = 25 \neq 2^2 + 3^2 = 13]$ (f) False $\left[(2+3)^{-2} = \frac{1}{(2+3)^2} = \frac{1}{25} \neq \frac{1}{2^2} + \frac{1}{3^2} = \frac{13}{36}\right]$

   (g) False $(3^{2\cdot 3} = 3^6 = 729 \neq 3^2 \cdot 3^3 = 243)$ (h) True $\left[\left(\frac{a}{b}\right)^{-1} = \frac{1}{\left(\frac{a}{b}\right)} = \frac{b}{a}\right]$

4. (a) $2^5 = 32 \Rightarrow 2^n = 2^5 \Rightarrow n = 5$ (b) $6^2 = 36$ and $({}^{-}6)^2 = 36 \Rightarrow n = 6$ or $n = {}^{-}6$

   (c) $2^{n+7} = 2^5 \Rightarrow n + 7 = 5 \Rightarrow n = {}^{-}2$ (d) $2^{n+7} = 2^3 \Rightarrow n + 7 = 3 \Rightarrow n = {}^{-}4$

   (e) $(2+n)(2+n) = 2^2 + n^2 \Rightarrow 2^2 + 4n + n^2 = 2^2 + n^2 \Rightarrow 4n = 0 \Rightarrow n = 0$

   (f) $3^n = (3^3)^5 \Rightarrow 3^n = 3^{15} \Rightarrow n = 15$

5. (a) Each cell has a "length" equal to twice its radius $\Rightarrow$ length of the line would be twice the radius times the number of cells, or:
   $2(4 \cdot 10^{-3})(25 \cdot 10^{12}) = (2 \cdot 4 \cdot 25) \cdot (10^{-3} \cdot 10^{12}) = 200 \cdot 10^9 = (2 \cdot 10^2) \cdot 10^9 = 2 \cdot 10^{11}$ mm.

   (b) $2 \cdot 10^{11} \div 10^6 = 2 \cdot (10^{11-6}) = 2 \cdot 10^5$ km (at 1.6 km/mile, $2 \cdot 10^5$ km $= \frac{2 \cdot 10^5}{1.6} = 125{,}000$ miles)

6. (a) $3^x \leq 3^4 \Rightarrow x \leq 4$

   (b) $(2^2)^x < 2^3 \Rightarrow 2x < 3 \Rightarrow x < \frac{3}{2} \Rightarrow x \leq 1$ and $x \in I$

   (c) $3^{2x} > 3^3 \Rightarrow 2x > 3 \Rightarrow x > \frac{3}{2} \Rightarrow x \geq 2$ and $x \in I$

   (d) $2^x > 2^0 \Rightarrow x > 0 \Rightarrow x \geq 1$

7. (a) $\left(\frac{1}{2}\right)^3 = \frac{1}{8};\ \left(\frac{1}{2}\right)^4 = \frac{1}{16} \Rightarrow \left(\frac{1}{2}\right)^3 > \left(\frac{1}{2}\right)^4$

(b) $3^{10} \cdot 4^8 < 4^{10} \cdot 3^8 \Rightarrow \left(\frac{3}{4}\right)^8 > \left(\frac{3}{4}\right)^{10}$

(c) $4^{10} \cdot 3^8 > 3^{10} \cdot 4^8 \Rightarrow \left(\frac{4}{3}\right)^{10} > \left(\frac{4}{3}\right)^8$

(d) $\frac{4}{5} > \frac{3}{4} \Rightarrow \left(\frac{4}{5}\right)^{10} > \left(\frac{3}{4}\right)^{10}$

(e) $\frac{4}{3} > \frac{5}{4} \Rightarrow \left(\frac{4}{3}\right)^{10} > \left(\frac{5}{4}\right)^{10}$

(f) $\frac{3}{4} > \frac{3 \cdot 9}{4 \cdot 10} \Rightarrow \left(\frac{3}{4}\right)^{100} > \left(\frac{3}{4} \cdot \frac{9}{10}\right)^{100}$

8. (a) $Q(0) = 10^{10}\left(\frac{6}{5}\right)^0 = 10^{10} \cdot 1 = 10^{10}$ bacteria when $t = 0$

(b) $Q(2) = 10^{10}\left(\frac{6}{5}\right)^2 = 10^{10} \cdot \frac{36}{25} = 1.44 \cdot 10^{10}$ (or 14.4 trillion) bacteria when $t = 2$

9. (a) $f(0) = \frac{3}{4} \cdot 2^0 = \frac{3}{4} \cdot 1 = \frac{3}{4}$

(b) $f(5) = \frac{3}{4} \cdot 2^5 = \frac{3}{4} \cdot 32 = 24$

(c) $f({}^-5) = \frac{3}{4} \cdot 2^{{}^-5} = \frac{3}{4} \cdot \frac{1}{32} = \frac{3}{128}$

(d) We are looking for the largest integer n for which $\frac{3}{4} \cdot 2^n < \frac{3}{400}$, where $\frac{3}{4} \cdot 2^n = \frac{3}{2^2} \cdot \frac{1}{2^{-n}} = \frac{3}{2^{2-n}}$.
Thus $\frac{3}{2^{2-n}} < \frac{3}{400} \Rightarrow 2^{2-n} > 400$. $2^9 = 512$ is the first integer power of 2 greater than 400 $\Rightarrow 2 - n = 9 \Rightarrow n = {}^-7$. Thus ${}^-7$ is the largest integer for which the statement is true.

10. (a) $a_1 = 3 \cdot 2^{{}^-1} = 3 \cdot \frac{1}{2} = \frac{3}{2}$; $a_2 = 3 \cdot 2^{{}^-2} = 3 \cdot \frac{1}{4} = \frac{3}{4}$; $a_3 = 3 \cdot 2^{{}^-3} = 3 \cdot \frac{1}{8} = \frac{3}{8}$;
$a_4 = 3 \cdot 2^{{}^-4} = 3 \cdot \frac{1}{16} = \frac{3}{16}$; $a_5 = 3 \cdot 2^{{}^-5} = 3 \cdot \frac{1}{32} = \frac{3}{32}$

(b) The first five terms are a geometric sequence because there is a common ratio of $\frac{1}{2}$

(c) $a_n < \frac{3}{1000}$ when $2^n > 1000 \Rightarrow n = 10$ and $a_{10} = \frac{3}{1024}$

11. (a) $32^{50} = (2^5)^{50} = 2^{250}$ and $4^{100} = (2^2)^{100} = 2^{200} \Rightarrow 32^{50} > 4^{100}$

(b) $({}^-27)^{{}^-15} = [({}^-3)^3]^{{}^-15} = ({}^-3)^{{}^-45} = \frac{1}{({}^-3)^{45}} = {}^-\left[\frac{1}{3^{45}}\right]$ and $({}^-3)^{{}^-75} = \frac{1}{({}^-3)^{75}} = {}^-\left[\frac{1}{3^{75}}\right] \Rightarrow ({}^-3)^{{}^-75} > ({}^-27)^{{}^-15}$
$\left(\frac{1}{3^{45}} > \frac{1}{3^{75}}\right.$, but their negatives reverse the direction of the inequality$\left.\right)$

12. (a) $0.023 = 0 \cdot 10^0 + 0 \cdot 10^{-1} + 2 \cdot 10^{-2} + 3 \cdot 10^{-3}$

(b) $206.06 = 2 \cdot 10^2 + 0 \cdot 10^1 + 6 \cdot 10^0 + 0 \cdot 10^{-1} + 6 \cdot 10^{-2}$

(c) $312.0103 = 3 \cdot 10^2 + 1 \cdot 10^1 + 2 \cdot 10^0 + 0 \cdot 10^{-1} + 1 \cdot 10^{-2} + 0 \cdot 10^{-3} + 3 \cdot 10^{-4}$

(d) $0.000132 = 0 \cdot 10^0 + 0 \cdot 10^{-1} + 0 \cdot 10^{-2} + 0 \cdot 10^{-3} + 1 \cdot 10^{-4} + 3 \cdot 10^{-5} + 2 \cdot 10^{-6}$

13. (a) $4000 + 300 + 50 + 6 + 0.7 + 0.08 = 4356.78$

(b) $4000 + 0.6 + 0.008 = 4000.608$

(c) $40{,}000 + 0.03 = 40{,}000.03$

(d) $0.2 + 0.0004 + 0.0000007 = 0.2004007$

14. (a) 536.0076

(b) 3.008

(c) 0.000436

(d) 5,000,000.2

15. (a) $0.436 = \frac{436}{1000} = \frac{109}{250}$

(b) $25.16 = 25\frac{16}{100} = \frac{2516}{100} = \frac{629}{25}$

15. (c) $^{-}316.027 = {^{-}316}\frac{27}{1000} = \frac{^{-}316027}{1000}$

(d) $28.1902 = 28\frac{1902}{10000} = \frac{281902}{10000} = \frac{140951}{5000}$

(e) $^{-}4.3 = {^{-}4}\frac{3}{10} = \frac{^{-}43}{10}$

(f) $^{-}62.01 = {^{-}62}\frac{1}{100} = \frac{^{-}6201}{100}$

16. (a) Terminating decimal (denominator contains only 5 as a prime factor)

(b) Terminating decimal (denominator contains no prime factors other than 2 and 5)

(c) Terminating decimal (reduced denominator contains only 2 as a prime factor)

(d) Terminating decimal (denominator contains only 2 as a prime factor)

(e) Terminating decimal (denominator contains only 5 as a prime factor)

(f) Terminating decimal (denominator contains only 5 as a prime factor)

(g) Nonterminating decimal (denominator contains 3 as a prime factor)

(h) Terminating decimal (denominator contains only 5 as a prime factor)

(i) Nonterminating decimal (denominator contains 13 as a prime factor)

17. (a) 0.8 (b) 3.05

(c) 0.5 (d) 0.03125

(e) 0.01152 (f) 0.2128

(g) Nonterminating decimal (h) 0.08

(i) Nonterminating decimal

18. (a) Lining up by place value:
13.49190
13.49200
13.49183
13.49199

Then from greatest to least they are: 13.492, 13.49199, 13.4919, 13.49183

(b) Lining up by place value:
$^{-}1.45300$
$^{-}1.45000$
$^{-}1.40530$
$^{-}1.49300$

Then from greatest (i.e., closest to 0) to least they are: $^{-}1.45053$, $^{-}1.45$, $^{-}1.453$, $^{-}1.493$

19. (a) $3.2 \div 10^9 = 0.0000000032$ (b) $3.2 \cdot 10^9 = 3{,}200{,}000{,}000$

(c) $4.2 \div 10^1 = 0.42$ (d) $6.2 \cdot 10^5 = 620{,}000$

20. (a) About $1.27 \cdot 10^7$ km (b) $5.797 \cdot 10^6$ km

(c) About $5 \cdot 10^7$ discarded cans

21. (a) 0.0000044 sec (b) About 19,900 km

21. (c) Approximately 3,000,000,000 years

22. (a) $(8 \cdot 10^{12}) \cdot (6 \cdot 10^{15}) = 8 \cdot 6 \cdot 10^{12} \cdot 10^{15} = 48 \cdot 10^{27} = 4.8 \cdot 10^{28}$

(b) $(16 \cdot 10^{12}) \div (4 \cdot 10^{5}) = \frac{16}{4} \cdot 10^{12} \cdot 10^{-5} = 4 \cdot 10^{7}$

(c) $(5 \cdot 10^{8}) \cdot (6 \cdot 10^{9}) \div (15 \cdot 10^{15}) = \frac{5 \cdot 6}{15} \cdot 10^{8} \cdot 10^{9} \cdot 10^{-15} = 2 \cdot 10^{2}$

23. The number of digits in the terminating decimal is the greater of m or n

24. $100{,}000^3 = (1 \cdot 10^5)^3 = 10^{15}$; $1000^5 = (1 \cdot 10^3)^5 = 10^{15}$; $100{,}000^2 < 100{,}000^3$
$\Rightarrow (100{,}000^3 = 1000^5) > 100{,}000^2$

On-going Assessment 6-2

1. Maura bought a total of:

\$17.95
13.59
14.86
179.98
2.43
2.43
\$231.24 in her shopping

2. (2.082 lbs per quart)(29.922 quarts per cubic foot) = 62.297604 pounds. Rounding to the nearest thousandth $\Rightarrow$ 62.298 pounds per cubic foot

3. Sum along the diagonal, obtaining 16.5 ; in rows and columns with two figures, subtract their sum from 16.5 to obtain the missing element, to obtain:

8.2	1.9	6.4
3.7	5.5	7.3
4.6	9.1	2.8

4. There would be a total of 30 + 20 + 10 = 60 pounds of nuts. At an average price per pound of \$4.50, Keith would pay (\$4.50)(60) = \$270.00 for the 60 pounds.

He has already paid (\$3.00)(30) + (\$5.00)(20) = \$90.00 + \$100.00 = \$190.00 for nuts, so he has \$270.00 – \$190.00 = \$80.00 left to pay for the additional 10 pounds $\Rightarrow$ \$80.00 ÷ 10 pounds = \$8.00 per pound

5. (a) (3 heaters)(1200 watts per hour each)(24 hours per day) = 86,400 watt hours = 86.4 kilowatt hours. (86.4 kilowatt hours)(\$0.03715 per kilowatt hour) = \$3.20976, which rounds to \$3.21 per day.

(b) 75 watts is 0.075 kilowatts. Then (0.075 kw)(1 hour)(\$0.03715 per kw hour) = \$0.00278625 to operate one bulb for one hour. \$1.00 ÷ \$0.00278625 = 358.9 hours (rounded).

6. (a) If there are 2.54 cm per inch, there are $(2.54)^3 = 16.387064$ cm^3 per cubic inch. (16.387064 cm^3 per in^3)(390 cubic inches) = 6391 cm^3 (rounded to the nearest cm^3) in the engine.

(b) (3000 cm^3) ÷ (16.387064 cm^3 per in^3) = 183 in^3 (rounded to the nearest in^3) in the engine.

7. (39.37 in per m)(100 m) = 3937 inches traveled. (3937 in) ÷ (63360 in per mi) = 0.062137 miles traveled.
(10.49 sec) ÷ (3600 sec per hr) = 0.002914 hours spent.
(0.062137 miles) ÷ (0.002914 hour) = 21.3 (rounded to the nearest tenth) miles per hour.

8. (a) There is a difference of 0.9 between each element of the sequence, so it is arithmetic.
   $\Rightarrow$ 5.4, 6.3, 7.2, 8.1, 9.0, $\cdots$

   (b) There is a difference of 0.2 between each element of the sequence, so it is arithmetic.
   $\Rightarrow$ 1.3, 1.5, 1.7, 1.9, 2.1, $\cdots$

   (c) Each element of the sequence is 0.5 times the previous element, so it is geometric.
   $\Rightarrow$ 0.0625, 0.03125, , 0.015625, 0.0078125, $\cdots$

   (d) There is a difference of 1.3 between each element of the sequence, so it is arithmetic.
   $\Rightarrow$ 6.7, 8.0, 9.3, 10.6, 11.9, $\cdots$

9. (a) $\frac{4}{9} = 4 \div 9 = 0.\overline{4}$ (b) $\frac{2}{7} = 2 \div 7 = 0.\overline{285714}$

   (c) $\frac{3}{11} = 3 \div 11 = 0.\overline{27}$ (d) $\frac{1}{15} = 1 \div 15 = 0.0\overline{6}$

   (e) $\frac{2}{75} = 2 \div 75 = 0.02\overline{6}$ (f) $\frac{1}{99} = 1 \div 99 = 0.\overline{01}$

   (g) $\frac{5}{6} = 5 \div 6 = 0.8\overline{3}$ (h) $\frac{1}{13} = 1 \div 13 = 0.\overline{076923}$

10. We would divide 93,000,000 by 1565, or $\boxed{9}\boxed{3}\boxed{0}\boxed{0}\boxed{0}\boxed{0}\boxed{0}\boxed{0}\boxed{\div}\boxed{1}\boxed{5}\boxed{6}\boxed{5}\boxed{=}$ (It would take 59,425 hours, or about $6\frac{3}{4}$ years)

11. The total of outstanding checks is \$54.19. Adding the total of outstanding checks to the checkbook balance, we have \$75.88, which differs from the bank statement. The bank is not correct.

12. (a) $1 \div 13 = 0.\overline{075923}$ (b) $1 \div 21 = 0.\overline{047619}$

    (c) $3 \div 19 = 0.\overline{157894736842105263}$

13. (a) $\underline{2}03.651 \Rightarrow$ the number to the right of the $\underline{\text{hundred}}$ position $< 5 \Rightarrow$ round down to 200

    (b) $2\underline{0}3.651 \Rightarrow$ the number to the right of the $\underline{\text{ten}}$ position $< 5 \Rightarrow$ round down to 200

    (c) $20\underline{3}.651 \Rightarrow$ the number to the right of the $\underline{\text{unit}}$ position $\geq 5 \Rightarrow$ round up to 204

    (d) $203.\underline{6}51 \Rightarrow$ the number to the right of the $\underline{\text{tenth}}$ position $\geq 5 \Rightarrow$ round up to 203.7

    (e) $203.6\underline{5}1 \Rightarrow$ the number to the right of the $\underline{\text{hundredth}}$ position $< 5 \Rightarrow$ round down to 203.65

14. $\frac{224 \text{ miles}}{12 \text{ gallons}} = 18.\overline{6} = 19$ mpg rounded to the nearest mile

15. (a) $n = 0.\overline{4}$; a one-digit repetend:

$$
\begin{array}{r}
10n = 4.4444\ldots \\
-n = -0.4444\ldots \\
\hline
9n = 4 \Rightarrow n = \dfrac{4}{9}
\end{array}
$$

15. (b) $n = 0.\overline{6}$; a one-digit repetend:

$$\begin{array}{l} 10n = 6.6666\ldots \\ {}^-n = {}^-0.6666\ldots \\ \hline 9n = 6 \Rightarrow n = \frac{6}{9} = \frac{2}{3} \end{array}$$

(c) $n = 1.3\overline{9}$; $10n = 13.\overline{9}$; now a one-digit repetend:

$$\begin{array}{l} 100n = 139.9999\ldots \\ {}^-10n = {}^-13.9999\ldots \\ \hline 90n = 126 \Rightarrow n = \frac{126}{90} = \frac{7}{5} \end{array}$$

(Note: $1.3\overline{9} = 1.3 + 0.0\overline{9} = 1.3 + 0.1 = 1.4$, which is $7 \div 5$)

(d) $n = 0.\overline{55} = 0.\overline{5}$; a one-digit repetend:

$$\begin{array}{l} 10n = 5.5555\ldots \\ {}^-n = {}^-0.5555\ldots \\ \hline 9n = 5 \Rightarrow n = \frac{5}{9} \end{array}$$

(e) $n = {}^-2.3\overline{4}$; $10n = {}^-23.\overline{4}$; now a one-digit repetend:

$$\begin{array}{l} 100n = {}^-234.4444\ldots \\ {}^-10n = 23.4444\ldots \\ \hline 90n = {}^-211 \Rightarrow n = \frac{{}^-211}{90} \end{array}$$

(f) $n = {}^-0.\overline{02}$; a two-digit repetend:

$$\begin{array}{l} 100n = {}^-2.02020202\ldots \\ {}^-n = 0.02020202\ldots \\ \hline 99n = {}^-2 \Rightarrow n = \frac{{}^-2}{99} \end{array}$$

16. Line up the decimal points:

$$\begin{array}{l} {}^-145454545\ldots \\ {}^-1.4544544\ldots \\ {}^-1.4545454\ldots \\ {}^-1.4544444\ldots \\ {}^-1.4540000 \end{array}$$

$\Rightarrow$ Ordering from greatest (i.e., closest to 0) to least yields: ${}^-1.454 > {}^-1.45\overline{4} > {}^-1.\overline{454} > {}^-1.4\overline{54} = {}^-1.\overline{45}$

17. Answers may vary, but:

(a) $3.2 < 3.201 < 3.202 < 3.203 < 3.22$

(b) $462.24 < 462.2401 < 462.2402 < 462.2403 < 462.243$

18. (a) $0.5 - 0.4 = 0.1$; $0.1 \div 2 = 0.05$; $0.4 + 0.05 = 0.45$ (b) $1.1 - 0.9 = 0.2$; $0.2 \div 2 = 0.1$; $0.9 + 0.1 = 1.0$

19. Camera – about \$55
Film – about \$5
Case – about \$18 ; total estimated cost about \$78

20. (a) (*i*) 65.84 rounds to 66
24.29 rounds to 24
12.18 rounds to 12
19.75 rounds to 20
$\Rightarrow$ Rounded total = 122

(*ii*) 66 might be rounded to 65.5 or 66.4
24 might be rounded to 23.5 or 24.4
12 might be rounded to 11.5 or 12.4
20 might be rounded to 19.5 or 20.4
$\Rightarrow$ Total could be between 120.0 and 123.6

(*iii*) The actual sum is 122.06

(b) (*i*) 89.47 rounds to 89
$^-$32.16 rounds to $^-$32
$\Rightarrow$ Rounded difference = 57

(*ii*) 89 might be rounded to 88.5 or 89.4
32 might be rounded to 31.5 or 32.4
$\Rightarrow$ Difference could be between 56.1 and 57.9

(*iii*) The actual difference is 57.31

(c) (*i*) 5.85 rounds to 6
6.13 rounds to 6
9.10 rounds to 9
4.32 rounds to 4
$\Rightarrow$ Rounded sum = 25

(*ii*) 6 might be rounded to 5.5 or 6.4
6 might be rounded to 5.5 or 6.4
9 might be rounded to 8.5 or 9.4
4 might be rounded to 3.5 or 4.4
$\Rightarrow$ Sum could be between 23.0 and 26.6

(*iii*) The actual sum is 25.4

(d) (*i*) 223.75 rounds to 224
$^-$87.60 rounds to $^-$88
$\Rightarrow$ Rounded difference = 136

(*ii*) 224 might be rounded to 223.5 or 224.4
88 might be rounded to 87.5 or 88.4
$\Rightarrow$ Difference could be between 135.0 and 136.9.

(*iii*) The actual difference is 136.15

21. Light travels ($1.86 \cdot 10^5$ miles per sec) $\cdot$ ($3.1536 \cdot 10^7$ secs per year) $\doteq$ $5.87 \cdot 10^{12}$ miles per year.
($5.87 \cdot 10^{12}$ miles per year) $\cdot$ (4 years) $\doteq$ $2.35 \cdot 10^{13}$ miles that Alpha Centauri is away from the earth.

22. (a) We add $0.\overline{3}$ to each term to obtain the next term, so the continuing pattern is $1.\overline{6}, 2, 2.\overline{3}, \ldots$.

22. (b) If we convert each of these terms to fractions, we have 0, $\frac{1}{2}$, $\frac{2}{3}$, $\frac{3}{4}$, $\frac{4}{5}$, and $\frac{5}{6}$; it can be seen that each term is arrived at by adding 1 to the numerator and denominator of the previous term. Thus, the next terms are $\frac{6}{7}, \frac{7}{8}, \frac{8}{9}, \ldots$. Converting back to decimals, the next terms are $0.\overline{857142}$, 0.875, $0.\overline{8}$, … .

23. (a) $a + b = 0.32323232\ldots + 0.123123123\ldots = 0.446355446355\ldots$. There are six digits in the repetend.

(b) $a + b = 1.3\overline{5775}$. Since the sum is a repeating decimal, it is a rational number $\left(\frac{67981}{49995}\right.$, specifically$\left.\right)$. There are four digits in the repetend.

24. (a) nth term $= (0.9)^n \Rightarrow a_{100} = (0.9)^{100} \doteq 2.66 \cdot 10^{-5}$

(b) nth term $= (0.99)^n \Rightarrow a_{1000} = (0.99)^{1000} \doteq 4.32 \cdot 10^{-5}$

(c) nth term $= (1.01)^n \Rightarrow a_{10,000} = (1.01)^{10,000} \doteq 1.64 \cdot 10^{43}$

(d) nth term $= (1.001)^n \Rightarrow a_{10^6} = (1.001)^{10^6} = \left[(1.001)^{100,000}\right]^{10} \doteq \left(2.56 \cdot 10^{43}\right)^{10} \doteq \left(1.21 \cdot 10^{4}\right) \cdot 10^{430}$ $\doteq 1.21 \cdot 10^{434}$

(e) When taken to the power n, as n grows very large:
Powers of numbers between 0 and 1approach 0
Powers of numbers greater than 1increase without bound

25. (18 shares of stock) $\cdot$ (\$61.48 per share) = \$1106.64 net return
(350 shares) $\cdot$ (\$85.35 per share) = \$29,872.50 gross return − \$495 commission = \$29,377.50 net return
Total net return = \$1106.64 + \$29,377.50 = \$30,484.14
Total cost = \$964.00 + \$27,422.50 = \$28,386.50
$\Rightarrow$ Profit = \$30,484.14 net return − \$28,386.50 cost = \$2097.64

26. (a) Exchange rate (for cash) of 1.19:1 $\Rightarrow$ \$235 $\cdot$ 1.19 = 279.65 francs

(b) 452.85 francs + 284.65 francs = 737.50 francs $\Rightarrow \frac{737.50}{1.19} \doteq$ \$619.75 ; rounding up, she must exchange \$620

(c) $\frac{\text{687.75 francs}}{\text{1.2:1 exchange ratio}} \doteq$ \$573.13 ; she must exchange five \$100's and four \$20's

On-going Assessment 6-2; Review Problems

37. (a) True $\left[\frac{x^{-n}}{y^{-n}} = \frac{1}{x^n} \cdot \frac{y^n}{1} = \frac{y^n}{x^n} = \left(\frac{y}{x}\right)^n\right]$

(b) False $\left(xy^{-1} = x \cdot \frac{1}{y} = \frac{x}{y}\right)$

(c) False $\left[(x + y)^0 \neq x^0 + y^0\right]$

(d) False $\left[(x^m + y^m)^n \neq x^{mn} + y^{mn}\right]$

(e) False $\left[(4^2 \cdot 5^3) = 16 \cdot 125 = 2000 \neq (4 \cdot 5)^{2+3} = 3{,}200{,}000\right]$

(f) False $\left(0^{-3} = \frac{1}{0^3} = \frac{1}{0} \Rightarrow \text{undefined}\right)$

38. (a) $2^9 = 512$ and $2^{10} = 1024 \Rightarrow 2^9 \leq 1000$ and $x = 9$ is the greatest integer

(b) $2^{-(-9)} = 512$ and $2^{-(-10)} = 1024 \Rightarrow 2^{-(-10)} \geq 1000$ and $x = {}^{-}10$ is the greatest integer

(c) $3^4 = 3^{2 \cdot 2} = 81$ and $3^{2 \cdot 3} > 81 \Rightarrow x = 3$ is the least integer

38. (d) $10^x \le \frac{1}{34{,}789} \Rightarrow 10^x \le \frac{1}{3.4789 \cdot 10^4} \Rightarrow 1 \cdot 10^x \le 2.87 \cdot 10^{{}^{-}5} \Rightarrow x = {}^{-}5$ is the greatest integer

39. (a) $(a^4)^5 = a^4 \cdot a^4 \cdot a^4 \cdot a^4 \cdot a^4 = a^{4+4+4+4+4} = a^{5 \cdot 4} = a^{4 \cdot 5}$

(b) $\left(a^{{}^{-}4}\right)^{{}^{-}5} = \frac{1}{(a^{{}^{-}4})^5} = \frac{1}{a^{{}^{-}4} \cdot a^{{}^{-}4} \cdot a^{{}^{-}4} \cdot a^{{}^{-}4} \cdot a^{{}^{-}4}} = \frac{1}{a^{{}^{-}4-4-4-4-4}} = \frac{1}{a^{{}^{-}20}} = a^{20} = a^{({}^{-}4)({}^{-}5)}$

40. (a) $4\,\boxed{9}\,\boxed{7}\,3\,\boxed{6}\,.\,\boxed{5}\,\boxed{2}\,8\,\boxed{1}$ (b) $4\,\boxed{1}\,\boxed{2}\,3\,\boxed{5}\,.\,\boxed{6}\,\boxed{7}\,8\,\boxed{9}$

41. Total deductions were \$1520.63 + \$723.30 + \$2843.62 = \$5087.55
Gross pay less deductions was \$27,849.50 – \$5057.55 = \$22,761.95

On-going Assessment 6-3

1. Answers may vary. One such number could be 0.232233222333… .

2. Line up the decimal points:

$0.78 = 0.78000000\ldots$
$0.\overline{7} = 0.77777777\ldots$
$0.\overline{78} = 0.78787878\ldots$
$0.788 = 0.78800000\ldots$
$0.7\overline{8} = 0.78888888\ldots$
$0.7\overline{88} = 0.78888888\ldots$ (Note that $0.7\overline{88} = 0.7\overline{8}$)
$0.77 = 0.77000000\ldots$
$0.787787778\ldots = 0.787787778\ldots$

From least to greatest $\Rightarrow$ $0.77, 0.\overline{7}, 0.78, 0.787787778\ldots, 0.\overline{78}, 0.788, 0.7\overline{8} = 0.7\overline{88}$

3. Line up the decimal points:

$0.9 = 0.90000000\ldots$
$0.\overline{9} = 0.99999999\ldots$
$0.\overline{98} = 0.98989898\ldots$
$0.9\overline{88} = 0.98888888\ldots$
$0.9\overline{98} = 0.99898989\ldots$
$0.\overline{898} = 0.89889889\ldots$

From greatest to least $\Rightarrow$ $0.\overline{9}, 0.9\overline{98}, 0.\overline{98}, 0.9\overline{88}, 0.9, 0.\overline{898}$

4. (a) Irrational (there is no number *s* such that $s^2 = 51$) (b) Rational

(c) Rational (d) Irrational

(e) Irrational (the sum of a rational number and an irrational number is irrational)

(f) Irrational (the quotient of a rational number and an irrational number is irrational)

5. (a) $15 \cdot 15 = 225 \Rightarrow \sqrt{225} = 15$ (b) $15.8 < \sqrt{251} < 15.9$; $(15.8)^2$ is closer to 251

(c) $13 \cdot 13 = 169 \Rightarrow \sqrt{169} = 13$

(d) $22^2 = 484$; $23^2 = 529 \Rightarrow 22 < \sqrt{512} < 23$
$(22.6)^2 = 510.76$; $(22.7)^2 = 515.29 \Rightarrow 22.6 < \sqrt{512} < 22.7$ and $(22.6)^2$ is closer to 512

(e) ${}^{-}81$ has no square root (there is no number *n* such that $n^2 = {}^{-}81$)

5. (f) $25 \cdot 25 = 625 \Rightarrow \sqrt{625} = 25$

6. (a) $4 < \sqrt{17} < 5$
$(4.1)^2 = 16.81$; $(4.2)^2 = 17.64 \Rightarrow 4.1 < \sqrt{17} < 4.2$
$(4.12)^2 = 16.97$; $(4.13)^2 = 17.06 \Rightarrow 4.12 < \sqrt{17} < 4.13$
17 is closer to 16.97 than to 17.06 $\Rightarrow \sqrt{17} \doteq 4.12$ to the nearest hundredth

(b) $2 < \sqrt{7} < 3$
$(2.6)^2 = 6.76$; $(2.7)^2 = 7.29 \Rightarrow 2.6 < \sqrt{7} < 2.7$
$(2.64)^2 = 6.9696$; $(2.65)^2 = 7.0225 \Rightarrow 2.6 < \sqrt{7} < 2.7$
7 is closer to 7.0225 than to 6.9696 $\Rightarrow \sqrt{7} \doteq 2.65$ to the nearest hundredth

(c) $4 < \sqrt{21} < 5$
$(4.5)^2 = 20.25$; $(4.6)^2 = 21.16 \Rightarrow 4.5 < \sqrt{21} < 4.6$
$(4.58)^2 = 20.98$; $(4.59)^2 = 21.07 \Rightarrow 4.58 < \sqrt{21} < 4.59$
21 is closer to 20.98 than to 21.07 $\Rightarrow \sqrt{21} \doteq 4.58$ to the nearest hundredth

(d) $0.1 < \sqrt{0.0120} < 0.2$
$(0.10)^2 = 0.0100$; $(0.11)^2 = 0.0121 \Rightarrow 0.10 < \sqrt{0.0120} < 0.11$
0.0120 is closer to 0.0121 than to 0.0100 $\Rightarrow \sqrt{0.0120} \doteq 0.11$ to the nearest hundredth

(e) $4 < \sqrt{20.3} < 5$
$(4.5)^2 = 20.25$; $(4.6)^2 = 21.16 \Rightarrow 4.5 < \sqrt{20.3} < 4.6$
$(4.50)^2 = 20.25$; $(4.51)^2 = 20.34 \Rightarrow 4.50 < \sqrt{20.3} < 4.51$
20.3 is closer to 20.34 than to 20.25 $\Rightarrow \sqrt{20.3} \doteq 4.51$ to the nearest hundredth

(f) $1 < \sqrt{1.64} < 2$
$(1.2)^2 = 1.44$; $(1.3)^2 = 1.69 \Rightarrow 1.2 < \sqrt{1.64} < 1.3$
$(1.28)^2 = 1.6384$; $(1.29)^2 = 1.6641 \Rightarrow 1.28 < \sqrt{1.64} < 1.29$
1.64 is closer to 1.6384 than to 1.6641 $\Rightarrow \sqrt{1.64} \doteq 1.28$ to the nearest hundredth

7. Answers may vary:

(a) False ($0 + \sqrt{2}$ is irrational)

(b) False ($^{-}\sqrt{2} + \sqrt{2} = 0$ which is rational)

(c) False ($\sqrt{2} \cdot \sqrt{2} = 2$ which is rational)

(d) False ($\sqrt{2} - \sqrt{2} = 0$ which is rational)

8. Answers may vary; $\sqrt{2}$, $\sqrt{3}$, and $\sqrt{5}$ are three

9. Answers may vary; 0.536336333633336... is one

10. (a) The set of real numbers contains the set of rational numbers <u>or</u> the set of irrational numbers, <u>or</u> both $\Rightarrow Q \cup S = R$

(b) A rational number cannot be an irrational number $\Rightarrow Q \cap S = \emptyset$

(c) $Q \subset R \Rightarrow Q \cap R = Q$

(d) No whole number can be irrational $\Rightarrow S \cap W = \emptyset$

(e) The union of the set of whole numbers and the set of real numbers is the set of real numbers (since W is contained in R). Thus $W \cup R = R$.

10. (f) $Q \subset R \Rightarrow Q \cup R = R$

11.

		$x =$	N	I	Q	R	S
(a)	$x^2 + 1 = 5$	$2, {}^-2$	X	X	X	X	
(b)	$2x - 1 = 32$	$\frac{33}{2}$			X	X	
(c)	$x^2 = 3$	$\sqrt{3}, {}^-\sqrt{3}$				X	X
(d)	$x^2 = 4$	$2, {}^-2$	X	X	X	X	
(e)	$\sqrt{x} = {}^-1$	$\emptyset$					
(f)	$\frac{3}{4}x = 4$	$\frac{16}{3}$			X	X	

12. (a) $x = 64 \ (\sqrt{64} = 8)$ (b) No real values

(c) $x = {}^-64 \ \left(\sqrt{{}^-({}^-64)} = 8\right)$ (d) No real values

(e) All real numbers > 0 (f) No real values

13. The sides of the gate form the sides of a right triangle with the diagonal brace as the hypotenuse. If c is the length of the hypotenuse, then $c^2 = a^2 + b^2 = 4^2 + 5^2 = 16 + 25 = 41$. Thus the length of the brace = $\sqrt{41} \doteq 6.4$ feet.

14. (a) $T = 2\pi\sqrt{\frac{20}{9.8}} \doteq 8.98$ seconds (b) $T = 2\pi\sqrt{\frac{100}{9.8}} \doteq 20.07$ seconds

15. The sequence 0.13, 0.1313, 0.131313, … , can be represented by the repeating decimal $0.\overline{13} = \frac{13}{99}$. Since any term of the repeating decimal $0.\overline{13}$ is less than $\frac{13}{99}$, that is the rational number for which we are looking.

16. (a) $\sqrt{180} = \sqrt{36 \cdot 5} = \sqrt{36} \cdot \sqrt{5} = 6\sqrt{5}$ (b) $\sqrt{363} = \sqrt{121 \cdot 3} = 11\sqrt{3}$

(c) $\sqrt{252} = \sqrt{36 \cdot 7} = 6\sqrt{7}$

17. (a) $\sqrt[3]{{}^-54} = \sqrt[3]{{}^-27 \cdot 2} = \sqrt[3]{{}^-27} \cdot \sqrt[3]{2} = {}^-3\sqrt[3]{2}$ (b) $\sqrt[5]{96} = \sqrt[5]{32 \cdot 3} = \sqrt[5]{32} \cdot \sqrt[5]{3} = 2\sqrt[5]{3}$

(c) $\sqrt[3]{250} = \sqrt[3]{125 \cdot 2} = \sqrt[3]{125} \cdot \sqrt[3]{2} = 5\sqrt[3]{2}$ (d) $\sqrt[5]{{}^-243} = {}^-3$

18. (a) $a_1 = 5;\ a_4 = 10;\ n = 4 \Rightarrow 10 = 5(r)^3 \Rightarrow 2 = r^3 \Rightarrow r = \sqrt[3]{2}$
So the terms are: 5, $5\sqrt[3]{2}$, $5\sqrt[3]{4}$, 10

(b) $a_1 = 2;\ a_5 = 1;\ n = 5 \Rightarrow 1 = 2(r)^4 \Rightarrow r = \sqrt[4]{\frac{1}{2}}$
So the terms are: 2, $2\sqrt[4]{\frac{1}{2}}, 2\sqrt[4]{\frac{1}{4}}, 2\sqrt[4]{\frac{1}{8}}$, 1

18. (c) $a_2 = \sqrt{2}$, $a_5 = \sqrt{5}$, $n = 5$

$\Rightarrow \quad \sqrt{2} = a_1 \cdot r^{2-1} \Rightarrow a_1 = \frac{\sqrt{2}}{r}$ (*i*)

$\sqrt{5} = a_1 \cdot r^{5-1} \Rightarrow \sqrt{5} = \frac{\sqrt{2}}{r} \cdot r^4 = \sqrt{2}\, r^3 \Rightarrow r = \sqrt[3]{\sqrt{\frac{5}{2}}} = \sqrt[6]{\frac{5}{2}}$ (*ii*)

If $r = \frac{a_2}{a_1} \Rightarrow \sqrt[6]{\frac{5}{2}} = \frac{\sqrt{2}}{a_1} \Rightarrow a_1 = \frac{\sqrt{2}}{\sqrt[6]{\frac{5}{2}}} = \sqrt{2} \cdot \sqrt[6]{\frac{2}{5}}$

$a_2 = \sqrt{2}$

$a_3 = \sqrt{2} \cdot \sqrt[6]{\frac{5}{2}}$

$a_4 = \left(\sqrt{2} \cdot \sqrt[6]{\frac{5}{2}}\right) \cdot \sqrt[6]{\frac{5}{2}} = \sqrt{2} \cdot \sqrt[6]{\frac{25}{4}}$

$a_5 = \sqrt{5}$

19. (a) $E(0) = 2^{10} \cdot 16^0 = 2^{10} \cdot 1 = 2^{10}$ bacteria (b) $E\left(\frac{1}{4}\right) = 2^{10} \cdot 16^{1/4} = 2^{10} \cdot 2 = 2^{11}$ bacteria

(c) $E(\frac{1}{2}) = 2^{10} \cdot 16^{1/2} = 2^{10} \cdot 4 = 2^{10} \cdot 2^2 = 2^{12}$ bacteria

20. (a) $\sqrt{3}$ ($1.7 < \sqrt{3} < 1.8$; $1.5 < \sqrt[3]{4} < 1.6$) (b) $\sqrt[3]{3}$ ($1.44 < \sqrt[3]{3} < 1.45$; $1.41 < \sqrt{2} < 1.42$)

(c) $3.46 < \sqrt{12} < 3.47$ and $3.74 < \sqrt{14} < 3.75$. Assuming that the root lies close to the midpoint of each interval, $\sqrt{12} + \sqrt{14}$ is about $3.465 + 3.745 = 7.21$.
$3.31 < \sqrt{11} < 3.32$ and $3.87 < \sqrt{15} < 3.88$, so $\sqrt{11} + \sqrt{15}$ is about 7.19.

21. $\sqrt{2\sqrt{2\sqrt{2}}} = \sqrt{2\sqrt{2 \cdot 2^{1/2}}} = \sqrt{2\sqrt{2^{3/2}}} = \sqrt{2(2^{3/2})^{1/2}} = \sqrt{2 \cdot 2^{3/4}} = \sqrt{2^{7/4}} = (2^{7/4})^{1/2} = 2^{7/8}$
and $2^{7/8} = \sqrt[8]{2^7}$

22. (a) $81 = 3^4$, so if $3^x = 3^4$ then $x = 4$ (b) $(2^2)^x = 2^3$, so $2x = 3$ and $x = \frac{3}{2}$

(c) $(2^7)^{-x} = 2^4$, so $-7x = 4$ and $x = -\frac{4}{7}$ (d) $\left[\left(\frac{2}{3}\right)^2\right]^{3x} = \left(\frac{2}{3}\right)^5$, so $6x = 5$ and $x = \frac{5}{6}$

23. $\sqrt[3]{(6-2)^{-2}} = \sqrt[3]{\frac{1}{4^2}} = \sqrt[3]{\frac{1}{16}}$

24. (a) *n* must be an odd number.

(b) If *m* is even, *n* can be any number except 0. If *m* is odd, *n* must be odd.

25. (a) $\sqrt{2} - \frac{2}{\sqrt{2}} = \frac{\sqrt{2} \cdot \sqrt{2} - 2 \cdot 1}{1 \cdot \sqrt{2}} = 0$ (rational) (b) $\left(\sqrt{2}\right)^{-4} = \frac{1}{(\sqrt{2})^4} = \frac{1}{4}$ (rational)

(c) Irrational (rational ÷ irrational is irrational) (d) $\frac{1}{1+\sqrt{2}} + 1 - \sqrt{2} = 0$ (rational)

26. (a) If $f(x) = x^2$:

x	$^-5$	$^-4$	$^-3$	$^-2$	$^-1$	0	1	2	3	4	5
$f(x)$	25	16	9	4	1	0	1	4	9	16	25

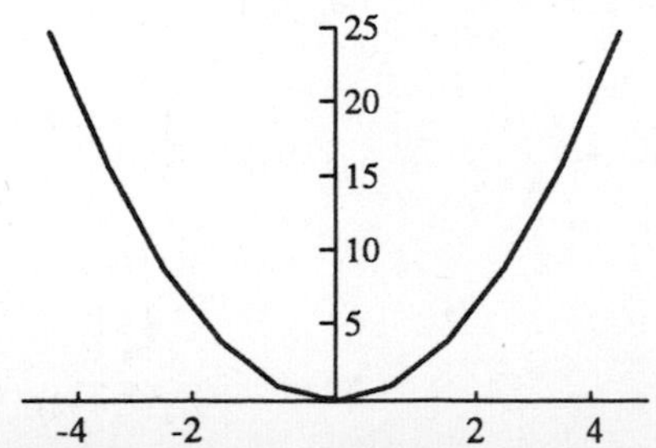

26. (b) If $f(x) = \sqrt{x}$:

x	0	1	2	3	4	5	6	7	8	9	10	11	12	13	14	15	16
$f(x)$	0	1	1.4	1.7	2	2.2	2.4	2.6	2.8	3	3.2	3.3	3.5	3.6	3.7	3.9	4

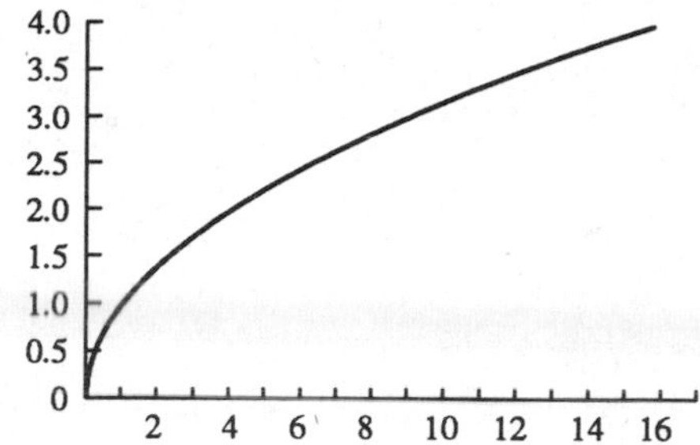

(c) If $f(x) = \sqrt{^{-}x}$:

x	$^{-}15$	$^{-}12.5$	$^{-}10$	$^{-}7.5$	$^{-}5$	$^{-}2.5$	0
f(x)	3.9	3.5	3.2	2.7	2.2	1.6	0

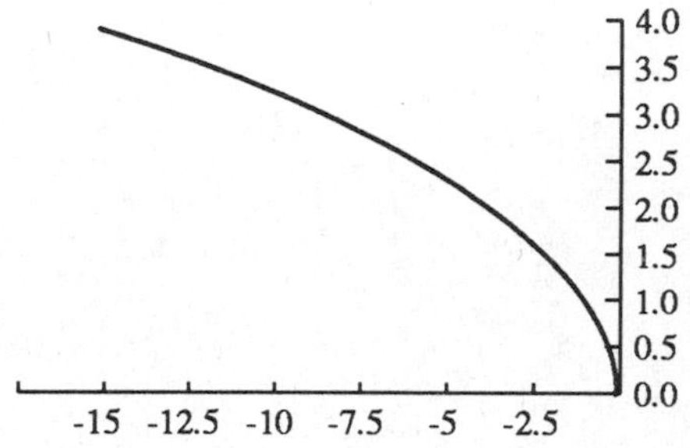

27. Suppose $\sqrt{3}$ is rational. If so, then $\sqrt{3} = \frac{a}{b}$, where *a* and *b* are integers and $b \neq 0$. Therefore, $3 = \frac{a^2}{b^2}$, or $3b^2 = a^2$. a^2 has an even number of 3's in its prime factorization but $3b^2$ has an odd number of 3's in its prime factorization. If $3b^2 = a^2$, this is impossible. Thus, $\sqrt{3}$ cannot be a rational number and therefore must be irrational.

28. Suppose $\sqrt{p}$ is rational. If so, then $\sqrt{p} = \frac{a}{b}$, where *a* and *b* are integers and $b \neq 0$. Therefore $p = \frac{a^2}{b^2}$, or $pb^2 = a^2$. a^2 must have an even number of p's in its prime factorization, as must b^2. In pb^2, another factor of p is introduced, resulting in an odd number of p's in the prime factorization of pb^2 and hence of a^2. But p cannot appear both an odd number of times and an even number of times in the same prime factorization, so we have a contradiction. Consequently, $\sqrt{p}$ must be an irrational number.

29. (a) *m* is a perfect square

(b) If *n* is a whole number and $n^2 = m$, then the prime factorization of n^2 and m must be the same. Since each will have the same number of prime factors, they are both rational numbers.

30. (a) $0.5 + \frac{1}{0.5} = 0.5 + 2 = 2.5 \geq 2$

(b) Suppose $x + \frac{1}{x} < 2$. Since $x > 0$, $x^2 + 1 < 2x$ so that $x^2 - 2x + 1 < 0$, or $(x - 1)^2 < 0$, which is false.

43. (a) (0.18 of body weight) $\cdot$ (120 lbs) = 21.6 pounds of bones

    (b) (0.4 of body weight) $\cdot$ (120 lbs) = 48 pounds of muscle

44. Total deductions were \$1520.63 + \$723.30 + \$2843.62 = \$5087.55
    Gross pay less deductions was \$27,849.50 – \$5057.55 = \$22,761.95

45. (a) $\frac{16}{1} + \frac{72}{100} = \frac{16 \cdot 100 + 1 \cdot 72}{1 \cdot 100} = \frac{1672}{100} = \frac{418}{25}$ (b) $\frac{3}{1000}$

    (c) $^{-}\left(\frac{5}{1} + \frac{7}{100}\right) = {}^{-}\left(\frac{5 \cdot 100 + 1 \cdot 7}{1 \cdot 100}\right) = \frac{^{-}507}{100}$ (d) $\frac{123}{1000}$

46. (a) $4.\overline{9}$ (b) $5.0\overline{9}$

    (c) $0.4\overline{9}$

47. $0.00024 = \frac{24}{100{,}000} = \frac{3}{12{,}500}$

48.
$$\begin{aligned} 4.09 &= 4.090000\ldots \\ 4.099 &= 4.099000\ldots \\ 4.0\overline{9} &= 4.099999\ldots \\ 4.09\overline{1} &= 4.091111\ldots \end{aligned}$$
So the numbers from least to greatest are 4.09, $4.09\overline{1}$, 4.099, $4.0\overline{9}$.

49.
$$\begin{aligned} 100n &= 24.\overline{24} \\ -\ n &= -\ .\overline{24} \\ \hline 99n &= 24, \text{ so } n = \tfrac{24}{99} = \tfrac{8}{33} \end{aligned}$$

50. (a) 208,000 (b) 0.00038

51. (a) $2^n + 2^{n+1} = 2^n(1+2) = 3 \cdot 2^n$ (b) $3^n + 3^{n+1} = 3^n(1+3) = 4 \cdot 3^n$

52. (a) False $(2^3 + 2^4 \neq 2^7)$ (b) False $(2^3 \cdot 3^2 \neq 6^5)$

    (c) False $(0^{-13} = \frac{1}{0^{13}} \Rightarrow$ undefined) (d) True. $\left(a^{-m}\right)^{-n} = a^{mn} = \frac{1}{a^{-mn}}$

53. (a) This is a geometric sequence with $a_1 = 25$; $r = 2$; $n = 6 \Rightarrow a_{25\ years} = 25(2)^5 = 800$ ppm salt content

    (b) $C(n) = 25 \cdot (2^{1/5})^n = 25 \cdot 2^{n/5}$ parts per million

    (c) Guess and check: The least n for which $25 \cdot 2^{n/5} > 10{,}000 \Rightarrow 2^{n/5} > 400 \Rightarrow 2^n > 400^5$
    $\Rightarrow 2^n > 1.024 \cdot 10^{13}$ is $n = 44$

Chapter 6 Review

1. (a) $\left(\frac{1}{2}\right)^4\left(\frac{1}{2}\right)^7 = \left(\frac{1}{2}\right)^{4+7} = \left(\frac{1}{2}\right)^{11}$ or $\frac{1}{2^{11}}$ (b) $5^{-16} \div 5^4 = 5^{-16} \cdot 5^{-4} = 5^{-16+^{-}4} = 5^{-20} = \frac{1}{5^{20}}$

   (c) $\left[\left(\frac{2}{3}\right)^7\right]^{-4} = \left(\frac{2}{3}\right)^{-28} = \left(\frac{3}{2}\right)^{28}$ (d) $3^{16} \cdot 3^2 = 3^{16+2} = 3^{18}$

2. (a) $3 \cdot 10 + 2 \cdot 10^0 + 0 \cdot 10^{-1} + 1 \cdot 10^{-2} + 2 \cdot 10^{-3}$

   (b) $0 \cdot 10^0 + 0 \cdot 10^{-1} + 0 \cdot 10^{-2} + 1 \cdot 10^{-3} + 0 \cdot 10^{-4} + 3 \cdot 10^{-5}$

3. If the denominator of a fraction in simplest form contains no prime factors other than 2 or 5, then the fraction can be written as a terminating decimal. If the denominator of a fraction is a power of 10, it can be written as a terminating decimal by proper placement of a decimal point in the numerator. If the denominator of the fraction is not a power of 10, we convert it to a power of 10 by mulitplying it by whatever factor is necessary. If we try to rewrite $\frac{a}{b}$ as a terminating decimal, we try to find a natural number c such that $\frac{a}{b} = \frac{ac}{bc}$, where c is a power of 10. By the Fundamental Theorem of Arithmetic, the only prime factors of a power of 10 are 2 and 5. If b has a factor other than 2 or 5, we cannot write bc as a power of 10, and therefore $\frac{a}{b}$ cannot be written as a terminating decimal.

4. $442.4 \div 55.3 = 8 \Rightarrow$ 8 shelves can be cut

5. (a) $4 \div 7 = 0.\overline{571428}$ (b) $1 \div 8 = 0.125$

   (c) $2 \div 3 = 0.\overline{6}$ (d) $5 \div 8 = 0.625$

6. (a) $\frac{28}{100} = \frac{4 \cdot 7}{4 \cdot 25} = \frac{7}{25}$ (b) $^-5.07 = {}^-\left(5\frac{7}{100}\right) = \frac{^-507}{100}$

   (c) $0.\overline{3} = \frac{3}{9} = \frac{1}{3}$ (d) $2.0\overline{8} = \frac{1880}{900} = \frac{94}{45}$

7. (a) 307.63 (b) 307.6

   (c) 308 (d) 300

8. (a) No ($^-\sqrt{2} + \sqrt{2} = 0$ is rational) (b) No ($\sqrt{2} - \sqrt{2} = 0$ is rational)

   (c) No ($\sqrt{2} \cdot \sqrt{2} = 2$ is rational) (d) No $\left(\frac{\sqrt{2}}{\sqrt{2}} = 1 \text{ is rational}\right)$

9. $4.795 < \sqrt{23} < 4.796$; squeezing further $\Rightarrow \sqrt{23} \doteq 4.7958$

10. (a) $4.26 \cdot 10^5$ (b) $2.37 \cdot 10^{-6}$

    (c) $3.2 \cdot 10^1$ (d) $3.25 \cdot 10^{-1}$

11. (a) Three (b) Three

    (c) Two (d) Three

12. (a) Irrational (b) Irrational

    (c) Rational (d) Irrational

13. (a) $\sqrt{121 \cdot 2} = 11\sqrt{2}$ (b) $\sqrt{144 \cdot 2} = 12\sqrt{2}$

    (c) $\sqrt{36 \cdot 10} = 6\sqrt{10}$ (d) $\sqrt[3]{27 \cdot 6} = 3 \cdot \sqrt[3]{6}$

14. (a) $Q(0) = 10^{14}\left(\frac{5}{6}\right)^0 = 10^{14} \cdot 1 = 10^{14}$ bacteria (b) $Q(10) = 10^{14}\left(\frac{5}{6}\right)^{10} \doteq 1.615 \cdot 10^{13}$ bacteria

14. (c) Find the point at which there is less than one bacteria remaining: $10^{14}\left(\frac{5}{6}\right)^{t} < 1 \Rightarrow \left(\frac{5}{6}\right)^{t} < 10^{-14}$

Trial and error will show that $\left(\frac{5}{6}\right)^{176} \doteq 1.16 \cdot 10^{-14}$ and $\left(\frac{5}{6}\right)^{177} \doteq 0.96 \cdot 10^{-14}$

So at t = 177 seconds there will be less than one bacteria $\Rightarrow$ all the bacteria will have died

15. (a) $3^6 = 729$ and $3^7 = 2187 \Rightarrow$ greatest integer value of x is 6 in order that $3^x \leq 1000$

(b) $3^{-(^-6)} = 729$ and $3^{-(^-7)} = 2187 \Rightarrow$ least integer of x is $^-6$ in order that $3^{-x} \leq 1000$

(c) $2^9 = 512$ and $2^{10} = 1024 \Rightarrow$ least integer value of x is 10 in order that $2^x \geq 900$

(d) Greatest integer value of x is 9 in order that $2^x \leq 900$

16.

$1.4519 = 1.45190000\ldots$

$1.451\overline{9} = 1.45199999\ldots$

$1.45\overline{19} = 1.45191919\ldots$

$1.4\overline{519} = 1.45195195\ldots$

$^-0.134 = {}^-0.13400000\ldots$

$^-0.13401 = {}^-0.13401000\ldots$

$^-0.13\overline{401} = {}^-0.13401401\ldots$

Ordering from greatest to least $\Rightarrow$ $1.451\overline{9} > 1.4\overline{519} > 1.45\overline{19} > 1.4519 > {}^-0.13\overline{401} > {}^-0.13401 > {}^-0.134$

17. (a) $10 = 5(r)^2 \Rightarrow r = \sqrt{2} \Rightarrow$ terms are: $5,\ 5\sqrt{2},\ 10$

(b) $\frac{1}{4} = 1(r)^4 \Rightarrow r = \frac{1}{\sqrt[4]{4}} \Rightarrow$ terms are: $1,\ \frac{1}{\sqrt[4]{4}},\ \frac{1}{2},\ \frac{1}{\sqrt[4]{4^3}},\ \frac{1}{4}$

(c) $0.4 = {}^-0.4(r)^3 \Rightarrow r = {}^-1 \Rightarrow$ terms are: $^-0.4,\ 0.4,\ {}^-0.4,\ 0.4$

(d) $100 = 10(r)^5 \Rightarrow r = \sqrt[5]{10} \Rightarrow$ terms are: $10,\ 10 \cdot \sqrt[5]{10},\ 10 \cdot \sqrt[5]{10^2},\ 10 \cdot \sqrt[5]{10^3},\ 10 \cdot \sqrt[5]{10^4},\ 100$

18. (a) $1.78341156 \cdot 10^6$

(b) $347 \cdot 10^{-8} = 3.47 \cdot 10^{-6}$

(c) $4.93 \cdot 10^9$

(d) $29.4 \cdot 10^{12} \cdot 10^4 = 2.94 \cdot 10^1 \cdot 10^{16} = 2.94 \cdot 10^{17}$

(e) $0.47 \cdot (10^3)^{12} = 4.7 \cdot 10^{-1} \cdot 10^{36} = 4.7 \cdot 10^{35}$

(f) $\frac{3}{5^9} = \frac{3 \cdot 2^9}{5^9 \cdot 2^9} = \frac{3 \cdot 2^9}{10^9} = 3 \cdot 2^9 \cdot 10^{-9} = 1536 \cdot 10^{-9} = 1.536 \cdot 10^{-6}$

19. (a) Answers may vary; one is: 0.11, 0.105, 0.104, 0.103, 0.102, 0.101, 0.1

(b) 0, 0.00625, 0.0125, 0.025, 0.05, 0.1

(c) 0.1, 0.15, 0.175, 0.1875, 0.19375, 0.2

20. (a) A: 0.02; B: 0.05; C: 0.11

(b) D: Halfway between 0.5 and 0.6; E: Halfway between 0.1 and 0.2

CHAPTER 7 - APPLICATIONS

1. (a) $d = (60t)$ miles (b) $c = \$(20 + 25x)$

   (c) Let n, d, and q be the number of nickels, dimes, and quarters, respectively.
   We are given that $n = 3d$ and $q = 2n = 6d$
   $\Rightarrow$ amount of money = value of dimes + value of nickels + value of quarters
   $= 10d + 5(3d) + 25(6d) = 175d$ ¢

   (d) Sum (S) $= x + (x + 1) + (x + 2) = 3x + 3$

   (e) Let b be the number of bacteria after n minutes
   Making a table of the number of bacteria:

n	b
1	$q \cdot 2$
2	$(q \cdot 2) \cdot 2 = q \cdot 2^2$
3	$(q \cdot 2^2) \cdot 2 = q \cdot 2^3$
$\vdots$	$\vdots$
n	$q \cdot 2^n$

   (f) Let T be the temperature after t hours $\Rightarrow$ $T = (40 - 3t)°F$

   (g) Salary $= \$[s + (s + 5000) + 2(s + 5000)] = \$(4s + 15{,}000)$

   (h) Sum $= x + (x + 2) + (x + 4) = 3x + 6$

   (i) Sum $= (m - 1) + m + (m + 1) = 3m$

   (h) Product $= (m - 1) \cdot m \cdot (m + 1) = m \cdot (m^2 - 1) = m^3 - m$

2. (a) $\frac{E}{P} = \frac{1}{0.04} \Rightarrow P = 0.04E$ (b) $E = \frac{P}{0.04} = 25P$

   (c) $P = 0.04 \cdot 150 = 6$ pounds (d) $E = \frac{100}{0.04} = 2500$ pounds

3. Let d, f, and g be the number of dollars, francs, and gilders, respectively.
   We are given that $f = 1.35d$ and $g = 1.22f$.

   (a) $g = 1.22f = 1.22(1.35d) = 1.647d \Rightarrow$ each dollar is worth 1.647 gilders
   Inversely, the value of a gilder $= \frac{1}{1.647} \doteq 0.607$ times the value of a dollar

   (b) $d = \frac{f}{1.35}$ and $f = \frac{g}{1.22}$. So $d = \frac{\left(\frac{g}{1.22}\right)}{1.35} = \frac{g}{(1.22)(1.35)} \Rightarrow d = \frac{g}{1.647} \doteq 0.607g$
   Inversely, the value of a dollar $= \frac{1}{\frac{1}{1.647}} = 1.647$ times the value of a gilder

4. The number of match sticks required to make the successive figures are 4, 12, 24, … . In each nth figure, there are $n(n + 1)$ vertical sticks and $n(n + 1)$ horizontal sticks. Thus in the third square, for example, there are $3 \cdot 4 + 3 \cdot 4 = 24$ match sticks.

   (a) In a 10×10 square, there are $10 \cdot 11 + 10 \cdot 11 = 220$ match sticks

   (b) If S is the number of match sticks in an $n \times n$ square, then
   $S = n(n + 1) + n(n + 1) = 2n(n + 1)$

5. (a) $F = \frac{9}{5} \cdot 32 + 32 = \frac{288}{5} + \frac{32 \cdot 5}{5} = \frac{448}{5} = 89\frac{3}{5}°\,F$, or 89.6° F

   (b) $^{-}40 = \frac{9}{5}C + 32 \Rightarrow {}^{-}72 = \frac{9}{5}C \Rightarrow \frac{5}{9}({}^{-}72) = \frac{5}{9} \cdot \frac{9}{5}C \Rightarrow C = {}^{-}40°\,C$ (This is the only temperature where Celsius and Fahrenheit are numerically the same)

6. $C = \frac{5}{9}(F - 32)$

7. (a) $K = C + 273.15$

   (b) $K - 273.15 = C + 273.15 - 273.15 \Rightarrow C = K - 273.15$

   (c) (*i*) $F = \frac{9}{5}C + 32 \Rightarrow F = \frac{9}{5}(K - 273.15) + 32$

   (*ii*) $K = C + 273.15 \Rightarrow K = \frac{5}{9}(F - 32) + 273.15$

8. (a) $P = \$(8t)$ (b) $P = \$[15 + 10(t - 1)]$

   (c) $P = \$(20 + 10t)$ (d) $C = \$(300 + 4n)$

   (e) $C = \$(30 + 0.35m)$

9. (a) $3 - x = {}^{-}15 \Rightarrow 3 - 3 - x = {}^{-}15 - 3 \Rightarrow {}^{-}x = {}^{-}15 + {}^{-}3 \Rightarrow x = 18$

   (b) $^{-}x + 3 > {}^{-}15 \Rightarrow {}^{-}x > {}^{-}15 - 3 \Rightarrow {}^{-}x > {}^{-}18 \Rightarrow x < 18$

   (c) $^{-}x - 3 = 15 \Rightarrow {}^{-}x = 15 + 3 \Rightarrow {}^{-}x = 18 \Rightarrow x = {}^{-}18$

   (d) $^{-}x - 3 \geq 15 \Rightarrow {}^{-}x \geq 15 + 3 \Rightarrow {}^{-}x \geq 18 \Rightarrow x \leq {}^{-}18$

   (e) $^{-}3x + 5 = 11 \Rightarrow {}^{-}3x = 11 - 5 \Rightarrow x = \frac{6}{^{-}3} \Rightarrow x = {}^{-}2$

   (f) $^{-}3x + 5 \leq 11 \Rightarrow {}^{-}3x \leq 11 - 5 \Rightarrow x \geq \frac{6}{^{-}3} \Rightarrow x \geq {}^{-}2$

   (g) $^{-}5(x + 3) > 0 \Rightarrow {}^{-}5x + {}^{-}15 > 0 \Rightarrow {}^{-}5x > 15 \Rightarrow x < {}^{-}3$

   (h) $3(x + 5) = {}^{-}4(x + 5) + 21 \Rightarrow 3x + 15 = {}^{-}4x + {}^{-}20 + 21 \Rightarrow 3x + 15 = {}^{-}4x + 1$
   $\Rightarrow 3x + 4x = 1 - 15 \Rightarrow 7x = {}^{-}14 \Rightarrow x = {}^{-}2$

9. (i) $2.04 - 2.24x = {}^{-}10.3 \Rightarrow {}^{-}2.24x = {}^{-}10.3 - 2.04 \Rightarrow x = \frac{{}^{-}12.34}{{}^{-}2.24} \Rightarrow x \doteq 5.51$

(j) ${}^{-}0.02 + 3.14x = {}^{-}0.05 \Rightarrow 100({}^{-}0.02 + 3.14x) = 100({}^{-}0.05) \Rightarrow {}^{-}2 + 314x = {}^{-}5$
$\Rightarrow 314x = {}^{-}5 + 2 \Rightarrow x = \frac{{}^{-}3}{314} \Rightarrow x \doteq {}^{-}0.0096$

(k) ${}^{-}\sqrt{3}\,x \leq {}^{-}\sqrt{3} \Rightarrow x \geq \frac{{}^{-}\sqrt{3}}{{}^{-}\sqrt{3}} \Rightarrow x \geq 1$

(l) ${}^{-}10^{-3}x \geq {}^{-}0.001 \Rightarrow {}^{-}0.001x \geq {}^{-}0.001 \Rightarrow 1000({}^{-}0.001x) \geq 1000({}^{-}0.001) \Rightarrow {}^{-}x \geq {}^{-}1$
$\Rightarrow x \leq 1$

10. (a) $4 + 3x \geq \sqrt{5} - 7x \Rightarrow 10x \geq \sqrt{5} - 4 \Rightarrow x \geq \frac{\sqrt{5}-4}{10}$

(b) $(2x - 1)^2 = 2 \Rightarrow \sqrt{(2x - 1)^2} = \pm\sqrt{2} \Rightarrow 2x - 1 = \pm\sqrt{2} \Rightarrow 2x = 1 \pm \sqrt{2}$
$\Rightarrow x = \frac{1 \pm \sqrt{2}}{2}$

(c) $|x| \geq \sqrt{7} \Rightarrow x \leq {}^{-}\sqrt{7}$ or $x \geq \sqrt{7}$

(d) $|x| \leq \sqrt{2} \Rightarrow {}^{-}\sqrt{2} \leq x \leq \sqrt{2}$

(e) $\frac{\left(\frac{1}{x} - \frac{1}{2}\right)}{0.875} = 1 \Rightarrow \text{LCD} = 0.875 \Rightarrow 0.875 \cdot \frac{\left(\frac{1}{x} - \frac{1}{2}\right)}{0.875} = 0.875 \cdot 1 \Rightarrow \frac{1}{x} - \frac{1}{2} = 0.875$
$\Rightarrow \text{LCD} = 2x \Rightarrow 2x\left(\frac{1}{x} - \frac{1}{2}\right) = 2x(0.875) \Rightarrow 2 - x = 1.75x$
$\Rightarrow 100(2 - x) = 100(1.75x) \Rightarrow 200 - 100x = 175x \Rightarrow 200 = 275x \Rightarrow x = \frac{200}{275} = \frac{8}{11}$

(f) $\frac{2(x-3)}{3(x-2)} = 4 \Rightarrow \text{LCD} = 3(x - 2) \Rightarrow 3(x - 2)\left[\frac{2(x-3)}{3(x-2)}\right] = 3(x - 2)[4] \Rightarrow 2(x - 3) = 12(x - 2)$
$\Rightarrow 2x - 6 = 12x - 24 \Rightarrow 18 = 10x \Rightarrow x = \frac{18}{10} = \frac{9}{5}$

11. (a) $\frac{{}^{-}2}{x} + 3 = \frac{2}{3} \Rightarrow \text{LCD} = 3x \Rightarrow 3x\left(\frac{{}^{-}2}{x} + 3\right) = 3x\left(\frac{2}{3}\right) \Rightarrow {}^{-}6 + 9x = 2x \Rightarrow {}^{-}6 = {}^{-}7x \Rightarrow \frac{{}^{-}6}{{}^{-}7} = x$
$\Rightarrow x = \frac{6}{7}$
Check: $\frac{{}^{-}2}{\left(\frac{6}{7}\right)} + 3 = \frac{{}^{-}14}{6} + \frac{18}{6} = \frac{2}{3}$

(b) $\frac{1}{5} = \frac{7}{3}x \Rightarrow \frac{3}{7} \cdot \frac{1}{5} = \frac{3}{7} \cdot \frac{7}{3}x \Rightarrow \frac{3}{35} = x$
Check: $\frac{1}{5} = \frac{7}{3} \cdot \frac{3}{35}$

(c) $\frac{1}{2}x - 7 = \frac{3}{4}x \Rightarrow \text{LCD} = 4 \Rightarrow 4\left(\frac{1}{2}x - 7\right) = 4\left(\frac{3}{4}x\right) \Rightarrow 2x - 28 = 3x \Rightarrow {}^{-}28 = x$
Check: $\frac{1}{2} \cdot {}^{-}28 - 7 = \frac{3}{4} \cdot {}^{-}28 \Rightarrow {}^{-}14 - 7 = {}^{-}21$

11. (d) $\frac{2}{3}\left(\frac{1}{2}x - 7\right) = \frac{3}{4}x \Rightarrow \frac{1}{3}x - \frac{14}{3} = \frac{3}{4}x \Rightarrow \text{LCD} = 12 \Rightarrow 12\left(\frac{1}{3}x - \frac{14}{3}\right) = 12\left(\frac{3}{4}x\right)$
$\Rightarrow 4x - 56 = 9x \Rightarrow {}^-56 = 5x \Rightarrow \frac{^-56}{5} = x$

(e) $\frac{^-2}{x-3} + 1 = \frac{4}{5} \Rightarrow \text{LCD} = 5(x-3) \Rightarrow 5(x-3)\left[\frac{^-2}{x-3} + 1\right] = 5(x-3)\left[\frac{4}{5}\right]$
$\Rightarrow {}^-10 + 5(x-3) = 4(x-3) \Rightarrow {}^-10 + 5x - 15 = 4x - 12 \Rightarrow 5x - 25 = 4x - 12$
$\Rightarrow x = 13$

(f) $x \div \frac{3}{4} = \frac{5}{8} \Rightarrow x \cdot \frac{4}{3} = \frac{5}{8} \Rightarrow \frac{3}{4} \cdot \frac{4}{3}x = \frac{3}{4} \cdot \frac{5}{8} \Rightarrow x = \frac{15}{32}$

(g) $\frac{2}{3-x} - \frac{4}{5} = {}^-1 \Rightarrow \text{LCD} = 5(3-x) \Rightarrow 5(3-x)\left[\frac{2}{3-x} - \frac{4}{5}\right] = 5(3-x)[{}^-1]$
$\Rightarrow 10 - 4(3-x) = {}^-5(3-x) \Rightarrow 10 - 12 + 4x = {}^-15 + 5x \Rightarrow 13 = x$

(h) $\frac{^-2}{5}(10x + 1) = 1 - x \Rightarrow {}^-4x - \frac{2}{5} = 1 - x \Rightarrow \text{LCD} = 5 \Rightarrow 5\left({}^-4x - \frac{2}{5}\right) = 5(1 - x)$
$\Rightarrow {}^-20x - 2 = 5 - 5x \Rightarrow {}^-15x = 7 \Rightarrow x = \frac{^-7}{15}$

12. Given $w = \frac{xy}{z}$, if z is multiplied by 8 and y is divided by 2, we have $w = \frac{x\cdot\frac{y}{2}}{8\cdot z} = \frac{\left(\frac{xy}{2}\right)}{8z} = \frac{xy}{16z}$
Thus the new value of w will be $\frac{1}{16}$ as large as the original.

13. Let n be the students' number. Then $\frac{\frac{3n+49}{7} - 7}{3} \Rightarrow \frac{\left(\frac{3n+49-49}{7}\right)}{3} = \frac{3n}{21} = \frac{n}{7}$ is the new number.
If the teacher then multiplied each student's answer by 7 she would come back to the original number.

14. Let n be the student's number $\Rightarrow 1000\left(\frac{0.3n-0.6}{3\cdot 100} - 0.55\right) = \frac{300n-600}{300} - 550 = n - 552$
Adding 552 to the student's answer gives the original number

15. (a) True $(3x + 3 = 3x + 3)$

(b) False, except when $x = 3$ $[x - 3 = {}^-(3 - x)]$

(c) True $(x + 3 = x + 3)$

(d) True $(2x - 2 + 2 = 3x - x \Rightarrow 2x = 2x)$

(e) True ($x^2 + 1$ is always positive, or greater than 0)

(f) False (3x is not greater than 3x)

(g) True (absolute value of any real numer is always positive $\Rightarrow \geq {}^-\sqrt{2}$)

On-going Assessment 7-2

1. Translating: ${}^-6n + 20 = 50 \Rightarrow {}^-6n = 30 \Rightarrow n = {}^-5$

2. Let D and R be the amount of money David and Rick, respectively, have. Then:
$D = 3R \Rightarrow 3R + R = 400 \Rightarrow R = 100$. Rick has \$100 and David has three times as much, or \$300

3. Let A, B, and C be the number of cars per day from factories A, B, and C, respectively. Then:
$A + B + C = 7300 \quad (i)$
$A = 2B \quad (ii)$
$C = A + 300 = 2B + 300 \quad (iii)$
Substituting (ii) and (iii) into (i), we then have: $2B + B + (2B + 300) = 7300$
$5B + 300 = 7300 \Rightarrow 5B = 7000 \Rightarrow B = 1400 \Rightarrow A = 2B = 2800$ and $C = 2B + 300 = 3100$

4. If s is the number of student tickets sold, then $812 - s$ = the number of nonstudent tickets. Adding their value gives the total amount taken in:
$\$2 \cdot s + \$3 \cdot (812 - s) = \$1912$
$2s + 2436 - 3s = 1912 \Rightarrow s = 524$ student tickets sold

5. The three consecutive integers may be represented by n, $n + 1$, and $n + 2$. Then:
$n + (n + 1) + (n + 2) = 237$
$3n + 3 = 237 \Rightarrow 3n = 234 \Rightarrow n = 78$
The three integers are thus 78, 78 + 1, and 78 + 2 ; or 78, 79, and 80

6. The three consecutive even integers may be represented by n, $n + 2$, and $n + 4$. Then:
$n + (n + 2) + (n + 4) = 240 \Rightarrow n = 78$
The three integers are 78, 80, and 82

7. Let the two integers be represented by x and y. Then:
$x + y = 21 \quad (i)$
$x = 2y \quad (ii)$
Substituting (ii) into (i), we have: $2y + y = 21 \Rightarrow 3y = 21 \Rightarrow y = 7$
Substituting $y = 7$ into (ii), $x = 2(7) = 14$, and the two integers are 14 and 7

8. Let E, M, and Y be money given to the eldest, middle, and youngest children, respectively. Then:
$E + M + Y = \$64{,}000 \quad (i)$
$E = 3Y \quad (ii)$
$M = Y + \$14{,}000 \quad (iii)$
Substituting (ii) and (iii) into (i), we have: $3Y + (Y + 14000) + Y = 64000 \Rightarrow Y = 10000$
Substituting $Y = 10000$ into (ii), we have: $E = 3(10000) = 30000$
Substituting $Y = 10000$ into (iii), we have $M = (10000) + 14000 = 24000$
So the three children receive \$30,000, \$24,000, and \$10,000, respectively

9. Let n, $n + 1$, and $n + 2$ be the three consecutive even integers. Then:
$7n = 5(n + 4) \Rightarrow 7n = 5n + 20 \Rightarrow 2n = 20 \Rightarrow n = 10$
The three integers are 10, 12, and 14

10. Let F be the original number of faculty. Then:
$F - \frac{1}{5}F = 320 \Rightarrow \frac{4}{5}F = 320 \Rightarrow F = \frac{5}{4} \cdot 320 \Rightarrow F = 400$

11. Let n be the number for which we are looking. Then:

$$3n - \frac{7}{18} = 2n + \frac{5}{12} \Rightarrow \text{LCD} = 36 \Rightarrow 36\left(3n - \frac{7}{18}\right) = 36\left(2n + \frac{5}{12}\right)$$

$$\Rightarrow 108n - 14 = 72n + 15 \Rightarrow 36n = 29 \Rightarrow n = \frac{29}{36}$$

Checking: $3\left(\frac{29}{36}\right) - \frac{7}{18} = \frac{73}{36}$ and $2\left(\frac{29}{36}\right) + \frac{5}{12} = \frac{73}{36}$

12. Let P be the total student population. Then:

$$\frac{5}{8}P = 6000 \Rightarrow P = \frac{8}{5} \cdot 6000 \Rightarrow P = 9600 \text{ students}$$

13. Let P be the original price of the suit. Then:

$$P - \frac{1}{4} \text{ of } P = \$180 \Rightarrow \frac{3}{4}P = 180 \Rightarrow P = \frac{4}{3} \cdot 180 \Rightarrow P = \$240$$

14. (a) Increasing a salary by $\frac{1}{10}$ means the new salary will be $1 + \frac{1}{10}$, or $\frac{11}{10}$, of its previous value. With two such raises, Martha will make $\left(\$100{,}000 \cdot \frac{11}{10}\right) \cdot \frac{11}{10} = \$121{,}000$

(b) \$99,000 is $\frac{11}{10}$ of what Aaron made last year; i.e., $99{,}000 = \frac{11}{10}S$ (where S is Aaron's salary one year ago). Then $S = \frac{10}{11} \cdot 99{,}000 \Rightarrow S = \$90{,}000$, Aaron's salary one year ago

(c) Let S be Juanita's salary two years ago. Then $\$363{,}000 = \frac{11}{10} \cdot \left(\frac{11}{10} \cdot S\right) \Rightarrow \frac{121}{100}S = 363000$

$$\Rightarrow S = \frac{100}{121} \cdot 363{,}000 \Rightarrow S = \$300{,}000$$

15. Let W be the number of women who apply. Then:

$3W$ is the number of men who apply

$W + 3W = 4W$ is the total number who apply

It is given that $\frac{1}{10} \cdot 4W = \frac{2}{5}W$ is the total number hired

and $\frac{1}{20} \cdot 3W = \frac{3}{20}W$ is the number of men hired

Thus the number of women hired is $\frac{2}{5}W - \frac{3}{20}W = \frac{1}{4}W$, or, $\frac{1}{4}$ of the women who apply are hired

16. Jasmine has read $\frac{3}{4}$ of the book, so she has $1 - \frac{3}{4} = \frac{1}{4}$ yet to read; i.e., 82 pages $= \frac{1}{4}$ of the book

If p is the number of pages in the book, then:

$$\frac{1}{4}p = 82 \Rightarrow p = 4 \cdot 82 = 328 \text{ pages}$$

And Jasmine has read $\frac{3}{4} \cdot 328 = 246$ pages

17. Let A be the amount of money in the account. Then:

After spending \$50 there was $A - 50$ left

He spent $\frac{3}{5}$ of that, or $\frac{2}{5}(A - 50)$ was left

Half that, or $\frac{1}{2} \cdot \frac{2}{5}(A - 50) = \frac{1}{5}(A - 50)$ went back into the bank

The other half was \$35, or $\frac{1}{5}(A - 50) = 35$

Solving: $\frac{1}{5}A - 10 = 35 \Rightarrow A - 50 = 175 \Rightarrow A = \$225$

18. Let S be the total number of students. Then:

$\frac{1}{5}S$ is the number with A's

$\frac{1}{4}\left(S - \frac{1}{5}S\right) = \frac{1}{4} \cdot \frac{4}{5}S = \frac{1}{5}S$ is the number with B's

600 is the number with C's

So if A's + B's + C's = S:

$\frac{1}{5}S + \frac{1}{5}S + 600 = S \Rightarrow \frac{2}{5}S + 600 = S \Rightarrow 600 = \frac{3}{5}S \Rightarrow S = \frac{5}{3} \cdot 600 = 1000$ students in the school

19. Let t be the temperature after m minutes.

In reaction A the temperature changed $28 - (^-12) = 40°$ in 5 minutes, or $^-8°$ per minute, so

$t = (28 - 8m)°$ C

In reaction B, $t = (^-57 - 3m)°$ C

(*i*) If termperatures are equal, $28 - 8m = {^-57} - 3m \Rightarrow 85 = 5m \Rightarrow m = 17$ minutes to equalize

(*ii*) After 17 minutes of reaction A, $t = 28 - 8(17) = {^-108}°$ C

of reaction B, $t = {^-57} - 3(17) = {^-108}°$ C

On-going Assessment 7-3

1. Both graphs have slope $^-1$, so they are parallel. One has y-intercept = 0 and the other has y-intercept = 3

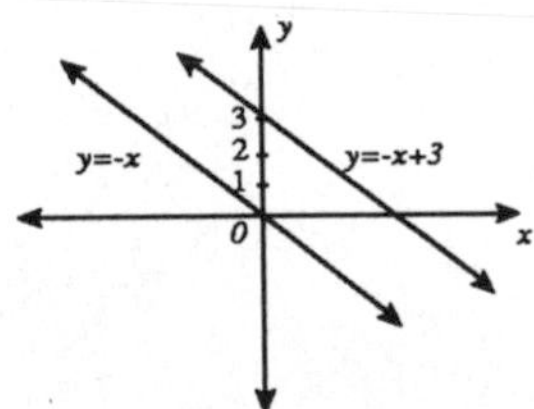

2. Both are parallel to the given line, since the slopes are the same.

(a) Parallel line; y-intercept = 3

(b) Parallel line; y-intercept = $^-3$

3. (a) Given $y = \frac{^-3}{4}x + 3$

(*i*) The y-intercept = 3

(*ii*) The x-intercept occurs where y = 0, or: $0 = \frac{^-3}{4}x + 3 \Rightarrow \frac{3}{4}x = 3 \Rightarrow x = \frac{4}{3} \cdot 3 = 4$

(*iii*) Draw a line through (0,3) and (4,0)

3. (a)

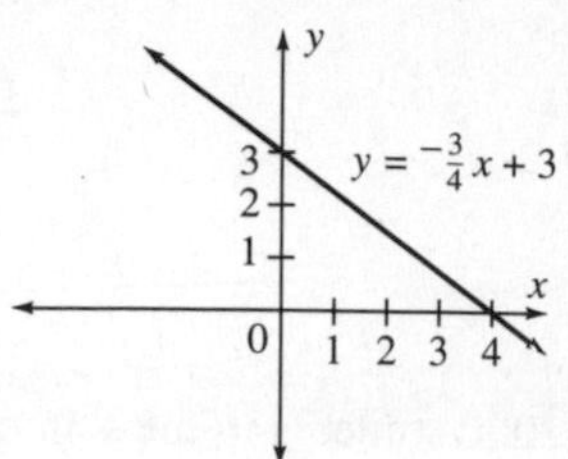

(b) $y = {}^-3$ may be written $y = 0x + {}^-3 \Rightarrow$ slope is $0 \Rightarrow$ the line is horizontal.
Draw a line through all points where $y = {}^-3$

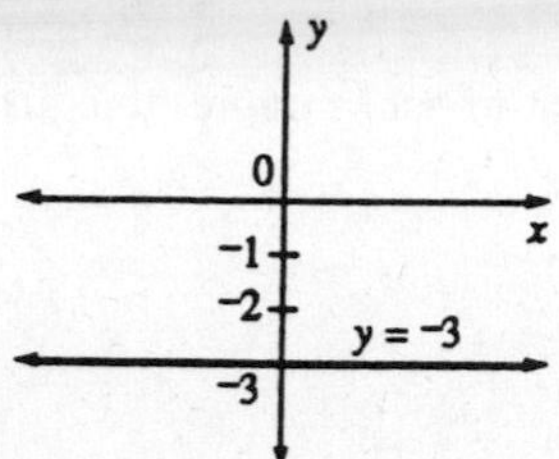

(c) Given $y = 15x - 30$

(*i*) The y-intercept = $^-30$

(*ii*) The x-intercept occurs where $y = 0$, or: $0 = 15x - 30 \Rightarrow 15x = 30 \Rightarrow x = 2$

(*iii*) Draw a line through $(0,{}^-30)$ and $(2,0)$

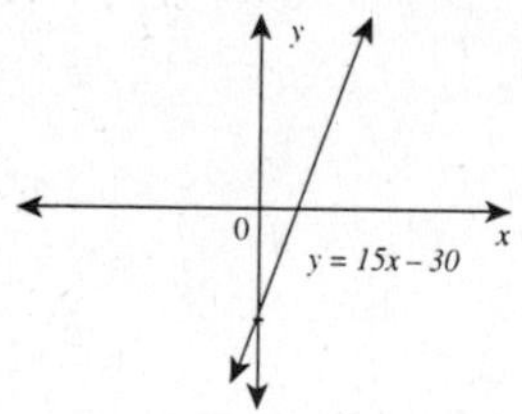

(d) The line corresponding to $x = {}^-2$ is vertical and passes through all points where $x = {}^-2$

(e) Given $y = 3x - 1$

(*i*) The y-intercept = $^-1$

(*ii*) The x-intercept occurs where $y = 0$, or: $0 = 3x - 1 \Rightarrow 3x = 1 \Rightarrow x = \frac{1}{3}$

(*iii*) Draw a line through $(0,{}^-1)$ and $\left(\frac{1}{3},0\right)$

3. (e)

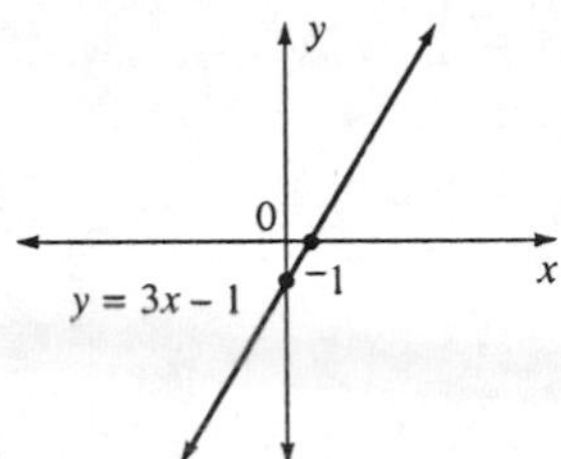

(f) Given $y = \frac{1}{20}x$

(*i*) The line passes through the origin

(*ii*) To find another point, arbitrarily assign a value to x and solve for y.
If $x = 20 \Rightarrow y = \frac{1}{20} \cdot 20 = 1$

(*iii*) Draw a line through (0,0) and (20,1)

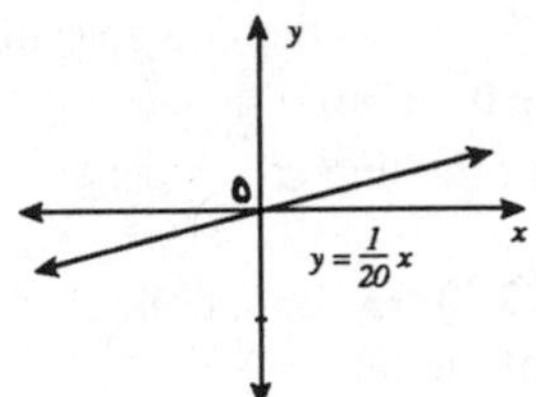

4.

	x-intercept	y-intercept
(a)	(4,0)	(0,3)
(b)	None	(0,⁻3)
(c)	(2,0)	(0,⁻30)
(d)	(⁻2,0)	None
(e)	$\left(\frac{1}{3},0\right)$	(0,⁻1)
(f)	(0,0)	(0,0)

5. (a) For ease of calculating, use the points (0,32) and (100,212)
Substituting in F = mC + b (i.e., y = mx + b):

$$32 = m(0) + b \text{ and } 212 = m(100) + b \Rightarrow b = 32 \text{ and } b = 212 - 100m \Rightarrow 32 = 212 - 100m$$

$$\Rightarrow 100m = 180 \Rightarrow m = \frac{180}{100} = \frac{9}{5}$$

If $32 = m(0) + b$, $b = 32$

So $F = \frac{9}{5}C + 32$

(b) $F = \frac{9}{5}C + 32 \Rightarrow 5 \cdot F = 5 \cdot \left(\frac{9}{5}C + 32\right) \Rightarrow 5F = 9C + 160 \Rightarrow 9C = 5F - 160 = 5(F - 32)$

So $C = \frac{5}{9}(F - 32)$

6. (a) $3y - x = 0 \Rightarrow 3y = x \Rightarrow y = \frac{1}{3}x$ (b) $x + y = 3 \Rightarrow y = {}^-x + 3$

6. (c) $\frac{x}{3} + \frac{y}{4} = 1 \Rightarrow 12\left(\frac{x}{3} + \frac{y}{4}\right) = 12(1) \Rightarrow 4x + 3y = 12 \Rightarrow 3y = {}^{-}4x + 12 \Rightarrow y = \frac{{}^{-}4}{3}x + 4$

(d) $3x - 4y + 7 = 0 \Rightarrow {}^{-}4y = {}^{-}3x - 7 \Rightarrow y = \frac{3}{4}x + \frac{7}{4}$

(e) $x = 3y \Rightarrow y = \frac{1}{3}x$

(f) $x - y = 4(x - y) \Rightarrow x - y = 4x - 4y \Rightarrow 3y = 3x \Rightarrow y = x$

7. (a) Given $({}^{-}4,3)$ and $(1,{}^{-}2)$ and substituting:

$3 = m \cdot {}^{-}4 + b$ or $b = 4m + 3$ *(i)*

${}^{-}2 = m \cdot 1 + b$ or $b = {}^{-}m - 2$ *(ii)*

Equating: $4m + 3 = {}^{-}m - 2 \Rightarrow 5m = {}^{-}5 \Rightarrow m = {}^{-}1$

Substituting into *(ii)*: $b = {}^{-}({}^{-}1) - 2 \Rightarrow b = {}^{-}1$

So the equation of the line is $y = {}^{-}x - 1$

(b) Given (0,0) and (2,1) $\Rightarrow$ the line goes through the origin, so $b = 0$. Substituting:

$1 = m \cdot 2 + 0 \Rightarrow m = \frac{1}{2}$

So the equation of the line is $y = \frac{1}{2}x$

(c) Given (0,1) and (2,1) $\Rightarrow$ both points include the coordinate point $y = 1$

So the equation of the line is $y = 1$

(d) Given (2,1) and $(2,{}^{-}1)$ $\Rightarrow$ both points include the coordinate point $x = 2$

So the equation of the line is $x = 2$

(e) Given $\left(0,\frac{{}^{-}1}{2}\right)$ and $\left(\frac{1}{2},0\right)$ and substituting:

$\frac{{}^{-}1}{2} = m \cdot 0 + b \Rightarrow b = \frac{{}^{-}1}{2}$

$0 = m \cdot \frac{1}{2} + b \Rightarrow 0 = \frac{1}{2}m - \frac{1}{2} \Rightarrow \frac{1}{2}m = \frac{1}{2} \Rightarrow m = 1$

So the equation of the line is $y = x - \frac{1}{2}$

(f) Given $({}^{-}a,0)$ and $(a,0)$ $\Rightarrow$ both points include the coordinate point $y = 0$

So the equation of the line is $y = 0$

8. Answers may vary

(a) The points are on the line $y = 2$ $\Rightarrow$ other points could be $({}^{-}3,2)$, (5,2), ...

(b) The points are on the line $x = {}^{-}1$ $\Rightarrow$ other points could be $({}^{-}1,7)$, $({}^{-}1,{}^{-}5)$, ...

(c) The points are on the line $x = 0$ (i.e., the y-axis) $\Rightarrow$ other points could be (0,1), (0,6), ...

(d) The points are on the line $y = x$ $\Rightarrow$ all points are of the form (a,a)

So other points could be (3,3), $({}^{-}1,{}^{-}1)$, ...

9. (a) If ($^-2$,0), ($^-2$,1), and (x,y) are collinear, the value of x is $^-2$ at each point $\Rightarrow$
   (*i*) $x = {}^-2$
   (*ii*) y may assume any real value

   (b) If ($^-2$,1), (0,1), and (x,y) are collinear, the value of y is 1 at each point $\Rightarrow$
   (*i*) $y = 1$
   (*ii*) x may assume any real value

   (c) $x > 0$, $y > 0$, x and y are real numbers

10. The rectangle has dimensions $2 - 0 = 2$ and $4 - 0 = 4$

   (*i*) The area is $2 \cdot 4 = 8$ square units (*ii*) The perimeter is $2 \cdot 2 + 2 \cdot 4 = 12$ units

11. (a) This is a vertical line through (3,0) $\Rightarrow$ its equation is $x = 3$

   (b) This is a horizontal line through (0,$^-2$) $\Rightarrow$ its equation is $y = {}^-2$

   (c) This is a horizontal line through ($^-4$,5) $\Rightarrow$ its equation is $y = 5$

   (d) This is a vertical line through ($^-4$,5) $\Rightarrow$ its equation is $x = {}^-4$

12. Answers may vary, depending on estimates from the fitted line. For example:

   (a) From the fitted line, estimate coordinates of the two points (50,8) and (60,18)
   Substituting into $C = mT + b$ (where *C* represents the number of chirps in 15 seconds):
   $8 = m \cdot 50 + b$ or $b = 8 - 50m$ (*i*)
   $18 = m \cdot 60 + b$ or $b = 18 - 60m$ (*ii*)
   Equating: $8 - 50m = 18 - 60m \Rightarrow 10m = 10 \Rightarrow m = 1$
   Substituting into equation (*ii*): $b = 18 - 60 \cdot (1) \Rightarrow b = {}^-42$
   So the equation of the fitted line is $C = T - 42$

   (b) If $T = 90°$: $C = (90) - 42 \Rightarrow$ 48 chirps in 15 seconds

   (c) $N = 4C$; i.e., there are four 15-second periods in one minute $\Rightarrow N = 4(T - 42)$
   $\Rightarrow N = 4T - 168$

13. (a)

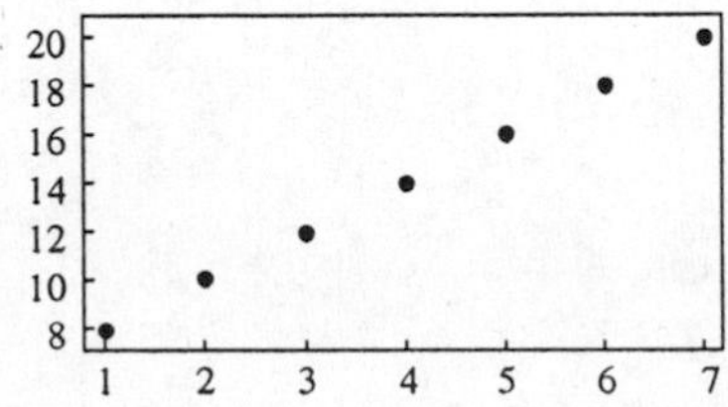

13. (a) Arbitrarily (because they appear on the best-fit line) use points (1,8.1) and (6,18):
Substituting into $y = mx + b$:

$8.1 = m \cdot 1 + b$ or $b = 8.1 - m$ (*i*)

$18 = m \cdot 6 + b$ or $b = 18 - 6b$ (*ii*)

Equating (*i*) and (*ii*): $8.1 - m = 18 - 6m \Rightarrow 5m = 9.9 \Rightarrow m \doteq 1.98$
Substituting into equation (*ii*): $b = 18 - 6 \cdot 1.98 \Rightarrow b \doteq 6.12$
So the equation of a line that seems to fit the data best would be: $y = 1.98x + 6.12$

(b) When $x = 100$, $y = 1.98 \cdot 100 + 6.12 = 204.12$

14. (a) Solutions may be found by selecting any value of x or y and then solving algebraically for the other; or it may be easier to first solve the equation for y $\Rightarrow y = \frac{2}{3}x - \frac{5}{3}$ and then find values of y for any (arbitrarily) chosen value of x. Using either method, some solution possibilities include (4,1), (7,3), $(3,\frac{1}{3})$, $(1,{}^-1)$, ...

(b) $2x - 3y = 5$ is a straight line. To graph the specified portion, find its endpoints by substituting $x = 2$ and $x = {}^-2$ into the equation:

$2 \cdot (2) - 3y = 5 \Rightarrow {}^-3y = 1 \Rightarrow y = \frac{{}^-1}{3} \Rightarrow$ endpoint is $\left(2,\frac{{}^-1}{3}\right)$

$2 \cdot ({}^-2) - 3y = 5 \Rightarrow {}^-3y = 9 \Rightarrow y = {}^-3 \Rightarrow$ endpoint is $({}^-2,{}^-3)$

Connecting these points gives the graph below:

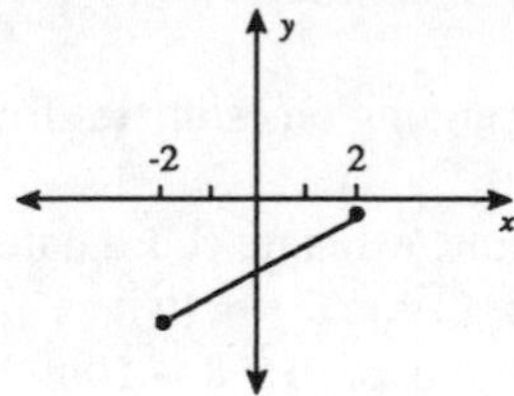

(c) Use $y = 0$ and $y = 2$ to obtain the endpoints:

$2x - 3 \cdot (0) = 5 \Rightarrow 2x = 5 \Rightarrow x = \frac{5}{2} \Rightarrow$ endpoint is $\left(\frac{5}{2},0\right)$

$2x - 3 \cdot (2) = 5 \Rightarrow 2x = 11 \Rightarrow x = \frac{11}{2} \Rightarrow$ endpoint is $\left(\frac{11}{2},2\right)$

Connecting these points gives the graph below:

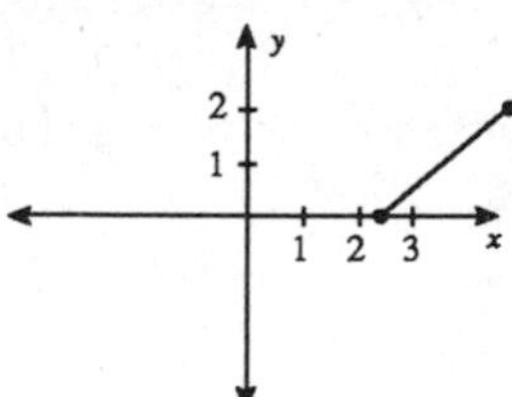

15. (a) Equating $y = 3x - 1$ (*i*) and $y = x + 3$ (*ii*):

$3x - 1 = x + 3 \Rightarrow 2x = 4 \Rightarrow x = 2$

Substitute $x = 2$ into equation (*ii*): $y = (2) + 3 \Rightarrow y = 5$
So (2,5) is a unique solution

15. (b) Given equations $2x - 6y = 7$ (i) and $3x - 9y = 10$ (ii):

Multiply (i) by 3: $3 \cdot (2x - 6y) = 3 \cdot 7 \Rightarrow 6x - 18y = 21$

Multiply (ii) by $^-2$: $^-2 \cdot (3x - 9y) = {}^-2 \cdot 10 \Rightarrow {}^-6x + 18y = {}^-20$

Adding the equations:
$$\begin{array}{rcl} 6x - 18y &=& 21 \\ {}^-6x + 18y &=& {}^-20 \\ \hline 0 + 0 &=& {}^-1 \end{array}$$

The sum $0 = {}^-1$ indicates there are no solutions (if the two equations were graphed, it would be seen that they represent parallel lines and thus have no point (x,y) that belongs to both)

(c) Given equations $3x + 4y = {}^-17$ (i) and $2x + 3y = {}^-13$ (ii):

Multiply (i) by 2: $2 \cdot (3x + 4y) = 2 \cdot {}^-17 \Rightarrow 6x + 8y = {}^-34$

Multiply (ii) by $^-3$: $^-3 \cdot (2x + 3y) = {}^-3 \cdot {}^-13 \Rightarrow {}^-6x - 9y = 39$

Adding the equations:
$$\begin{array}{rcl} 6x + 8y &=& {}^-34 \\ {}^-6x - 9y &=& 39 \\ \hline {}^-y = 5 &\Rightarrow& y = {}^-5 \end{array}$$

Substitute $y = {}^-5$ into (i): $3x + 4 \cdot ({}^-5) = {}^-17 \Rightarrow 3x = 3 \Rightarrow x = 1$

So $(1, {}^-5)$ is a unique solution

(d) Given $8y - 6x = 78$ (i) and $9x - 12y = 12$ (ii):

Solve (i) for y: $8y = 6x + 78 \Rightarrow y = \frac{6}{8}x + \frac{78}{8} \Rightarrow y = \frac{3}{4}x + \frac{39}{4}$

Substitute into (ii): $9x - 12\left(\frac{3}{4}x + \frac{39}{4}\right) = 12 \Rightarrow 9x - 9x - 117 = 12 \Rightarrow 0x = 129$

The result $0 = 129$ indicates there are no solutions

(e) Given $5x - 18y = 0$ (i) and $x - 24y = 0$ (ii):

Solve (i) for x: $5x = 18y \Rightarrow x = \frac{18}{5}y$

Substitute into (ii): $\left(\frac{18}{5}y\right) - 24y = 0 \Rightarrow \frac{{}^-102}{5}y = 0 \Rightarrow y = 0$

Substitute $y = 0$ into (i): $5x - 18 \cdot (0) = 0 \Rightarrow 5x = 0 \Rightarrow x = 0$

So (0,0) is a unique solution

(f) Given $2x + 3y = 1$ (i) and $3x - y = 1$ (ii):

Solve (ii) for y: ${}^-y = 1 - 3x \Rightarrow y = 3x - 1$

Substitute into (i): $2x + 3(3x - 1) = 1 \Rightarrow 2x + 9x - 3 = 1 \Rightarrow 11x = 4 \Rightarrow x = \frac{4}{11}$

Substitute $x = \frac{4}{11}$ into (ii): $y = 3 \cdot \left(\frac{4}{11}\right) - 1 \Rightarrow y = \frac{1}{11}$

So $\left(\frac{4}{11}, \frac{1}{11}\right)$ is a unique solution

16. The equation of the segment connecting (5,0) and (6,8) is $y = 8x - 40$ (use techniques previously demonstrated)

The equation of the segment connecting (10,0) and (3,4) is $y = \frac{{}^-4}{7}x + \frac{40}{7}$

The equation of the segment connecting (0,0) and (8,4) is $y = \frac{1}{2}x$

Equate: $8x - 40 = \frac{{}^-4}{7}x + \frac{40}{7}$, $8x - 40 = \frac{1}{2}x$, and $\frac{{}^-4}{7}x + \frac{40}{7} = \frac{1}{2}x$ to find $x = \frac{16}{3}$

Substitute $x = \frac{16}{3}$ into any of the three equations to find $y = \frac{8}{3}$

So the coordinates of the common intersection are $\left(\frac{16}{3}, \frac{8}{3}\right)$

17. Write one equation for the contents of the truck (where G is the number of gallons of gasoline and K is the number of gallons of kerosene); write another for the profit:

$$G + K = 5000 \text{ or } G = 5000 - K \quad (i)$$
$$\$0.13G + \$0.12K = \$640 \text{ or } 13G + 12K = 64000 \quad (ii)$$

Substituting (i) into (ii): $13(5000 - K) + 12K = 64000 \Rightarrow 65000 - 13K + 12K = 64000 \Rightarrow K = 1000$
Substituting $K = 1000$ into (i): $G = 5000 - (1000) \Rightarrow G = 4000$
So there are 4000 gallons of gasoline and 1000 gallons of kerosene on the truck

18. (a) In eight months, \$80 interest was earned. Since it is simple interest, this is \$10 per month; thus in the first ten months, (10 months) · (\$10 per month) = \$100 interest was earned. The original balance was \$2100 − \$100 = \$2000

(b) Simple interest (I) = Principal (P) · Rate (R) · Time in years (T) $\Rightarrow R = \frac{I}{P \cdot T}$

So $R = \frac{100}{2000 \cdot \frac{10}{12}} = 0.06$, or 6% annually (or $\frac{1}{2}$% per month)

19. Let D be the number of dimes and Q be the number of quarters. Then:

$$D + Q = 27 \text{ or } D = 27 - Q \quad (i)$$
$$\$0.10D + \$0.25Q = \$5.25 \text{ or } 10D + 25Q = 525 \quad (ii)$$

Substituting (i) into (ii): $10(27 - Q) + 25Q = 525 \Rightarrow 270 - 10Q + 25Q = 525 \Rightarrow Q = 17$
Substituting $Q = 17$ into (i): $D = 27 - (17) = 10$
So there are 17 quarters and 10 dimes in the bank

20. (a) All solutions are $(^-1,2)$

(b) Answers may vary; one set would be $9x + 10y = 11$ and $12x + 13y = 14 \Rightarrow$ the solution is $(^-1,2)$

(c) (i) These equations are of the form $nx + (n+1)y = (n+2)$ and $(n+3)x + (n+4)y = (n+5)$

(ii) All solutions will be $(^-1,2)$

(iii) $^-1(a) + 2(a+1) = {}^-a + 2a + 2 = a + 2$

On-going Assessment 7-3; Review Problems

30. Let P be the population of the city and T be the time in years after a population of 120,000. Then:

$$P = 1800T + 120{,}000$$

When population is 165,000: $165{,}000 = 1800T + 120{,}000 \Rightarrow T = 25$
So the population will exceed 165,000 after 25 years

31. Let the first number be n. Then the next three consecutive odd numbers would be $n + 2$, $n + 4$, and $n + 6$. Thus:

$$n + (n+2) + (n+4) + (n+6) = 1024 \Rightarrow 4n + 12 = 1024 \Rightarrow n = 253$$

So the four consecutive odd integers are 253, 255, 257, and 259

32. Let L be the length of a short side
Then $L + L + 3L = 550 \Rightarrow 5L = 550 \Rightarrow L = 110$
So the rectangle will be 110 feet by 330 feet

1. (a) There are five vowels and 21 consonants; the ratio is thus $\frac{5 \text{ vowels}}{21 \text{ consonants}} = \frac{5}{21}$

(b) Answers may vary; **break** or **minor** are two

2. We know that $\frac{a}{b} = \frac{c}{d}$ only if $a \cdot d = b \cdot c$. Thus:

(a) Given $\frac{12}{x} = \frac{18}{45} \Rightarrow 18 \cdot x = 12 \cdot 45 \Rightarrow x = \frac{12 \cdot 45}{18} = 30$

(b) Given $\frac{x}{7} = \frac{^-10}{21} \Rightarrow 21 \cdot x = 7 \cdot {^-10} \Rightarrow x = \frac{7 \cdot {^-10}}{21} = \frac{^-10}{3}$ or $^-3\frac{1}{3}$

(c) Given $\frac{5}{7} = \frac{3x}{98} \Rightarrow 3x \cdot 7 = 5 \cdot 98 \Rightarrow x = \frac{5 \cdot 98}{3 \cdot 7} = \frac{70}{3}$ or $23\frac{1}{3}$

(d) $3\frac{1}{2}$ is to 5 as x is to 15 $\Rightarrow \frac{3\frac{1}{2}}{5} = \frac{x}{15} \Rightarrow 5 \cdot x = 3\frac{1}{2} \cdot 15 \Rightarrow x = \frac{3\frac{1}{2} \cdot 15}{5} = \frac{21}{2}$ or $10\frac{1}{2}$

3. $\frac{2 \text{ pounds muscle}}{5 \text{ pounds body weight}} = \frac{x \text{ pounds muscle}}{90 \text{ pounds body weight}} \Rightarrow 5 \cdot x = 2 \cdot 90 \Rightarrow x = \frac{2 \cdot 90}{5} = 36$
So there are 36 pounds of muscle in a 90-pound child

4. $\frac{5 \text{ adults}}{1 \text{ teen}} = \frac{12{,}345 \text{ adults}}{x \text{ teens}} \Rightarrow 5 \cdot x = 1 \cdot 12{,}345 \Rightarrow x = \frac{12{,}345}{5} = 2469$
So there are 2469 teenage drivers in Aloussim

5. $\frac{4 \text{ grapefruit}}{79¢} = \frac{6 \text{ grapefruit}}{x\ ¢} \Rightarrow 4 \cdot x = 6 \cdot 79 \Rightarrow x = \frac{6 \cdot 79}{4} = 118\frac{1}{2}$
So, rounding, six grapefruit would cost \$1.19

6. $\frac{\frac{1}{3} \text{ inch}}{5 \text{ miles}} = \frac{18 \text{ inches}}{x \text{ miles}} \Rightarrow \frac{1}{3} \cdot x = 5 \cdot 18 \Rightarrow x = \frac{5 \cdot 18}{\frac{1}{3}} = 270$
So there are 270 miles between New York and Aloussim

7. $\frac{40 \text{ pages}}{50 \text{ minutes}} = \frac{x \text{ pages}}{80 \text{ minutes}} \Rightarrow 50 \cdot x = 40 \cdot 80 \Rightarrow x = \frac{40 \cdot 80}{50} = 64$
So David can read 64 pages in 80 minutes

8. The candle has burned 5 inches in 12 minutes; thus:
$\frac{5 \text{ inches}}{12 \text{ minutes}} = \frac{30 \text{ inches}}{x \text{ minutes}} \Rightarrow 5 \cdot x = 12 \cdot 30 \Rightarrow x = \frac{12 \cdot 30}{5} = 72$
So the candle would burn completely (i.e., 30 inches) in 72 minutes

9. (a) $3x + 4x = 98 \Rightarrow 7x = 98 \Rightarrow x = 14 \Rightarrow 3x = 42$ and $4x = 56$
The numbers are 42 and 56

(b) $3x \cdot 4x = 768 \Rightarrow 28x = 768 \Rightarrow x = 8 \Rightarrow 3x = 24$ and $4x = 32$
The numbers are 24 and 32 (or $^-24$ and $^-32$)

10. Let 5x represent width and 9x represent length. Knowing that the perimeter of a rectangle is 2W + 2L:
$2(5x) + 2(9x) = 2800 \Rightarrow 28x = 2800 \Rightarrow x = 100$
So width = 500 feet and length = 900 feet

11. $2+4+5=11 \Rightarrow \frac{2}{11}=\frac{\text{Gary}}{\$82{,}000}$, $\frac{4}{11}=\frac{\text{Bill}}{\$82{,}000}$, and $\frac{5}{11}=\frac{\text{Carmella}}{\$82{,}000}$. Thus:

$\text{Gary}\cdot 11 = 2\cdot 82{,}000 \Rightarrow \text{Gary}=\frac{2\cdot 82{,}000}{11}=\$14{,}909.09$ (Gary's share)

$\text{Bill}\cdot 11 = 4\cdot 82{,}000 \Rightarrow \text{Bill}=\frac{4\cdot 82{,}000}{11}=\$29{,}818.18$ (Bill's share)

$\text{Carmella}\cdot 11 = 5\cdot 82{,}000 \Rightarrow \text{Carmella}=\frac{5\cdot 82{,}000}{11}=\$37{,}272.73$ (Carmella's share)

12. The ratio of Sheila's to Dora's hours is $3\frac{1}{2}:4\frac{1}{2}$; thus:

$3\frac{1}{2}x+4\frac{1}{2}x=\$176 \Rightarrow 8x=176 \Rightarrow x=22$

So Sheila's earnings are $3\frac{1}{2}\cdot 22=\$77$

Dora's earnings are $4\frac{1}{2}\cdot 22=\$99$

13. Success:Failure = 5:4 $\Rightarrow \frac{5\text{ successes}}{4\text{ failures}}=\frac{75\text{ successes}}{x\text{ failures}} \Rightarrow 5\cdot x=4\cdot 75 \Rightarrow x=\frac{4\cdot 75}{5}=60$ failures

So 75 successes + 60 failures = 135 total attempts

14. (a) $\frac{\text{Rise}}{\text{Half-Span}}=\frac{10}{14}=\frac{5}{7} \Rightarrow$ The pitch is $\frac{5}{7}$, or 5:7

(b) $\frac{\text{Rise}}{\text{Half-Span}}=\text{Pitch} \Rightarrow \frac{\text{Rise}}{8}=\frac{3}{4} \Rightarrow \text{Rise}\cdot 4=8\cdot 3 \Rightarrow \text{Rise}=\frac{8\cdot 3}{4}=6$

So the rise is 6 feet

15. $\frac{\text{Jump}}{\text{Length}}=\frac{20}{1} \Rightarrow \frac{\text{Jump}}{6\text{ feet}}=\frac{20}{1} \Rightarrow \text{Jump}\cdot 1=6\cdot 20 \Rightarrow \text{Jump}=\frac{6\cdot 20}{1}=120$

So a 6-foot human would be able to jump 120 feet

16. $\frac{9\text{ months}}{6\text{ vacation days}}=\frac{12\text{ months}}{x\text{ vacation days}} \Rightarrow 9\cdot x=6\cdot 12 \Rightarrow x=\frac{6\cdot 12}{9}=8$

So Jim will earn 8 vacation days per year

17. (a) $\frac{4\text{ rpm on large gear}}{6\text{ rpm on small gear}}=\frac{18\text{ teeth on small gear}}{x\text{ teeth on large gear}} \Rightarrow 4\cdot x=6\cdot 18 \Rightarrow x=\frac{6\cdot 18}{4}=27$

So the large gear has 27 teeth

(b) $\frac{200\text{ rpm on large gear}}{600\text{ rpm on small gear}}=\frac{x\text{ teeth on small gear}}{60\text{ teeth on large gear}} \Rightarrow 600\cdot x=200\cdot 60 \Rightarrow x=\frac{200\cdot 60}{600}=20$

So the small gear has 20 teeth

18. $\frac{230\text{ foot length}}{195\text{ foot wingspan}}=\frac{40\text{ cm length}}{x\text{ cm wingspan}} \Rightarrow 230\cdot x=195\cdot 40 \Rightarrow x=\frac{195\cdot 40}{230}=33\frac{21}{23}$

So the model has about 34 cm wingspan

19. $\frac{160\text{ lbs on earth}}{416\text{ lbs on Jupiter}}=\frac{120\text{ lbs on earth}}{x\text{ lbs on Jupiter}} \Rightarrow 160\cdot x=416\cdot 120 \Rightarrow x=\frac{416\cdot 120}{160}=312$

Amy weighs 312 pounds on Jupiter

20. (a) 2:5 (In an average group of 2 boys and 3 girls, there are 5 total students)

(b) $\frac{m}{m+n}$ or $m:(m+n)$

21. (a) $\frac{3\text{ cups tomato sauce}}{2\text{ cups tomato sauce}}=\frac{3}{2}$, so:

(*i*) $\frac{1\text{ teaspoon mustard seed}}{x\text{ teaspoon mustard seed}}=\frac{3}{2} \Rightarrow 3x=1\cdot 2 \Rightarrow x=\frac{2}{3}$ teaspoon mustard seed

21. (a) (*ii*) $\frac{1\frac{1}{2}\text{ cups scallions}}{\text{x cups scallions}} = \frac{3}{2} \Rightarrow 3x = 1\frac{1}{2} \cdot 2 \Rightarrow x = 1$ cup scallions

(*iii*) $\frac{3\frac{1}{4}\text{ cups beans}}{\text{x cups beans}} = \frac{3}{2} \Rightarrow 3x = 3\frac{1}{4} \cdot 2 \Rightarrow x = 2\frac{1}{6}$ cups beans

(b) $\frac{1\frac{1}{2}\text{ cups scallions}}{\text{1 cup scallions}} = \frac{3}{2}$, which is the same ratio as in (a)
$\Rightarrow \frac{2}{3}$ teaspoon mustard seed, 2 cups tomato sauce, $2\frac{1}{6}$ cups beans

(c) $\frac{3\frac{1}{4}\text{ cups beans}}{1\frac{3}{4}\text{ cups beans}} = \frac{13}{7}$, so:

(*i*) $\frac{\text{1 teaspoon mustard seed}}{\text{x teaspoons mustard seed}} = \frac{13}{7} \Rightarrow 13x = 1 \cdot 7 \Rightarrow x = \frac{7}{13}$ teaspoon mustard seed

(*ii*) $\frac{\text{3 cups tomato sauce}}{\text{x cups tomato sauce}} = \frac{13}{7} \Rightarrow 13x = 3 \cdot 7 \Rightarrow x = \frac{21}{13} = 1\frac{8}{13}$ cups tomato sauce

(*iii*) $\frac{1\frac{1}{2}\text{ cups scallions}}{\text{x cups scallions}} = \frac{13}{7} \Rightarrow 13x = 1\frac{1}{2} \cdot 7 \Rightarrow x = \frac{21}{26}$ cups scallions

22. $\frac{4.2\ \Omega}{\text{5 feet}} = \frac{x\ \Omega}{\text{18 feet}} \Rightarrow 5 \cdot x = 4.2 \cdot 18 \Rightarrow x = \frac{4.2 \cdot 18}{5} = 15.12$
So the resistance of an 18-foot wire is 15.12 ohms

23. (a) $By = Ax \Rightarrow \frac{x}{y} = \frac{B}{A}$; $A = 3B \Rightarrow \frac{x}{y} = \frac{B}{3B} = \frac{1}{3}$

(b) $\frac{x}{y} = \frac{10}{1} = \frac{B}{A} \Rightarrow 1 \cdot B = 10 \cdot A \Rightarrow B = 10A$
So if A = 100 pounds, $B = 10 \cdot 100 = 1000$ pounds

(c) Given $y = 3x$ and $A + B = 10$ (or $B = 10 - A$), and if $By = Ax$, then:
$A = B \cdot \frac{y}{x} = (10 - A) \cdot \frac{3x}{x} = (10 - A) \cdot 3 = 30 - 3A \Rightarrow 4A = 30 \Rightarrow A = 7\frac{1}{2}$
$B = 10 - A = 10 - (7\frac{1}{2}) = 2\frac{1}{2}$
So A weighs $7\frac{1}{2}$ pounds and B weighs $2\frac{1}{2}$ pounds

24. $\frac{\text{30 feet tall}}{\text{12 foot shadow}} = \frac{\text{x feet tall}}{\text{14 foot shadow}} \Rightarrow 12 \cdot x = 30 \cdot 14 \Rightarrow x = \frac{30 \cdot 14}{12} = 35$
So the tree is 35 feet tall

25. $\frac{\text{2.3 cm (daughter)}}{\text{5.8 cm (father)}} = \frac{\text{x cm (daughter)}}{\text{188 cm (father)}} \Rightarrow 5.8 \cdot x = 2.3 \cdot 188 \Rightarrow x = \frac{2.3 \cdot 188}{5.8} \doteq 74.6$
So the daughter is about 74.6 cm tall

26. Assume $d_x = 7$ units and $d_y = 8$ units, where d_x and d_y are distances of x and y, respectively, from the fulcrum. Then:

(a) $7x = 8y$

(b) $y = \frac{7}{8}x$

(c)

x	0	5	10	15	20	25
y	0	5.25	8.75	13.125	17.5	21.875

26. (c)

17.5 15 12.5 10 7.5 5 2.5 0

0 5 10 15 20

(d) $y = \frac{7}{8} \cdot (6) = 5.25$ pounds

27. Since weight and distance from the fulcrum are in inverse proportion, then:

$\frac{50 \text{ pounds}}{100 \text{ pounds}} = \frac{x \text{ feet}}{6 \text{ feet}} \Rightarrow 100 \cdot x = 50 \cdot 6 \Rightarrow x = \frac{50 \cdot 6}{100} = 3$

So 100 pounds should be applied 3 feet from the fulcrum

28. (a)

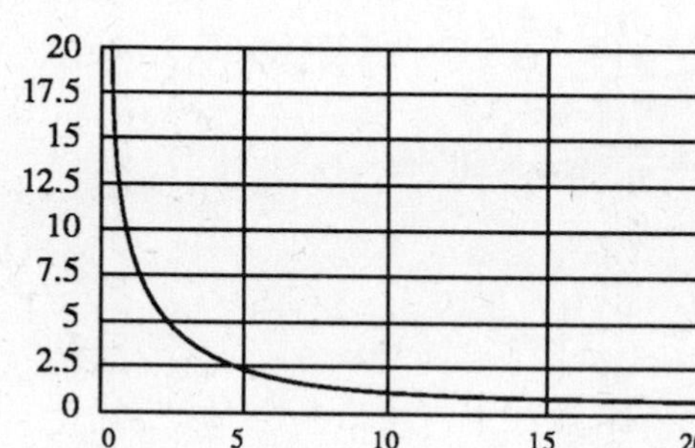

(b) $W \cdot L = 10$ (or $WL = 10$)

(c) Inverse [see (d) and (e)]

(d) $W = \frac{10}{L}$

(e) $L = \frac{10}{W}$

29. (a) (*i*) $d = 15 \cdot t$

(*ii*) Direct variation

(*iii*)

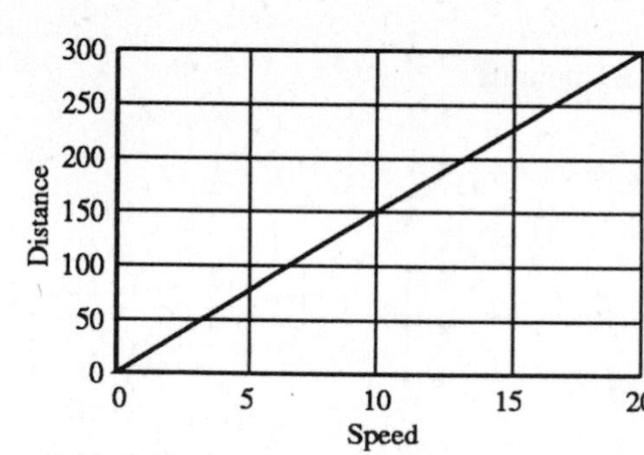

(b) (*i*) $t = \frac{400}{w}$

(*ii*) Inverse variation

29. (b) (*iii*)

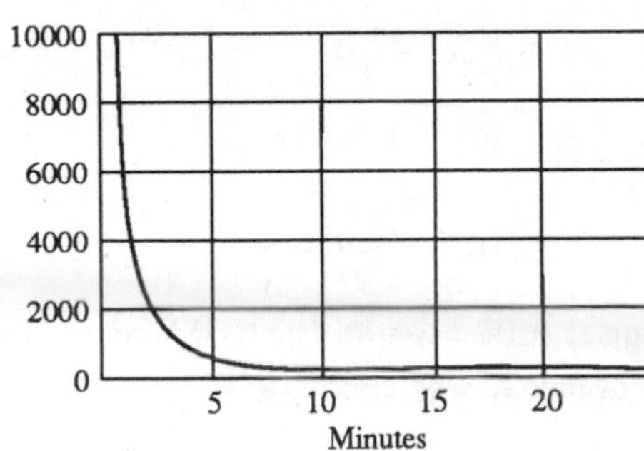

29. (c) (*i*) L = 25 · S (*ii*) Direct variation

(*iii*)

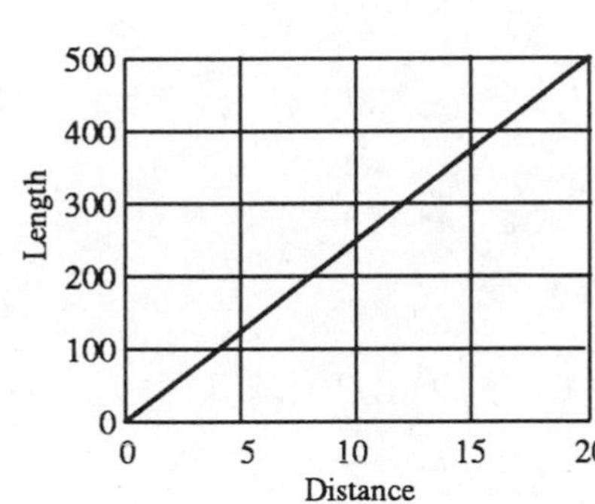

(d) (*i*) W = 100 − L (*ii*) Neither direct nor inverse variation

(*iii*)

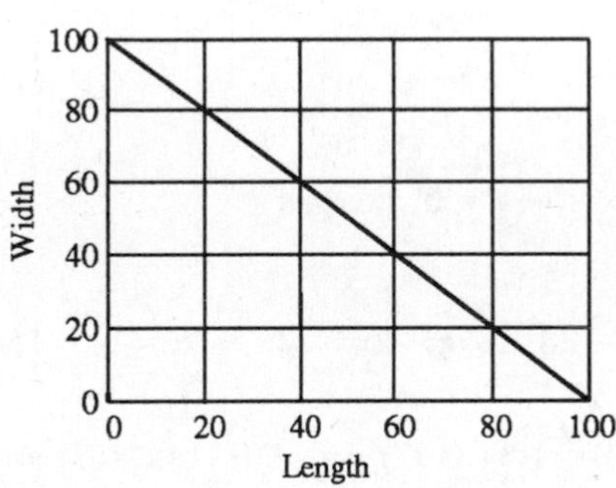

(e) (*i*) J = 2.64 · E (*ii*) Direct variation

(*iii*)

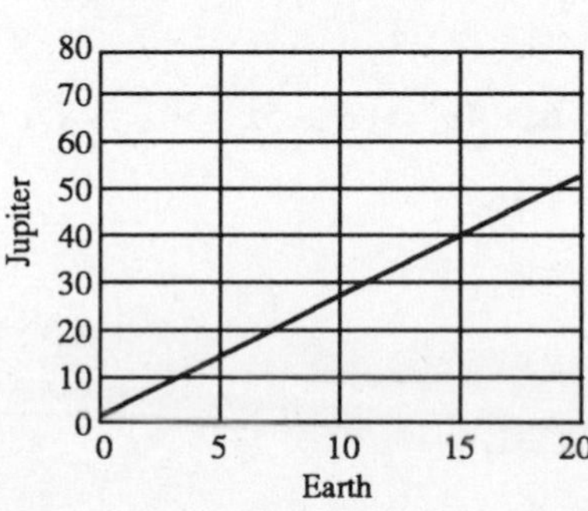

30. (a) Directly $\left(y = \frac{1}{2}x\right)$ (b) Directly $(y = 10x)$

(c) Inversely $\left(y = \frac{15}{x}\right)$ (d) Directly

(e) Neither $(y = 2 - x)$ (f) Neither

31. (a) The total number of men in all three rooms is $1 + 2 + 5 = 8$. The total number of women in all three rooms is $2 + 4 + 10 = 16$. Thus the ratio of men to women is $\frac{8}{16} = \frac{1}{2}$.

(b) If $\frac{a}{b} = \frac{c}{d} = \frac{e}{f}$, then $\frac{c}{d} = \frac{a \cdot m}{b \cdot m}$ and $\frac{e}{f} = \frac{a \cdot n}{b \cdot n}$. So $\frac{a+c+e}{b+d+f} = \frac{a+am+an}{b+bm+bn} = \frac{a(1+m+n)}{b(1+m+n)} = \frac{a}{b}$.

32. (a) $\frac{a}{b} = \frac{c}{d} \Rightarrow \frac{a}{b} + 1 = \frac{c}{d} + 1 \Rightarrow \frac{a}{b} + \frac{b}{b} = \frac{c}{d} + \frac{d}{d} \Rightarrow \frac{a+b}{b} = \frac{c+d}{d}$

(b) $\frac{a}{b} = \frac{c}{d} \Rightarrow ad = bc \Rightarrow ac + ad = ac + bc \Rightarrow a(c + d) = c(a + b) \Rightarrow \frac{a}{a+b} = \frac{c}{c+d}$

(c) $\frac{a}{b} = \frac{c}{d} \Rightarrow \frac{a}{a+b} = \frac{c}{c+d} \Rightarrow \frac{2a}{a+b} = \frac{2c}{c+d} \Rightarrow \frac{2a}{a+b} - 1 = \frac{2c}{c+d} - 1$
$\Rightarrow \frac{2a-(a+b)}{a+b} = \frac{2c-(c+d)}{c+d} \Rightarrow \frac{a-b}{a+b} = \frac{c-d}{c+d}$

On-going Assessment 7-4; Review Problems

43. If *n* is an odd number, then:
Sum $= n + (n + 2) + (n + 4) = 3n + 6$
Subtracting 6 gives $3n$
Dividing by 3 gives $\frac{3n}{3} = n$
And the numbers are n, $n + 2$, and $n + 4$

44. (a) $\frac{1}{3}x = \frac{3}{4}x \Rightarrow \frac{3}{4}x - \frac{1}{3}x = 0 \Rightarrow \frac{5}{12}x = 0 \Rightarrow x = \frac{0}{\left(\frac{5}{12}\right)} = 0$

(b) $\frac{1}{2}x - 7 = \frac{3}{4} \Rightarrow 4\left(\frac{1}{2}x - 7\right) = 4\left(\frac{3}{4}\right) \Rightarrow 2x - 28 = 3 \Rightarrow 2x = 31 \Rightarrow x = \frac{31}{2} = 15\frac{1}{2}$

(c) $^-0.01 + 3.14x = {}^-0.07 \Rightarrow 100(^-0.01 + 3.14x) = 100(^-0.07) \Rightarrow {}^-1 + 314x = {}^-7 \Rightarrow 314x = {}^-6$
$\Rightarrow x \doteq {}^-0.019$

(d) $\frac{5}{x} - 0.34 = 0.91 \Rightarrow x\left(\frac{5}{x} - 0.34\right) = x(0.91) \Rightarrow 5 - 0.34x = 0.91x \Rightarrow 100(5 - 0.34x) = 100(0.91x)$
$\Rightarrow 500 - 34x = 91x \Rightarrow 500 = 125x \Rightarrow x = 4$

(e) $\frac{^-1}{2}x + 3 > 2x \Rightarrow 2\left(\frac{^-1}{2}x + 3\right) > 2(2x) \Rightarrow {}^-x + 6 > 4x \Rightarrow 6 > 5x \Rightarrow \frac{6}{5} > x$ or $x < \frac{6}{5}$

(f) $|x| \geq \sqrt{2} \Rightarrow x \leq {}^-\sqrt{2}$ or $x \geq \sqrt{2}$

1. (a) $7.89 = (100 \cdot 7.89)\% = 789\%$ (b) $0.032 = (100 \cdot 0.032)\% = 3.2\%$

(c) $193.1 = (100 \cdot 193.1)\% = 19{,}310\%$ (d) $0.2 = (100 \cdot 0.2)\% = 20\%$

(e) $\frac{5}{6} = 0.83\frac{1}{3} = \left(100 \cdot 0.83\frac{1}{3}\right)\% = 83\frac{1}{3}\%$ (f) $\frac{3}{20} = 0.15 = (100 \cdot 0.15)\% = 15\%$

(g) $\frac{1}{8} = 0.125 = (100 \cdot 0.125)\% = 12.5\%$ (h) $\frac{3}{8} = 0.375 = (100 \cdot 0.375)\% = 37.5\%$

(i) $\frac{5}{8} = 0.625 = (100 \cdot 0.625)\% = 62.5\%$ (j) $\frac{1}{6} = 0.16\frac{2}{3} = \left(100 \cdot 0.16\frac{2}{3}\right)\% = 16\frac{2}{3}\%$

(k) $\frac{4}{5} = 0.8 = (100 \cdot 0.8)\% = 80\%$ (l) $\frac{1}{40} = 0.025 = (100 \cdot 0.025)\% = 2.5\%$

2. (a) $16\% = \frac{16}{100} = 0.16$ (b) $4\frac{1}{2}\% = 4.5\% = \frac{4.5}{100} = 0.045$

(c) $\frac{1}{5}\% = 0.2\% = \frac{0.2}{100} = 0.002$ (d) $\frac{2}{7}\% = \frac{\frac{2}{7}}{100} = \frac{0.\overline{285714}}{100} = 0.00\overline{285714}$

(e) $13\frac{2}{3}\% = \frac{13\frac{2}{3}}{100} = \frac{13.\overline{6}}{100} = 0.13\overline{6}$ (f) $125\% = \frac{125}{100} = 1.25$

(g) $\frac{1}{3}\% = \frac{\frac{1}{3}}{100} = \frac{0.\overline{3}}{100} = 0.00\overline{3}$ (h) $\frac{1}{4}\% = \frac{\frac{1}{4}}{100} = \frac{0.25}{100} = 0.0025$

3. (a) $4\% = \frac{4}{100} \Rightarrow$ Four (b) $4\% = \frac{4}{100} = \frac{2}{50} \Rightarrow$ Two

(c) $4\% = \frac{4}{100} = \frac{1}{25} \Rightarrow 25$ (d) $4\% = \frac{4}{100} = \frac{8}{200} \Rightarrow 200$

(e) $4\% = \frac{4}{100} = \frac{0.5}{12.5} \Rightarrow 12.5$

4. Depending on the calculator:

(a) Yes (most calculators) (b) Yes (most calculators)

5. (a) 6% of $34 = 0.06 \cdot 34 = 2.04$

(b) $17 = n \cdot 34 \Rightarrow n = \left(100 \cdot \frac{17}{34}\right)\% = (100 \cdot 0.5)\% \Rightarrow n = 50\%$

(c) $18 = 30\% \cdot n \Rightarrow 18 = 0.3 \cdot n \Rightarrow n = \frac{18}{0.3} = 60$

(d) 7% of $49 \Rightarrow 0.07 \cdot 49 = 3.43$

(e) $61.5 = n \cdot 20.5 \Rightarrow n = \left(100 \cdot \frac{61.5}{20.5}\right)\% = (100 \cdot 3)\% \Rightarrow n = 300\%$

(f) $16 = 40\% \cdot n \Rightarrow 16 = 0.4 \cdot n \Rightarrow n = \frac{16}{0.4} = 40$

6. 75% of 84 boxes $\Rightarrow 0.75 \cdot 84 = 63$ boxes sold

7. 6% of \$16,000 is $0.06 \cdot 16{,}000 = \$960$, which is the amount of the raise
She now makes \$16,000 + \$960 = \$16,960

8. (7% of last salary) + (100% of last salary) = \$15,515 $\Rightarrow$ 107% of last salary is \$15,515; or:
$1.07 \cdot (\text{Last salary}) = 15{,}515 \Rightarrow \text{Last salary} = \frac{15{,}515}{1.07} = \$14{,}500$

9. (a) Joe sold 180 newspapers
Bill sold $(0.85) \cdot (260) = 221$ newspapers
Ron sold 212 newspapers $\Rightarrow$ Bill sold the most (221) newspapers

(b) Joe sold $\left(100 \cdot \frac{180}{200}\right)\% = 90\%$ of his newspapers
Bill sold 85% of his newspapers
Ron sold 80% of his newspapers $\Rightarrow$ Joe sold the greatest percentage (90%) of his newspapers

(c) Joe started with 200 newspapers
Bill started with 260 newspapers
Ron started with $\frac{212}{0.80} = 265$ newspapers $\Rightarrow$ Ron started with the greatest number of newspapers

10. The amount of the discount is \$35 – \$28 = \$7 $\Rightarrow$ find \$7 as a percentage of \$35, or:
$\frac{7}{35} = 0.2 = (100 \cdot 0.2)\% = 20\%$ discount

11. The amount of depreciation was \$1700 – \$1400 = \$300 $\Rightarrow$ find \$300 as a percentage of \$1700, or:
$\frac{300}{1700} \doteq 0.1765 = (100 \cdot 0.176)\%$, or approximately 17.65% depreciation

12. The number of eagles by which the population decreased was 728 – 594 = 134
Decrease as a percentage of the original population is $\frac{134}{728} \doteq 0.184 = (100 \cdot 0.184)\% = 18.4\%$ decrease

13. The amount of increase in value was \$95,000 – \$59,000 = \$36,000
Increase as a percentage of the original value is $\frac{36{,}000}{59{,}000} \doteq 0.61 = (100 \cdot 0.61)\%$, or about 61% increase

14. The amount of Xuan's weight increase was 18 – 9 = 9 pounds
Increase of a percentage of birth weight was $\frac{9}{9} = 1 = (100 \cdot 1)\% = 100\%$ increase

15. Sale price was regular price – 20% of regular price, or:
\$28.00 – 20% of \$28.00 = \$28.00 – (0.20 · \$28.00) = \$28.00 – \$5.60 $\Rightarrow$ Sale price was \$22.40

16. The amount of the discount is 25% of \$6.80, or $0.25 \cdot \$6.80 = \$1.70$
The sale price is \$6.80 – \$1.70 = \$5.10

17. Set up a proportion: $\frac{\frac{1}{4}\text{ cup}}{\text{x cups}} = \frac{0.5\%}{100\%} \Rightarrow \frac{\frac{1}{4}\text{ cup}}{\text{x cups}} = \frac{0.005}{1}$

So $0.005x = \frac{1}{4} \cdot 1 \Rightarrow x = \frac{\frac{1}{4}}{0.005} = 50 \Rightarrow$ 50 cups of Crunchies needed

18. The amount of the tax is 5% of \$320, or $0.05 \cdot \$320 = \$16$
So the total cost is \$320 + \$16 = \$336

19. Bill answered $\frac{80-52}{80} = 0.35 = (100 \cdot 0.35)\%$, or 35% of the questions correctly

20. The broker receives 4% of \$80,000, or $0.04 \cdot \$80{,}000 = \$3200$

21. $66\frac{2}{3}\%$ of 1800 employees is $\frac{66\frac{2}{3}}{100} = \frac{\frac{200}{3}}{100} = \frac{200}{300} = \frac{2}{3}$ of 1800 employees, or:
$\frac{2}{3} \cdot 1800 = 1200$ employees favoring the program

22. The house payment as a percentage of total income is $\frac{\$800}{\$3400} \doteq 0.235 = (100 \cdot 0.235)\% = 23.5\%$

23. Last year + 110% of last year = 210% of last year $\Rightarrow$ 210% of last year = \$19.80 $\Rightarrow$ last year = $\frac{\$19.80}{210\%}$
$= \frac{\$19.80}{2.1} = \$9.43 \Rightarrow$ there was a \$19.80 – \$9.43 = \$10.37 increase

24. 6 cans at 45¢ each is \$2.70 $\Rightarrow$ the savings would be \$2.70 – \$2.40 = \$0.30 by buying the 6-pack
Savings as a percentage of 6-can cost is $\frac{\$0.30}{\$2.70} \doteq 0.111 = (100 \cdot 0.111) = 11.1\%$

25. The amount of John's 20% profit is $\frac{20}{100} \cdot \$330 = \$66 \Rightarrow$ net price of the bike after a 10% discount must be:
\$330 + \$66 = \$396
Let L be list price; then L – 10% of L = net price $\Rightarrow L - \frac{10}{100} \cdot L = \$396 \Rightarrow 0.9L = 396 \Rightarrow L = \frac{396}{0.9} = \$440$
If John prices the bike at \$440 he can offer a 10% discount of \$44 and still realize his \$66 profit

26. 25% of \$200 was $\frac{25}{100} \cdot \$200 = \$50$, so the sale price was \$200 – \$50 = \$150
Then increasing the price by \$50 (to bring the price back to \$200) is $\frac{50}{150} = \frac{1}{3} = \left(100 \cdot \frac{1}{3}\right)\% = 33\frac{1}{3}\%$
So the sale price must be increased by $33\frac{1}{3}\%$

27. 12.13% of price = \$1116.88 $\Rightarrow$ price = $\frac{\$1116.88}{\left(\frac{12.13}{100}\right)} \doteq \$9207.58$ purchase price

28. (a) 10% of \$22 = \$2.20 ; 5% of \$22 is half 10%, or \$1.10 $\Rightarrow$ \$2.20 + \$1.10 = \$3.30

(b) 10% of \$120 = \$12; 20% is twice 10%, or \$24

(c) 10% of \$38 = \$3.80; 5% is half 10%, or \$1.90

(d) 25% is $\frac{1}{4} \Rightarrow \frac{1}{4} \cdot \$98 = \$98 \div 4 = \$24.50$

29. (a) Only the four corner blocks will have four faces painted $\Rightarrow$ there are $\frac{4}{100} = 4\%$ painted

(b) The blocks along each edge, exclusive of the corner blocks, will have three faces painted
There are 8 of these along each edge, or 32 blocks $\Rightarrow$ there are $\frac{32}{100} = 32\%$ painted

(c) Each of the interior blocks will have two faces painted; there are 100 – 32 – 4 = 64 of these
There are $\frac{64}{100} = 64\%$ painted

30. (a) (*i*) Four corner blocks painted $\Rightarrow \frac{4}{81} \doteq 0.049 = (100 \cdot 0.049)\% = 4.9\%$ painted

(*ii*) Edge blocks (except corners) painted $\Rightarrow \frac{4 \cdot 7}{81} \doteq 0.346 = (100 \cdot 0.346)\% = 34.6\%$ painted

(*iii*) Interior blocks painted $\Rightarrow \frac{81-28-4}{81} \doteq 0.605 = (100 \cdot 0.605)\% = 60.5\%$ painted

(b) (*i*) Four corner blocks painted $\Rightarrow \frac{4}{64} = 0.0625 = (100 \cdot 0.0625)\% = 6.25\%$ painted

(*ii*) Edge blocks (except corners) painted $\Rightarrow \frac{4 \cdot 6}{64} = 0.375 = (100 \cdot 0.375)\% = 37.5\%$ painted

(*iii*) Interior blocks painted $\Rightarrow \frac{64-24-4}{64} = 0.5625 = (100 \cdot 0.5625)\% = 56.25\%$ painted

(c) (*i*) Four corner blocks painted $\Rightarrow \frac{4}{49} \doteq 0.082 = (100 \cdot 0.082)\% = 8.2\%$ painted

(*ii*) Edge blocks (except corners) painted $\Rightarrow \frac{4 \cdot 5}{49} \doteq 0.408 = (100 \cdot 0.408)\% = 40.8\%$ painted

(c) (*iii*) Interior blocks painted $\Rightarrow \frac{49-20-4}{49} \doteq 0.510 = (100 \cdot 0.510)\% = 51\%$ painted

(d) (*i*) Four corner blocks painted $\Rightarrow \frac{4}{144} = 0.02\overline{7} = (100 \cdot 0.02\overline{7})\% = 2.\overline{7}\%$ painted

(*ii*) Edge blocks (except corners) painted $\Rightarrow \frac{4 \cdot 10}{144} = 0.27\overline{7} = (100 \cdot 0.27\overline{7})\% = 27.\overline{7}\%$ painted

(*iii*) Interior blocks painted $\Rightarrow \frac{144-40-4}{144} = 0.69\overline{4} = (100 \cdot 0.69\overline{4})\% = 69.\overline{4}\%$ painted

31. (a) Answers may vary. If you are 20 years old, your range would be a rate of 60% of (220 – 20), or $0.60 \cdot 200 = 120$ to 80% of (220 – 20), or $0.80 \cdot 200 = 160$

(b) (*i*) $\frac{15 \text{ seconds}}{41 \text{ beats}} = 0.\overline{36585}$ seconds, or about 0.37 seconds between beats

(*ii*) $\frac{\frac{1}{4} \text{ minute}}{41 \text{ beats}} = 0.00\overline{60975}$ minutes, or about 0.006 minutes between beats

32. (a) $50 - 40 = 10 \Rightarrow$ 10 as a percentage of 40 $= \frac{10}{40} = 0.25 = (100 \cdot 0.25)\% = 25\%$

(b) 10 as a percentage of 50 $= \frac{10}{50} = 0.20 = (100 \cdot 0.20)\% = 20\%$

33. Purchasing power would increase by the amount of the raise, 20%

34. You can now buy $\frac{100\%}{80\%} = 1.25 = 125\%$ of the previous amount of goods, so your purchasing power has increased by 25%

35. A journeyman makes 200% of an apprentice's pay
A master makes 150% of a journeyman's pay $\Rightarrow$ 150% of 200% = $1.5 \cdot 2 = 3$ = 300% of an apprentice's pay
Thus the \$4200 needs $1 + 2 + 3 = 6$ shares, or \$700 per share
And the apprentice earns \$700; the journeyman earns 200% of \$700 = \$1400; the master earns 150% of \$1400 = 300% of \$700 = \$2100

36. (a) $\frac{\text{20 math majors}}{\text{500 incoming students}} = 0.04 = (100 \cdot 0.04)\% = 4\%$ math majors

(b) (*i*) There were 480 students who were nonmath majors $\Rightarrow$ 5% of 480 = $0.05 \cdot 480 = 24$ switchers
20 original + 24 switchers = 44 math majors now

(*ii*) $\frac{\text{44 math majors}}{\text{500 students}} = 0.088 = (100 \cdot 0.088)\% = 8.8\%$ math majors

37. Let S be the salary of the previous year $\Rightarrow$ 100% of S + 10% of S = 110% of S = 1.1S is current salary
$1.1S = \$100{,}000$ (this year) $\Rightarrow S = \frac{100{,}000}{1.1} \doteq \$90{,}909.09$ (last year)
$1.1S = \$90{,}909.09$ (last year) $\Rightarrow S = \frac{90{,}909.09}{1.1} \doteq \$82{,}644.63$
So she earned \$82,644.63 two years ago

38. In these charts, x ¢ = x % ; for example, 6¢ of revenue = 6%, since $\frac{6¢}{100¢} = 6\%$

(a) (6¢ = 6% corporate taxes) + (84¢ = 84% personal taxes) = 90%

(b) $\frac{\text{6¢ corporate income taxes}}{\text{90¢ of income taxes}} = 0.06\frac{2}{3} = \left(100 \cdot 0.06\frac{2}{3}\right)\% = 6\frac{2}{3}\%$

(c) (29% primary/secondary) + (3% community colleges) + (15% higher education) + (1% other) = 48%

(d) $\frac{\text{29¢ primary/secondary}}{\text{48¢ for education}} \doteq 0.604 = (100 \cdot 0.604)\% = 60.4\%$

(e) Human resources includes: other (6¢); corrections (6¢); seniors (3¢); adults/families (5¢); children (4¢); mental health (8¢); for a total of 32¢
50% of the human resources budget would be 16¢ ; or
Mental health + adults/families + seniors ; or
Children + corrections + other

(f) Yes

39. Let G be gross annual income; then:
\$550 per month $\cdot$ 12 months + 8% of (G – \$250,000) = \$18,550
$\Rightarrow 6600 + 0.08G - 20{,}000 = 18{,}550 \Rightarrow 0.08G = 31{,}950 \Rightarrow G = 399{,}375$
Or gross income was \$399,375

On-going Assessment 7-5; Review Problems

46. On the scale drawing, 14.5 in. by 5.5 in. = 79.75 in.^{2} and 4.25 in. by 8.75 in. = 37.1875 in.^{2}
$\Rightarrow \frac{\text{79.75 sq. in. scale}}{\text{1872 sq ft floor area}} = \frac{\text{37.1875 sq. in. scale}}{\text{x sq. ft. floor area}} \Rightarrow 79.75x = 37.1875 \cdot 1872 \Rightarrow x \doteq 873 \text{ ft.}^2$

47. Plant A: 30 people · 30 hours = 900 person-hours $\Rightarrow \frac{\text{900 person-hours}}{\text{30 items}}$ = 30 p-h per item

Plant B: 60 people · 60 hours = 3600 person-hours $\Rightarrow \frac{\text{3600 person-hours}}{\text{60 items}}$ = 60 p-h per item

So Plant A is more productive

48. There are 3 boys and 4 girls in each class unit of 7

There are $\frac{3}{7} \doteq 0.429 = 42.9\%$ boys in each class

There are $\frac{4}{7} \doteq 0.571 = 57.1\%$ girls in each class

On-going Assessment 7-6

1.

	(a)	(b)	(c)	(d)
Compounding Period	Semiannual	Quarterly	Monthly	Daily
Principal	$1000	$1000	$1000	$1000
Annual Rate	6%	8%	10%	12%
Time (Years)	2	3	5	4
Interest Rate Per Period	$\frac{6\%}{2} = 3\%$	$\frac{8\%}{4} = 2\%$	$\frac{10\%}{12} = 0.8\overline{3}\%$	$\frac{12\%}{365} \doteq 0.000329\%$
Number of Periods	4	12	60	1460
Interest Paid*	$125.51	$268.24	$645.31	$615.95

* In each case, where: A = compound amount

P = principal ($1000 in this problem)

i = interest rate per period

n = number of periods

I = interest paid

$A = P(1 + i)^n$ and $I = A - P$

2. If I is interest, P is principal, r is rate, and t is time in years:

$I = Prt = \$42{,}000 \cdot 13\% \cdot 1 \text{ year} \Rightarrow I = 42{,}000 \cdot 0.13 \cdot 1 = \$5460$ owed

3. Carolyn is compounding $125 for 12 periods at 1.5% per period, so:

$A = 125(1 + 0.015)^{12} \doteq \$149.45$ (i.e., principal and interest)

And interest owed is $149.45 – $125.00 = $24.45

4. If $I = Prt$, then $r = \frac{I}{Pt}$

The interest charged (I) was $28,500 – $25,000 = $3500; then:

$r = \frac{3500}{25{,}000 \cdot 4} = 0.035$

So he was charged at 3.5%

5. Look for the principal to be invested: if $A = P(1 + i)^n$, then $P = \frac{A}{(1+i)^n}$

Where $A = \$50{,}000$; $i = \frac{9\%}{4} = 2.25\%$; and $n = 5 \text{ years} \cdot 4 \text{ periods per year} = 20$; then:

$P = \frac{50{,}000}{(1+0.0225)^{20}} = 32{,}040.82$

So $32,040.82 must be invested now to realize $50,000 in five years

6. $I = Prt \Rightarrow$ Interest = \$320,000 · 13.5% · $1\frac{1}{2}$ years = 320,000 · 0.135 · 1.5 = 64,800
So the company must pay \$64,800 interest

7. $A = P(1 + i)^n$, where P = \$4000, $i = \frac{9\%}{4} = 2.25\%$, n = 20 years · 4 periods per year; then:
$A = 4000(1 + 0.0225)^{80} \doteq 23{,}720.58$
The couple's investment will be worth \$23,720.58

8. Interest = \$7200 · 9% · 3 years $\Rightarrow$ I = 7200 · 0.09 · 3 = \$1944 charged

9. (*i*) Interest as a percentage of savings is $\frac{\$53.90}{\$980} = 0.055 = 5.5\%$

(*ii*) Interest as a percentage of savings is $\frac{\$55.20}{\$600} = 0.092 = 9.2\%$

(*iii*) Interest as a percentage of savings is $\frac{\$158.40}{\$1200} = 0.132 = 13.2\%$

10. Hamburger prices starting at \$1.35 are compounding at 11% annually for 6 years; thus:
$A = P(1 + i)^n = 1.35(1 + 0.11)^6 \doteq 2.53 \Rightarrow$ A hamburger would cost about \$2.53 after six years

11. College tuition starting at \$10,000 is compounding at 9% annually for 10 years; thus:
$A = P(1 + i)^n = 10{,}000(1 + 0.09)^{10} \doteq 23{,}673.64 \Rightarrow$ College tuition would be about \$23,673.64

12. (See problem 5) $A = P(1 + i)^n \Rightarrow P = \frac{A}{(1+i)^n}$; thus if \$P compounded quarterly at 6.5% for 4 years yields \$4650:
$P = \frac{4650}{\left(1+\frac{0.065}{4}\right)^{4 \cdot 4}} \doteq 3529.89 \Rightarrow$ Sara had invested \$3529.89

13. \$300 compounded monthly at 1.1% per month for 11 months will yield:
$A = \$300(1 + 0.011)^{11} \doteq \$338.36$
And interest earned will be \$338.36 – \$300 = \$38.36
So interest as a percentage of the amount deposited is $\frac{\$38.36}{\$300} \doteq 0.128 = 12.8\%$ effective annual yield

14. We can develop a formula for compound decay:
Let A be the amount remaining after 1 period, r be the rate of decay, and B be the beginning amount;
Then A = B – decay = B – rB = B(1 – r). After n periods, then, $A = B(1 - r)^n$
So in the rain forest, where $B = 2.34 \cdot 10^9$, r = 0.5% = 0.005, and n = 12 · 20 = 240:
$A = 2.34 \cdot 10^9(1 - 0.005)^{240} \doteq 7.03 \cdot 10^8 \Rightarrow$ There will be about $7.03 \cdot 10^8$ trees left after 20 years

15. (*i*) First 3 years: P = \$3000, $i = \frac{5\%}{4} = 1.25\% = 0.0125$, and n = 4 · 3 = 12
$\Rightarrow A = \$3000(1 + 0.0125)^{12} \doteq \$3482.26$

(*ii*) Second 3 years: P = \$3482.26, $i = \frac{8\%}{4} = 2\% = 0.02$, and n = 4 · 3 = 12
$\Rightarrow A = \$3482.26(1 + 0.02)^{12} \doteq \$4416.35$

(*iii*) The balance in the account after six years was \$4416.35

16. If \$10,000 is compounded daily at 14% annual interest for 15 years:
$$A = \$10{,}000\left(1 + \frac{0.14}{365}\right)^{365\cdot 15} \doteq \$81{,}628.83 \text{ is in the fund}$$

17. Suppose \$1 were to be invested in each institution for 1 year. Then:

(*i*) At New Age, $i = \frac{0.09}{365}$ and $n = 365 \Rightarrow A = \$1\left(1 + \frac{0.09}{365}\right)^{365} \doteq \$1.094$
Subtracting the \$1 invested, interest = 9.4¢ , corresponding to an effective rate of $\frac{9.4¢}{100¢} = 9.4\%$

(*ii*) At Pay More, $i = \frac{0.105}{1}$ and $n = 1 \cdot 1 \Rightarrow A = \$1(1 + 0.105)^1 = \$1.105$
Subtracting the \$1 invested, interest = 10.5¢ , corresponding to an effective rate of 10.5%

(*iii*) Pay More Bank has a higher effective interest rate

18. (See problem 14) We can develop a formula for compound depreciation: $A = P(1 - i)^n$; thus:
where $P = \$15{,}000$, $i = 0.10$, and $n = 3 \Rightarrow A = \$15{,}000(1 - 0.1)^3 = \$10{,}935$ depreciated value

Chapter 7 Review

1. (a) $t = \frac{d}{65}$ (b) $C = [15 + 8(t - 1)]¢$

(c) $C = [0.6\,(14t)]¢ = (8.4t)¢$ (d) $S = \frac{100}{2}[(x - 99) + x] = 50(2x - 99)$

(e) $\frac{V}{m} = \frac{88}{100} \Rightarrow V = \frac{88}{100}m$

(f) Year 1: $E = S + 0.05S = 1.05S$
Year 2: $E = 1.05S + 0.10(1.05S) = 1.155S$
Year 3: $E = 1.155S + 0.15(1.155S) = 1.32825S$

2. (a) $\frac{1}{4}x - \frac{3}{5} \leq \frac{1}{2}(3 - 2x) \Rightarrow \frac{1}{4}x - \frac{3}{5} \leq \frac{3}{2} - x \Rightarrow 20\left(\frac{1}{4}x - \frac{3}{5}\right) \leq 20\left(\frac{3}{2} - x\right)$
$\Rightarrow 5x - 12 \leq 30 - 20x \Rightarrow 25x \leq 42 \Rightarrow x \leq \frac{42}{25}$

(b) $\frac{x}{3} - \frac{x}{2} \geq \frac{^-1}{4} \Rightarrow 12\left(\frac{x}{3} - \frac{x}{2}\right) \geq 12\left(\frac{^-1}{4}\right) \Rightarrow 4x - 6x \geq {}^-3 \Rightarrow {}^-2x \geq {}^-3 \Rightarrow x \leq \frac{3}{2}$

(c) $\frac{2}{3}\left(\frac{3}{4}x - 1\right) = \frac{2}{3} - x \Rightarrow \frac{1}{2}x - \frac{2}{3} = \frac{2}{3} - x \Rightarrow 6\left(\frac{1}{2}x - \frac{2}{3}\right) = 6\left(\frac{2}{3} - x\right) \Rightarrow 3x - 4 = 4 - 6x$
$\Rightarrow 9x = 8 \Rightarrow x = \frac{8}{9}$

(d) $\frac{5}{6} = \frac{4-x}{3} \Rightarrow 6\left(\frac{5}{6}\right) = 6\left(\frac{4-x}{3}\right) \Rightarrow 5 = 2(4 - x) \Rightarrow 5 = 8 - 2x \Rightarrow {}^-3 = {}^-2x \Rightarrow x = \frac{3}{2}$

3. Let x be the number of 2-kg packages $\Rightarrow$ $150 - x$ = the number of 1-kg packages
Total weight: $2x + 1(150 - x) = 265 \Rightarrow 2x + 150 - x = 265 \Rightarrow x = 115$
So there are 115 2-kg packages and 150 − 115 = 35 1-kg packages

4. Let d be the number of dimes and n be the number of nickels; then:

$$d = 2n + 3 \quad (i)$$
$$10¢ \cdot d + 5¢ \cdot n = 205¢ \Rightarrow 10d + 5n = 205 \quad (ii)$$

Substituting (i) into (ii): $10(2n+3) + 5n = 205 \Rightarrow 20n + 30 + 5n = 205 \Rightarrow 25n = 175 \Rightarrow n = 7$
Substituting $n = 7$ into (i): $d = 2(7) + 3 \Rightarrow d = 17$
So there are 17 dimes and 7 nickels

5. Let s be the number of seniors; j be the number of juniors; p be the number of sophomores; and f be the number of freshmen; then:

$$s + j + p + f = 5715 \quad (i)$$
$$s = j + 115 \quad (ii)$$
$$p = 2s = 2(j + 115) = 2j + 230 \quad (iii)$$
$$f = 2j \quad (iv)$$

Substituting (ii), (iii), and (iv) into (i):

$$(j + 115) + j + (2j + 230) + (2j) = 5715 \Rightarrow 6j + 345 = 5715 \Rightarrow 6j = 5370 \Rightarrow j = 895$$

Substituting $j = 895$ into (ii): $s = (895) + 115 = 1010$
Substituting $j = 895$ into (iii): $p = 2(895) + 230 = 2020$
Substituting $j = 895$ into (iv): $f = 2(895) = 1790$
So there are 1010 seniors, 895 juniors, 2020 sophomores, and 1790 freshmen

6. Let q be the quantity originally in each keg $\Rightarrow q - 37$ and $q - 7$, respectively, remains after beer is drawn
The amount $q - 7$ (the larger quantity) is 7 times the quantity $q - 37$, or:

$$q - 7 = 7(q - 37) \Rightarrow q - 7 = 7q - 259 \Rightarrow {}^{-}6q = {}^{-}252 \Rightarrow q = 42$$

So there were 42 gallons in each keg originally

7. The ratio of O weight to H_2 weight is 8:1; then:

$$8x + 1x = 16 \text{ (ounces)} \Rightarrow x = \tfrac{16}{9}$$

And $1x = \frac{16}{9} = 1\frac{7}{9}$ ounces of hydrogen per pound of water ($14\frac{2}{9}$ ounces O)

8. On the drawing scale, $\frac{1}{4}$ inch = 1 mile; answers may vary because of variations in measurement:

(a) The widest map distance is about $1\frac{1}{2}$ inches; then:

$$\frac{\frac{1}{4}\text{ inch}}{1\text{ mile}} = \frac{1\frac{1}{2}\text{ inches}}{x\text{ miles}} \Rightarrow \tfrac{1}{4}x = 1 \cdot 1\tfrac{1}{2} \Rightarrow x = \tfrac{4}{1} \cdot \tfrac{3}{2} = 6 \text{ miles}$$

(b) The map distance is about $1\frac{3}{8}$ inches; then:

$$\frac{\frac{1}{4}\text{ inch}}{1\text{ mile}} = \frac{1\frac{3}{8}\text{ inches}}{x\text{ miles}} \Rightarrow \tfrac{1}{4}x = 1 \cdot 1\tfrac{3}{8} \Rightarrow x = \tfrac{4}{1} \cdot \tfrac{11}{8} = 5\tfrac{1}{2} \text{ miles}$$

9. Given $\frac{t}{n} = \frac{T}{x}$, $tx = Tn \Rightarrow x = \frac{Tn}{t}$; then if $T = 173$, $n = 68$, and $t = 21$:

$$x = \frac{173 \cdot 68}{21} \doteq 560 \text{ fish}$$

10. The buyer could not know the overall ratio in her order without knowing the ratio of the number of chips from each plant. The first plant will have $\frac{2}{3}$ the number of defective chips as the second; $\left(\text{i.e., } \frac{\text{first}}{\text{second}} = \frac{\frac{2}{100}}{\frac{3}{100}} = \frac{2}{3} \Rightarrow \text{first} = \frac{2}{3}\text{ second}\right)$ but without knowing the total number of chips no further inferences can be drawn.

11. (a)

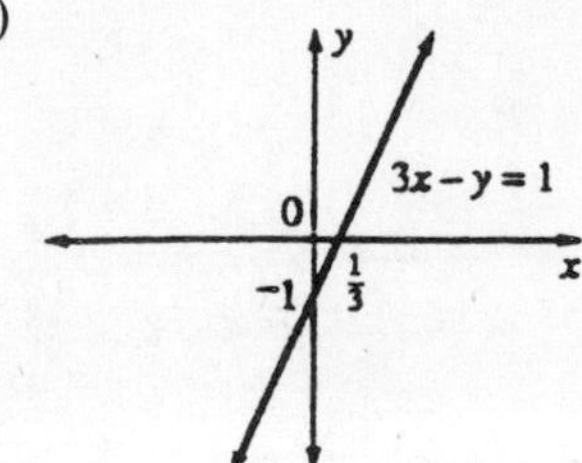

(b)

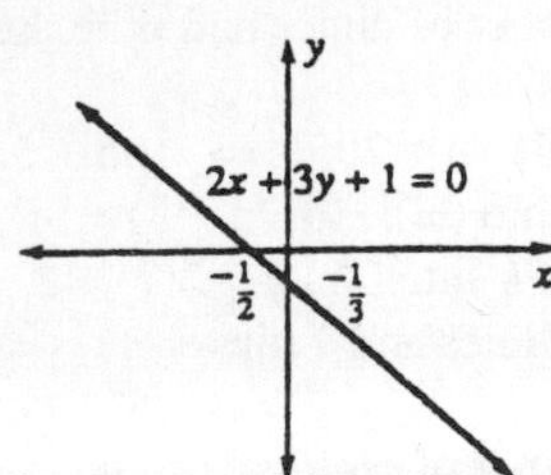

12. Let R be the number of Roosevelt's votes and H be the number of Hoover's votes; then:

$$\mathrm{R = H + 6{,}563{,}988} \qquad (i)$$

$$\mathrm{H} + \tfrac{1}{5}\mathrm{R} = \mathrm{R} - \tfrac{1}{5}\mathrm{R} + 2{,}444{,}622 \Rightarrow 5\mathrm{H} + \mathrm{R} = 4\mathrm{R} + 12{,}223{,}110 \Rightarrow 5\mathrm{H} = 3\mathrm{R} + 12{,}223{,}110 \qquad (ii)$$

Substituting (i) into (ii): $5\mathrm{H} = 3(\mathrm{H} + 6{,}563{,}988) + 12{,}223{,}110 \Rightarrow 2\mathrm{H} = 31{,}915{,}074 \Rightarrow \mathrm{H} = 15{,}957{,}537$

Substituting $\mathrm{H} = 15{,}957{,}537$ into (i): $\mathrm{R} = (15{,}957{,}537) + 6{,}563{,}988 = 22{,}521{,}525$

So Roosevelt won 22,521,525 votes and Hoover won 15,957,537 votes

13. (a) Given the points $(2,{}^{-}3)$ and $({}^{-}1,1)$:

$${}^{-}3 = \mathrm{m} \cdot 2 + \mathrm{b} \Rightarrow \mathrm{b} = {}^{-}2\mathrm{m} - 3 \qquad (i)$$

$$1 = \mathrm{m} \cdot {}^{-}1 + \mathrm{b} \Rightarrow \mathrm{b} = \mathrm{m} + 1 \qquad (ii)$$

Equating (i) and (ii): ${}^{-}2\mathrm{m} - 3 = \mathrm{m} + 1 \Rightarrow {}^{-}3\mathrm{m} = 4 \Rightarrow \mathrm{m} = \frac{{}^{-}4}{3}$

Substituting $\mathrm{m} = \frac{{}^{-}4}{3}$ into (ii): $\mathrm{b} = \left(\frac{{}^{-}4}{3}\right) + 1 = \frac{{}^{-}1}{3}$

So $\mathrm{y} = \frac{{}^{-}4}{3}\mathrm{x} - \frac{1}{3}$

(b) Given the points $({}^{-}3,0)$ and $({}^{-}3,2)$:
Both points have x-coordinate ${}^{-}3$ $\Rightarrow$ the equation of the line is $\mathrm{x} = {}^{-}3$

(c) Given the points $({}^{-}2,3)$ and $(2,3)$
Both points have y-coordinate 3 $\Rightarrow$ the equation of the line is $\mathrm{y} = 3$

14. (a) Given:

$$\mathrm{x} + 2\mathrm{y} = 3 \Rightarrow \mathrm{x} = 3 - 2\mathrm{y} \qquad (i)$$

$$2\mathrm{x} - \mathrm{y} = 9 \qquad (ii)$$

Substituting (i) into (ii): $2(3 - 2\mathrm{y}) - \mathrm{y} = 9 \Rightarrow 6 - 4\mathrm{y} - \mathrm{y} = 9 \Rightarrow {}^{-}5\mathrm{y} = 3 \Rightarrow \mathrm{y} = \frac{{}^{-}3}{5}$

Substituting $\mathrm{y} = \frac{{}^{-}3}{5}$ into (i): $\mathrm{x} = 3 - 2\left(\frac{{}^{-}3}{5}\right) \Rightarrow \mathrm{x} = 4\frac{1}{5}$

So the unique solution is $\left(4\frac{1}{5}, \frac{{}^{-}3}{5}\right)$

(b) Given:

$$\frac{\mathrm{x}}{2} + \frac{\mathrm{y}}{3} = 1 \Rightarrow 3\mathrm{x} + 2\mathrm{y} = 6 \qquad (i)$$

$$4\mathrm{y} - 3\mathrm{x} = 2 \Rightarrow {}^{-}3\mathrm{x} + 4\mathrm{y} = 2 \qquad (ii)$$

Adding (i) and (ii): $6\mathrm{y} = 8 \Rightarrow \mathrm{y} = \frac{8}{6} = \frac{4}{3}$

Substituting $\mathrm{y} = \frac{4}{3}$ into (i): $3\mathrm{x} + 2\left(\frac{4}{3}\right) = 6 \Rightarrow 3\mathrm{x} = 6 - \frac{8}{3} \Rightarrow \mathrm{x} = \frac{10}{9}$

So the unique solution is $\left(\frac{10}{9}, \frac{4}{3}\right)$

14. (c) Given:

$$x - 2y = 1 \Rightarrow {}^{-}2y = {}^{-}x + 1 \Rightarrow y = \tfrac{1}{2}x - \tfrac{1}{2} \quad (i)$$
$$4y - 2x = 0 \Rightarrow 4y = 2x \Rightarrow y = \tfrac{1}{2}x \quad (ii)$$

(i) and (ii) have the same slope and different y-intercepts $\Rightarrow$ they are parallel and there is no solution

15. (a) $6 = n \cdot 24 \Rightarrow n = \left(100 \cdot \frac{6}{24}\right)\% = 25\%$ (b) $n = 320\% \cdot 60 = \frac{320}{100} \cdot 60 = 192$

(c) $17 = 30\% \cdot n \Rightarrow n = \frac{17}{\frac{30}{100}} = 56.\overline{6}$ (d) $0.2 = n \cdot 1 \Rightarrow n = \left(100 \cdot \frac{0.2}{1}\right)\% = 20\%$

16. (a) $\frac{1}{8} = 0.125 = (100 \cdot 0.125)\% = 12.5\%$ (b) $\frac{3}{40} = 0.075 = (100 \cdot 0.075)\% = 7.5\%$

(c) $6.27 = (100 \cdot 6.27)\% = 627\%$ (d) $0.0123 = (100 \cdot 0.0123)\% = 1.23\%$

(e) $\frac{3}{2} = 1.5 = (100 \cdot 1.5)\% = 150\%$

17. (a) $60\% = \frac{60}{100} = 0.6$ (b) $\frac{2}{3}\% = \frac{\frac{2}{3}}{100} = \frac{2}{300} = 0.00\overline{6}$

(c) $100\% = \frac{100}{100} = 1$

18. $11\% \cdot \text{investment} = \$1020.80 \Rightarrow \text{investment} = \frac{\$1020.80}{0.11} = \$9280$

19. Percent defective = $\left(100 \cdot \frac{5}{150}\right)\% = 3.\overline{3}\,\%$

20. Percent correct = $\left(100 \cdot \frac{70-8}{70}\right)\% \doteq 88.6\%$

21. Let C be the cost four years ago $\Rightarrow 60\% \cdot C = \$3450 \Rightarrow C = \frac{\$3450}{0.60} = \$5750$

22. A discount of d% means the customer pays $1 - \frac{d}{100}$ for the purchase; so:
Discounts of 5%, 10%, and 20% means the customer pays 0.95. 0.90, and 0.80, respectively, of cost $\Rightarrow$ their product is the same in any order $\Rightarrow$ there is no difference in the total discount

23. Let C be the cost of the bicycle; then:

$$100\% \text{ of } C + 30\% \text{ of } C = \$104 \Rightarrow C + 0.3C = 104 \Rightarrow 1.3C = 104 \Rightarrow C = \frac{104}{1.3} = 80$$

So Jane paid \$80 for the bicycle

24. $I = Prt$, where $P = \$30{,}000$, $r = 12.5\% = 0.125$, and $t = 4$ years, so:

$$I = 30{,}000 \cdot 0.125 \cdot 4 = \$15{,}000 \text{ interest due}$$

25. \$10,000 compounded quarterly at 14% annual interest for 3 years will yield:

$$A = 10{,}000\left(1 + \frac{0.14}{4}\right)^{3\cdot 4} \doteq \$15{,}110.69 \text{ in the account}$$

CHAPTER 8 - PROBABILITY

1. (a) P(point up) = $\frac{n(up)}{n(s)} = \frac{56}{80} = \frac{7}{10}$ (b) P(point down) = $\frac{n(down)}{n(s)} = \frac{24}{80} = \frac{3}{10}$

(c) Probably not. When running an experiment again, with only a relatively small number of tries, the outcome will probably not be identical. Experimental probability is based only on the number of times the experiment is repeated--not what will happen in the long run.

(d) Yes. The thumbtack is unchanged, so the results will be determined by the same dynamics (but remember that experimental probability does not guarantee exact results).

2. (a) {0, 1, 2, 3, 4, 5, 6, 7, 8, 9}. (b) {0, 1, 2, 3, 4}.

(c) {1, 3, 5, 7, 9}. (d) {0, 1, 3, 4, 5, 6, 7, 8, 9}.

(e) (*i*) $\frac{5}{10} = \frac{1}{2}$ (*ii*) $\frac{5}{10} = \frac{1}{2}$ (*iii*) $\frac{9}{10}$

3. (a) P(1, 5, or 7) = $\frac{1}{8} + \frac{1}{8} + \frac{1}{8} = \frac{3}{8}$ (b) P(3 or 6) = $\frac{1}{8} + \frac{1}{8} = \frac{1}{4}$

(c) P(2, 4, 6, or 8) = $\frac{1}{8} + \frac{1}{8} + \frac{1}{8} + \frac{1}{8} = \frac{1}{2}$ (d) P(6 or 2) = $\frac{1}{8} + \frac{1}{8} = \frac{1}{4}$

(e) P(11) = 0 (f) P(4, 6, or 8) = $\frac{1}{8} + \frac{1}{8} + \frac{1}{8} = \frac{3}{8}$

(g) P(neither prime nor composite) = P(1) = $\frac{1}{8}$

4. (a) P(red) = $\frac{n(\text{red})}{n(S)} = \frac{26}{52} = \frac{1}{2}$ (b) P(face card) = $\frac{n(\text{face card})}{n(S)} = \frac{12}{52} = \frac{3}{13}$

(c) P(red or ten) = $\frac{n(\text{red})}{n(S)} + \frac{n(\text{ten})}{n(S)} - \frac{n(\text{red and ten})}{n(S)} = \frac{26}{52} + \frac{4}{52} - \frac{2}{52} = \frac{7}{13}$

(d) P(queen) = $\frac{n(\text{queen})}{n(S)} = \frac{4}{52} = \frac{1}{13}$ (e) P(not a queen) = 1 – P(queen) = $1 - \frac{1}{13} = \frac{12}{13}$

(f) P(face card or club) = $\frac{n(\text{face card})}{n(S)} + \frac{n(\text{club})}{n(S)} - \frac{n(\text{face card and club})}{n(S)} = \frac{12}{52} + \frac{13}{52} - \frac{3}{52} = \frac{11}{26}$

(g) P(face card and club) = $\frac{n(\text{face card and club})}{n(S)} = \frac{3}{52}$

(h) P(not a face card and not a club) = 1 – P(face card or club) = $1 - \frac{11}{26} = \frac{15}{26}$ (Note: Use a Venn diagram to verify this use of the complementary property) OR $\frac{40}{52} \cdot \frac{39}{52} = \frac{10}{13} \cdot \frac{3}{4} = \frac{30}{52} = \frac{15}{26}$

5. (a) There are 4 brown socks out of the total of 12 in the drawer, so P(brown) = $\frac{n(\text{brown})}{n(S)} = \frac{4}{12} = \frac{1}{3}$

(b) The events are mutually exclusive, so P(black or green) = $\frac{n(\text{black})}{n(S)} + \frac{n(\text{green})}{n(S)} = \frac{6}{12} + \frac{2}{12} = \frac{2}{3}$

(c) There are no red socks in the drawer, so P(red) = 0

(d) P(not black) = 1 – P(black) = $1 - \frac{n(\text{black})}{n(S)} = 1 - \frac{6}{12} = \frac{1}{2}$

6. (a) P(vowel) = $\frac{n(\text{vowel})}{n(S)} = \frac{5}{26}$ (b) P(consonant) = 1 – P(vowel) = $1 - \frac{5}{26} = \frac{21}{26}$

7. P(missing flight) = 1 – P(boarding flight) = 1 – 0.2 = 0.8

8. (a) P(English disk) = $\frac{n(\text{English disk})}{n(S)} = \frac{1}{6}$ (b) P(not Math nor Chemistry) = $\frac{n(\overline{M \cup C})}{n(S)} = \frac{4}{6} = \frac{2}{3}$

9. (a) There are 36 equally likely outcomes when rolling two dice. Of these 36, a 7 may be obtained in six different ways: {(1, 6), (2, 5), (3, 4), (4, 3), (5, 2), (6, 1)}
11 may be obtained in only two ways: {(5, 6), (6, 5)}
These events are mutually exclusive $\Rightarrow$ P(7 or 11) = $\frac{n(7)}{n(S)} + \frac{n(11)}{n(S)} = \frac{6}{36} + \frac{2}{36} = \frac{2}{9}$

(b) Two may be obtained in only one way: {(1, 1)}
Three may be obtained in two ways: {(1, 2), (2, 1)}
Twelve may be obtained in only one way: {(6, 6)}
These events are mutually exclusive $\Rightarrow$ P(Loss on first roll) = $\frac{n(2)}{n(S)} + \frac{n(3)}{n(S)} + \frac{n(12)}{n(S)} = \frac{1}{36} + \frac{2}{36} + \frac{1}{36} = \frac{1}{9}$

(c) A 4 may be rolled in three ways: {(1, 3), (2, 2), (3, 1)}
A 5 may be rolled in four ways: {(1, 4), (2, 3), (3, 2), (4, 1)}
A 6 may be rolled in five ways: {(1, 5), (2, 4), (3, 3), (4, 2), (5, 1)}
A 8 may be rolled in five ways: {(2, 6), (3, 5), (4, 4), (5, 3), (6, 2)}
A 9 may be rolled in four ways: {(3, 6), (4, 5), (5, 4), (6, 3)}
A 10 may be rolled in three ways: {(4, 6), (5, 5), (6, 4)}
These events are mutually exclusive $\Rightarrow$
P(Neither win nor loss) = $\frac{n(4)}{n(S)} + \frac{n(5)}{n(S)} + \frac{n(6)}{n(S)} + \frac{n(8)}{n(S)} + \frac{n(9)}{n(S)} + \frac{n(10)}{n(S)} = \frac{3}{36} + \frac{4}{36} + \frac{5}{36} + \frac{5}{36} + \frac{4}{36} + \frac{3}{36} = \frac{2}{3}$

(d) 6 or 8, with probabilities of $\frac{5}{36}$, have the highest probability of occurring again (7 has a probability of $\frac{6}{36}$)

(e) It is not possible to roll a sum of 1 with two dice, so P(1) = 0

(f) The largest number which can be rolled with two dice is 12, so P(< 13) = 1

(g) There is a $\frac{6}{36} = \frac{1}{6}$ probability of rolling 7 on any one roll
$\Rightarrow$ in 60 rolls one would expect $\frac{1}{6} \cdot 60 = 10$ sevens

10. 70%. P(no rain) = 1 – P(rain) = 1 – 0.30 = 0.70, or 70%

11. (a) There are 18 black slots on the roulette wheel $\Rightarrow$ P(black) = $\frac{n(\text{black})}{n(S)} = \frac{18}{38} = \frac{9}{19}$

(b) P(0 or 00) = $\frac{n(0 \text{ or } 00)}{n(S)} = \frac{2}{38} = \frac{1}{19}$

(c) This problem is easier if we find the probability that the ball <u>does</u> land on a number 1 through 12, and then use the property of complementary events. Thus:
P(not 1-12) = 1 – P(1-12) = 1 – $\frac{n(1\text{-}12)}{n(S)} = 1 - \frac{12}{38} = \frac{13}{19}$

(d) Since there are no green numbers other than 0 and 00, the events are mutually exclusive. Thus:
P(odd or green) = $\frac{n(\text{odd})}{n(S)} + \frac{n(\text{green})}{n(S)} = \frac{18}{38} + \frac{2}{38} = \frac{10}{19}$

12. P(0 or 00) = $\frac{1}{19}$, so in 190 spins one would expect the ball to land in one of these slots $\frac{1}{19} \cdot 190 = 10$ times

13. (a) P(I win or you lose) = P(H) + P(T) = $\frac{1}{2} + \frac{1}{2} = 1$ $\Rightarrow$ each player's probability of winning is not equal

(b) Equal [P(heads I win) = P(H) = $\frac{1}{2}$; P(tails you win) = P(T) = $\frac{1}{2}$]

13. (c) Equal $\left[P(1;\text{ I win}) = \frac{n(1)}{n(S)} = \frac{1}{6};\ P(6;\text{ you win}) = \frac{n(6)}{n(S)} = \frac{1}{6}\right]$

(d) Equal $\left[P(\text{even; I win}) = \frac{n(\text{even})}{n(S)} = \frac{3}{6};\ P(\text{odd; you win}) = \frac{3}{6}\right]$

(e) Not equal $\left[P(\geq 3;\text{ I win}) = \frac{n(\geq 3)}{n(S)} = \frac{4}{6};\ P(< 3;\text{ you win}) = \frac{n(< 3)}{n(S)} = \frac{2}{6}\right]$

(f) Equal $\left[P(1\text{ on each; I win}) = \frac{1}{36};\ P(6\text{ on each; you win}) = \frac{1}{36}\right]$

(g) Not equal: $P(3;\text{ I win}) = \frac{n(3)}{n(S)} = \frac{2}{6};\ P(2;\text{ you win}) = \frac{n(2)}{n(S)} = \frac{1}{6}$

(h) Not equal: red greater than white can occur in 15 ways:

Red	White
2	1
3	2, 1
4	3, 2, 1
5	4, 3, 2, 1
6	5, 4, 3, 2, 1

There are also 15 ways in which the white die could be greater than the red die and 6 ways in which they could be equal $\Rightarrow P(\text{red} > \text{white; I win}) = \frac{15}{36};\ P(\text{white} \geq \text{red; you win}) = \frac{21}{36}$

14. Assuming that the bowler's performance is consistent, and that 45 strikes in 150 frames is an unbiased empirical probability, then $P(\text{strike}) = \frac{n(\text{strikes})}{n(S)} = \frac{45}{150} = \frac{3}{10}$

15. (a) The sample space, S, is {(H, H), (H, T), (T, H), (T, T)}; exactly one head appears in two of the events $\Rightarrow P(\text{exactly 1 head}) = \frac{n(1\text{ head})}{n(S)} = \frac{2}{4} = \frac{1}{2}$

(b) At least one head means 1 head or 2 heads $\Rightarrow P(\text{at least 1}) = \frac{n(1\text{ head})}{n(S)} + \frac{n(2\text{ head})}{n(S)} = \frac{2}{4} + \frac{1}{4} = \frac{3}{4}$

(c) At most one head means 0 heads or 1 head $\Rightarrow P(\text{at most 1}) = \frac{1}{4} + \frac{1}{2} = \frac{3}{4}$

16. There are 350 + 320 + 310 + 400 = 1380 students in all $\Rightarrow P(\text{freshman}) = \frac{n(f)}{n(s)} = \frac{350}{1380} = \frac{35}{138}$

17. (a)

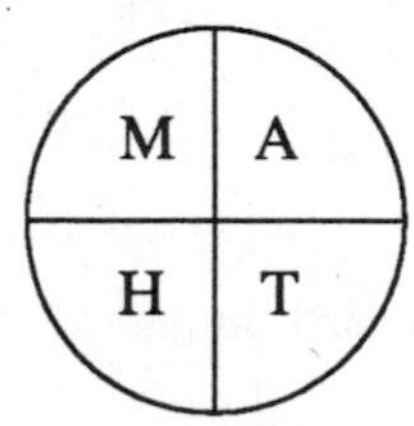

(b)

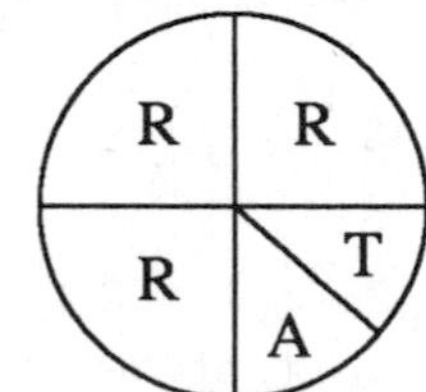

18. (a) There are five cards between 5 and J in each of the four suits $\Rightarrow P(\text{win}) = \frac{5\cdot 4}{52} = \frac{20}{52} = \frac{5}{13}$

(b) There are ten cards between 2 and K in each of the four suits $\Rightarrow P(\text{win}) = \frac{10\cdot 4}{52} = \frac{40}{52} = \frac{10}{13}$

(c) There are no cards between 5 and 6 $\Rightarrow P(\text{win}) = 0$

19. (a) Segment *a* will be lit for the digits 0, 2, 3, 5, 6, 7, 8, and 9 $\Rightarrow P(a) = \frac{8}{10} = \frac{4}{5}$

(b) Segment *b* will be lit for the digits 0, 1, 2, 3, 4, 7, 8, and 9 $\Rightarrow P(b) = \frac{8}{10} = \frac{4}{5}$

19. (c) Segments e and b will be lit for the digits 0, 1, 3, 4, 7, 8, and 9 $\Rightarrow$ $P(e \cap b) = \frac{7}{10}$

(d) Segment e will be lit for the digits 0, 1, 3, 4, 5, 6, 7, 8, and 9 $\Rightarrow$ $P(e) = \frac{9}{10}$
Segment b will be lit for the digits 0, 1, 2, 3, 4, 7, 8, and 9 $\Rightarrow$ $P(b) = \frac{8}{10}$
So $P(e \cup b) = P(e) + P(b) - P(e \cap b) = \frac{9}{10} + \frac{8}{10} - \frac{7}{10} = \frac{10}{10} = 1$
That is, either e or b will be lit for all digits

20. (a) The probability of students taking Algebra or Chemistry, or both

(b) The probability of students taking both Algebra and Chemistry

(c) $1 - P(C)$ is the probability that students are not taking chemistry

21. Because they are mutually exclusive, $P(A \cup B) = P(A) + P(B) = 0.3 + 0.4 = 0.7$

22. (a) The sample space, S, is $35 + 45 = 80 \Rightarrow P(\text{female}) = \frac{n(\text{female})}{n(S)} = \frac{35}{80} = \frac{9}{16}$

(b) $P(\text{Computer Science}) = \frac{n(\text{Computer Science})}{n(S)} = \frac{10}{80} = \frac{1}{8}$

(c) Since we know we have 20 Mathematics majors, this problem is easier if we use the property of complementary events $\Rightarrow P(\text{not Math}) = 1 - P(\text{Math}) = 1 - \frac{20}{80} = \frac{3}{4}$

(d) Since these events are mutually exclusive, $P(\text{Computer Science or Math}) = \frac{10}{80} + \frac{20}{80} = \frac{3}{8}$

On-going Assessment 8-2

1. (a)

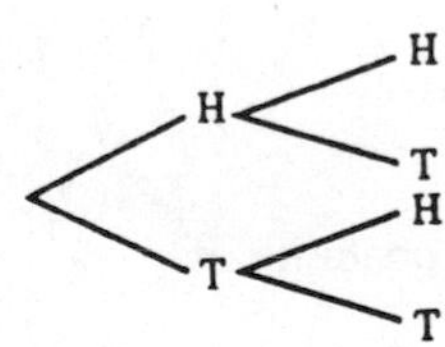

$S = \{HH, HT, TH, TT\}$

(b)

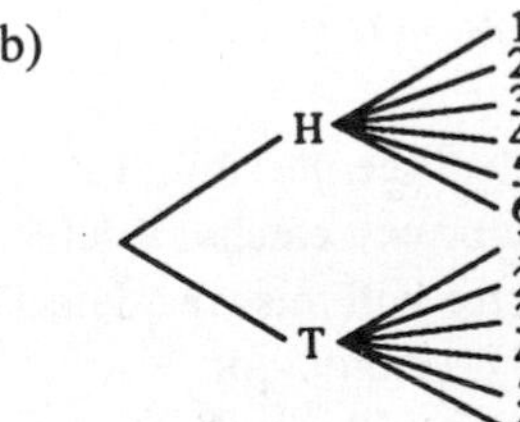

$S = \{H1, H2, H3, H4, H5, H6, T1, T2, T3, T4, T5, T6\}$

2. (a) $S = \{(1, 1), (1, 2), (1, 3), (2, 1), (2, 2), (2, 3)\}$ (b) $A = \{(2, 2)\}$

(c) $B = \{(1, 2), (2, 1), (2, 2), (2, 3)\}$ (d) $C = \{(1, 2), (2, 1), (2, 3)\}$

3. (a) $P(D) = \frac{1}{6}$; $P(A) = \frac{1}{6}$; $P(N) = \frac{1}{6} \Rightarrow P(DAN) = \frac{1}{6} \cdot \frac{1}{6} \cdot \frac{1}{6} = \frac{1}{216}$

(b) $P(D) = \frac{1}{6}$; $P(A) = \frac{1}{5}$; $P(N) = \frac{1}{4} \Rightarrow P(DAN) = \frac{1}{6} \cdot \frac{1}{5} \cdot \frac{1}{4} = \frac{1}{120}$

4. (a) $P(HAT) = \frac{1}{4} \cdot \frac{1}{3} \cdot \frac{1}{2} = \frac{1}{24}$ (b) $P(HAT) = \frac{1}{4} \cdot \frac{1}{4} \cdot \frac{1}{4} = \frac{1}{64}$

(c) $P(HAT) = \frac{1}{4} \cdot \frac{1}{3} \cdot \frac{1}{7} = \frac{1}{84}$

4. (d) Box 1: $P(A) = \frac{1}{3} \cdot \frac{1}{4} = \frac{1}{12}$ (because the probability of choosing Box 1 is $\frac{1}{3}$ and the probability of choosing an A, given Box 1, is $\frac{1}{4}$)
Box 2: $P(A) = \frac{1}{3} \cdot \frac{1}{3} = \frac{1}{9}$; Box 3: $P(A) = \frac{1}{3} \cdot 0 = 0$.
These are mutually exclusive events $\Rightarrow P(A) = \frac{1}{12} + \frac{1}{9} + 0 = \frac{7}{36}$

5. This problem is similar to that of drawing colored marbles out of a box without replacement; i.e., three woman-colored marbles from a box with four woman-colored and six man-colored in it. Thus:
$P(\text{3 women}) = \frac{4}{10} \cdot \frac{3}{9} \cdot \frac{2}{8} = \frac{1}{30}$

6. (a) (*i*) If we choose Box 1: $P(SOS) = \frac{2}{3} \cdot \frac{1}{2} \cdot 1 = \frac{1}{3}$

(*ii*) If we choose Box 2: $P(SOS) = \frac{4}{6} \cdot \frac{2}{5} \cdot \frac{3}{4} = \frac{1}{5}$

Thus we choose Box 1

(b) (*i*) If we choose Box 1: $P(SOS) = \frac{2}{3} \cdot \frac{1}{3} \cdot \frac{2}{3} = \frac{4}{27}$

(*ii*) If we choose Box 2: $P(SOS) = \frac{4}{6} \cdot \frac{2}{6} \cdot \frac{4}{6} = \frac{4}{27}$

So we may choose either box

7. (a) This problem is best illustrated by a tree diagram showing four mutually exclusive paths for the probabilities of a white ball being drawn. For example, the first path would show probabilities of $\frac{1}{5}$ for drawing a white ball from the first box, $\frac{3}{5}$ of drawing a white ball from the second box given that white had been drawn from box one, and $\frac{2}{3}$ of drawing a white ball from the third box given that white had been drawn from boxes one and two. Other paths would be similarly drawn. Thus:
$P(\text{white from 3}) = \frac{1}{5} \cdot \frac{3}{5} \cdot \frac{2}{3} + \frac{1}{5} \cdot \frac{2}{5} \cdot 1 + \frac{4}{5} \cdot \frac{2}{5} \cdot \frac{2}{3} + \frac{4}{5} \cdot \frac{3}{5} \cdot 1 = \frac{6}{75} \cdot \frac{2}{25} \cdot \frac{16}{75} \cdot \frac{12}{25} = \frac{64}{75}$

(b) $P(\text{black}) = 1 - P(\text{white}) = 1 - \frac{64}{75} = \frac{11}{75}$

8. A tree diagram would show three possibilities:
(*i*) First inspector will catch the defect, with a probability of 0.95; or
(*ii*) First inspector will miss the defect and the second will catch it, with a probability of $(0.05)(0.99) = 0.0495$; or
(*iii*) First inspector will miss the defect and the second will miss it, with a probability of $(0.05)(0.01) = 0.0005$
So the probability of a defect passing both inspectors (i.e., both inspectors missing) is 0.0005

9. (a) $P(\text{white from box 1}) = \frac{3}{5}$; $P(\text{white from box 2}) = \frac{2}{6} \Rightarrow P(\text{two whites}) = \frac{3}{5} \cdot \frac{2}{6} = \frac{1}{5}$

(b) "At least 1" means either one or two; i.e., black from 1 and black from 2, or, black from 1 and white from 2, or, white from 1 and black from 2. These events are mutually exclusive, so:
$P(\text{at least 1 black}) = \frac{2}{5} \cdot \frac{4}{6} + \frac{2}{5} \cdot \frac{2}{6} + \frac{3}{5} \cdot \frac{4}{6} = \frac{8}{30} + \frac{4}{30} + \frac{12}{30} = \frac{4}{5}$

(c) "At most 1" means either zero or one. Since we can have a maximum of 2 black balls, it is easier to find the probability of 2 black balls and then use the property of complementary events. Thus:
$P(\text{two blacks}) = \frac{2}{5} \cdot \frac{4}{6} = \frac{4}{15} \Rightarrow P(\text{0 or 1 black}) = 1 - P(\text{two blacks}) = 1 - \frac{4}{15} = \frac{11}{15}$

(d) $P(\text{black-white or white-black}) = \frac{2}{5} \cdot \frac{2}{6} + \frac{3}{5} \cdot \frac{4}{6} = \frac{4}{30} + \frac{12}{30} = \frac{8}{15}$

10. "At least 3 heads" means either 3 heads or 4 heads.
There is only one way four heads can be tossed; there are four ways 3 heads can be tossed: {HHHT, HHTH, HTHH, THHH}, each with probability $\frac{1}{2} \cdot \frac{1}{2} \cdot \frac{1}{2} \cdot \frac{1}{2} = \frac{1}{16}$
Thus P(at least 3 heads) = $\frac{1}{16} + \frac{1}{16} + \frac{1}{16} + \frac{1}{16} + \frac{1}{16} = \frac{5}{16}$

11. P(all boys) = $\frac{1}{2} \cdot \frac{1}{2} \cdot \frac{1}{2} \cdot \frac{1}{2} = \frac{1}{16}$

12. (a) There are five different ways of ascending four steps in either 1 or 2 strides: S = {(1, 1, 1, 1), (1, 2, 1), (1, 1, 2), (2, 1, 1), (2, 2)}, with probabilities of $\frac{1}{8}$, $\frac{1}{4}$, $\frac{1}{8}$, $\frac{1}{4}$, and $\frac{1}{4}$, respectively.
Thus, P(2 strides) = $\frac{1}{4}$

(b) P(3 strides) = $\frac{1}{4} + \frac{1}{8} + \frac{1}{4} = \frac{5}{8}$

(c) P(4 strides) = $\frac{1}{8}$

13. Draw a tree diagram with two sets of branches:
(*i*) One branch with each of the numbers 4, 6, 7, 8, 9 as choices, each with probability $\frac{1}{5}$
(*ii*) For each branch of (*i*), four branches with the remaining numbers as choices, each with probability $\frac{1}{4}$
(*iii*) There are 5 · 4 = 20 branches, each of which will have probability $\frac{1}{5} \cdot \frac{1}{4} = \frac{1}{20}$

(a) Add the two numbers in each branch of the tree diagram; there are 8 even sums
$\Rightarrow$ P(even sum = win) = $\frac{8}{20} = \frac{2}{5}$

(b) Yes [only two of the 20 products are odd (7 · 9 and 9 · 7) $\Rightarrow$ P(even = win) = $\frac{18}{20} = \frac{9}{10}$]

14. There are 4 · 4 = 16 possible numerator-denominator combinations, each with probability $\frac{1}{16}$. Of these, there are two combinations in which the numerator is more than $1\frac{1}{2}$ times the denominator (6 and 3; 5 and 3)
$\Rightarrow$ P(greater than $1\frac{1}{2}$) = $\frac{1}{16} + \frac{1}{16} = \frac{2}{16} = \frac{1}{8}$

15. (a) P(3 plums) = $\frac{5}{20} \cdot \frac{1}{20} \cdot \frac{5}{20} = \frac{1}{320}$

(b) P(3 oranges) = $\frac{3}{20} \cdot \frac{6}{20} \cdot \frac{7}{20} = \frac{63}{4000}$

(c) P(3 lemons) = $\frac{3}{20} \cdot \frac{0}{20} \cdot \frac{4}{20} = 0$

(d) P(No plums) = $\frac{15}{20} \cdot \frac{19}{20} \cdot \frac{15}{20} = \frac{171}{320}$

16. Each question has a $\frac{1}{2}$ probability of being right, and the results of each question have no effect on subsequent questions $\Rightarrow$ P(100%) = $\frac{1}{2} \cdot \frac{1}{2} \cdot \frac{1}{2} \cdot \frac{1}{2} \cdot \frac{1}{2} = \frac{1}{32}$

17. (a) P(Paxson loses) = P(Rattlesnake wins) $\Rightarrow$ P(4 Paxson losses) = $\frac{2}{3} \cdot \frac{2}{3} \cdot \frac{2}{3} \cdot \frac{2}{3} = \frac{16}{81}$

(b) There are six ways in which each school wins two games: D = {(PPRR), (PRPR), (PRRP), (RPPR), (RPRP), (RRPP)} ; each occurs with probability $\frac{2}{3} \cdot \frac{2}{3} \cdot \frac{1}{3} \cdot \frac{1}{3} = \frac{4}{81}$
$\Rightarrow$ P(Draw) = $6 \cdot \frac{4}{81} = \frac{8}{27}$

18. The set of multiples of 9 = {0, 9, 18, 27, 36}. The set of multiples of 4 = {0, 4, 8, 12, 16, 20, 24, 28, 32, 36}. There are 5 multiples of 9, 10 multiples of 4, and 40 numbers between 0 and 39.
Thus P(9 ×, 9 ×, 4 ×) = $\frac{5}{40} \cdot \frac{5}{40} \cdot \frac{10}{40} = \frac{1}{256}$

19. P(MISSISSIPPI) = $\frac{1}{11} \cdot \frac{4}{10} \cdot \frac{4}{9} \cdot \frac{3}{8} \cdot \frac{3}{7} \cdot \frac{2}{6} \cdot \frac{1}{5} \cdot \frac{2}{4} \cdot \frac{2}{3} \cdot \frac{1}{2} \cdot 1 = \frac{1152}{39916800} = \frac{1}{34650}$

20. (a) The total area of the dart board is 5x by 5x, or $25x^2$. The area of A is x by x, or x^2
$\Rightarrow$ P(Section A) = $\frac{x^2}{25x^2} = \frac{1}{25}$

(b) The area of B is $(3x)^2 - x^2 = 8x^2$ $\Rightarrow$ P(Section B) = $\frac{8x^2}{25x^2} = \frac{8}{25}$

20. (c) The area of C is $(5x)^2 - (3x)^2 = 16x^2 \Rightarrow$ P(Section C) = $\frac{16}{25}$

21. (a) Total area is 10 units by 10 units = 100 square units

(b) (*i*) P(region A) = $\frac{4}{100} = \frac{1}{25}$ (*ii*) P(region B) = $\frac{12}{100} = \frac{3}{25}$

(*iii*) P(region C) = $\frac{20}{100} = \frac{1}{5}$ (*iv*) P(region D) = $\frac{28}{100} = \frac{7}{25}$

(*v*) P(region E) = $\frac{36}{100} = \frac{9}{25}$

(c) 20 points with two darts can only be scored if both land in region A $\Rightarrow$ P(20 points) = $\frac{1}{25} \cdot \frac{1}{25} = \frac{1}{625}$

(d) If the dart lands in neither D nor E, then it must land in either A, B, or C
$\Rightarrow$ P(A, B, or C) = P(neither D nor E) = $\frac{4}{100} + \frac{12}{100} + \frac{20}{100} = \frac{9}{25}$

22. The total area of the earth is about 197,100,00 square miles. Thus:
P(Hitting water) = $\frac{139{,}600{,}000}{197{,}100{,}000}$ = 0.7 (to the nearest tenth)

23. Assuming that we have an analog and not a digital display, the second hand will cover the distance between 3 and 4 in five seconds $\Rightarrow$ P(between 3 and 4) = $\frac{5}{60} = \frac{1}{12}$

24. There are 7 ways of infecting at least 1 child: (YNN), (NYN), (NNY), (YYN), (YNY), (NYY), (YYY)
Each Y has probability 0.1; each N has probability 0.9
Thus P(At least 1) = $3(0.1)(0.9)(0.9) + 3(0.1)(0.1)(0.9) + (0.1)^3 = 0.271$

25. Set A covers 2 units ($1 - {}^-1$); set B covers 5 units ($2 - {}^-3$) $\Rightarrow$ P(B $\in$ A) = $\frac{2}{5}$

26. We want the probability that a randomly-selected patient has lung cancer, given that the patient smokes.
We know that of the 30 smokers 25 have lung cancer, so :
P(cancer given smoker) = $\frac{n(\text{cancer} \cap \text{smoker})}{n(\text{smoker})} = \frac{25}{30} = \frac{5}{6}$

27. Of the ten secretaries two are male, so P(secretary given male) = $\frac{n(\text{male} \cap \text{secretary})}{n(\text{male})} = \frac{2}{28} = \frac{1}{14}$

28. As shown in Problem 26, the probability of an event given another happening, or P(A given B), is:
P(A given B) = $\frac{P(A \cap B)}{P(B)}$ $\Rightarrow$ P(A $\cap$ B) = P(B) $\cdot$ P(A given B). Thus:
P(eaten $\cap$ sickly) = P(sickly) $\cdot$ P(eaten given sickly) = $\frac{1}{20} \cdot \frac{1}{3} = \frac{1}{60}$;
P(eaten $\cap$ not sickly) = P(not sickly) $\cdot$ P(eaten given not sickly) = $\frac{19}{20} \cdot \frac{1}{150} = \frac{19}{3000}$;
$\Rightarrow$ P(Eaten) = $\frac{1}{60} + \frac{19}{3000} = \frac{23}{1000}$

29. (*i*) Billie-Bobby-Billie: Carolyn can win the prize only if she wins the first two games or the last two games.
P(beats Billie and beats Bobbie) = (0.5)(0.8) = 0.4
P(loses to Billie; beats Bobby and Billie) = (0.5)(0.8)(0.5) = 0.2
P(wins prize) = 0.4 + 0.2 = 0.6

(*ii*) Bobby-Billie-Bobby:
P(beats Bobby and beats Billie) = (0.8)(0.5) = 0.4
P(loses to Bobby; beats Billie and Bobby) = (0.2)(0.5)(0.8) = 0.08
P(wins prize) = 0.4 + 0.08 = 0.48

Carolyn should choose to play Billie-Bobby-Billie.

30. (*i*) HS: P(win) = P(1st in) · P(Point) + P(1st out) · P(2nd in) · P(Point)
= (0.50)(0.75) + (0.50)(0.75)(0.50) = 0.5625

(*ii*) HH: P(win) = (0.50)(0.75) + (0.50)(0.50)(0.75) = 0.5625

(*iii*) SH: P(win) = (0.75)(0.50) + (0.25)(0.50)(0.75) = 0.46875

(*iv*) SS: P(win) = (0.75)(0.50) + (0.25)(0.75)(0.50) = 0.46875

Jane should always serve hard the first time. It does not matter what her second serve is.

On-going Assessment 8-2; Review Problems

40. (a) A certain event ↔ (v), or a certain event has a probability of 1

(b) An impossible event ↔ (iii), or an impossible event has a probability of 0

(c) A very likely event ↔ (ii), or a very likely event has a probability close to 1

(d) An unlikely event ↔ (i), or an unlikely event has a probability close to 0

(e) A 50% chance ↔ (iv), or a 50% chance has a probability of $\frac{1}{2}$

41. (a) P(April 7) = $\frac{1}{30}$ (b) P(April 31) = 0

(c) P(Before April 20) = $\frac{19}{30}$

On-going Assessment 8-3

1. Answers may vary. One way would be to let a red card represent either a boy or a girl and a black card represent the other ... the deck would then be shuffled and cards selected randomly

2. Answers may vary

(a) Use a table of random numbers; pick one at random, letting digits 0 through 8 represent rain and 9 represent no rain

(b) From a representative sample of seven random numbers, where R is rain and N is no rain:

Day	1	2	3	4	5	6	7
Weather	R	R	R	R	R	R	N

You would perform a large number of simulations; then find the proportion in which rain was observed for seven days in a row. Your proportion should be close to $(0.9)^7 \doteq 0.48$.

(c) P(not rain for seven days in a row) = 1 – P(seven days in a row) = 1 – 0.48 = 0.52

3. If trial 1 produces 2, 5, 1, 3, then Bridge #1 is open, Bridge #2 is closed, Bridge #3 is closed, and Bridge #4 is closed $\Rightarrow$ there was no open route
If trial 2 produces 7, 4, 4, 6, then Bridge #1 is closed, Bridge #2 is open, Bridge #3 is open, and Bridge #4 is open $\Rightarrow$ there was an open route

You may use a spinner, a random number generator, a table, or any other means of producing random numbers; continue the experiment for 20 trials and record your results

4. Answers may vary

(a) Let the numbers 1, 2, 3, 4, 5, 6 represent the numbers of the die and ignore the numbers 0, 7, 8, 9

(b) Number the persons 01, 02, 03, ... , 20. Pick 3 two-digit numbers at random (discard any that are more than 20 and draw again); these are the numbers of the 3 out of 20 that will be chosen

(c) Let red be numbers 1, 2, 3, 4, 5; green be numbers 6, 7, 8; yellow be 9; and white be 0; then pick a number at random $\Rightarrow$ its value will represent the color upon which the needle rests

5. Number the students from 001 to 500. Pick 30 three-digit numbers at random (discard 000 or any that are more than 500 and draw again); these are the numbers of the 30 out of 500 students that will be chosen.

6. Monday: Pick 10 random numbers; let the digits 0 to 7 represent rain and 8, 9 represent dry
Tuesday: Pick 10 random numbers; if it rained on Monday let 0 to 7 represent rain and if not, let 0 to 2 represent rain
Wednesday through Saturday: Repeat.

7. In a random-number table, mark off 100 two-digit blocks. Let numbers 00-14 represent contraction of strep throat. Pick a two-digit number at random from the group of 100; if it is within 00-14 it simulates having caught the disease. Do the experiment three times to represent three children. If at least one of the numbers is in the range 00 to 14, this represents a child in the 3-child family having strep.

8. $\text{P(less than 30)} = \frac{n(\text{numbers} < 30)}{100} = \frac{30}{100} = \frac{3}{10}$

9. Assuming an unbiased random sample of fish in the pond are caught, then $\frac{50}{300} = \frac{1}{6}$ of the total population is marked. Let n be the fish population $\Rightarrow$ $\frac{1}{6}n = 200$ $\Rightarrow$ $n = 1200$ fish in the pond

10. (a) Since it is possible for the losing team to win three games in a series, the maximum number that could be played is 7

(b) Since the teams are evenly matched, use a table of random digits and let a number between 0 and 4 represent a win by Team A; let a number between 5 and 9 represent a win by Team B. Pick a starting spot and count the number of digits it takes before a Team A or Team B series win is recorded. Repeat the experiment many times and then base your answers on:

$$\text{P(4-game series)} = \frac{n(\text{4-game series})}{n(\text{Total series})} \text{ and P(7-game series)} = \frac{n(\text{7-game series})}{n(\text{Total series})}.$$

Given evenly matched teams, the probability of a 4-game series would be expected to be low

On-going Assessment 8-3; Review Problems

21. No [there are $2 \cdot 2 \cdot 2 \cdot 2 = 16$ possible outcomes, of which six have exactly two heads: {(HHTT), (HTHT), (HTTH), (THHT), (THTH), (TTHH)} $\Rightarrow$ P(win) $= \frac{6}{16} = \frac{3}{8}$]

22. (a) $\frac{13}{52} = \frac{1}{4}$ (b) $\frac{4}{52} \cdot \frac{13}{52} = \frac{52}{2704} = \frac{1}{52}$

22. (c) $1 - \frac{4}{52} = \frac{48}{52} = \frac{12}{13}$ (d) $1 - \frac{1}{4} = \frac{3}{4}$

(e) $\frac{1}{4} + \frac{1}{4} = \frac{1}{2}$ (f) $\frac{1}{52}$

(g) $\frac{1}{13} + \frac{1}{4} - \frac{1}{13} \cdot \frac{1}{4} = \frac{4}{13}$ (h) $\frac{1}{2} + \frac{1}{2} = 1$

23. (a) $\frac{7}{19} + \frac{8}{19} = \frac{15}{19}$ (b) $\frac{7}{19} \cdot \frac{8}{19} = \frac{56}{361}$

(c) $\frac{7}{19} \cdot \frac{8}{18} = \frac{28}{171}$

On-going Assessment 8-4

1. (a) P(drawing a face card) = $\frac{12}{52} = \frac{3}{13}$ $\Rightarrow$ odds in favor = $\frac{\text{P(face card)}}{1 - \text{P(face card)}} = \frac{3}{13} \div \frac{10}{13} = \frac{3}{10}$ or 3:10

   (b) Odds in favor are 3:10 $\Rightarrow$ odds against = 10:3

2. $P(7) = \frac{1}{6}$ $\Rightarrow$ odds against = $\frac{1-P(7)}{P(7)} = \frac{5}{6} \div \frac{1}{6} = \frac{5}{1}$ or 5:1

3. If P(boy) = $\frac{1}{2}$, then P(4 boys) = $(\frac{1}{2})^4 = \frac{1}{16}$ $\Rightarrow$ odds against = $\frac{1-\text{P(4 boys)}}{\text{P(4 boys)}} = \frac{15}{16} \div \frac{1}{16} = \frac{15}{1}$ or 15:1

4. (a) P(tail on 10th toss) = $\frac{1}{2}$

   (b) P(10 more tails) = P(10 tails in any 10 tosses) = $(\frac{1}{2})^{10} = \frac{1}{1024}$

   (c) Odds against = $\frac{1-\text{P(10 tails)}}{\text{P(10 tails)}} = \frac{1023}{1}$ or 1023:1

5. $\frac{1-\text{P(win)}}{\text{P(win)}} = \frac{3}{5}$, given that the odds against are 3:5 $\Rightarrow$ 5[1 – P(win)] = 3[P(win)]
   $\Rightarrow$ 5 – 5[P(win)] = 3[P(win)] $\Rightarrow$ 5 = 8[P(win)] $\Rightarrow$ P(win) = $\frac{5}{8}$

6. S = {HHH, HHT, HTH, HTT, THH, THT, TTH, TTT}. At least 2 heads appear in 4 of the 8 outcomes
   $\Rightarrow$ P(at least 2 heads) = $\frac{1}{2}$ $\Rightarrow$ odds in favor = $\frac{\text{P(At least 2 heads)}}{1 - \text{P(At least 2 heads)}} = \frac{1}{1}$ or 1:1

7. Odds against raining = $\frac{1 - \text{P(Rain)}}{\text{P(Rain)}} = \frac{1 - 0.60}{0.60} = \frac{0.40}{0.60} = \frac{2}{3}$ or 2:3

8. P(red slot) = $\frac{18}{38} = \frac{9}{19}$ $\Rightarrow$ odds against red slot = $\frac{1 - \frac{9}{19}}{\frac{9}{19}} = \frac{10}{9}$ or 10:9

9. Odds are 26:1 that Gameylegs will lose $\Rightarrow$ $\frac{\text{P(loss)}}{1-\text{P(loss)}} = \frac{26}{1}$ $\Rightarrow$ P(loss) = $\frac{26}{27}$ $\Rightarrow$ probability of Gameylegs winning is $1 - \frac{26}{27} = \frac{1}{27}$

10. E = 1(0.15) + 2(0.20) + 3(0.40) + 4(0.10) + 5(0.05) + 6(0.10) = 3 hours

11. There are six ways two dice can roll 7 $\Rightarrow$ $P(7) = \frac{6}{36} = \frac{1}{6}$
    So E = $\left(\frac{1}{6}\right) \cdot 10 + \left(\frac{5}{6}\right) \cdot {}^{-}2 = \frac{10}{6} - \frac{10}{6} = 0$ $\Rightarrow$ on average, there will be 0 expected gain on each throw
    $\Rightarrow$ In the long run you will come out about even

12. (a) $P(17) = \frac{1}{38}$

    (b) Odds against 17 = $\frac{1 - P(17)}{P(17)} = \frac{37}{38} \div \frac{1}{38} = \frac{37}{1}$ or 37:1

12. (c) $E = \left(\frac{1}{38}\right) \cdot \$36 = \$\frac{36}{38} = \$\frac{18}{19}$, or about 95¢ $\Rightarrow$ expected payoff is $^{-}\$\frac{1}{19}$, or about $^{-}5$¢

13. $E = \$0.25(\frac{5}{25}) + \$0.10(\frac{5}{25}) + \$0.05(\frac{5}{25}) + \$0.01(\frac{10}{25}) = \$0.084$, or about 8¢

14. Odds in favor of winning = 5:2 $\Rightarrow$ $\frac{\text{P(win)}}{1 - \text{P(win)}} = \frac{5}{2}$ $\Rightarrow$ $\text{P(win)} = \frac{5}{7}$
Then $E = \$14{,}000(\frac{5}{7}) = \$10{,}000$

15. (a) There are two outcomes of further tossing that would provide Al with a win: {H, TH}, so P(Al wins) = $\frac{1}{2} + \frac{1}{2} \cdot \frac{1}{2} = \frac{3}{4}$ and P(Betsy wins) = 1 – P(Al wins) = $\frac{1}{4}$ $\Rightarrow$ an equitable division would be $\frac{1}{4}$ for Betsy and $\frac{3}{4}$ for Al, or \$25 for Betsy and \$75 for Al

(b) Odds against Betsy = $\frac{1 - \text{P(Betsy wins)}}{\text{P(Betsy wins)}} = 3:1$

(c) There are 15 outcomes of further tossing that would give Al a win: {HH, HTH, HTTH, HTTTH, HTTTTH, THH, THTH, THTTH, THTTTH, TTHH, TTHTH, TTHTTH, TTTHH, TTTHTH, TTTTHH} $\Rightarrow$ P(Al wins) = $\frac{1}{4} + \frac{1}{8} + \frac{1}{16} + \frac{1}{32} + \frac{1}{64} + \frac{1}{8} + \frac{1}{16} + \frac{1}{32} + \frac{1}{64} + \frac{1}{16} + \frac{1}{32} + \frac{1}{64} + \frac{1}{32} + \frac{1}{64} + \frac{1}{64} = \frac{57}{64}$ $\doteq 0.8906$. Rounding to the nearest dollar, Al should receive \$89 and Betsy \$11

(d) Odds for Al = $\frac{\text{P(Al wins)}}{1 - \text{P(Al wins)}} = \frac{\frac{57}{64}}{1 - \frac{57}{64}} = 57:7$

16. P(2 heads) = $\frac{1}{4}$; P(1 head) = $\frac{1}{2}$; P(0 heads) = $\frac{1}{4}$ $\Rightarrow$ $E = \$10(\frac{1}{4}) + \$5(\frac{1}{2}) + \$0(\frac{1}{4}) = \$5.00$
Because you pay the same as the expected gain, it is a fair game

17. $E = \$100(\frac{1}{200}) = \$0.50$ $\Rightarrow$ since expected gain is less than cost, it is not a fair game

On-going Assessment 8-4; Review Problems

23. (a) S = {1, 2, 3, 4}

(b) S = {Red, Blue}

(c) If R means red and B means blue: S = {(1, R), (1, B), (2, R), (2, B), (3, R), (3, B), (4, R), (4, B)}

(d) S = {(R, 1), (R, 2), (R, 3), (R, 4), (R, 5), (R, 6), (B, 1), (B, 2), (B, 3), (B, 4), (B, 5), (B, 6)}

(e) S = {(1, 1), (1, 2), (1, 3), (1, 4), (2, 1), (2, 2), (2, 3), (2, 4), (3, 1), (3, 2), (3, 3), (3, 4), (4, 1), (4, 2), (4, 3), (4, 4)}

(f) S = {(R, R), (R, B), (B, R), (B, B)}

24. $P(B) = \sqrt{P(B, B)} = \sqrt{\frac{25}{36}} = \frac{5}{6}$
$\Rightarrow$ the blue section must have $\frac{5}{6} \cdot 360° = 300°$ and the red section must have $360° - 300° = 60°$

25. P(2 Vowels) = $\frac{5}{26} \cdot \frac{5}{26} = \frac{25}{676}$

On-going Assessment 8-5

1. $\frac{12!}{6!4!2!} = 13{,}860$ ways for the 12 cars to finish

2. There are $16 \cdot 14 = 224$ different ways of pairing 16 boys and 14 girls

3. Each coin toss will result in two possible outcomes (H or T) $\Rightarrow$ five tosses will result in $2^5 = 32$ different combinations of heads and tails

4. The number of ways the four digits may be arranged is $10^4 = 10{,}000$ $\Rightarrow$ 10,000 numbers can be associated with each prefix (assuming all can be used)

5. Assume all letters after the first can be repeated. Then:

   (*i*) There are $2 \cdot 26 \cdot 26 = 1352$ possible three-letter call signs

   (*ii*) There are $2 \cdot 26 \cdot 26 \cdot 26 = 35{,}152$ possible four-letter call signs

6. There are $3 \cdot 15 \cdot 4 = 180$ possible different three-course meals

7. (a) True $[6 \cdot 5! = 6 \cdot (5 \cdot 4 \cdot 3 \cdot 2 \cdot 1) = 6!]$

   (b) False $(3! + 3! = 3 \cdot 2 \cdot 1 + 3 \cdot 2 \cdot 1 \neq 6!)$

   (c) False $\left(\frac{6!}{3!} = \frac{6 \cdot 5 \cdot 4 \cdot 3 \cdot 2 \cdot 1}{3 \cdot 2 \cdot 1} = 6 \cdot 5 \cdot 4 \neq 2!\right)$

   (d) False $\left(\frac{6!}{3} = \frac{6 \cdot 5 \cdot 4 \cdot 3 \cdot 2 \cdot 1}{3} \neq 2!\right)$

   (e) True $\left(\frac{6!}{5!} = \frac{6 \cdot 5 \cdot 4 \cdot 3 \cdot 2 \cdot 1}{5 \cdot 4 \cdot 3 \cdot 2 \cdot 1} = 6\right)$

   (f) True $\left[\frac{6 \cdot 5 \cdot 4 \cdot 3 \cdot 2 \cdot 1}{(4 \cdot 3 \cdot 2 \cdot 1)(2 \cdot 1)} = \frac{6 \cdot 5}{2 \cdot 1} = 15\right]$

   (g) True $[(n + 1) \cdot n! = (n + 1) \cdot n \cdot (n - 1) \cdot (n - 2) \cdot \cdots \cdot 3 \cdot 2 \cdot 1 = (n + 1)!]$

8. There are no letters repeated in "SCRAMBLE" $\Rightarrow$ $8! = 40{,}320$ possible arrangements

9. Since order is not distinct, the number of two-person committees is a combination of six people taken two at a time, or ${}_6C_2 \Rightarrow {}_6C_2 = \frac{6!}{2!(6-2)!} = 15$ different committees

10. (a) There are two letters repeated in "OHIO" $\Rightarrow$ $\frac{4!}{2!} = 12$ possible arrangements

    (b) $\frac{7!}{4!} = 210$ possible arrangements

    (c) There are two and three letters repeated in "ILLINOIS" $\Rightarrow$ $\frac{8!}{2!3!} = 3360$ possible arrangements

    (d) $\frac{11!}{4!4!2!} = 34{,}650$ possible arrangements

    (e) $\frac{9!}{4!2!2!} = 3780$ possible arrangements

11. (a) Since order is distinct, this is a permutation of 30 members taken 3 at a time: ${}_{30}P_3 = \frac{30!}{(30-3)!} = 24{,}360$ possible ways

    (b) In this case order is not distinct; this is a combination: ${}_{30}C_3 = \frac{30!}{3!(30-3)!} = 4060$ possible ways

12. The combination of 12 players taken 5 at a time is: ${}_{12}C_5 = \frac{12!}{5!(12-5)!} = 792$ different teams

13. Five volumes may be placed in $5! = 120$ different ways; only one will be in order $\Rightarrow$ P(in order) $= \frac{1}{120}$

14. We want the number of ways of choosing 10 points, 2 at a time. Since a line may be drawn either way, order is not distinct; i.e., we have a combination $\Rightarrow$ ${}_{10}C_2 = \frac{10!}{2!(10-2)!} = 45$ possible straight lines

15. Sally can run $\frac{9!}{4!3!2!} = 1260$ nine-flag signals up the pole

16. (a) Each shortest path involves one face of the cube. Since there are 6 faces, there are 6 shortest paths

16. (b) There are $6 \cdot 6 = 36$ total shortest paths

17. If there were n people at the party, there were n combinations of people two at a time shaking hands. That is: ${}_nC_2 = \frac{n!}{(n-2)!2!} = \frac{n \cdot (n-1)}{2!} = 28 \Rightarrow n \cdot (n - 1) = 56 \Rightarrow n = 8$ people at the party

18. (a) The number of ways of selecting a committee of 3 from the group of 7 Americans is ${}_7C_3 = 35$
There are ${}_{15}C_3 = 455$ ways of selecting 3 members from the whole set
$\Rightarrow$ P(3 Americans) $= \frac{35}{455} = \frac{1}{13}$

(b) If no Americans are selected, there are ${}_8C_3 = 56$ ways of selecting the 3 members from among the French and English
$\Rightarrow$ P(no American) $= \frac{56}{455} = \frac{8}{65}$

19. Order is not important $\Rightarrow$ this is a combination of 52 cards taken 5 at a time:
${}_{52}C_5 = \frac{52!}{47!5!} = 2{,}598{,}960$ possible five-card hands

20. If no letter or number repetitions are allowed, there are $26 \cdot 25 \cdot 24 \cdot 10 \cdot 9 \cdot 8 = 11{,}232{,}000$ possible numbers

21. There are ${}_{54}C_6 = \frac{54!}{48!6!} = 25{,}827{,}165$ possible combinations of numbers, only one of which will win
$\Rightarrow$ P(win) $= \frac{1}{25{,}827{,}165}$

22. There are $10 \cdot 10 \cdot 10 - 10 \cdot 10 - 10 \cdot 10 \cdot 10 \cdot 10 = 10^9$ possible social security numbers

23. If six free throws are made, then four are missed
If the probability of making one is $\frac{2}{3}$, then the probability of missing is $\frac{1}{3}$
Thus P(6 made and 4 missed) $= (\frac{2}{3})^6 \cdot (\frac{1}{3})^4$
There are ${}_{10}C_6 = 210$ different ways of making 6 free throws out of 10
$\Rightarrow$ P(exactly 6 free throws) $= 210 \cdot (\frac{2}{3})^6 \cdot (\frac{1}{3})^4 = \frac{13{,}440}{59{,}049} \doteq 0.23$

24. If we treat this as 5 people to be seated in 5 chairs (since the couples cannot be separated), there are $5! = 120$ different ways of being seated. Each couple, though, can be alternated, and there are $2^5 = 32$ ways of doing this $\Rightarrow 120 \cdot 32 = 3840$ possible combinations

On-going Assessment 8-5; Review Problems

30. (a) P(at least one ace) = P(1 ace) + P(2 aces)
P(1 ace) = P(ace and other) + P(other and ace) $= \frac{4}{52} \cdot \frac{48}{51} + \frac{48}{52} \cdot \frac{4}{51} = \frac{16}{221} + \frac{16}{221} = \frac{32}{221}$
P(2 aces) $= \frac{4}{52} \cdot \frac{3}{51} = \frac{1}{221}$
$\Rightarrow$ P(at least one ace) $= \frac{32}{221} + \frac{1}{221} = \frac{33}{221}$

(b) P(one red card) = P(red and black) + P(black and red) $= \frac{26}{52} \cdot \frac{26}{51} + \frac{26}{52} \cdot \frac{26}{51} = \frac{13}{51} + \frac{13}{51} = \frac{26}{51}$

31. P(sum > 10) = P(11) + P(12)
11 can be tossed in two ways {(5, 6), (6,5)} $\Rightarrow$ P(11) $= \frac{2}{36}$
12 can be tossed in only one way $\Rightarrow$ P(12) $= \frac{1}{36}$
$\Rightarrow$ P(sum > 10) $= \frac{2}{36} + \frac{1}{36} = \frac{1}{12}$

32. The possible outcomes are {HH, HT, TH, TT}
Then P(both heads) = $\frac{1}{4}$; P (both tails) = $\frac{1}{4}$; P(no match) = $\frac{1}{2}$
$\Rightarrow$ E = \$5($\frac{1}{4}$) + \$3($\frac{1}{4}$) – \$4($\frac{1}{2}$) = $\frac{5}{4} + \frac{3}{4} - \frac{8}{4} = 0$
So this is a fair game if you do not pay to play it

Chapter 8 Review

1. (a) S = {Monday, Tuesday, Wednesday, Thursday, Friday, Saturday, Sunday}

   (b) E = {Tuesday, Thursday}   (c) P(day starting with T) = $\frac{2}{7}$

2. (*i*) $\frac{4}{5} \cdot 1000 = 800 \Rightarrow$ there are 800 blue jelly beans

   (*ii*) $\frac{1}{8} \cdot 1000 = 125 \Rightarrow$ there are 125 red jelly beans

   (*iii*) $\frac{4}{5} + \frac{1}{8} < 1 \Rightarrow$ there are jelly beans in the jar that are neither blue nor red

   (*iv*) There are 1000 – 800 – 125 = 75 jelly beans that are neither blue nor red

3. (a) P(vote for Kennedy) = $\frac{34{,}226{,}731}{68{,}334{,}888} \doteq 0.501$

   (b) P(vote for Nixon) = $\frac{34{,}108{,}157}{68{,}334{,}888} \doteq 0.499$

   (c) Odds against Nixon were = $\frac{34{,}226{,}731}{34{,}108{,}157} = \frac{1-0.4991324}{0.4991324} \doteq 1.0034764$ to 1

4. (a) P(black) = $\frac{5}{12}$ (b) P(black or white) = $\frac{5}{12} + \frac{4}{12} = \frac{3}{4}$

   (c) P(neither red nor white) = P(black) = $\frac{5}{12}$

   (d) P(red not drawn) = 1 – P(red) = $1 - \frac{3}{12} = \frac{3}{4}$

   (e) Only one ball is drawn $\Rightarrow$ P(black and white) = 0

   (f) P(black or white or red) = 1

5. (a) P(club) = $\frac{13}{52} = \frac{1}{4}$ (b) P(spade and 5) = $\frac{1}{52}$

   (c) P(heart or face card) = $\frac{13}{52} + \frac{12}{52} - \frac{13}{52} \cdot \frac{12}{52} = \frac{11}{26}$

   (d) P(no Jack) = 1 – P(Jack) = $1 - \frac{4}{52} = \frac{12}{13}$

6. (a) $\frac{4}{9} \cdot \frac{4}{9} \cdot \frac{4}{9} = \frac{64}{729}$ (b) $\frac{4}{9} \cdot \frac{3}{8} \cdot \frac{2}{7} = \frac{1}{21}$

7. $\frac{1}{5} \cdot \frac{2}{5} + \frac{4}{5} \cdot \frac{1}{5} = \frac{6}{25}$

8. $\frac{1}{4} \cdot \frac{0}{2} + \frac{1}{4} \cdot \frac{1}{4} + \frac{1}{4} \cdot \frac{1}{4} + \frac{1}{4} \cdot \frac{1}{5} = \frac{7}{40}$

9. P(black) = $\frac{1}{3} \cdot \frac{3}{5} \cdot \frac{1}{3} + \frac{1}{3} \cdot \frac{2}{5} \cdot 0 + \frac{2}{3} \cdot \frac{2}{5} \cdot \frac{1}{3} + \frac{2}{3} \cdot \frac{3}{5} \cdot 0 = \frac{3}{45} + 0 + \frac{4}{45} + 0 = \frac{7}{45}$

10. P(Jack) = $\frac{1}{13}$ $\Rightarrow$ odds in favor of a Jack are $\frac{\frac{1}{13}}{1-\frac{1}{13}} = 1:12$

11. P(prime number) = $\frac{1}{2}$ $\Rightarrow$ odds against are 1:1

12. $\frac{P(\text{event})}{1 - P(\text{event})} = \frac{3}{5} \Rightarrow 5 \cdot P(\text{event}) = 3[1 - P(\text{event})] \Rightarrow P(\text{event}) = \frac{3}{8}$

13. $E = \$7.20(\frac{1}{36}) + \$3.60(\frac{1}{36}) = \$0.30$

14. Fair price = $E = \$1000(\frac{1}{3000}) = \$0.33\frac{1}{3}$ (or, rounded to the next cent, 34¢)

15. $9 \cdot 10 \cdot 10 \cdot 1 = 900$ possible different numbers

16. ${}_{10}C_3 = 120$ possible different ways

17. ${}_{10}P_4 = 5040$ possible different ways

18. P(both blue) = $\frac{{}_2C_2}{{}_5C_2} = \frac{1}{10}$

19. (a) ${}_5P_3 = 60$ possible different ways

(b) P(Deadbeat 1st and Bandy 2nd) = $\frac{1}{{}_5P_2} = \frac{1}{20}$

(c) P(Deadbeat, Egglegs, Cash) = $\frac{1}{60}$

20. There are 15 different ways that Ruby can roll a higher number than Al $\Rightarrow$ P(Ruby > Al) = $\frac{15}{36}$

21. There are ${}_5C_3 = 10$ ways of selecting 3 questions out of 5; 6 of these would include question 1 $\Rightarrow$ P(no question 1) = $\frac{4}{10} = \frac{2}{5}$

22. P(all green) = $(0.3)^3 = 0.027$

23. P(2nd stage success) = $\frac{7}{8}$; P(3rd stage success) = $\frac{9}{10}$ $\Rightarrow$ P(success given stage 1) = $\frac{7}{8} \cdot \frac{9}{10} = \frac{63}{80}$

24. Answers may vary

(a) Randomly select numbers 1-6 (discard numbers 0, 7-9)

(b) Pick 3 random two-digit numbers (discard numbers other than 01-12)

(c) Let random numbers 0-2 represent red; 3-5 represent white; 6-8 represent blue; discard any 9's

25. (a) Divide the figure into 16 equal triangles; A represents 2 of them $\Rightarrow$ P(A) = $\frac{2}{16} = \frac{1}{8}$

(b) P(B) = $\frac{1}{4}$

(b) P(C) = $\frac{1}{16}$

26. P(between N and O) = $\frac{8}{20} = \frac{2}{5}$

CHAPTER 9 - STATISTICS: AN INTRODUCTION

On-going Assessment 9-1

1.

Glasses of Lemonade Sold

Friday

Thursday

Wednesday

Tuesday

Monday

represents 10 glasses

2. (a) 225 million (b) 375 million

(c) 675 million − 125 million = 550 million

3. Student Ages at Washington School

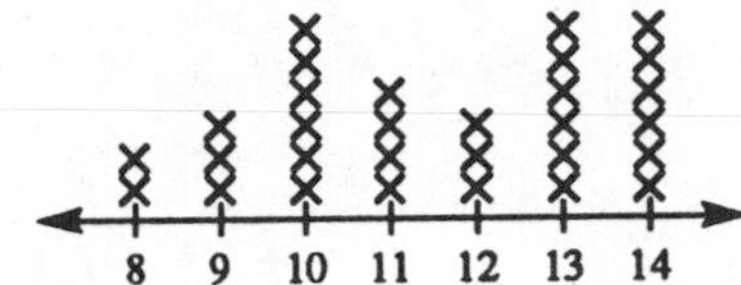

4. (a) 72, 74, 81, 81, 82, 85, 87, 88, 92, 94, 97, 98, 103, 123, 125

(b) 72 pounds (c) 125 pounds

5.

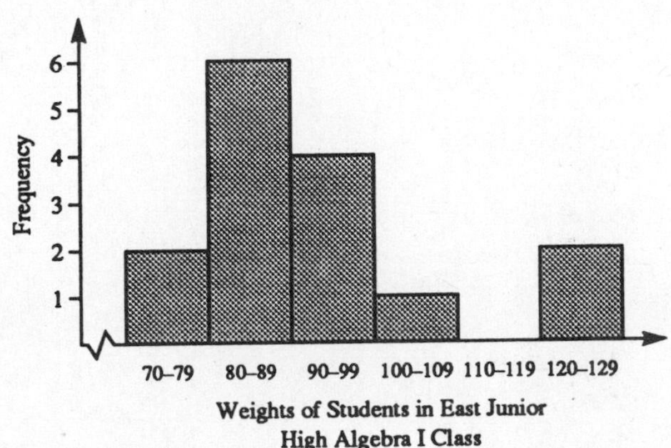

6. Data may vary

(a) A line plot will have two columns of x's; one for Heads and one for Tails

6. (b) A histogram will have two bars; one for Heads and one for Tails. The vertical axis will be partitioned to show frequencies of each.

7. (a) November, with approximately 30 cm of rain

(b) 15 (October) + 25 (December) + 10 (January) = 50 cm

8. (a)

Ages of HKM Employees

Stem	Leaves
6	332
5	8224
4	8561511
3	474224
2	14333617301365396
1	898

3 | 4 represents 34 years old

(b) There are seven in their 40's; 4 in their 50's

(c) The total of teens and 20's is 20 employees

(d) There are 7 age 50 or more; that is $\frac{7}{40} = 0.175 = 17.5\%$ of the total

9. (a) The Mississippi is approximately 3800 km long

(b) The Columbia is approximately 1900 km long

10.

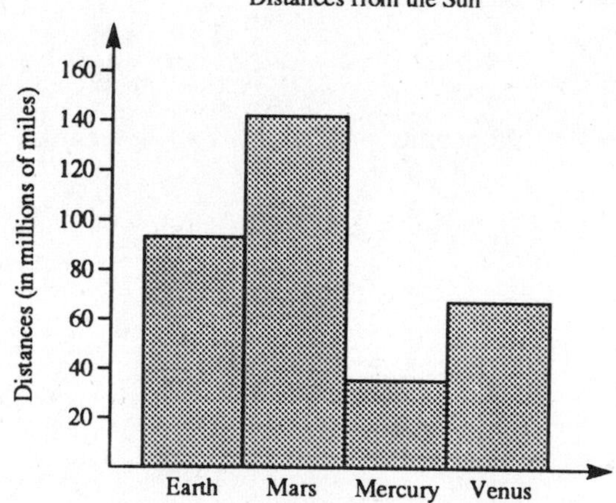

11.

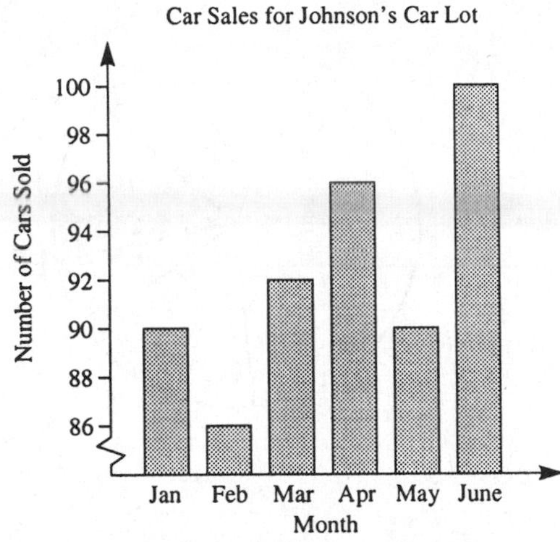
Car Sales for Johnson's Car Lot
Number of Cars Sold
100
98
96
94
92
90
88
86
Jan Feb Mar Apr May June
Month

12.

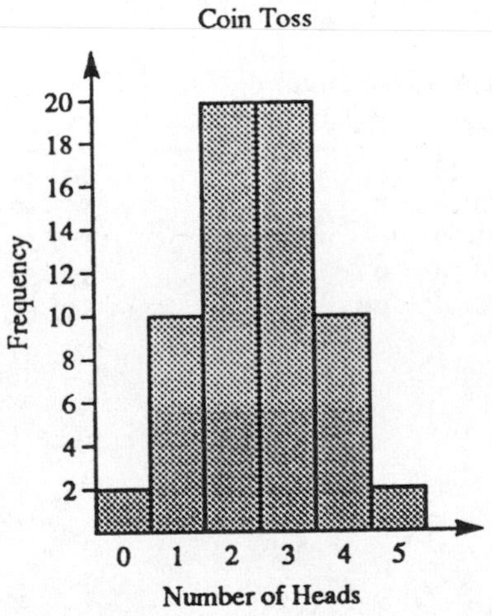
Coin Toss
Frequency
20
18
16
14
12
10
8
6
4
2
0 1 2 3 4 5
Number of Heads

13. (a)

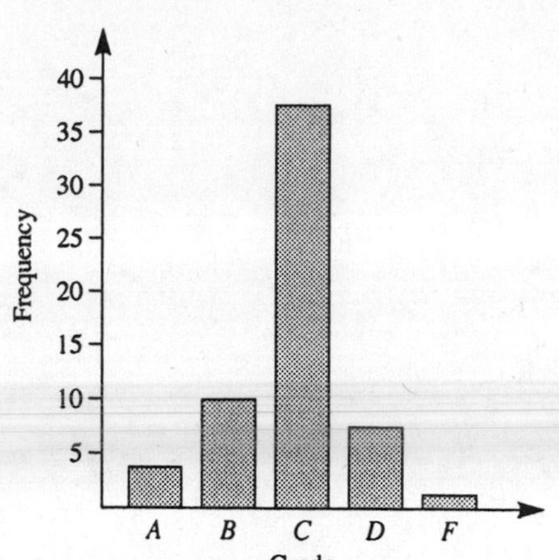

(b)

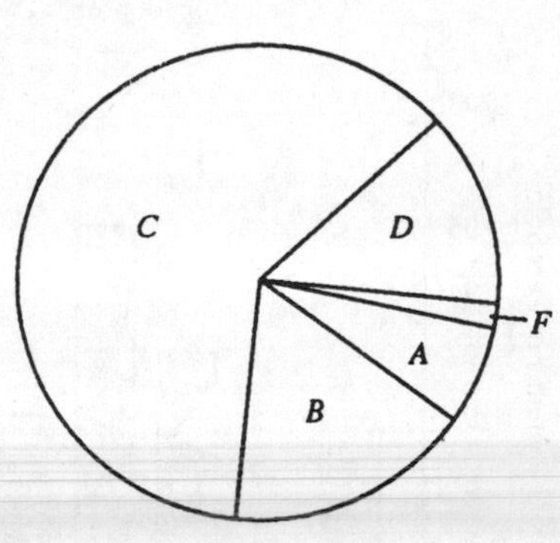

14. (a) Fall Textbook Costs

1	6
2	3 3
3	0 3 5 7 7 9 9
4	0 1 2 2 5 8 9
5	0 0 1 3 8
6	0 2 2

2 | 3 represents $23

(b)

Fall Textbook Costs

Classes	Tally	Frequency	Classes	Tally	Frequency
$15–19	I	1	$40–44	IIII	4
$20–24	II	2	$45–49	III	3
$25–29		0	$50–54	IIII	4
$30–34	II	2	$55–59	I	1
$35–39	IIII	5	$60–64	III	3
					25

14. (c) and (d) are shown on the same graph:

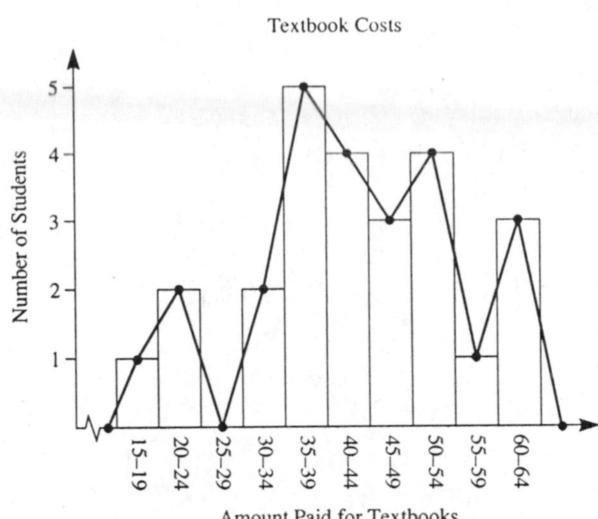

(e) The frequency polygon is not as appropriate, since it represents discrete rather than continuous data

15. (a) The chicken (it's graph has the shortest bar of the graph)

(b) 10 miles per hour (where the length of the chicken's bar intersects 10 on the horizontal axis)

(c) The cheetah (twice the rabbit's 35 mph is 70 mph, where the cheetah's bar ends)

(d) Yes (the lion's speed is 50 mph; the zebra's 40 mph)

16. (a) Women (b) Approximately one year

(c) Approximately 7.5 years

17. (a) Approximately 70% of $12,000 = $8400

(b) Approximately (100 – 30)% of $20,000 = 70% of $20,000 = $14,000

(c) Approximately 35% of $20,000 = $7000 (d) At about two years

18. (a) Asia (b) Africa

(c) $\frac{20\%}{30\%}$ = two-thirds as large (d) Asia and Africa

(e) $\frac{5\%}{16\%} = \frac{5}{16}$, or 5:16

(f) 7% of (total area) = 4.1 million $\Rightarrow$ total area = $\frac{4.1 \text{ million}}{0.07} \doteq$ 58.6 million square miles

19. (a)

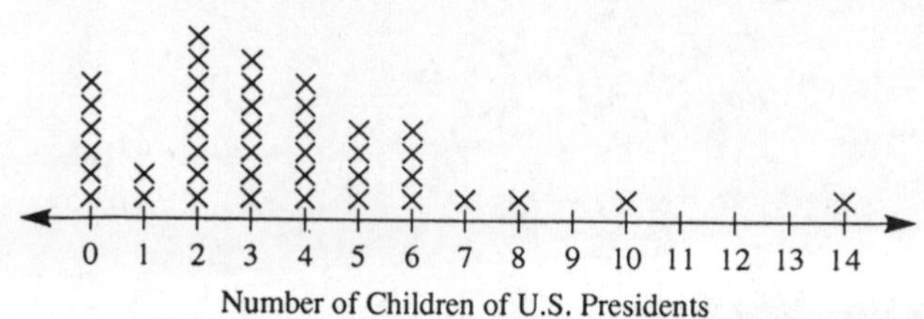

(b)

Nr. Children	Tally	Frequency
0								6
1				2
2										8
3									7
4								6
5						4
6						4
7			1
8			1
9		0
10			1
11		0
12		0
13		0
14			1
Total		41

(c) Two children

20. (a) The range of data is too diverse to lend itself to a stem-and-leaf plot

(b) The number of deaths in 1992 are significantly greater in each age category than in 1985

On-going Assessment 9-2

1. (a) Ordering the data, we have 2, 5, 5, 7, 8, 8, 8, 10

   (*i*) Mean $= \frac{2+5+5+7+8+8+8+10}{8} = \frac{53}{8} = 6.625$

   (*ii*) Median: The midpoint is between 7 and 8, or $\frac{7+8}{2} = 7.5$

   (*iii*) Mode: 8 occurs most frequently, so mode = 8

   (b) Ordering the data, we have 10, 11, 12, 12, 12, 14, 14, 16, 20

   (*i*) Mean $= \frac{10+11+12+12+12+14+14+16+20}{9} = \frac{121}{9} = 13.\overline{4}$

   (*ii*) Median: The midpoint is at 12, so median = 12

   (*iii*) Mode: 12 occurs most frequently, so mode = 12

1. (c) Ordering the data, we have 12, 17, 18, 18, 22, 22, 30

(*i*) Mean = $\frac{12+17+18+18+22+22+30}{7} = \frac{139}{7} \doteq 19.9$

(*ii*) Median: The midpoint is at 18, so median = 18

(*iii*) Mode: 18 and 22 occur most frequently, so there are dual modes of 18 and 22

(d) Ordering the data, we have 63, 75, 80, 80, 80, 80, 82, 90, 92, 92

(*i*) Mean = $\frac{63+75+80+80+80+80+90+92+92}{10} = \frac{814}{10} = 81.4$

(*ii*) Median: The midpoint is between 80 and 80, or median = 80

(*iii*) Mode: 80 occurs most frequently, so mode = 80

(e) (*i*) Mean = $\frac{5+5+5+5+5+10}{6} = \frac{35}{6} = 5.8\overline{3}$

(*ii*) Median: The midpoint is between 5 and 5, or median = 5

(*iii*) Mode: 5 occurs most frequently, so mode = 5

2. (a) (*i*) Mean: Since all values are 80, mean = 80

(*ii*) Median: Since all values are 80, median = 80

(*iii*) Mode: Since all values are 80, mode = 80

(b) Answers may vary, but one set would be 70, 80, 80, 80, 90

3. Mean = $\frac{\text{sum of test scores}}{\text{number of test scores}} \Rightarrow 75 = \frac{\text{sum}}{20} \Rightarrow$ sum = $20 \cdot 75 = 1500$

4. If 50 people average $\frac{7500}{50} = 150$ pounds, the tram will be at capacity

5. Mean of 28 scores = 80 $\Rightarrow$ sum of the scores = $28 \cdot 80 = 2240$
Adding scores of 60 and 50 $\Rightarrow$ new sum = 2350 $\Rightarrow$ new mean = $\frac{2350}{28+2} = 78.\overline{3}$

6. (a) Mean = $\frac{40+36+8+6+2}{5} = \frac{92}{5} = 18.4$ years

(b) Five years from now, the family's ages will be 45, 36, 13, 11, and 7
$\Rightarrow$ mean = $\frac{45+36+13+11+7}{5} = \frac{117}{5} = 23.4$ years

(c) Note that the mean five years from now is 5 more than the mean now
$\Rightarrow$ mean ten years from now will be $18.4 + 10 = 28.4$ years

(d) The mean in (b) is equal to the mean in (a) plus 5 years. The mean in (c) is equal to the mean in (a) plus 10 years, or the mean in (b) plus 5 years.

7. Select the mode; it is the size which sold most frequently.

8. The number of points for each course is the product of the number of credits and the point value of each, so
Jon will have 15 points for math, 12 for english, 10 for physics, 3 for German, and 4 for handball; a total of 44 points
$\Rightarrow$ GPA will be $\frac{44 \text{ points}}{17 \text{ credits}} \doteq 2.59$

9. Total tackle weight is $7 \cdot 230 = 1610$ pounds; total backfield weight is $4 \cdot 190 = 760$ pounds; so total player weight is $1610 + 760 = 2370$ pounds $\Rightarrow$ mean weight $= \frac{2370}{11} \doteq 215.5$ pounds per person

10. 99 people with mean of \$12,000 is \$1,188,000 total income. Increased by \$200,000, the new total income is \$1,388,000. Mean income is now $\frac{1388000}{100} = \$13,880 \Rightarrow$ there has been an increase of \$1880

11. (a) The total of salaries, in thousands of dollars, is:
$18 \cdot 2 + 22 \cdot 4 + 26 \cdot 4 + 35 \cdot 3 + 38 \cdot 12 + 44 \cdot 8 + 50 \cdot 4 + 80 \cdot 2 + 150$
$= 36 + 88 + 104 + 105 + 456 + 352 + 200 + 160 + 150 = 1651$, or \$1,651,000
There are 40 dancers $\Rightarrow$ mean annual salary $= \frac{1651000}{40} = \$41,275$

(b) The median is between the 20th and 21st (in order, from smallest to largest) salaries. Salaries between the 13th and 25th are all at \$38,000 $\Rightarrow$ median = \$38,000

(c) The largest number of salaries is 12 at \$38,000 $\Rightarrow$ mode = \$38,000

12. (a) Balance beam - Olga, with a mean score of 9.575
Uneven bars - Lisa, with a mean score of 9.85
Floor exercise - Lisa, with a mean score of 9.925

(b) Lisa - 29.20

13. Total trip miles = 43,390 − 42,800 = 590 miles; total gasoline used = 12 + 18 = 30 gallons
$\Rightarrow$ average fuel mileage for the trip $= \frac{590 \text{ miles}}{30 \text{ gallons}} = 19\frac{2}{3}$ mpg

14. $\frac{45 \text{ miles}}{1\frac{1}{2} \text{ hours}} = 30$ miles per hour

15. Mean hours per day $= \frac{5\frac{1}{2} + 3\frac{1}{2} + 5\frac{1}{4} + 6\frac{3}{4} + 8}{5} = \frac{29}{5} = 5\frac{4}{5}$ hours

16. The oldest person is 24 + 34 = 58 years old

17. (a) Set A: mean $= \frac{24}{4} = 6$; range $= 9 - 3 = 6$

(b) Set B: all elements are 11 $\Rightarrow$ mean, median, and mode = 11
Set C: mean $= \frac{77}{7} = 11$; median and mode = 11

(c) Set C: mean $= \frac{12}{4} = 3$; median $= \frac{2+4}{2} = 3$; no value occurs more than once $\Rightarrow$ no mode

18. $\bar{x} = \frac{1281}{7} = 183$ cm; summation of $(x - \bar{x})^2 = 64 + 1 + 49 + 9 + 81 + 121 + 49 = 374$
$\Rightarrow$ variance $= \frac{374}{7} \doteq 53.43 \text{ cm}^2$; $s = \sqrt{53.43} \doteq 7.31$ cm

19. (a) s = 0 (there are no deviations from the mean)

(b) Yes (otherwise, there would be some differences from the mean and the standard deviation would therefore not be zero)

20. (a) $\bar{x} = \frac{96+71+43+77+75+76+61+83+71+58+97+76+74+91+74+71+77+83+87+93+79}{21} \doteq 76.8$

(b) Ordering, the scores are:
43, 58, 61, 71, 71, 71, 74, 74, 75, 76, 76, 77, 77, 79, 83, 83, 87, 91, 93, 96, 97
$\Rightarrow$ median = the 11th score, or 76

(c) The most frequent score is 71 $\Rightarrow$ mode = 71

20. (d)

$\bar{x}$	$x - \bar{x}$	$(x - \bar{x})^2$
96	19.2	368.64
71	¯5.8	33.64
43	¯33.8	1142.44
77	0.2	0.04
75	¯1.8	3.24
76	¯0.8	0.64
61	¯15.8	249.64
83	6.2	38.44
71	¯5.8	33.64
58	¯18.8	353.44
97	20.2	408.04
76	¯0.8	0.64
74	¯2.8	7.84
91	14.2	201.64
74	¯2.8	7.84
71	¯5.8	33.64
77	0.2	0.04
83	6.2	38.44
87	10.2	104.04
93	16.2	262.44
79	2.2	4.84
		Total: 3293.24

$\Rightarrow \; v = \frac{3293.24}{21} \doteq 156.8$

(e) $s = \sqrt{156.8} \doteq 12.5$

21. If S is the score needed on the fifth exam, then $\frac{84+95+86+94+S}{5} = 90$, or $394 + S = 450$ $\Rightarrow S = 91$

22. Let Ginny's three scores be represented by F (first), S (second), and T (third); then:

$S = 90$ (median)

$\frac{F+S+T}{3} = 92$ (mean), or $F + S + T = 276$

$F - T = 6$ (range)

Solving as a system of equations $\Rightarrow$ $F = 96$, $S = 90$, $T = 90$

23. Mean of 5 numbers = 6 $\Rightarrow$ sum of the numbers $= 5 \cdot 6 = 30$

Removing a number, n $\Rightarrow$ $\frac{30 - n}{4} = 7 \Rightarrow n = 2$

24.

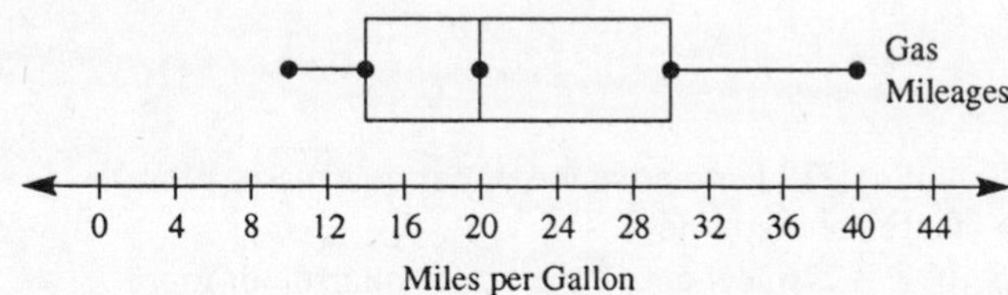

25. (a) The median in a box plot is the middle line through the box $\Rightarrow$ median of Theater A = \$25; median of Theater B = \$50

(b) The greatest range is that of Theater B: \$80 – \$15 = \$65

(c) The highest price of either is the upper value at Theater B, \$80

(d) Answers may vary. Some observations are that there is significantly more variation and generally higher prices at Theater B.

26. Lower extreme = 40; upper extreme = 95
Lower quartile = 70; upper quartile = 90
Median = 80
IQR = 90 – 70 = 20
Lower quartile – $1.5 \cdot$ IQR = 40 $\Rightarrow$ outlier of 20
Upper quartile + $1.5 \cdot$ IQR = 120 $\Rightarrow$ no outlier

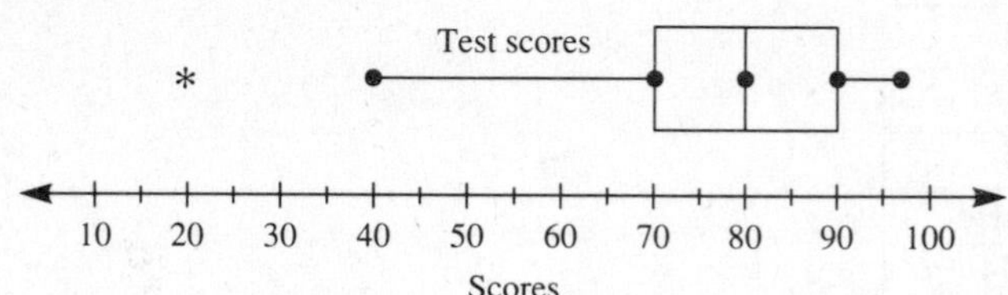

27. (a) Minneapolis: Lower extreme = 366
Lower quartile = 416
Median = $\frac{447 + 561}{2} = 504$
Upper quartile = 668
Upper extreme = 950
IQR = 668 – 416 = 252
LQ – $1.5 \cdot$ IQR = 38 $\Rightarrow$ no outlier
UQ + $1.5 \cdot$ IQR = 1046 $\Rightarrow$ no outlier

Los Angeles: Lower extreme = 516
Lower quartile = 571
Median = $\frac{620 + 625}{2} = 622.5$
Upper quartile = 735
Upper extreme = 858
IQR = 164
LQ – $1.5 \cdot$ IQR = 325 $\Rightarrow$ no outlier
UQ + $1.5 \cdot$ IQR = 981 $\Rightarrow$ no outlier

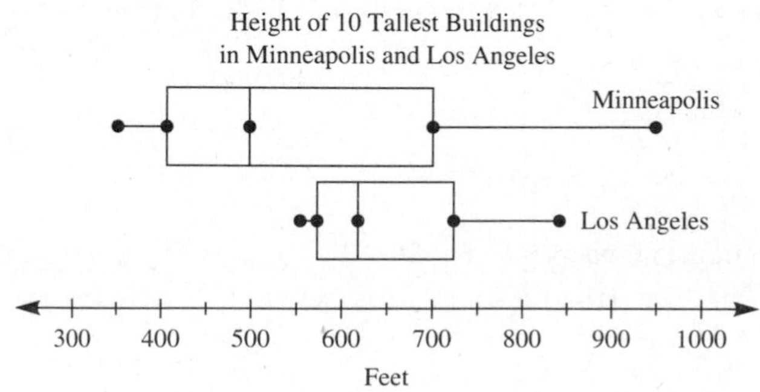

(b) In Minneapolis there are no values more than $1.5 \cdot$ IQR = 378 feet above the upper quartile or more than 378 feet below the lower quartile $\Rightarrow$ there are no outliers
In Los Angeles there are no values more than $1.5 \cdot$ IQR = 246 feet above the upper quartile or more than 246 feet below the lower quartile $\Rightarrow$ there are no outliers

28. (a) (*i*) The mean increases by \$1000 (*ii*) The median increases by \$1000

(*iii*) The extremes increase by \$1000 (*iv*) The quartiles increase by \$1000

(*v*) The standard deviation is unchanged

(b) (*i*) The mean increases by 5% (*ii*) The standard deviation increases by 5%

29. (a) (*i*) Mean = $\frac{1+3+5+7+9}{5}$ = 5; median = the middle value, or 5

(*ii*) 199 = 1 + (n − 1)2, so n = 100 ⇒ there are 100 terms in the sequence
The sum of 100 terms of this sequence is $\frac{100}{2}(1 + 199) = 10{,}000$
The 50th term is 1 + (50 − 1)2 = 99
⇒ mean = $\frac{10{,}000}{100} = 100$
⇒ median is between term 50 and 51, or $\frac{99 + 101}{2} = 100$

(*iii*) 607 = 7 + (n − 1)3, so n = 201 ⇒ there are 201 terms in the sequence
The sum of 201 terms of this sequence is $\frac{201}{2}(7 + 607) = 61{,}707$
The 101st term is 7 + (101 − 1)3 = 307
⇒ mean = $\frac{61{,}707}{201} = 307$
⇒ median is the 101st term, or 307

(b) The mean and median of an arithmetic sequence are the same

30. Mode (the mode represents the value most frequently used by the states--both mean and median might be decimals, and no state would use decimal age for a drivers license)

31. Mode (non-numerical data cannot be used without numerical coding)

32. Mean (the amount of rain is not a discrete number)

On-going Assessment 9-2; Review Problems

41. Stock female walking equipment and male swimming, biking, and fishing equipment

42. (a) Education: 53% of 360° ≐ 191°
General fund: 27% of 360° ≐ 97°
Cities, senior citizens, and other: 7% of 360° ≐ 25° each

(b) The graph totals to 101% (the reason for which is unknown, but might be the result of rounding of raw data)

43. (a) Mount Everest is the highest mountain, at approximately 8500 meters

(b) Mounts Aconcagus, Everest, and McKinley

44. (a)

History Test Scores

5	5
6	48
7	2334679
8	0255567889
9	00346

7 | 2 represents a score of 72

(b) History Test Scores

Classes	Tallies	Frequency
55-59	|	1
60-64	|	1
65-69	|	1
70-74	||||	4
75-79	|||	3
80-84	||	2
85-89	||||| |||	8
90-94	||||	4
95-99	|	1

(c)

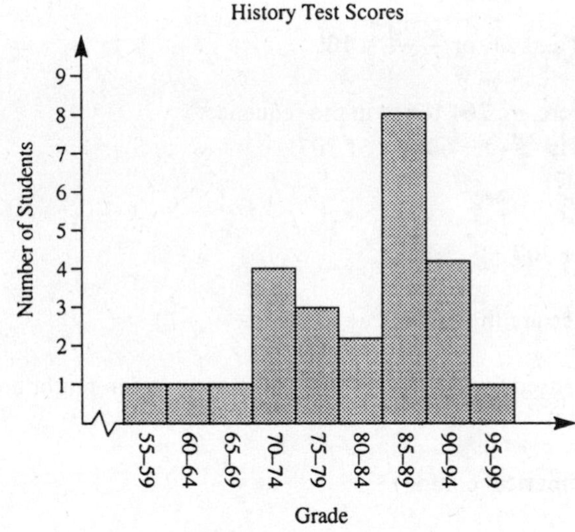

(d)

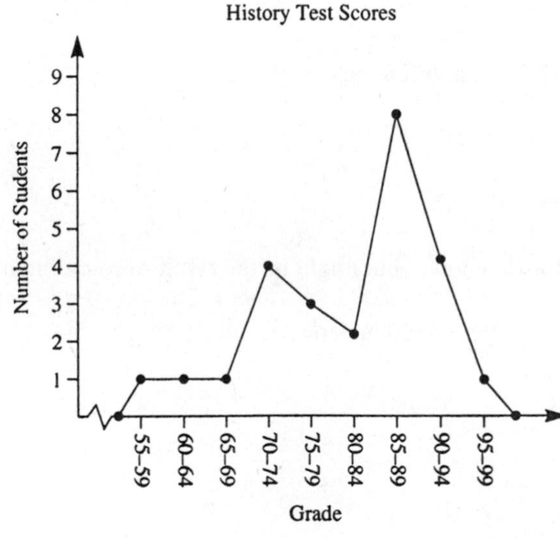

44. (e) Eight of the 25 scores are in the 85-89 range; represented by $\frac{8}{25}(360) \doteq 115°$

On-going Assessment 9-3

Note: Answers for this assessment may vary, depending upon whether you are using a calculator, a table, or appromimations for areas under the normal curve.

1. (a) 85 is one standard deviation below the mean; 115 is one standard deviation above the mean. That is:
$$Z_{85} = \frac{85 - 100}{15} = {}^-1, \text{ and } Z_{115} = \frac{115 - 100}{15} = 1$$
Since 34 + 34 = 68% of the area under the curve lies within ± 1 standard deviation from the mean, 68% of the students will have IQ's between 85 and 115. 68% of 1500 is 1020 students in that range.

   (b) 70 is two standard deviations below the mean; 130 is two standard deviations above the mean. 95% of the area under the curve lies within ± 2 standard deviations from the mean, and 95% of 1500 = 1425 students with IQ's between 70 and 130.

   (c) 145 is three standard deviations above the mean; only 0.1% of the area under the curve is more than three standard deviations from the mean. 0.01% of 1500 = 1.5, so one or two students will have an IQ of more than 145.

2. $Z_{16} = \frac{16 - 16.1}{0.05} = {}^-2$ ⇒ 16 ounces is 2 standard deviations below the mean. 13.5 + 34 + 50 = 97.5% of the area under the curve falls above 2 standard deviations below the mean; i.e., 97.5% of the boxes will actually contain more than 16 ounces.

3. $Z_{4.50} = \frac{4.50 - 5.00}{0.50} = {}^-1$ and $Z_{5.50} = \frac{5.00 - 5.00}{0.50} = 1$
The amount of data between ± 1 standard deviations is 68%, so there is a 0.68 probability that a worker picked at random will earn between \$4.50 and \$5.50 per hour.

4. (a) $Z_{verbal} = \frac{90 - 84}{10} = 0.60$; $Z_{quan} = \frac{133 - 118}{18} = 0.8\overline{3}$; $Z_{reason} = \frac{18 - 14}{4} = 1$

   (b) (*i*) She performed relatively the highest on the logical reasoning test

   (*ii*) She performed relatively the lowest on the verbal exam

   (*iii*) Mean = $\frac{0.60 + 0.8\overline{3} + 1}{3} \doteq 0.8\overline{1}$

5. $Z_{2\,min} = \frac{2-4}{2} = {}^-1$. Only 50 – 34 = 16% of the data under the curve falls below 2 standard deviations below the mean ⇒ 16% of the calls will last less than 2 minutes.

6. (a) $Z_{130} = \frac{130 - 100}{15} = 2$. 34 + 13.5 = 47.5% of the data under the curve lies within 2 standard deviations above the mean ⇒ 47.5% of the population will have IQ's between 100 and 130.

   (b) $Z_{85} = \frac{85 - 100}{15} = {}^-1$. 50 – 34 = 16% of the data under the curve falls below 1 standard deviation below the mean ⇒ 16% of the population will have IQ's of less than 85.

7. (a) 1.07% (b) 95.54%

   (c) 2.27%

8. $Z_{1.4} = 91.92$; $Z_{1.5} = 93.32$ ⇒ the percentage of scores between Z = 1.4 and 1.5 is 93.32 – 91.92 = 1.4%

9. $Z_{125} = \frac{125 - 105}{20} = 1 \Rightarrow 50\% + 34\% = 84\%$ will weigh less than 125 ounces

10. $Z = {}^{-}1.25 = \frac{53 - 63}{s} = \frac{{}^{-}10}{s} \Rightarrow {}^{-}1.25s = {}^{-}10 \Rightarrow s$ (standard deviation) $= 8$

11. Two standard deviations above the mean is a score of $72 + 2 \cdot 9 = 90 \Rightarrow$ the lowest score for an A is 90

12. 95% of all data under a normal curve is within $\pm$ 2 standard deviations of the mean. The range corresponding to $\pm$ 2 standard deviations is between $65.5 - 2 \cdot 2.5 = 60.5$ inches to $65.5 + 2 \cdot 2.5 = 70.5$ inches.

13. $Z_{23,000} = \frac{23,000 - 28,000}{2500} = {}^{-}2$. The amount of data falling below 2 standard deviations below the mean is 2.5% $\Rightarrow$ 2.5% of 2000 tires = 50 tires.

14. $Z_{440} = \frac{440 - 500}{60} = {}^{-}1$. A z-score of ${}^{-}1$ represents the 16th percentile $\Rightarrow 0.16 \cdot 10,000 = 1600$ students rated deficient.

15. (a)

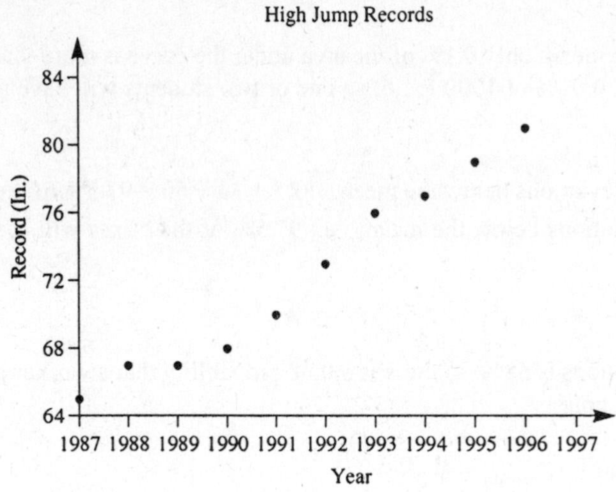

(b) Positive correlation (the trend line slopes upward to the right)

16. (a) Negative correlation (the trend line slopes downward to the right)

(b) Approximately 10

(c) Approximately 22 years old

On-going Assessment 9-3; Review Problems

23. (a) $\bar{x} = \frac{43 + 91 + 73 + 65 + 56 + 77 + 84 + 91 + 82 + 65 + 98 + 65}{12} \doteq 74.17$

(b) Ordering, the scores are 43, 56, 65, 65, 65, 73, 77, 82, 84, 91, 91, 98
Median $= \frac{73 + 77}{2} = 75$

(c) Mode is 65

23. (d) The sum of the $(x - \bar{x})^2$ terms is 2855.68 $\Rightarrow$ variance is $\frac{2855.68}{12} \doteq 237.97$

(e) $s = \sqrt{237.97} \doteq 15.43$

24. If the mean is 27, then the total of the scores is $36 \cdot 27 = 972$. Adding the two additional scores, the new total is 1054 $\Rightarrow$ mean $= \frac{1054}{38} \doteq 27.74$.

25. If the mean of 10 papers is 70 there are $10 \cdot 70 = 700$ points. Of 20 papers, there are $20 \cdot 80 = 1600$ points. The combined mean $= \frac{2300}{30} = 76.\bar{6}$.

26.

Men's Olympic
100 meter Run Times
1896–1964

1 0	0 2 3 3 3 4 5 6 8 8 8 8
1 1	0 0
1 2	0

10|0 represents 10.0 seconds

27. (*i*) Freestyle: 54.64, 54.79, 54.93, 55.65, 55.92, 58.59, 59.50, 60.00, 61.20
Lower extreme is 54.64; upper extreme is 61.20
Lower quartile is $\frac{54.79 + 54.93}{2} = 54.86$; upper quartile is $\frac{59.50 + 60.00}{2} = 59.75$
IQR is $59.75 - 54.86 = 4.89$
Lower quartile $- 1.5 \cdot \text{IQR} = 47.53 \Rightarrow$ no lower outliers
Upper quartile $+ 1.5 \cdot \text{IQR} = 67.09 \Rightarrow$ no upper outliers

(*ii*) Butterfly: 58.62, 59.00, 59.26, 60.13, 60.42, 63.34, 64.70, 65.50, 69.50
Lower extreme is 58.62; upper extreme is 69.50
Lower quartile is $\frac{59.00 + 59.26}{2} = 59.13$; upper quartile is $\frac{64.70 + 65.50}{2} = 65.10$
Median is 60.42
IQR is $65.10 - 59.13 = 5.97$
Lower quartile $- 1.5 \cdot \text{IQR} = 50.18 \Rightarrow$ no lower outliers
Upper quartile $+ 1.5 \cdot \text{IQR} = 74.06 \Rightarrow$ no upper outliers

(*iii*)

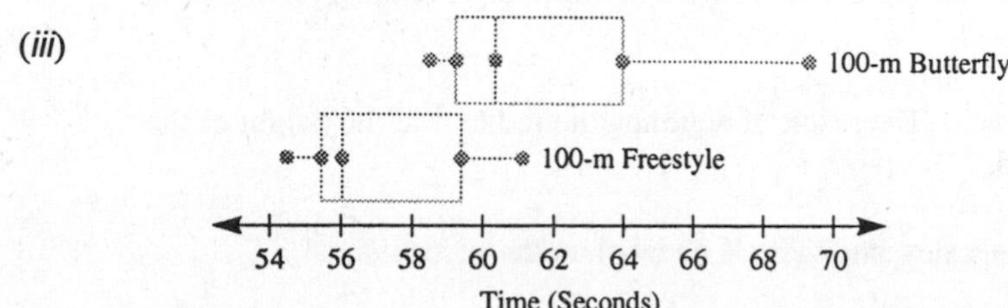

(*iv*) The 100 meter butterfly times are (relatively speaking) much greater than the 100 meter freestyle times

On-going Assessment 9-4

1. Answers may vary.

(a) The claim cannot be substantiated without knowing more about the noise characteristics of the car and glider in question. Many gliders are quite noisy, or the car may not be running.

1. (b) There is no way of knowing whether or not this claim is true. It may be that 95% of its cycles sold in the United States were sold in the last year.

   (c) 10% more than 10% (which is 11%) is not much of an increase.

   (d) Fresher than what? 40% of what?

   (e) "Up to" can cover a multitude of sins. The conditions under which 30 mpg was realized are not stated.

   (f) Brighter than what?

   (g) How many dentists responded? Who paid them?

   (h) This is an example of carrying an argument to a ridiculous and deceptive extreme

   (i) Is there another airline flying to the city?

2. Answers may vary. One possibility is that people might think the temperature is always 25°. Another is that, unfamiliar with the metric system, people would think it to be always cold (25° C = 77° F).

3. She could have taken a different number of quizzes during the first part of the quarter than in the second part.

4. When the radius of a circle is doubled, the area is quadrupled. This is misleading since the population has only doubled.

5. The horizontal axis does not have uniformly-sized intervals, and neither the horizontal axis nor the graph are labeled.

6. There were more scores above the mean than below, but the mean was affected more by low scores.

7. No. It could very well be that most of the pickups sold in the past 10 years were actually sold during the last two years. In such a case most of the pickups have been on the road for only two years, and therefore the given information would not imply that the average life of a pickup is around ten years.

8. Answers may vary, but General Cooster was assuming that there were no deep holes in the river where he was crossing.

9. The three-dimensional drawing distorts the graph. The result of doubling the radius and the height of the can are to increase the volume by a factor of 8.

10. There are no labels by which to compare actual sales, and there is no label on the vertical axis.

11. One would need more information; e.g., is the graph in percentage or actual numbers?

12. (a) False (prices vary by only $30)

    (b) False (the bar has four times the area but the price is only 3.5% higher)

    (c) True

13. (a) This bar graph would have perhaps 20 accidents as the baseline. Then 38 in 1992 would appear to be almost double the 24 of 1988, when in fact it is only 58% higher.

    (b) This bar graph would have 0 accidents as its baseline, and some larger number (such as 1000) as the maximum value. This would have the effect of showing values from 24 to 38 as lying on an essentially horizontal line.

14. Answers may vary, but one such would be 5, 5, 5, 5, 5, 5, 100, 100. The mean would be 28.75 and the median 5.

15. No (it is possible that either the population of the coastal east has decreased or that of the mountain west has increased)

16. Answers may vary.

    (*i*) The mean moved approximately 4 cm during the first 100 years and 3.5 cm during the next 100 years $\Rightarrow$ movement of 5.5 cm during the next 200 years (3 cm in the first 100 and 2.5 cm in the next 100)

    (*ii*) If the pattern continues, the mean would have moved another 3.5 cm at the end of 400 years

17. Answers may vary

    (a) A scattergram trend line representing this data may be approximated by the equation:

    $R = {}^{-}0.0175t + 44.45$, where R is the record and t is the year (e.g., 1936)

    $t = 1992 \Rightarrow R = {}^{-}0.0175(1992) + 44.45 = 9.59$ seconds

    (b) The 1992 record time was 9.86 seconds (set by Carl Lewis)

    (c) $t = 2996 \Rightarrow R = {}^{-}0.0175(2996) + 44.45 = {}^{-}7.98$ seconds

    (d) The pattern cannot continue using a straight line as a trend line. Trend lines, in general, are inaccurate predictors when used very far outside their scattergram data points.

18. The homeowner is expecting the trend of dropping interest rates to continue into the year 2000. It might not be a wise decision, since interest rates may begin to go up, or even if they continue to go down there may be an increase in home prices that would outweigh any lower interest costs.

19. What was the class average and standard deviation? What was the highest obtainable score?

20. Does the average of 32 cover all subjects? How large are the classrooms; is there adequate seating? What is the variation in class sizes? The question cannot be answered with one number alone.

21. The mode might be reported if enough randomly-selected spots were selected--although it is possible that a mode not exist. A median or mean might be misleading, depending upon the number of data points selected. A report of mean, median, and standard deviation would probably be the most helpful.

22. Yes (it would look like the Netherlands)

23. Answers may vary. First, the sample size must be determined (the larger the number of samples, the smaller the sampling error). Then one way to pick a random sample of adults in a town is to use the telephone book or voter registration lists (these will not list all adults in the town but are probably the most accessible). To pick the sample, one might consult a random number list for a number n; then starting at a random point in the adult list choose every nth person.

24. One of the primary reasons this could be true is that the cost of replacing defective chips is less than trying to correct the problems that caused the chips in the first place. It is absolutely essential that the company, to be successful, detects a very high percentage of defective chips.

25. Answers may vary. The writers may have based the statement on a large, nation-wide, representative population of grades 5-8. They may also have based it by observing magazines or TV show ratings.

1. If the average is 2.41 children, then the mean is probably being used. If the average is 2.5, then the mean *or* the median might have been used.

2. 10 part-timers with an average salary of \$50 means a total part-time payroll of \$500. That leaves \$3450 for full-timers $\Rightarrow \frac{3450}{150} = 23$ full-time employees.

3. (a) Mean = $\frac{10+50+30+40+10+60+10}{7} = 30$. Ordering, we have 10, 10, 10, 30, 40, 50, 60. The median is 30. The mode is 10.

   (b) Mean = $\frac{5+8+6+3+5+4+3+6+1+9}{10} = 5$. Ordering, we have 1, 3, 3, 4, 5, 5, 6, 6, 8, 9. The median is 5. The modes are 3, 5, and 6.

4. (a) The range is $60 - 10 = 50$. The sum of the $(x - \bar{x})^2$ terms is 2600 $\Rightarrow$ variance is $\frac{2600}{7} \doteq 371.4$. The standard deviation is $\sqrt{371.4} \doteq 19.3$.

   (b) The range is $9 - 1 = 8$. The sum of the $(x - \bar{x})^2$ terms is 52; the variance is $\frac{52}{10} = 5.2$. The standard deviation is $\sqrt{5.2} \doteq 2.28$.

5. (a)

Miss Rider's Class
Masses in Kilograms

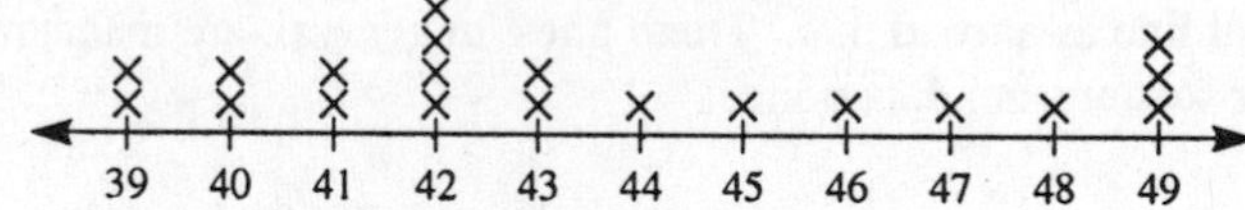

(b)

Miss Rider's Class
Masses in Kilograms

3	99
4	0011222233345678999

4 | 0 represents 40 kg

(c) Miss Rider's Class
Masses in Kilograms

Mass	Tally	Frequency
39	||	2
40	||	2
41	||	2
42	||||	4
43	||	2
44	|	1
45	|	1
46	|	1
47	|	1
48	|	1
49	|||	3
Total		20

5. (d)

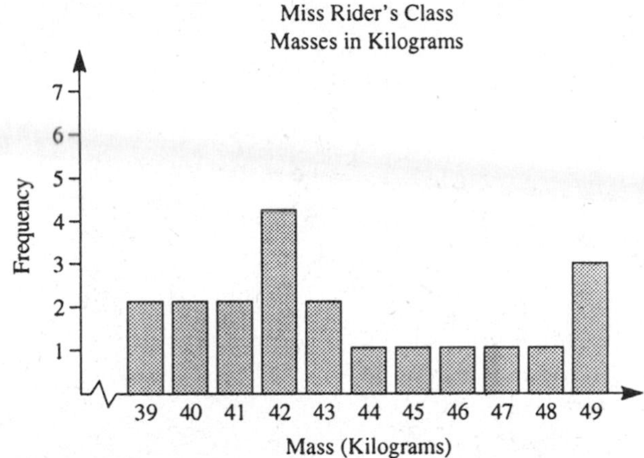

6. (a)

Test Grades

Classes	Tally	Frequency
61-70	|||||		6
71-80	||||| |||||		11
81-90	||||| ||	7
91-100	|||||		6
Total		30

(b) and (c) are shown on the same graph below (the frequency polygon is probably not appropriate inasmuch as it represents discrete data as continuous)

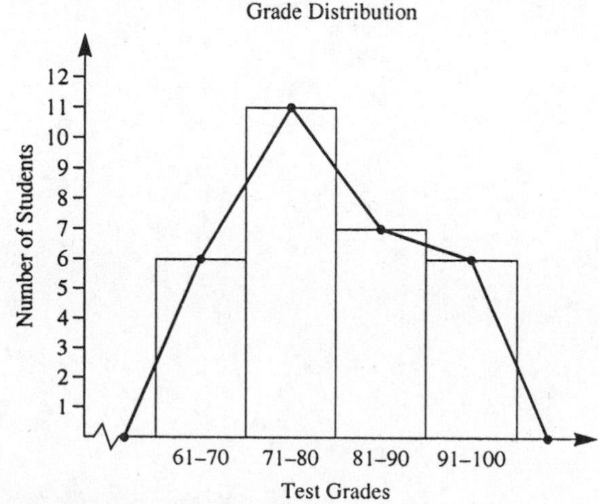

7.

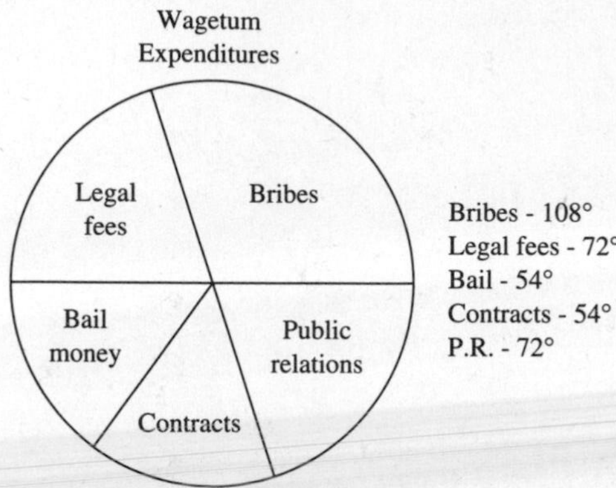

8. The width of the bars is not uniform and the graph has no title

9. The total salary is $24 \cdot 9000 = \$216{,}000$. An additional \$80,000 salary makes the total \$296,000. The new mean is $\frac{296{,}000}{25} = \$11{,}840 \Rightarrow$ the mean was increased by \$2840.

10.

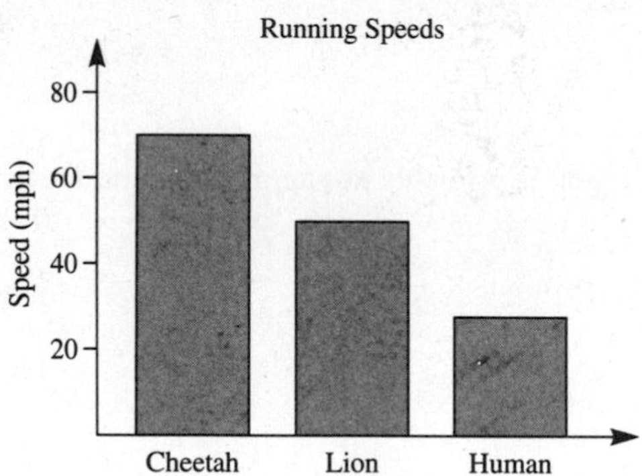

11. (a)

Life Expectancies
of Males and Females

Females		Males
	67	1446
	68	28
	69	156
	70	0049
	71	0223458
	72	
	73	
7	74	
9310	75	
86	76	
88532	77	
54332211	78	
	79	

7 | 74 | represents 74.7 years old

| 67 | 1 represents 67.1 years old

(b)

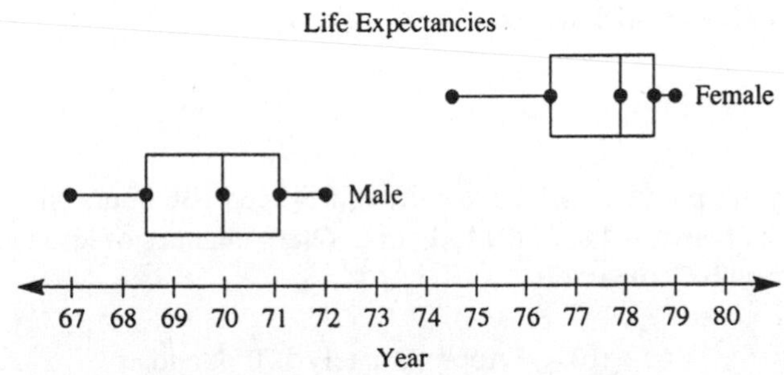

12. Larry's GPA is $\frac{4\cdot4+4\cdot4+3\cdot3+3\cdot2+1\cdot2}{4+4+3+3+1} = 3.2\overline{6}$. Marc's is $\frac{4\cdot2+4\cdot2+3\cdot3+3\cdot4+1\cdot4}{4+4+3+3+1} = 2.7\overline{3}$.
Larry is correct.

13. (a) Ordering, the lengths are 160, 180, 330, 350, 360, 380, 450, 460, 480 $\Rightarrow$ median is 360 yards

(b) There is no mode

(c) The mean is $\frac{160+180+330+350+360+380+450+460+480}{9} = 350$ yards

(d) The sum of the $(x - \bar{x})^2$ terms is 105,600 $\Rightarrow$ standard deviation is $\sqrt{\frac{105{,}600}{9}} \doteq 108.2$

14. (a) Ordering, the speeds are:
45, 54, 56, 58, 58, 60, 62, 64, 64, 64, 65, 65, 65, 66, 67, 67, 67, 67, 68, 68, 69, 72, 74, 74, 75, 75, 82, 86, 88, 90 $\Rightarrow$ median is 67

(b) The upper quartile is 74; the lower is 64

14. (c)

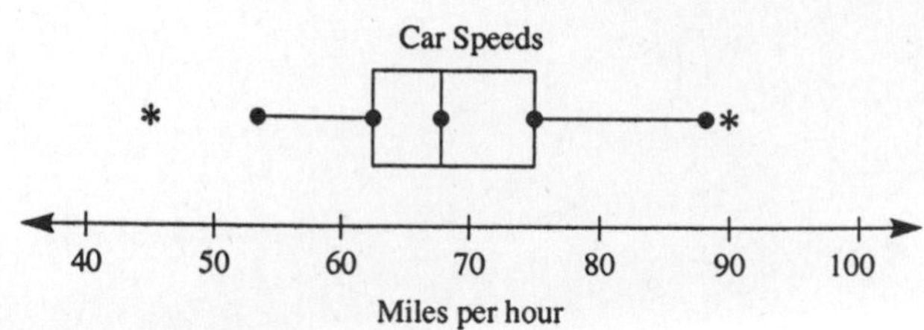

(d) About 40% in this case; 50% is usually expected

(e) $\frac{9}{30}$ = 30% of the drivers received tickets

(f) No (there are fewer speeds close to 67 in the 3rd quartile than in the 2nd quartile)

15. (a) $Z_{68} = \frac{68-64}{2} = 2$; 2.5% of the data is more than 2 standard deviations above the mean; 2.5% of 1000 = 25 girls over 68 inches tall.

(b) $Z_{60} = \frac{60-64}{2} = {}^{-}2$; 47.5% of the data is between the mean and 2 standard deviations below the mean. 47.5% of 1000 = 475 girls between 60 and 64 inches tall.

(c) $Z_{66} = \frac{66-64}{2} = 1$; 50 – 34 = 16% ⇒ 0.16 probability of a girl being over 66 inchs tall

16. $Z_{750} = \frac{750-600}{75} = 2$; 47.5% scored between 600 and 750 ⇒ 475 students

17. $Z_{725} = \frac{725-600}{75} = 1.\overline{6}$

18. Answers may vary. With 95% certainty, Company A's products will have a life of between 130 hours and 170 hours; Company B's products will have a life of between 141 and 149 hours. One's chances of knowing how long the product will really last would seem to be better with Company B.

19. (a) Positive correlation

(b) Approximately 170 pounds

(c) Approximately 67 inches

(d) 64 inches

(e) 170 – 120 = 50 pounds

20. Answers may vary.

(a) One way would be to leave the television on, even if no one was watching

(b) The networks air very popular shows during "ratings sweeps" periods

21. Answers may vary. Graphs may show area or volume instead of relative size; another way is to select a horizontal baseline that will support the point trying to be made.

22. Answers may vary. One might want a representation of hourly earnings versus cost of living, depending on the state. If your state is one with the darkest color representation, you would probably want to use this graph because it shows your state with 105% of the national average for hourly earnings.

23. Sum Live Weight values for corresponding dates and plot the sum as a total

24. Not reasonable (there is no information about snow in the middle of the runs--variations in shade could cause variations in snow level)

CHAPTER 10 - INTRODUCTORY GEOMETRY

On-going Assessment 10-1

1. No (a segment would have an infinite number of dots with no spaces between them; this symbol is finite)

2. (a) Skew lines are two lines that cannot be contained in the same plane $\Rightarrow$ $\overleftrightarrow{AB}$ and $\overleftrightarrow{FH}$; $\overleftrightarrow{AD}$ and $\overleftrightarrow{GH}$; $\overleftrightarrow{BC}$ and $\overleftrightarrow{DH}$; $\overleftrightarrow{AE}$ and $\overleftrightarrow{BD}$; etc.

   (b) Parallel (note that BDHF is a rectangle)

   (c) No (they are non-coplanar; i.e., skew)

   (d) No intersection (plane EFG is the bottom of the box; $\overleftrightarrow{BD}$ is parallel to plane EFG $\Rightarrow$ no common points)

   (e) {H} $\left(\overleftrightarrow{BH}\right.$, a diagonal, intersects the box at {B} and {H}$\left.\right)$

   (f) Any two planes containing lines perpendicular at a corner (e.g.; $\overleftrightarrow{EH}$ and $\overleftrightarrow{DH}$ $\Rightarrow$ AEH and CDH; $\overleftrightarrow{DH}$ and $\overleftrightarrow{FH}$ $\Rightarrow$ CDH and EFG; etc.)

   (g) $\overleftrightarrow{AE}$, $\overleftrightarrow{BF}$, $\overleftrightarrow{CG}$, and $\overleftrightarrow{DH}$ are four such lines

   (h) $\angle$ EFB (all planar angles associated with a given dihedral angle are congruent)

   (i) 90°

3. (a) $\emptyset$ (the lines are parallel)

   (b) $\angle$ A-BD-E

   (c) {C}

   (d) {A}

   (e) Answers may vary; $\overleftrightarrow{AB}$ and $\overleftrightarrow{BD}$ are two

   (f) $\overleftrightarrow{AC}$ and $\overleftrightarrow{DE}$ or $\overleftrightarrow{AD}$ and $\overleftrightarrow{CE}$

   (g) Plane BCD or plane BEA

4. 20 pairs (adjacent angles share a common vertex and a common side, and have nonoverlapping interiors)

5. Answers may vary; some examples are:

   (a) Edges of a room; vertical and horizontal parts of a window frame

   (b) Branches in a tree; clock hands at 7:30

   (c) The top angle of intersection of a guy wire and telephone pole; clock hands at 7:15

   (d) An open book resting on a lap; intersection at the peak of a rooftop

   (e) The peak of an army tent; an opened cabinet

   (f) Any two teeth of a zipper; buttons on a shirt

   (g) Ends of the legs of a tripod and the camera atop it; the tips of any four prongs of a child's jack

6. (a) 110°

   (b) $110° - 70° = 40°$

   (c) $180° - 160° = 20°$

   (d) $160° - 30° = 130°$

7. (a) Approximately 36° (b) Approximately 120°

8. (a) (*i*) $18°35'29'' + 22°55'41'' = 40°90'70'' = 40°91'10'' = 41°31'10''$

(*ii*) $93°38'14'' - 13°49'27'' = 93°37'74'' - 13°49'27'' = 92°97'74'' - 13°49'27'' = 79°48'47''$

(b) (*i*) $0.9° = (0.9 \cdot 60)' = 54'$

(*ii*) $15.13° = 15° + (0.13 \cdot 60)' = 15°7.8' = 15°7' + (0.8 \cdot 60)'' = 15°7'48''$

9. (a) (*i*) 90° (the hour hand will be pointed directly at the 3 $\Rightarrow$ it will have moved $\frac{1}{4}$ of 360°)

(*ii*) 12.5° = 12°30′ (the hand will be $\frac{25}{60}$ of the way from the 12 to the 1, or $\frac{25}{60}$ of 30° between numbers)

(*iii*) 205° (the hand will have moved 6 whole spaces at 30° each + $\frac{50}{60}$ of another 30°)

(b) Each minute moves the hour hand $\frac{30°}{60} = 0.5° \Rightarrow 75 \cdot 0.5° = 37.5°$ past 12
In 15 minutes the minute hand moves to 90° past 12
$90° - 37.5° = 52.5° = 52°30'$ between the minute and hour hands

(c) At noon, the angle between hands is 0°
There will be a 180° angle between hands when the minute hand has moved 180° more than the hour hand
Each minute, the minute hand moves $\frac{360}{6} = 6°$ and the hour hand moves 0.5° (from part b)
After x minutes, the hands will have moved 6x° and 0.5x°, respectively
$\Rightarrow 6x - 0.5x = 180 \Rightarrow x = 32.\overline{72}$ minutes $= 32$ minutes $+ 0.\overline{72} \cdot 60$ seconds $= 32$ minutes $+ \frac{72}{99} \cdot 60$ seconds
There will be a 180° angle approximately 32 minutes 43.6 seconds after noon

10. (*i*) Yes (a right angle is formed)

(*ii*) At 2:00, the minute hand is 60° in front of the hour hand
There will be a 90° angle when the minute hand has moved 150° more than the hour hand
$\Rightarrow 6x - \frac{x}{60} \cdot 30 = 150°$ (where x is the number of minutes)
$x = 27.\overline{27}$ minutes $\Rightarrow$ a right angle at approximately 2:27

11. (a) Draw a line with 3 points labeled A, B, and C $\Rightarrow$ there are four rays determined by the three points: $\overrightarrow{AB}$, $\overrightarrow{BC}$, $\overrightarrow{CB}$, and $\overrightarrow{BA}$ (remember that $\overrightarrow{AB} = \overrightarrow{AC}$, but $\overrightarrow{AB} \neq \overrightarrow{BA}$)

(b) Draw a line with 4 points labeled A, B, C, and D $\Rightarrow$ there are six rays: $\overrightarrow{AB}$, $\overrightarrow{BC}$, $\overrightarrow{CD}$, $\overrightarrow{DC}$, $\overrightarrow{CB}$, $\overrightarrow{BA}$

(c) 5 colinear points A, B, C, D, and E $\Rightarrow$ eight rays: $\overrightarrow{AB}$, $\overrightarrow{BC}$, $\overrightarrow{CD}$, $\overrightarrow{DE}$, $\overrightarrow{ED}$, $\overrightarrow{DC}$, $\overrightarrow{CB}$, $\overrightarrow{BA}$

(d) There are 4, 6, and 8 rays for 3, 4, and 5 points, respectively $\Rightarrow$ the general term for the number of rays given n points is $2(n - 1)$

12. (a) 3 (if the points are labeled A, B, and C, the lines are $\overleftrightarrow{AB}$, $\overleftrightarrow{AC}$, $\overleftrightarrow{BC}$)

(b) 6 ($\overleftrightarrow{AB}$, $\overleftrightarrow{AC}$, $\overleftrightarrow{AD}$, $\overleftrightarrow{BC}$, $\overleftrightarrow{BD}$, $\overleftrightarrow{CD}$)

(c) 10 (d) $\frac{n(n-1)}{2} = {}_nC_2$ (see Chapter 8)

13. (a)

Number of Intersection Points

Number of lines	0	1	2	3	4	5
2			Not Possible	Not Possible	Not Possible	Not Possible
3					Not Possible	Not Possible
4			Not Possible			
5			Not Possible	Not Possible		
6			Not Possible	Not Possible	Not Possible	

(b) The maximum number of intersections is the number of possible pairings of two lines: $\frac{n(n-1)}{2}$

14. Perspectives may vary

(a)

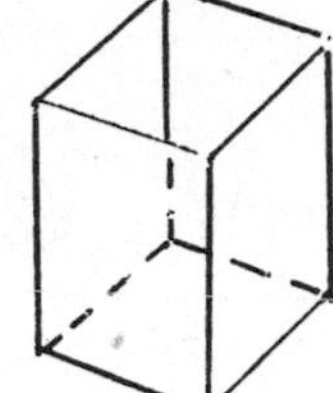

(b)

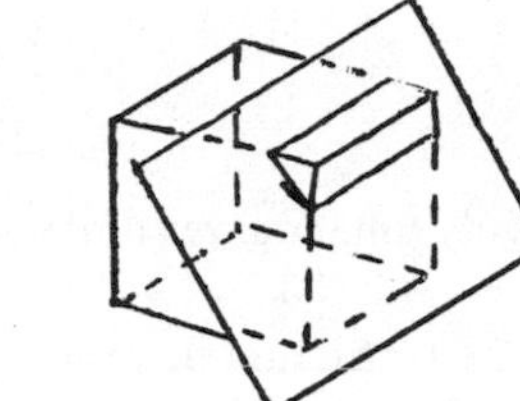

(c)

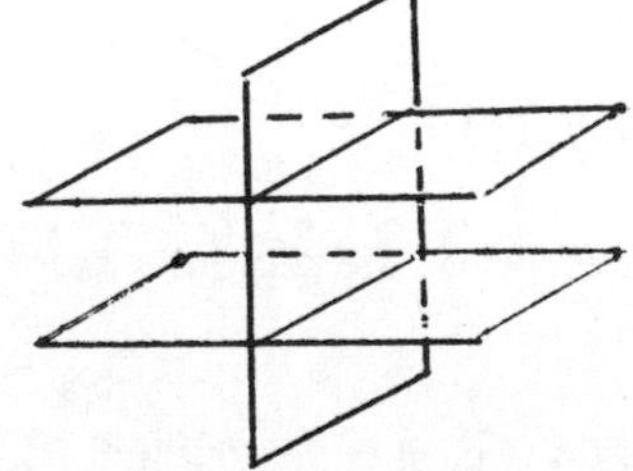

(d)

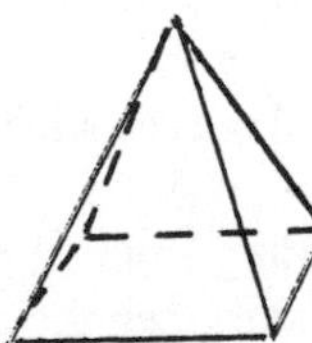

15. (a) 3

(b) 4

(c) 4

(d) 6

(e) 2n (extending each new line through the point will split a region on either side $\Rightarrow$ 2n regions)

16. (*i*) (b) is empty (lines cannot be both skew and coplanar)

(*ii*) (d) is empty (lines cannot be both skew and parallel)

(*iii*) (e) is empty (lines cannot be skew, coplanar, and parallel)

(*iv*) (g) is empty (lines cannot be parallel without being coplanar)

17. Suppose $\alpha \parallel \beta$ and γ intersects α in $\overleftrightarrow{AB}$, and γ intersects β in $\overleftrightarrow{CD}$. If $\overleftrightarrow{AB} \cap \overleftrightarrow{CD}$ is Q, then Q is a point of both plane α and plane β. This cannot happen $\Rightarrow$ $\overleftrightarrow{AB} \parallel \overleftrightarrow{CD}$.

18. Answers may vary; see the following:

18. (a)

```
TO ANGLE:SIZE
  FD 100 BK 100
  RT:SIZE FD 100
  BK 100 LT :SIZE
END
```

(b)

```
TO SEGMENT :LENGTH
  FD :LENGTH1 BK :LENGTH
END
```

(c)

```
TO PERPENDICULAR :LENGTH1 :LENGTH2
  FD :LENGTH1 BK :LENGTH2
  RT 90 FD :LENGTH2
  BK :LENGTH2 LT 90
  BK :LENGTH1/2
END
```

(d)

```
TO PARALLEL :LENGTH1 :LENGTH2
  DRAW
  FD :LENGTH1 PENUP
  RT 90 FD 10 RT 90
  PENDOWN FD :LENGTH2
  PENUP HOME
  RT 180 PENDOWN
END
```

(In LCSI replace DRAW with CLEARSCREEN)

On-going Assessment 10-2

1. (a) By definition, polygonal curves are made entirely of line segments ⇒ 1, 2, 5, 6, 7, 8, and 10

   (b) "Simple" adds the restriction that the polygonal curves may not cross themselves ⇒ 1, 6, 7, and 8

   (c) Closed polygonal curves are those that when traced have the same starting and stopping points ⇒ 1, 2, 5, 6, 7, 8

   (d) Polygons are polygonal curves which are both simple and closed ⇒ 1, 6, 7, 8

   (e) If all segments connecting any two points of a polygon are inside the polygon (i.e., the region is not dented inwards anywhere) then the polygon is a convex polygon ⇒ 6 and 7

   (f) If part of any segment joining two points of a polygon is outside the polygon (i.e., it is "caved in" somewhere), then it is concave ⇒ 1 and 8

2. D and O

3. A segment can pass through at most two sides of a triangle; if each side of the quadrilateral passes through two sides of the triangle ⇒ eight intersections

4. A concave polygon

5. (*i*) (a) and (c) are convex; (b) and (d) are concave

   (*ii*) In (a) and (c), a segment connecting any two points would lie fully inside the figure
   In (b) and (d), it is possible to connect two points of the figure with a segment that lies partially or fully outside the figure

6. (a) Possible (three sides of different lengths with an obtuse angle)

   (b) Possible (three sides of different lengths with three acute angles)

   (c) Possible (three sides of different lengths with a right angle)

   (d) Impossible (an equilateral triangle has three 60° angles)

6. (e) Impossible (an equilateral triangle has three 60° angles)

   (f) Possible (two sides of equal length forming an obtuse angle)

   (g) Possible (two sides of equal length forming an acute angle)

   (h) Possible (two sides of equal length forming a right angle)

7. From "Looking Back" in Section 10-2 example problem 1, the number of diagonals in an n-gon is $\frac{n(n-3)}{2}$

   (a) $\frac{10(7)}{2} = 35$ diagonals (b) $\frac{20(17)}{2} = 170$ diagonals

   (c) $\frac{100(97)}{2} = 4850$ diagonals

8. (a) Equilateral and isosceles (3 congruent sides) (b) Isosceles (2 congruent sides)

   (c) Scalene (no sides congruent)

9. (a) and (b) represent rhombuses and rectangles, respectively [a square is a parallelogram with two key properties; all sides congruent (rhombus) and right angles (rectangle); since each circle represents one of these properties, the intersection contains a parallelogram with both, or a square]

10. (a) T, Q, R, H, G, I, F, J (b) Y, Z, E

    (c) W, D, A, Z, U, E (d) Q, J, F, G, H

    (e) Y

11. Answers may vary

12. Answers may vary; examples are:

    (a)
```
TO SQUARE :SIDE
  REPEAT 4 [FD :SIDE RT 90]
END
```

    (b)
```
TO RECTANGLE :WIDTH :LENGTH
  REPEAT 2 [FD :WIDTH RT 90 FD :LENGTH RT 90]
END
```

On-going Assessment 10-2; Review Problems

17. Angles are formed by any two rays $\Rightarrow$ the number of angles is the number of pairs of rays; i.e., the combinations of all rays taken two at a time (see Chapt 8)

    (a) ${}_{10}C_2 = \frac{10!}{2!(10-2)!} = 45$ (b) ${}_nC_2 = \frac{n(n-1)(n-2)\cdots(1)}{2\cdot 1\cdot[(n-2)(n-3)\cdots(1)]} = \frac{n(n-1)}{2}$

18. $\emptyset$, 1 point, 2 points, or a ray

19. (a) False (a ray has one endpoint, continuing forever in the other direction)

19. (b) True

(c) False (by definition, skew lines are non-coplanar)

(d) False ($\overrightarrow{MN}$ has endpoint M and extends in the direction of point N; $\overrightarrow{NM}$ has endpoint N and extends in the direction of point M)

(e) True

(f) False (their intersection is a line)

On-going Assessment 10-3

1. (a) AB = 1.0 cm – 0.1 cm = 0.9 cm or 9 mm

(b) DE = 4.5 – 3.6 = 0.9 cm or 9 mm

(c) CJ = 10.0 – 2.0 = 8.0 cm or 80 mm

(d) EF = 5.0 – 4.5 = 0.5 cm or 5 mm

(e) IJ = 10.0 – 9.3 = 0.7 cm or 7 mm

(f) AF = 5.0 – 0.1 = 4.9 cm or 49 mm

(g) IC = 9.3 – 2.0 = 7.3 cm or 73 mm

(h) GB = 6.2 – 1.0 = 5.2 cm or 52mm

2. (a) $\frac{100 \text{ inches}}{36 \text{ inches per yard}} = \frac{25}{9} = 2\frac{7}{9}$ yards

(b) (400 yds) · (36 in. per yd) = 14,400 inches

(c) $\frac{300 \text{ feet}}{3 \text{ feet per yard}} = 100$ yards

(d) $\frac{372 \text{ inches}}{12 \text{ inches per foot}} = 31$ feet

3. (a) ——

(b) ————————————————————

(c) ——

(d) ————————————————————

(e) ——

(f) ————————————————————————————————

(g) ————————————————————

(h) —————

4. (a) 98 mm

(b) 9.8 cm

5. (a) Cm (a new pencil measures about 19 cm)

(b) Mm (the diameter is about 21 mm)

(c) Cm or m (the width is about 120 cm or 1.2 m)

(d) Cm or mm (the thickness is about 2 cm or 20 mm)

(e) Cm (about 23 cm)

(f) M or cm (the height is about 1.9 m or 190 cm)

(g) M or cm [an average man's height is about 1.80 m (180 cm); an average woman's about 1.65 m (165 cm)]

(h) Cm or mm (about 15-20 cm or 150-200 mm)

6. (a) Inches (b) Inches

(c) Feet (d) Inches

(e) Inches (f) Feet

(g) Feet (h) Inches

7. In each case, note that:
From m to cm move the decimal point two places to the right
From cm to mm move the decimal point one place to the right
From mm to cm move the decimal point one place to the left
From cm to m move the decimal point two places to the left

Item	m	cm	mm
(a) Length of a piece of paper	0.35	35	350
(b) Height of a woman	1.63	163	1630
(c) Width of a filmstrip	0.035	3.5	35
(d) Length of a cigarette	0.1	10	100
(e) Length of two meter sticks laid end to end	2	200	2000

8. (a) 10.00 mm (b) 0.770 m

(c) 10.0 m (d) 15.5 cm

(e) 195.0 cm (f) 8.100 cm

(g) 40.0 km/hr

9. Convert each to cm: 8 cm; 5218 mm = 521.8 cm; 245 cm; 91 mm = 9.1 cm; 6 m = 600 cm; 700 mm = 70 cm
Listing in decreasing order ⇒ 6 m > 5218 mm > 245 cm > 700 mm > 91 mm > 8 cm

10. Answers may vary, for example:

(a) An equilateral triangle with 4 cm sides or a hexagon with 2 cm sides

(b) A circle with radius about $\frac{5}{8}$ inch (c) A triangle with 1, $1\frac{1}{2}$, and $1\frac{1}{2}$ inch sides

(d) A four-point star with 1 inch sides

11. Listing lengths of sides starting clockwise from the top of each figure:

(a) $(2 + 2 + 2 + 2)$ cm = 8 cm (b) $(4 + 1 + 2 + 1 + 2 + 2)$ cm = 12 cm

(c) $(3 + 3 + 3)$ cm = 9 cm (d) $(4 + 1 + 3 + 1 + 3 + 1 + 4 + 3)$ cm = 20 cm

12. (a) 10 mm = 1 cm (b) 262 m = 0.262 km

(c) 3 km = 3000 m (d) 30 mm = 0.03 m

(e) 35 m = 3500 cm (f) 359 mm = 0.359 m

(g) 647 mm = 64.7 cm (h) 0.1 cm = 1 mm

12. (i) 5 km = 5000 m (j) 51.3 m = 5130 cm

13. The sum of the lengths of any two sides of a triangle is greater than the length of the third side:

 (a) AB + BC > AC (b) BC + CA > AB

 (c) AB + CA > BC

14. (a) Can be (23 + 50 > 60) (b) Cannot be ($10 + 40 \not> 50$)

 (c) Cannot be ($260 + 14 \not> 410$)

15. No (a diagonal forms a triangle with two sides whose sum must be greater than the diagonal $\Rightarrow$ four sides must total more than two diagonals)

16. The hypotenuse of the resultant right triangles is $\sqrt{(4.25)^2 + (11)^2} \doteq 11.8$ inches

 (a) Minimum perimeter: form an isosceles triangle with the two congruent sides formed by the diagonals, and the base formed by the two short ($4\frac{1}{4}$ inch) sides $\Rightarrow$ perimeter $\doteq$ 32.1 inches

 (b) Maximum perimeter: form the base with the two long (11 inch) sides $\Rightarrow$ perimeter $\doteq$ 45.6 inches

17. (a) Answers may vary; one way is to add four squares to each row to form a 7-square by 2-square rectangle

 (b) The minimum number of squares for a fixed perimeter is formed when the squares have the maximum number of sides exposed $\Rightarrow$ six squares with three sides exposed on each gives a perimeter of 18 (two given squares may have only a vertex in common, as long as there is a common edge with another; imagine three dominoes set in step fashion, touching only at corners)

 (c) Twenty squares forming a 4-square by 5-square rectangle are the maximum possible to achieve a perimeter of 18

18.

Number of Toothpicks	Possible Triangles	Type of Triangle
3	1-1-1	Equilateral
4	none	N/A
5	2-2-1	Isosceles
6	2-2-2	Equilateral
7	3-2-2 or 3-3-1	Isosceles
8	3-3-2	Isosceles
9	3-3-3, 4-4-1, or 4-3-2	Equilateral, Isosceles, or Scalene
10	4-4-2 or 3-3-4	Isosceles
11	5-3-3, 4-4-3, 5-5-1, or 5-4-2	Isosceles or Scalene
12	4-4-4, 5-5-2, or 5-4-3	Equilateral, Isosceles, or Scalene

19. Circumference = $2\pi \cdot$ radius $\Rightarrow r = \frac{C}{2\pi}$:

 (a) $r = \frac{12\pi \text{ cm}}{2\pi} = 6$ cm (b) $r = \frac{6 \text{ m}}{2\pi} = \frac{3}{\pi}$ m $\doteq 0.955$ m

 (c) $r = \frac{0.67 \text{ m}}{2\pi} = \frac{0.335}{\pi}$ m $\doteq 0.107$ m (d) $r = \frac{92\pi \text{ cm}}{2\pi} = 46$ cm

20. $C = 2\pi r = \pi d$:

(a) $C = 6\pi$ cm $\doteq 18.8$ cm

(b) $C = 2\pi(3) = 6\pi$ cm $\doteq 18.8$ cm

(c) $C = 2\pi\left(\frac{2}{\pi}\right) = 4$ cm

(d) $C = \pi(6\pi) = 6\pi^2$ cm $\doteq 59.2$ cm

21. The relationship between the two measures is linear $\Rightarrow$ the circumference doubles

22. The arc length of each half-circle is half the circumference of a circle with diameter r $\Rightarrow$ $L = \frac{1}{2}\pi r$
There are two half-circles $\Rightarrow$ total arc length $= \pi r$

23. (a) $\left(\frac{300{,}000 \text{ km}}{\text{sec}}\right)\left(\frac{60 \text{ sec}}{\text{min}}\right)\left(\frac{60 \text{ min}}{\text{hr}}\right)\left(\frac{24 \text{ hr}}{\text{day}}\right)\left(\frac{365 \text{ days}}{\text{yr}}\right) \doteq 9.5 \cdot 10^{12}$ km per year

(b) (4.34 light years)($9.5 \cdot 10^{12}$ km per yr) $\doteq 4.1 \cdot 10^{13}$ km

(c) $\left(\frac{4.1 \cdot 10^{13} \text{ km}}{60{,}000 \text{ km/hr}}\right) \doteq 6.8 \cdot 10^8$ hours, or about 78,000 years

(d) Light travels $(8 \cdot 60 + 19)$ sec $\cdot$ 300,000 km/sec $= 1.497 \cdot 10^8$ km in 8 minutes 19 seconds
$\frac{1.497 \cdot 10^8 \text{ km}}{6 \cdot 10^4 \text{ km/hr}} = 2495$ hours, or about 104 days

24. (a) $(2.5)\left(\frac{0.344 \text{ km}}{\text{sec}}\right)\left(\frac{3600 \text{ sec}}{\text{hr}}\right) \doteq 3096$ km/hr

(b) $(3)\left(\frac{344 \text{ m}}{\text{sec}}\right) = 1032$ m/sec

(c) $M = \frac{\text{Speed of airplane}}{\text{Speed of sound}} = \frac{\frac{5000 \text{ km}}{\text{hr}}}{\frac{0.344 \text{ km}}{\text{sec}} \cdot \frac{3600 \text{ sec}}{\text{hr}}} \doteq 4.04$, or Mach 4.04

25. By definition, 2 "footlongs" = 1 foot

(a) 1 yard = 3 feet = 6 footlongs

(b) 1 mile = 5280 feet = 10,560 footlongs

26. Perimeter $= 2 \cdot 19 + 12 + \frac{1}{2} \cdot \pi \cdot 12 = (50 + 6\pi)$ feet $\doteq 68.8$ feet

27. Assuming these are unit squares, all perimeters will be even integers ≥ 6. There are an even number of sides in each allowed total. For each side shared by two squares, this means that two sides are not on the perimeter $\Rightarrow$ the even total decreased by the shared pairs yields an even perimeter.

28.

Perimeter	Minimum Area	Maximum Area
4	1	1
6	2	2
8	3	4
10	4	6
12	5	9
14	6	12
16	7	16
18	8	20
20	9	25
22	10	30
24	11	36
26	12	42
2n	n − 1	*

28. * Let q be the whole number quotient when 2n is divided by 4
If 2n is a multiple of 4 $\Rightarrow$ the maximum area is q^2
If 2n is not a multiple of 4 $\Rightarrow$ the maximum area is $q(q + 1)$

On-going Assessment 10-3; Review Problems

34. (a) Yes $\left(\overleftrightarrow{BC} \parallel \overleftrightarrow{EH}\right)$

(b) Yes (every three points labeled are not colinear $\Rightarrow$ they determine a unique plane)

(c) No (C is not in the unique plane determined by E, H, and G)

35. Answers may vary; use the definitions of Table 10-5.

On-going Assessment 10-4

1. Answers may vary; some examples are:

(a)

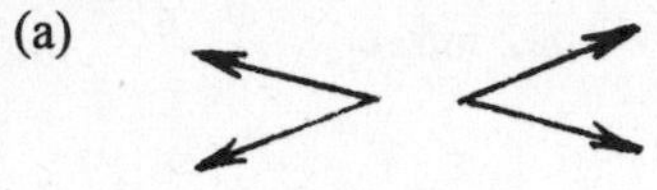

(b)

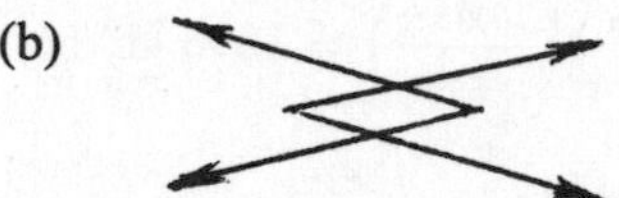

(c)

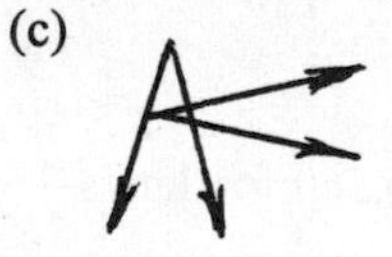

(d)

(e)

2. Every pair of lines forms two pairs of vertical angles $\Rightarrow$ $2[{}_5C_2] = 2 \cdot 10 = 20$ pairs

3. The angles of every triangle add to 180° $\Rightarrow$ subtract the given angles to find the third angle

(a) 60° $[180 - (70 + 50) = 60]$

(b) 45° $[180 - (90 + 45) = 45]$

(c) 60° $[180 - (90 + 30) = 60]$

(d) 60° $[180 - (60 + 60) = 60]$

4. (a) Yes (a pair of corresponding angles are 50° each)

(b) Yes (a pair of corresponding angles are 70° each)

(c) Yes (a pair of alternate interior angles are 40° each)

(d) Yes (a pair of corresponding angles are 90° each)

5. The ratio could be written 7x:2x ; the angles must add to 90°, so $7x + 2x = 90 \Rightarrow x = 10$
The angles are $7(10) = 70°$ and $2(10) = 20°$

6. (a) Each exterior angle is 180 – 162 = 18°. Since exterior angles add to 360°, there must be 360 ÷ 18 = 20 angles ⇒ 20 sides.

   (b) A dodecagon has 12 exterior angles so each is 360 ÷ 12 = 30°. The interior angles are then 180 – 30 = 150° each.

7. (a) 180° – (45 + 65)° = 70°

   (b) ACBD is a parallelogram; opposite angles are equal [see Example 10-6(b)] ⇒ $m(\angle D) = m(\angle 3) = 70°$

   (c) AECB is a parallelogram ⇒ $m(\angle E) = m(\angle 2) = 65°$

   (d) ACFB is a parallelogram ⇒ $m(\angle F) = m(\angle 1) = 45°$

8. (a) x = 40° (congruent vertical angles) ⇒ y = 180 – (90 + 40) = 50°

   (b) x + 4x = 90° (complementary angles) ⇒ x = 18° and 4x = 72°

   (c) $m(\angle BCD) = 50°$ (vertical angles) ⇒ x = 50° (alternate interior angles)
   ⇒ y = 180 – (70 + 50) = 60°

   (d) One angle of the triangle = 180 – 125 = 55° (supplementary angles)
   Another angle of the triangle = 42° (vertical angles)
   ⇒ the angle of the triangle vertical to x is 180 – (55 + 42) = 83°
   ⇒ x = 83° (vertical angles)

9. (a) Call the angle A; its complement is then (90 – A)°
   $m(\angle A)$ = twice its complement = 2(90 – A) = 180 – 2A ⇒ 3A = 180 ⇒ $m(\angle A) = 60°$

   (b) Two angles complementary ⇒ m(third angle) = 180 – 90 = 90°

10. (a) The six angles surrounding the center point add to 360°. They can be compared to three pairs of vertical angles with the angles contained by triangles equal to those not contained;
    the contained angles must then add to $\frac{1}{2}(360) = 180°$.
    The three triangles total 3(180) = 540° ⇒ the numbered angles = 540 – 180 = 360°.

    (b) $m(\angle 1) = m(\angle 3) = m(\angle 5) = 60°$ (equilateral triangle) ⇒ $m(\angle 1 + \angle 3 + \angle 5) = 180°$
    Likewise, $m(\angle 2 + \angle 4 + \angle 6) = 180°$
    ⇒ m(sum of marked angles) = 180 + 180 = 360°

    (c) 360° (sum of angle measurement in each large triangle is 180°)

11. The rightmost wall and wire are parallel; interior angles on the same side of the transversal are supplementary
    ⇒ ∠b is supplementary to 28° ⇒ $m(\angle b) = 152°$
    Angles a, b, and the right angle total 360° ⇒ $m(\angle a) = 360 - 90 - 152 = 118°$

12. The angles are 60, 60 + d, 60 + 2d, 60 + 3d, and 60 + 4d. Their sum is 300 + 10d = 540 ⇒ d = 24.
    The angles measure 60°, 84°, 108°, 132°, and 156°.

13. The measure of an octogon's interior angle is $\frac{(n-2)180}{n} = \frac{(6)180}{8} = 135°$. By using supplementary angles, the measure of each of the triangle's interior angles is 180 – 135 = 45°. Since the two interior angles of the isosceles triangle are each 45°, $m(\angle 1) = 180 - (45 + 45) = 90°$.

14. The sum of the interior angles in this convex hexagon is 720°
    $m(\angle x) = 720 - (110 + 105 + 142 + 122 + 130) = 111°$

15. $\angle$ APT is a right angle, so $m(\angle 1) = 90 - 30 = 60°$
From $\triangle$PTR, $m(\angle 2) = 180 - (90 + 60) = 30°$
From $\triangle$APR, $m(\angle 3) = 180 - (30 + 40) = 110°$

16. Home plate is a pentagon with a total of interior angles of 540°. The two congruent angles add to $540 - 3 \cdot 90 = 270° \Rightarrow 135°$ each.

17. Many options are possible; examples using a protractor and ruler will be given here:

(a) Each angle must be $\frac{(6-2)180}{6} = 120°$. Make one pair of opposite sides one length and the other four sides a different length, measuring a 120° angle each time a new side is drawn.

(b) Each angle must be $\frac{(5-2)180}{5} = 108°$. Construct as in (a), but make all sides the same length.

(c) Repeat (b) but with 120° angles.

(d) Repeat (b); this time angles should be $\frac{(8-2)180}{8} = 135°$ each.

18. (a) $m(\angle \text{ACB}) = 180 - (70 + 30) = 80° \Rightarrow m(\angle 1) = 180 - 80 = 100°$

(b) The measure of the exterior angle equals the sum of the remote interior angles.
Since $\angle 1$ and $\angle$ ACB are supplementary, then $m(\angle 1) + m(\angle \text{ACB}) = 180°$.
We also know that the sum of the measures of the angles of a triangle is 180°
$\Rightarrow m(\angle \text{A}) + m(\angle \text{B}) + m(\angle \text{C}) = 180°$.
Thus $m(\angle 1) = m(\angle \text{A}) + m(\angle \text{B})$

(c) (*i*) $m(\angle \text{ABD}) = 180 - (90 + 50) = 40°$ (*ii*) $m(\angle \text{ACB}) = 180 - (90 + 50) = 40°$

(*iii*) $m(\angle \text{DBC}) = 90 - 40 = 50°$

(d) (*i*) $m(\angle \text{ABD}) = 180 - (90 + \alpha) = (90 - \alpha)°$ (*ii*) $m(\angle \text{ACB}) = 180 - (90 + \alpha) = (90 - \alpha)°$

(*iii*) $m(\angle \text{DBC}) = 90 - (90 - \alpha) = \alpha°$

On-going Assessment 10-4; Review Problems

33. (a) 100 mm = 10 cm (b) 10.4 cm = 104 mm

(c) 350 mm = 0.35 m (d) 0.04 m = 40 mm

(e) 8 km = 8000 m (f) 6504 m = 6.504 km

34. (a) $4 + \frac{1}{2}(2\pi \cdot 2) = (4 + 2\pi)$ mm $\doteq 10.3$ mm

(b) $2 + \frac{1}{2}(2\pi \cdot 2) + 1 + 3 + \frac{1}{2}(2\pi \cdot 3) = (6 + 5\pi)$ mm $\doteq 21.7$ mm

35. All such polygons will have one of the four shapes shown below:

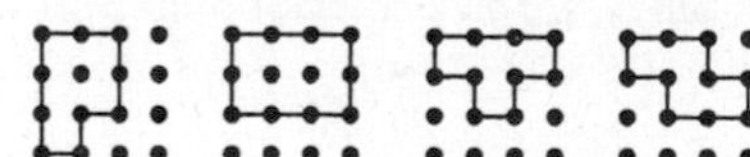

36. (a) All rectangles have four right angles and congruent diagonals

    (b) All sides are congruent and all angles are right angles

    (c) Impossible (all squares are parallelograms)

On-going Assessment 10-5

1. (a) Quadrilateral pyramid (possibly square pyramid)

   (b) Quadrilateral prism (possibly trapezoidal or right trapezoidal prism)

   (c) Pentagonal pyramid

2. (a) A, D, R, W (b) $\overline{AR}$, $\overline{RD}$, $\overline{AD}$, $\overline{AW}$, $\overline{WR}$, $\overline{WD}$

   (c) △ ARD, △ AWD, △ AWR, △ WDR (d) {R}

3. Answers may vary, but examples are: square prism (saltine crackers), rectangular prism (cereal), circular cylinder (canned corn)

4. (a) 5 (triangular prism) (b) 4 (triangular pyramid)

   (c) 4 (tetrahedron)

5. (a) True (definition of a right prism)

   (b) False (no pyramid is a prism; i.e., a pyramid has one base and a prism two bases)

   (c) True (the definition of a pyramid starts with the fact that it is a polyhedron)

   (d) False (they lie in parallel planes)

   (e) False (the base can be any simple closed curve)

   (f) False (it has two bases)

   (g) False (they are parallelograms; if they were rectangles they would be right prisms)

   (h) True (by definition)

6. (a)

   (b)

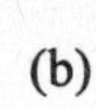

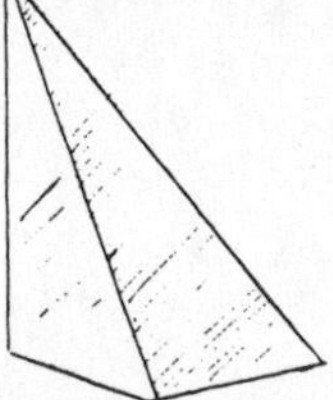

   (c)

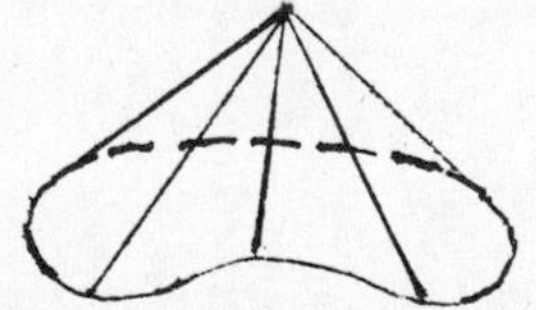

   (d)

7. (a)

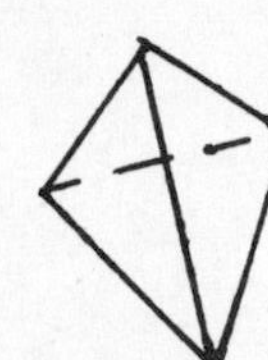

(b)

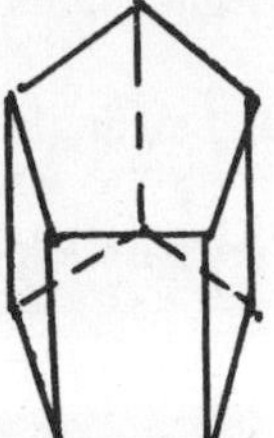
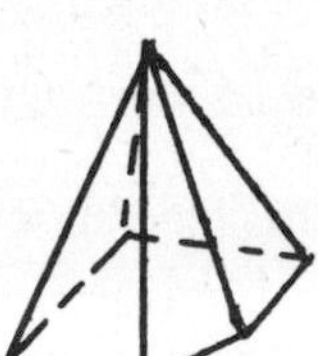

(c)

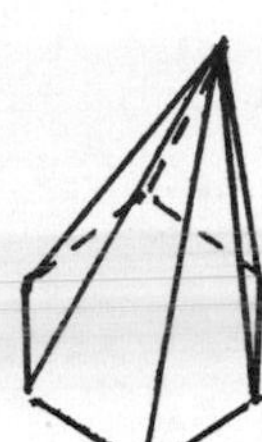

8. (a)

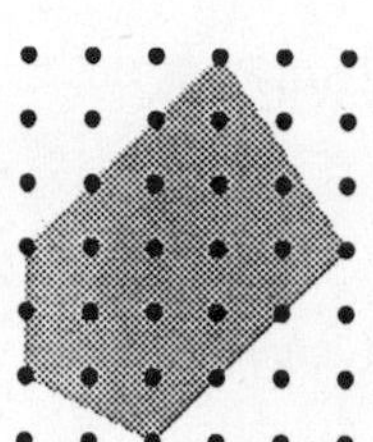

(b)

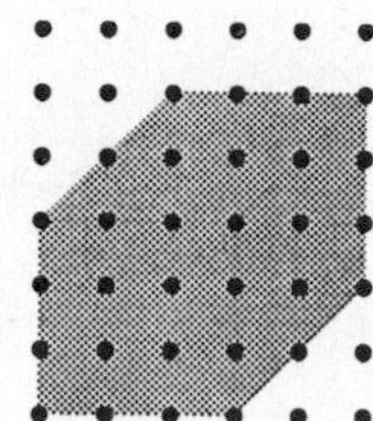

9. (a) Hexagonal pyramid

(b) Quadrilateral (square) pyramid

(c) Cube

(d) Rectangular prism

(e) Hexagonal prism

10. (a) (*iv*)

(b) (*ii*)

11. (a) (*i*): end view; (*ii*): topview; and (*iii*): side view

(b) (*ii*), (*iii*), and (*iv*): top view

12.

Prism	Vertices per Base	Diagonals per Vertex	Total Number of Diagonals
Quadrilateral	4	1	4
Pentagonal	5	2	10
Hexagonal	6	3	18
Heptagonal	7	4	28
Octagonal	8	5	40
⋮	⋮	⋮	⋮
n-gonal	n	n – 3	n(n – 3)

13. (a)

(b)

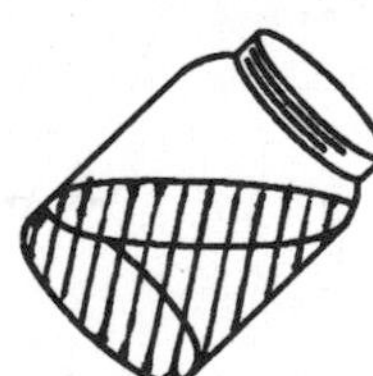

14. (a) Object 2 (note the relationship between numbered faces)

(b) Object 4 (the two figures cannot be on adjoining faces)

15. Intersections have the following shapes:

(a) Triangle (b) Rectangle

(c) Circle (d) Pentagon

(e) Circle (f) Ellipse

16. (a) Square, rectangle, triangle, trapezoid , or rhombus

(b) Rectangle, circle, or ellipse

17. The relationship V + F – E is known as Euler's formula:

(a) $V = 10, E = 15, F = 7 \Rightarrow V + F - E = 10 + 7 - 15 = 2$

(b) $V = 9, E = 16, F = 9 \Rightarrow V + F - E = 9 + 9 - 16 = 2$

18. Use Euler's formula to find the missing value in each case:

Polyhedron	Vertices	Faces	Edges
(a)	$V + 8 - 12 = 2 \Rightarrow V = 6$	8	12
(b)	20	30	$20 + 30 - E = 2 \Rightarrow E = 48$
(c)	6	$6 + F - 15 = 2 \Rightarrow F = 11$	15

19. (a) (*i*) A pyramid has n + 1 faces (*n* lateral faces plus 1 base)

(*ii*) A prism has n + 2 faces (*n* lateral faces plus 2 bases)

(b) (*i*) A pyramid has n + 1 vertices (*n* vertices on the base plus the apex)

(*ii*) A prism has 2n vertices (*n* vertices on each base)

(c) (*i*) A pyramid has 2n edges (*n* edges on the base plus 1 connecting each vertex of the base to the apex)

(*ii*) A prism has 3n edges (*n* on each base plus 1 connecting each corresponding pair of base vertices)

(d) (*i*) Pyramids: $(n + 1) + (n + 1) - 2n = 2$ (*ii*) Prisms: $(n + 2) + 2n - 3n = 2$

On-going Assessment 10-5; Review Problems

29. Yes (the sum of the angles in a triangle must be 180° ⇒ the measure of the third angle in each triangle must be 180° minus the sum of the measures of the other two angles)

30. $m(\angle ACB) = m(\angle DCE) = 60°$ and $m(\angle ACB) + m(\angle BCD) + m(\angle DCE) = 180°$
$\Rightarrow 60° + m(\angle BCD) + 60° = 180° \Rightarrow m(\angle BCD) = 60°$

31. A nonogon has nine sides ⇒ interior angle measurement = $\frac{180 \cdot 9 - 360}{9} = 140°$

32. (a) True (b) True

(c) False (all three may be acute; e.g., an equilateral triangle)

33. (a) Two lines on the same plane and perpendicular to the same line are parallel

(b) The right angles are corresponding; since they are congruent, *l* and *m* must be parallel

On-going Assessment 10-6

1. All except (d), (f), and (i) are traversable; (a), (b), and (j) are Euler networks (starting and stopping points are the same)

(a)

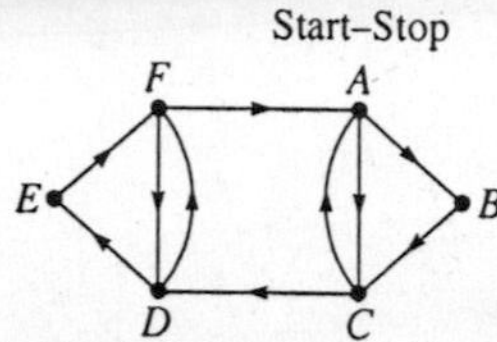

Path:
ABCACDEFDFA;
any point can be a starting point.

(b)

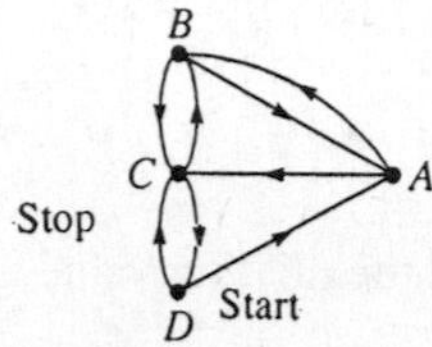

Path:
DACDCBABC;

(c)

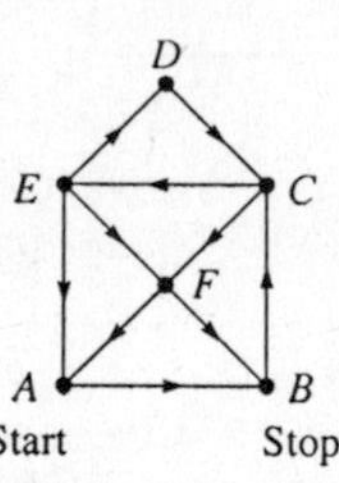

Path:
ABCFAEDCEFB;
only points *A* and *B* can be starting points.

(d) Not traversable; has more than two odd vertices.

(e)

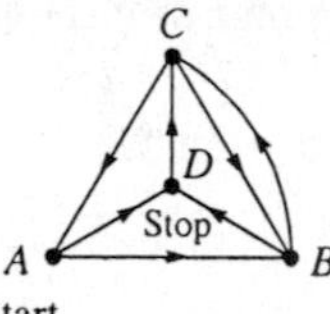

Path:
ABCBDCAD;
only points *A* and *D* can be starting points.

(f) Not traversable; has more than two odd vertices.

(g)

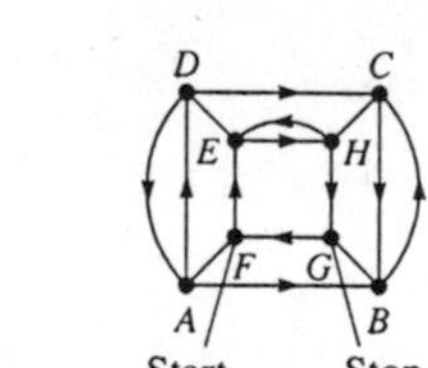

Path:
FADABCBGFEDCHEHG;
only points *F* and *G* can be starting points.

(h)

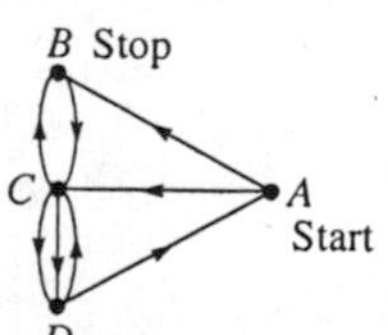

Path:
ACBCDCDAB;
only points *A* and *B* can be starting points.

1. (i) Not traversable; has more than two odd vertices.

(j)

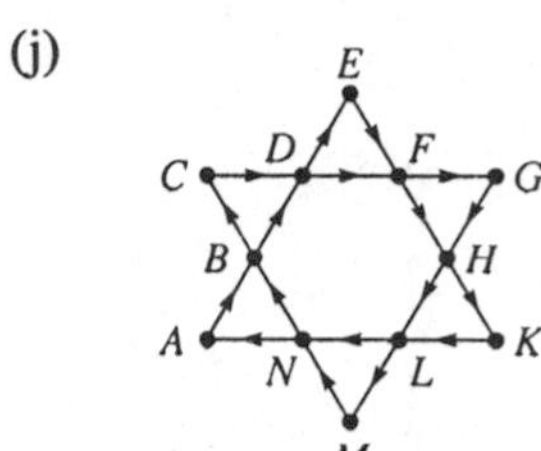

2. All are possible if the starting and stopping points are not the same. If the traveling salesperson must start and return home, then it depends on where home is.

3.

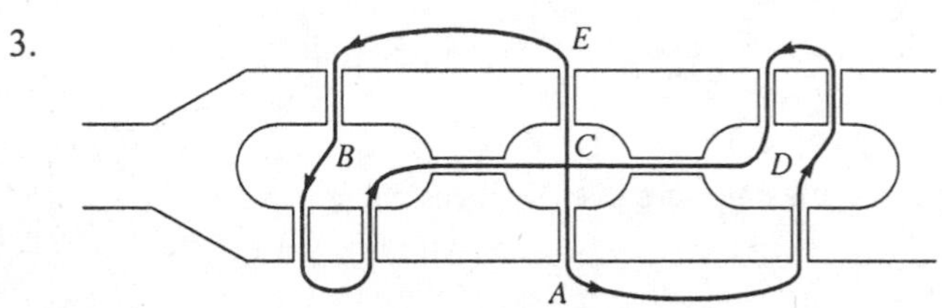

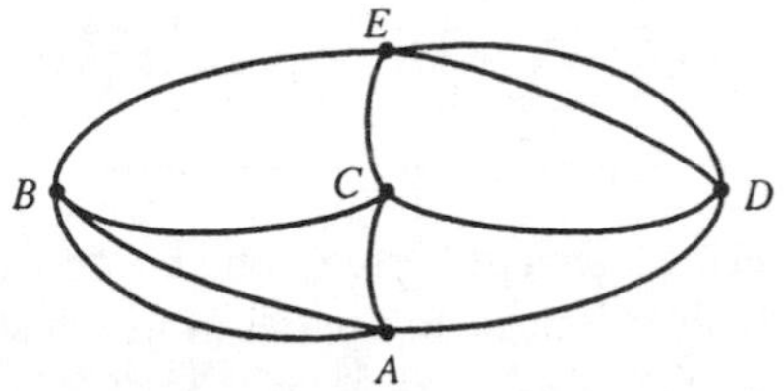

Path: *CEBABCADEDC*; any point can be a starting point.

4. (a) (*i*)

(*ii*)

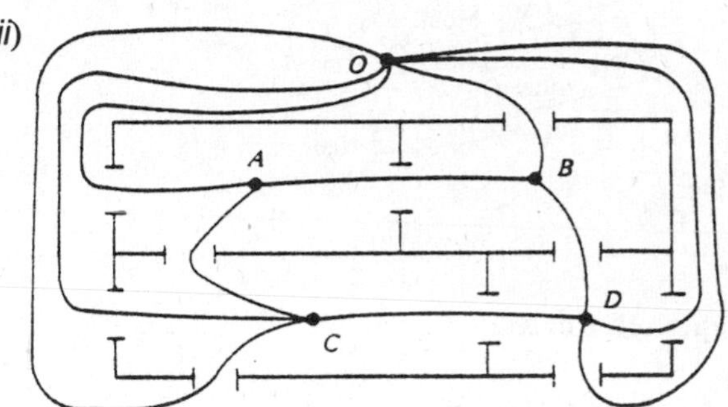

(b) Network (*i*) is not traversable, since it has four odd vertices. Network (*ii*) has two odd vertices, so it is traversable, as shown below.

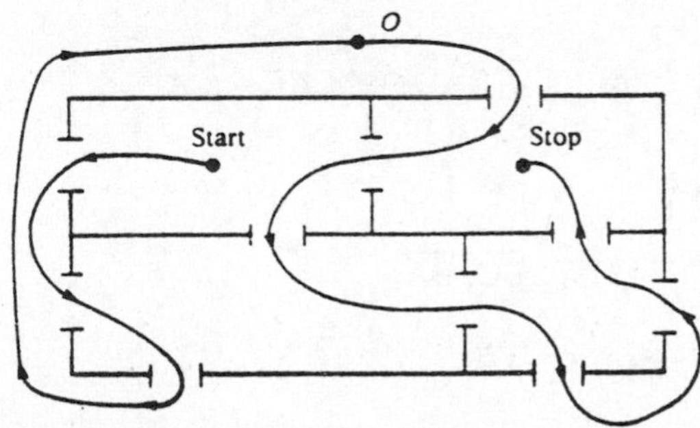

5. Yes. See below:

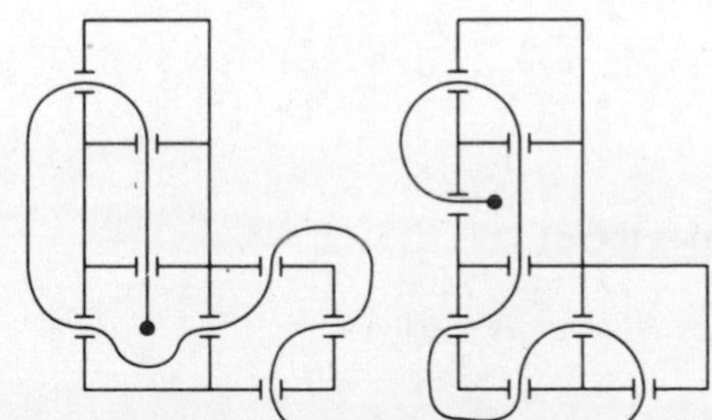

6. Not possible

7.

Network	R	V	A	R + V − A
(a)	6	6	10	2
(b)	7	4	9	2
(c)	6	6	10	2
(d)	4	4	6	2
(e)	5	4	7	2
(f)	8	8	14	2
(g)	9	8	15	2
(h)	6	4	8	2
(i)	7	7	12	2
(j)	8	12	18	2

8. Considering states as vertices and borders as arcs connecting them, all states are even vertices. The trip is thus possible; it does not matter in which state it begins.

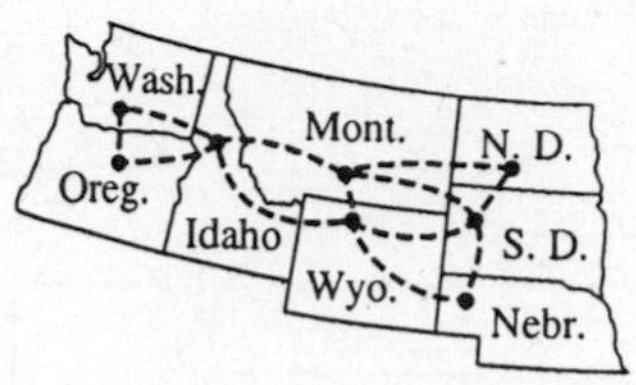

Chapter 10 Review

1. Answers may vary.

   (a) $\overline{AC} \cap \overline{BD} = \overline{BC}$

   (b) $\overrightarrow{AC} \cap \overrightarrow{BC} = \overrightarrow{BC}$

   (c) $\overrightarrow{AB} \cap \overrightarrow{CB} = \overline{AC}$

   (d) $\angle BAD \cap \angle CAE = \angle A$

   (e) $\angle BAC \cap \angle ACD = \overline{AC}$

2. (a) $\overleftrightarrow{AB}, \overleftrightarrow{BC}, \overleftrightarrow{AC}$

   (b) $\overrightarrow{BC}, \overrightarrow{BA}$

   (c) $\overline{AB}$

   (d) $\overline{AB}$

3. (a) $\overleftrightarrow{PQ}$ and $\overleftrightarrow{AB}$ are skew (i.e., they do not intersect and are non-coplanar)

   (b) Any plane containing $\overleftrightarrow{PQ}$ is perpendicular to α (from the diagram, planes APQ and BPQ are two such)

   (c) The planes have $\overleftrightarrow{AQ}$ in common

   (d) No ($\overleftrightarrow{AB}$ and $\overleftrightarrow{PQ}$ are skew lines, and no single plane contains them)

4. Answers may vary; refer to the text for samples.

5. (a) No (the sum of the measures of two obtuse angles is greater than 180°, which is the sum of the measures of the angles of any triangle)

   (b) No (the sum of the measures of the four angles in a parallelogram must be 360° $\Rightarrow$ if all the angles are acute, the sum would be less than 360°)

6. Let α be the measure of the smallest angle; then $\alpha + 2\alpha + 7\alpha = 180 \Rightarrow \alpha = 18°, 2\alpha = 36°, 7\alpha = 126°$

7. (a) Given any convex n-gon, pick any vertex and draw all possible diagonals from this vertex. This will determine n – 2 triangles. Because the sum of the measures of the angles in each triangle is 180°, the sum of the measures of the angles in the n-gon is (n – 2)180°.

   (b) $\frac{(n-2)180}{n} = 176 \Rightarrow 180n - 360 = 176n \Rightarrow n = 90$ sides

8. Answers may vary

9. Sketches may vary; the possibilities are a point, a segment, a triangle, a quadrilateral, or an empty set

10. $m(\angle 3) = m(\angle 4) = 45°$

11. $6°48'59'' + 28°19'36'' = 34°67'95'' = 34°68'35'' = 35°\,8'35''$

12. (a) 60° (vertical angle) (b) 120° (alternate interior and straight angles)

    (c) 120° (vertical angle)

13. (a) (*i*) The sum of the angles in a triangle is 180°

    (*ii*) The measure of an exterior angle of a triangle equals the sum of the measures of the two other angles which are not supplementary to the exterior angle

    (b) (See below) Construct $\angle BAD \simeq \angle B \Rightarrow \overline{AD} \parallel \overline{BC}$ by congruent alternate interior angles
    Thus $\angle DAE \simeq \angle BCA$ by corresponding angles formed by the parallels $\overline{BC}$ and $\overline{AD}$ and the transversal $\overrightarrow{AC}$
    Marking the measure of angles shown below: $b = b'$ and $c = c'$
    Consequently $a + b + c = a + b' + c' = 180°$

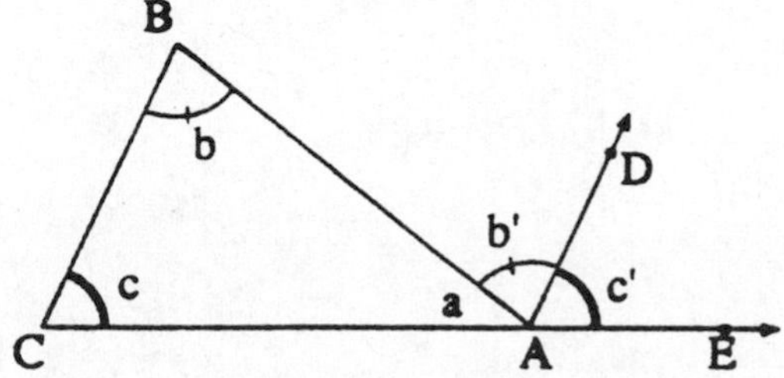

14. (a) Not possible ($p - q > r \Rightarrow p > q + r$ which violates the Triangle Inequality)

    (b) Not possible ($p - q = r \Rightarrow p = q + r$ which violates the Triangle Inequality)

15. (a) $\frac{50 \text{ yards}}{3 \text{ feet per yard}} = 16\frac{2}{3}$ yards (b) $\frac{947 \text{ yards}}{1760 \text{ yards per mile}} \doteq 0.538$ mile

    (c) 0.75 mile · 5280 feet per mile = 3960 feet (d) $\frac{349 \text{ inches}}{36 \text{ inches per yard}} \doteq 9.694$ yards

16. (a) The angles at O of each of the triangles is $\frac{360°}{6} = 60°$. Because all the sides which meet at O are radii, all the triangles are isosceles. Thus the angles at A and B in $\triangle OAB$ are congruent. The sum of their measures must be $180 - 60 = 120°$ so each angle measures 60°. Because all the angles of $\triangle ABC$ measure 60°, all the sides of the triangles are congruent $\Rightarrow$ AB = r. An identical argument applies to each of the remaining triangles $\Rightarrow$ the length of each side of the hexagon = r.

    (b) The perimeter of the hexagon = 6r $\Rightarrow$ the circumference of the circle = $2\pi r$
    Error = $2\pi r - 6r = (2\pi - 6)r$
    Percent error = $\left[\frac{(2\pi-6)r}{2\pi r}\right] \cdot 100\% = \left(\frac{2\pi-6}{2\pi}\right) \cdot 100\% \doteq 4.46\%$

17. Sketches may vary, but the possibilities are the empty set, a single point, a segment, a quadrilateral (various types possible), a triangle, a pentagon, and a hexagon

18. There are as many lateral faces as sides $\Rightarrow$ an octogonal pyramid has 8 lateral faces

19. $180° - 90° - 42° = 48°$

20. (a) *i* (all even vertices), *ii* (two odd vertices), and *iv* (two odd vertices) are traversable

    (b) (*i*)

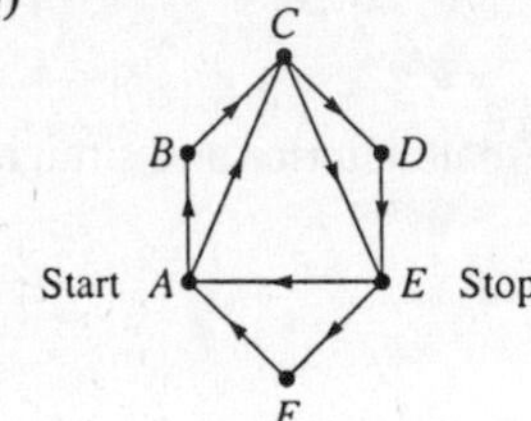

Path:
ABCDEFACEA;
any point can be used as a starting point.

(*ii*)

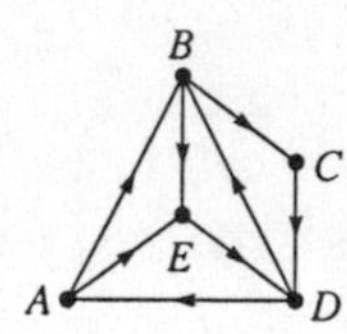

Path:
ABCDAEDBE;
points *A* and *E* are possible starting points.

(*iv*)

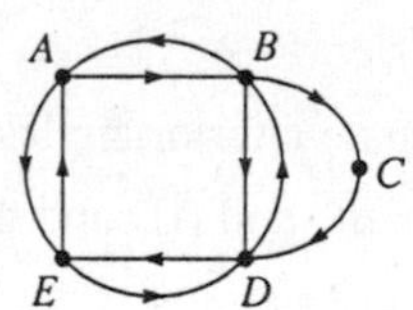

Path:
BDEABAEDBCD;
points *B* and *D* are possible starting points.

CHAPTER 11 - CONSTRUCTIONS AND SIMILARITY

1. (a) The angle opposite $\overline{BC}$ is larger than the angle opposite $\overline{AC}$ $[m(\angle A) > m(\angle B)]$

   (b) The side of greater length is opposite the angle of greater measure

2. Use the instructions in specified Figures for formal constructions. Use a protractor to measure desired angles. Methods may vary, depending upon the tools used.

   (a) See Figures 11-4 and 11-11 in the textbook   (b) See Figure 11-10

   (c) Scalene right triangle (see Figure 11-10)   (d) Not possible $(10 > 4 + 5)$

   (e) See Figure 11-10   (f) See Figure 11-15

   (g) Answers will vary; three triangles are possible (combine Figures 11-10 and 11-15)

   (h) Combine Figures 11-10 and 11-15, or determine the included angle of an isosceles triangle and use 11-15 only

   (i) Use SAS construction with 90° for the included angle

3. (b) Yes (SSS)   (c) Yes (SSS)

   (d) Not possible (triangle inequality)   (e) Yes (SSS)

   (f) Yes (SAS)

   (g) No (SSA can be ambiguous; the side not connected to the given angle may have two possible places to connect to complete the triangle, particularly if it is shorter than the other given side)

   (h) Yes (SAS; with one angle given in an isosceles triangle, others are determined)

   (i) Yes (SAS)

4. 22 (5-5-5, 5-5-4, 5-5-2, 5-5-1, 5-4-4, … , 1-1-1)

5. (a) Yes (SAS)   (b) Yes (SSS)

   (c) No (not SAS since the angles are non-included, and SSA is not sufficient to ensure a congruent triangle)

6. The diagonals form triangles, which are rigid structures and thus make the gate stronger (as well as keeping cows from squeezing through). They also ensure that the gate is and stays rectangular (assuming the diagonals are the same length).

7. The lengths must be the same (by SAS, they are corresponding parts of congruent triangles)

8. The construction makes $\triangle ABC \simeq \triangle DBC$ by SAS $\Rightarrow$ AB = DB

9. (a) See Figure 11-11 in the textbook

   (b) Use the procedure of Figure 11-10 in the textbook with all sides the length of $\overline{AB}$

   (c) Any angle in an equilateral triangle is 60° $\Rightarrow$ follow the procedure in (b) to construct a 60° angle

9. (d) Copy $\angle$ A, then mark off the desired length for the congruent sides on each side of the angle. Connect the two marked points.

10. (a) Use the "copy an angle" procedure, marking the span of $\angle$ B from the point where the span of $\angle$ A fell on the arc

(b) Same as (a), except mark the span of $\angle$ A back toward the starting point from where the span of $\angle$ B fell on the arc

11. (a) $\triangle$ ABC $\simeq$ $\triangle$ ABC; $\triangle$ ACB $\simeq$ $\triangle$ ABC; $\triangle$ BAC $\simeq$ $\triangle$ ABC; $\triangle$ BCA $\simeq$ $\triangle$ ABC; $\triangle$ CAB $\simeq$ $\triangle$ ABC; $\triangle$ CBA $\simeq$ $\triangle$ ABC

(b) Consider the correspondence $\triangle$ BCA $\simeq$ $\triangle$ ABC. Then $\angle$ B $\simeq$ $\angle$ A, $\angle$ C $\simeq$ $\angle$ B, and $\angle$ A $\simeq$ $\angle$ C; i.e., all angles are congruent to each other $\Rightarrow$ $\triangle$ ABC (and any equilateral triangle) is equiangular.

12. Answers may vary

(a) Cans of food, floor tiles, light bulbs, etc.

(b) Photos and their enlargements, slides and their images, original viewgraphs and their projected images, etc. (make sure sides are proportional; e.g., 4×6 and 8×10 pictures are not similar)

13. (a) Start at any point on the circle and mark off around the circle lengths equal to the radius. They should come out evenly.

(b) This construction will form a regular hexagon and its diagonals

(c) Congruent by SSS (all the radii of the circle are congruent; since the points are equally spaced around the circle, the segments joining them are congruent)

(d) Methods will vary depending on the drawing utility used

14. (a) F is the midpoint of both diagonals ($\triangle$ABC $\simeq$ $\triangle$ADC by SSS $\Rightarrow$ $\angle$ CAB $\simeq$ $\angle$ CAD by CPCTC. $\triangle$BAF $\simeq$ $\triangle$DAF by SAS $\Rightarrow$ $\overline{BF} \simeq \overline{FD}$ $\Rightarrow$ F is a midpoint. A similar argument will show $\overline{AF} \simeq \overline{FC}$)

(b) 90° [they are congruent ($\triangle$BAF $\simeq$ $\triangle$DAF) and supplementary]

15. Use the diagram of problem 14 to reference positions in the following:

(a) Parallelogram [using vertical angles, $\triangle$AFD $\simeq$ $\triangle$CFB by SAS; the congruent corresponding angles (e.g., $\angle$ BCF and $\angle$ DAF) are alternate interior angles $\Rightarrow$ $\overline{BC} \parallel \overline{AD}$ and $\overline{AB} \parallel \overline{CD}$]

(b) Rectangle [Since diagonals bisect each other, it must be a parallelogram, from (a). If they are congruent, then $\triangle$ABD $\simeq$ $\triangle$BCA $\simeq$ $\triangle$CDB $\simeq$ DAC $\Rightarrow$ $\angle$ A $\simeq$ $\angle$ B $\simeq$ $\angle$ C $\simeq$ $\angle$ D. These four angles must total 360° (a quadrilateral) $\Rightarrow$ they are 90° each]

(c) Rhombus ($\triangle$AFB $\simeq$ $\triangle$CFB $\simeq$ $\triangle$CFD $\simeq$ $\triangle$AFD $\Rightarrow$ $\overline{AB} \simeq \overline{BC} \simeq \overline{CD} \simeq \overline{AD}$ $\Rightarrow$ rhombus)

16. (a) The angles formed by the diagonals of a rhombus are right angles

(b) Let the rhombus be ABCD with O as the point of intersection of the diagonals
First show that $\triangle$ABO $\simeq$ $\triangle$CDO and conclude that $\overline{AO} \simeq \overline{OC}$
Then show that $\triangle$ABO $\simeq$ $\triangle$CBO by SSS
Therefore conclude that $\angle$ AOB $\simeq$ $\angle$ COB $\Rightarrow$ each angle is a right angle

17. Parallelogram (For quadrilateral ABCD, let $\overline{AB} \simeq \overline{CD}$ and $\overline{BC} \simeq \overline{AD}$ as given. Then $\triangle ABC \simeq \triangle CDA$ by SSS $\Rightarrow \overline{BC} \parallel \overline{AD}$. Similarly, $\overline{AB} \parallel \overline{CD}$.)

18. Congruent arcs are arcs of circles with equal radii whose central angles have the same measure

19. The side of one cube is congruent to a side of the other cube

20. Two parts (e.g., the length of a side of the base and the height

21. (a) 6 [see problem 11(a)]

    (b) 24 (the first can be paired with any of 4, the second with any of the remaining 3, . . . $\Rightarrow 4 \cdot 3 \cdot 2 \cdot 1 = 24$ different pairs)

    (c) $n(n-1)(n-2) \cdot \cdots \cdot 3 \cdot 2 \cdot 1$ [following the pattern in (b)]

22. Congruent by SAS

23. Perimeters are equal (if sides are congruent the sums of their lengths must be the same)

24. Answers may vary; e.g.:

```
TO EQUITRI :SIDE
  REPEAT 3 [FD :SIDE RT 120]
END
```

25. (a) and (b): Execute the program

26. (a) A triangle is constructed (the computer does not know the difference between angle measure and compass heading)

    (b) No (no triangle has one angle with measure 190°)

    (c) IF NOT (:ANGLE < 180) PRINT [NO TRIANGLE IS POSSIBLE.] STOP

On-going Assessment 11-2

1. (a)

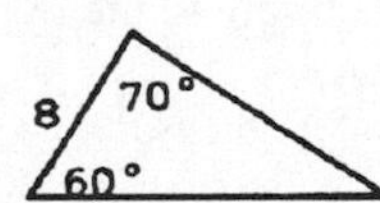

(b)

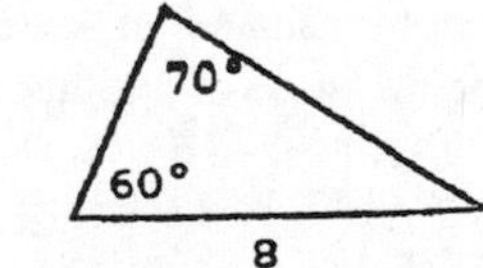

(c)

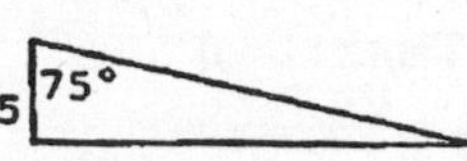

(d) Infinitely many are possible; all would be the shape, but sizes may vary

2. (a) No (the triangle is unique by ASA) (b) No (the triangle is unique by AAS)

2. (c) No (the triangle is unique by ASA)

   (d) Yes (AAA determines a unique shape, but not size)

3. (a) Yes (congruent by ASA) (b) Yes (congruent by AAS)

   (c) No (SSA does not assure congruence) (d) No (AAA does not assure congruence)

4. Drawing $\overline{AD}$ forms $\triangle ADC \simeq \triangle DAB$ by SSS. $\angle BAD$ and $\angle CDA$ are alternate interior angles formed by $\overleftrightarrow{AB}$ and $\overleftrightarrow{DC}$ with transversal $\overleftrightarrow{AD} \Rightarrow \overline{AB} \parallel \overline{DC}$.

5. (a) Parallelogram

   (b) None (one must know it is a parallelogram before it can be known that it is a rectangle; otherwise it could be an isosceles trapezoid)

   (c) None (it could be a kite if parallelogram is not specified)

   (d) Rectangle (e) Rhombus

   (f) Square (g) Parallelogram

6. An isosceles trapezoid is formed. With parallel sides horizontal, the bottom base angles are contruent, as are the top base angles. Either of the bottom base angles is supplementary to either of the top base angles.

7. The third angles must also be congruent (the sum of the measures of the three angles of a triangle must be 180°; with two angles given the third is determined)

8. (a) (*i*) ASA: If one leg and an acute angle of one right triangle are congruent respectively to a leg and an acute angle of another right triangle, the triangles are congruent

   (*ii*) AAS: if the hypotenuse and an acute angle of a right triangle are congruent respectively to the hypotenuse and an acute angle of another right triangle, the triangles are congruent

   (b) (*i*) If one leg and an acute angle of one right triangle are congruent respectively to a leg and an acute angle of another right triangle, the triangles are congruent by ASA

   (*ii*) If the hypotenuse and an acute angle of a right triangle are congruent respectively to the hypotenuse and an acute angle of another right triangle, the triangles are congruent by AAS

9. (a) True (b) True

   (c) True (d) True

   (e) True

   (f) False [a trapezoid may have only one pair of parallel sides (see the example in Table 11-1)]

   (g) True

   (h) False (a square is both a rectangle and a rhombus)

   (i) False (a square satisfies all conditions of a trapezoid, so some trapezoids must be squares)

   (j) True (in fact, all are)

10. (a) Possibilities include:

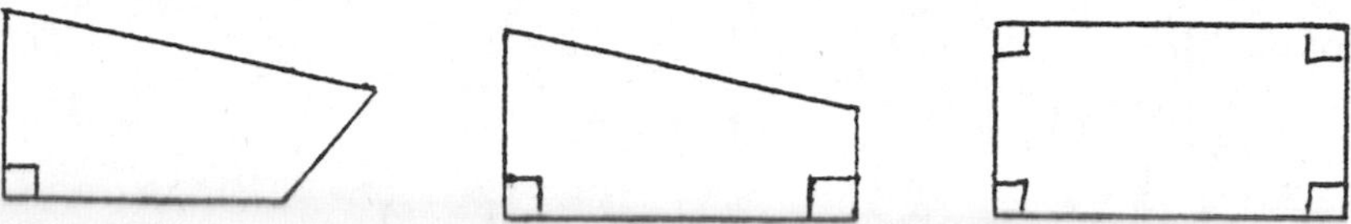

(b) No (the sum of all four angles is 360° ⇒ if three are right angles, the fourth is $360° - 3 \cdot 90° = 90°$, or a fourth right angle)

(c) No (opposite angles are congruent and all angles add to 360° ⇒ making any two angles right forces the other two to be right as well)

11. There are five possibilities; one parallelogram and four kites.

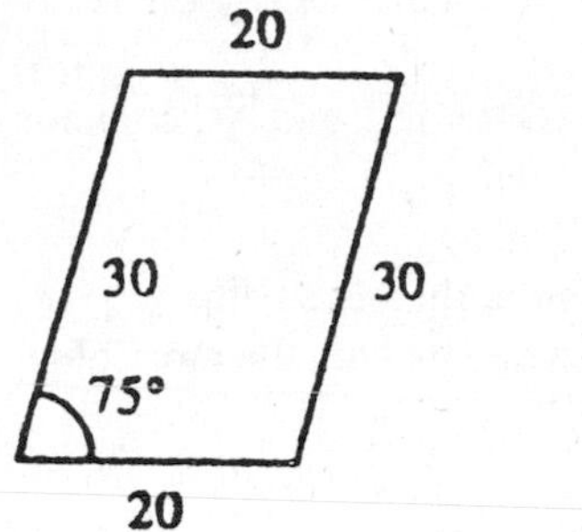

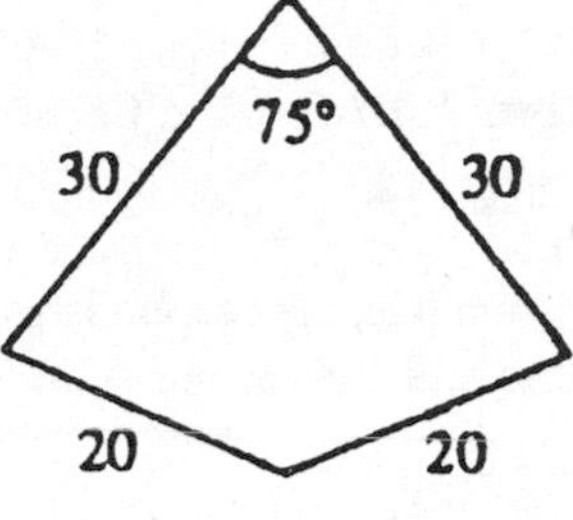

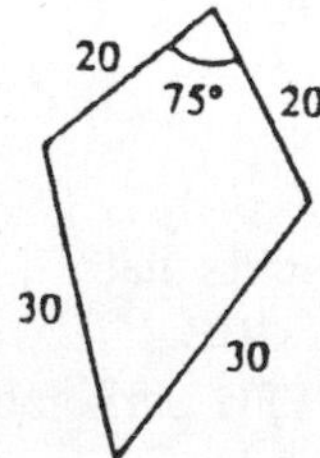

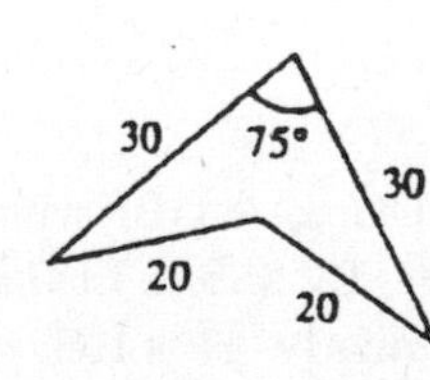

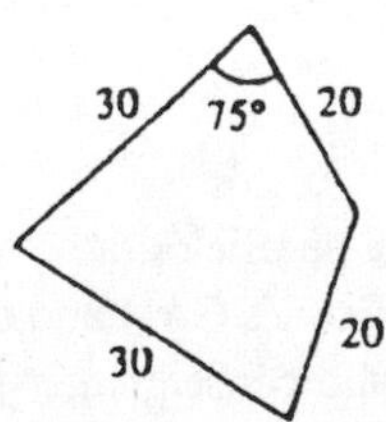

12. Rhombus (all sides are congruent)

13. The polygons must have the same number of sides with one pair congruent (all regular polygons with the same number of sides are similar, so if they have the same number of sides with one pair congruent they are the same shape and size; i.e., congruent)

14. Either the arcs or the central angles must have the same measure (radii are the same since the sectors are part of the same circle)

15. Make one of the quadrilaterals a square and the other a rectangle

16. (a) $\triangle ABC \simeq \triangle ADC$ by SSS ⇒ $\angle BCA \simeq \angle DCA$ and $\angle BAC \simeq \angle DAC$
Therefore $\overleftrightarrow{AC}$ bisects $\angle A$ and $\angle C$

(b) The diagonals intersect at right angles ($\triangle BCM \simeq \triangle DCM$ by SAS ⇒ $\angle BMC \simeq \angle DMC$. These two add to 180°, so must be 90° each)

(c) $\triangle BCM \simeq \triangle DCM$ by SAS ⇒ $\overline{BM} \simeq \overline{DM}$ by CPCTC

17. Let ABCD be an isosceles trapezoid with $\angle A \simeq \angle D$ and $\overline{BC} \parallel \overline{AD}$ (see below)

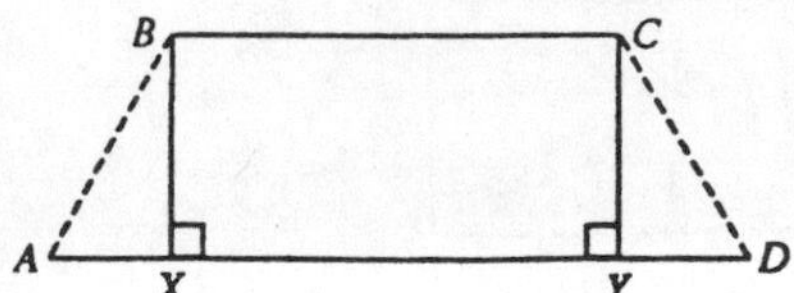

(a) Sides opposite congruent angles in an isosceles trapezoid are congruent ($\overline{AB} \simeq \overline{DC}$)

(b) The diagonals are congruent ($\overline{AC} \simeq \overline{BD}$)

(c) (*i*) Draw $\overline{BX}$ and $\overline{CY}$ perpendicular to $\overline{AD}$. $\overline{BC} \parallel \overline{AD} \Rightarrow$ the distances between them must be constant; i.e., $\overline{BC} \simeq \overline{CY}$. Then $\triangle ABX \simeq \triangle DCY$ by AAS $\Rightarrow \overline{AB} \simeq \overline{DC}$ by CPCTC.

(*ii*) $\triangle ABD \simeq \triangle DCA$ by SAS (given $\angle BAD \simeq \angle CDA$, $\overline{AB} \simeq \overline{DC}$, and $\overline{AC}$ common). Thus $\overline{BD} \simeq \overline{AC}$ by CPCTC.

18. There are two possibilities: (*i*) The first kite is a rhombus, the second is another rhombus with different angles; or (*ii*) the first is any non-rhombic kite, the second is the same kite with the more blunt point indented (the convex restriction is only on the first kite).

19. (a) Rhombus.

(b) Use SAS to prove that $\triangle ECF \simeq \triangle GBF \simeq \triangle EDH \simeq \triangle GAH$, then $\overline{EF} \simeq \overline{GF} \simeq \overline{EH} \simeq \overline{GH}$

(c) Parallelogram.

(d) Suppose ADCB in part (a) is a parallelogram. By SAS $\triangle EDH \simeq \triangle GBF$ which implies that $\overline{EH} \simeq \overline{GF}$. Similarly, $\triangle ECF \simeq \triangle GAH$ and thus $\overline{EF} \simeq \overline{GH}$. By SSS $\triangle EFG \simeq \triangle GHE$. Therefore $\angle GEH \simeq \angle EGF$ and consequently $\overline{FG} \parallel \overline{EH}$. Similarly, $\overline{EF} \parallel \overline{HG} \Rightarrow$ HEFG is a parallelogram. (It is not known that $\overline{EH} \simeq \overline{GH}$, so the figure is not necessarily a rhombus)

(e) Parallelogram (which can be seen by making a few quadrilaterals, concave or convex)

20. (a) One side of each square must be congruent

(b) Two adjacent sides of one must be congruent to those of the other

(c) Answers vary; one solution is that two adjacent sides and an angle of one must be congruent to those of the other

21. (a) $\angle ABD \simeq \angle CDB$ and $\angle CBD \simeq \angle ADB$ (alternate interior angles with respect to parallel lines), so $\triangle ABD \simeq \triangle CDB$ (ASA). Thus $\angle BAD \simeq \angle DCB$ (CPCTC); similarly, $\angle ABC \simeq \angle CDA$.

(b) $\triangle ABD \simeq \triangle CDB \Rightarrow \overline{AB} \simeq \overline{CD}$ and $\overline{AD} \simeq \overline{CB}$

(c) $\angle BAC \simeq \angle DCA$ and $\angle ABD \simeq \angle CDB$ (alternate interior angles), and $\overline{AB} \simeq \overline{DC}$ [from (b)], so $\triangle BAF \simeq \triangle DCF$ and thus $\overline{AF} \simeq \overline{CF}$ and $\overline{BF} \simeq \overline{DF}$

21. (d) As for any triangle, in $\triangle$ ABD $m(\angle$ BAD) + $m(\angle$ ABD) + $m(\angle$ ADB) = 180°.
From (a), $\angle$ CBD $\simeq$ $\angle$ ADB; substitution gives $m(\angle$ BAD) + $m(\angle$ ABD) + $m(\angle$ CBD) = 180°.
Since $m(\angle$ ABC) = $m(\angle$ ABD) + $m(\angle$ CBD), then $m(\angle$ BAD) + $m(\angle$ ABC) = 180°.
Thus $\angle$ ABC and $\angle$ BAD are supplementary.

22. (a) Execute the program

(b) (*i*) Two intersecting line segments

(*ii*) Three segments that do not close into a triangle

(c) Add the following (answers may vary):

```
IF NOT (ALLOF (:ANGLE1 + :ANGLE2 < 180) (:ANGLE 1 > 0) (:ANGLE2 > 0))
PRINT [NO TRIANGLE IS POSSIBLE.] STOP
```

In LSCI, use the following line:

```
IF NOT (AND (:ANGLE1 + :ANGLE2 < 180) (:ANGLE1 > 0) (:ANGLE2 > 0)
[PRINT [NO TRIANGLE IS POSSIBLE.] STOP
```

23. (a) Answers may vary.

```
TO RHOMBUS :SIDE :ANGLE
 REPEAT 2 [FD :SIDE RT (180 – :ANGLE) FD :SIDE RT :ANGLE]
END
```

(b) They are congruent

(c)

```
TO SQ. RHOM :SIDE
 RHOMBUS :SIDE 90
END
```

24. Answers may vary (consider carefully the inputs to :ANGLE):

```
TO ISOSTRI :SIDE :ANGLE
 HOME FD :SIDE
 RIGHT (2*:ANGLE)
 FD :SIDE RIGHT :ANGLE
 HOME
END
```

On-going Assessment 11-2; Review Problems

31. $\triangle$DEA, $\triangle$CDE (By the definition of a regular pentagon, all five sides and angles are congruent $\Rightarrow$ $\triangle$ABC, $\triangle$BCD, $\triangle$CDE, $\triangle$DEA, and $\triangle$EAB are all congruent by SAS. $\triangle$DEA and $\triangle$CDE satisfy the condition of having one point in common with $\triangle$ABC)

32. Use the procedure of Figure 11-10 in the textbook

33. Follow the procedure of Figure 11-10, using the given segment for all three sides

34. (a) Yes (SAS) (b) Yes (SSS)

(c) No (SSA is not a congruous relation)

1. (a) Follow the procedure in Figure 11-20 with the given modifications. Copy α below and left of P (so that it is alternate interior rather than corresponding).

   (b) Copy the angle vertical to α in Figure 11-20, in the position shown

2. The Mira is easy to use when the paper on which the constructions are to be perfomred may not be altered. The compass and straightedge is the classical way to do constructions. Paperfolding adds a tactile approach to the problem. The geometric drawing utility demands that exact measurements must be used on the screen unless similar figures are desired.

   (a) *(i)* Match up the sides of $\angle$ A and crease, being sure that the fold passes through A (Figure 11-24)

   (ii) Use the technique of Figure 11-25 in the textbook

   (iii) Use the technique of Figure 11-23

   (iv) Run the program, if available

   (b) *(i)* Match vertices A and B, then fold making sure to keep the halves of $\overline{AB}$ flush with each other

   (ii) Use the techniques of Figure 11-29(b); line up so that A reflects onto B

   (iii) Use the technique of Figure 11-27 in the textbook

   (iv) Run the program, if available

   (c) *(i)* Fold the paper so that m lands upon itself while being sure to make the crease pass through P

   (ii) Place the drawing edge on P and align so that m reflects onto itself

   (iii) Use the technique of Figure 11-26 in the textbook

   (iv) Run the program, if available

3. (a) A right triangle (assuming the ground is level, the cable will hang perpendicularly to the ground)

   (b) The altitude is the extension of the cable of (a); it will lie outside the triangle (see Figure 11-32)

4. (a) The perpendicular bisectors meet at a point inside the triangle

   (b) The perpendicular bisectors meet at the midpoint of the hypotenuse of the right triangle

   (c) The perpendicular bisectors meet at a point outside the triangle

5. (a) Any point on the perpendicular bisector is equidistant to the endpoints of the segment it bisects

   (b) Construct the perpendicular bisectors of $\overline{AB}$ and $\overline{BC}$. Any point on the perpendicular bisector of $\overline{AB}$ is equidistant to A and B. Any point on the perpendicular bisector of $\overline{BC}$ is equidistant to B and C. The intersection of the two gives P, equidistant to A, B, and C.

   (c) Same as (b). The difference is that P will be outside the triangle, where in (b) it was inside.

   (d) The circle will pass through A, B, and C

6. Construct the bisector of each side to find its midpoint; then connect each midpoint to the opposite vertex

7. (a) Distances are the same (b) Follow textbook Figure 11-26 for each angle

   (c) Follow Figure 11-26

   (d) The circle is tangent to the sides of the triangle; i.e., it touches each side at one point only

8. (a) The perpendicular bisector of a chord passes through the center of the circle

   (b) The perpendicular bisector of a segment contains all points equidistant to the segment's endpoints. It must then contain the center, since it is equidistant to the endpoints of any chord (equal radii).

   (c) Construct two non-parallel chords and find their perpendicular bisectors. The intersection of the bisectors is the center of the circle.

9. Extend $\overline{AB}$ and construct a right angle (perpendicular) at A, using Figure 11-28. Measure $\overline{AB}$ and use it to mark off side $\overline{AC}$ along the perpendicular. From C and B, mark off the length of $\overline{AB}$ at the approximate location of the final vertex. Call the intersection of these two arcs D. Connect to form square ABDC.

10. Answers may vary. One possibility is to:
    (*i*) Draw a line segment (10¢)
    (*ii*) Draw two intersecting arcs (20¢) to construct a perpendicular segment (10¢)
    (*iii*) With compass point at the intersection of the two segments, sweep a wide arc (10¢) intersecting both segments
    (*iv*) Maintain the same compass setting and measure an arc from each of these points to determine the fourth point (20¢)
    (*v*) Draw the two segments to complete the square (20¢)
    The total is 90¢

11. Make an arc of radius BC with center A and one with radius AB and center C so that the two intersect. This intersection is the location of the fourth vertex. A second option would be to construct a parallel to $\overline{BC}$, then mark off the distance BC from A.

12. (a) $\overrightarrow{PQ}$ is the perpendicular bisector of $\overline{AB}$

    (b) Q is on the perpendicular bisector of AB because AQ $\simeq$ QB. Similarly, P is on the perpendicular bisector of AB. Because a unique line contains two points, the perpendicular bisector contains PQ.

    (c) $\overrightarrow{PQ}$ is the angle bisector of $\angle$ APB; $\overrightarrow{QC}$ is the angle bisector of $\angle$ AQB

    (d) $\triangle$ APQ $\simeq$ $\triangle$ BPQ by SSS $\Rightarrow$ $\angle$ APQ $\simeq$ $\angle$ BPQ by CPCTC. Similarly, $\triangle$ AQC $\simeq$ $\triangle$ BQC $\Rightarrow$ $\angle$ AQC $\simeq$ $\angle$ BQC.

13. APBQ is a kite (it has two distinct pairs of congruent consecutive sides)

14. (a) See problem 9

    (b) Construct two perpendicular segments bisecting each other and congruent to the given diagonal

    (c) There is no unique rectangle (the endpoints of two segments bisecting each other and congruent to the given diagonal determine a rectangle $\Rightarrow$ since the segments may intersect at any angle, there are infinitely many such rectangles)

    (d) See problem 11 (without the angle between the sides, there is no unique parallelogram)

    (e) Construct two perpendicular segments bisecting each other and congruent to the given diagonals

14. (f) Not possible (the sum of the measures of the angles would be greater than 180°)

(g) Not possible (given three right angles the fourth angle must also be a right angle)

(h) The right angles will be formed by the non-congruent sides (the kite would not be unique without knowing lengths of some sides)

(i) Three right angles implies a fourth $\Rightarrow$ a square (the kite would not be unique without knowing lengths of some sides)

(j) Consider isosceles $\triangle$ ABC with base $\overline{AB}$ and the angle bisector $\overline{CD}$. Since $\overline{AC} \simeq \overline{BC}$, then $\overline{CD} \perp \overline{AB}$. It is possible to construct $\triangle$ ADC, since $\overline{AD}$ is half as long as the base and $m(\angle DAC) = 90° - \frac{1}{2}m(\angle ACB)$. With C located, complete $\triangle$ABC.

(k) There is no unique trapezoid unless two sides are designated as parallel. If this is the case, consider trapezoid ABCD as shown below to be the final product; i.e., lengths AB, BC, CD, and AD are given with $\overline{BC} \parallel \overline{AD}$. Construct $\overline{AD} - \overline{BC}$ and label it $\overline{AE}$. From A mark off length AB, from E mark off length CD. The intersection of these markings is B. Copy $\angle$ AEB at D. Mark off length CD to locate C. Connecting B and C will complete trapezoid ABCD. (The construction is not always possible; if the four given sides are such that $\triangle$ABE cannot be constructed, the trapezoid cannot be constructed either)

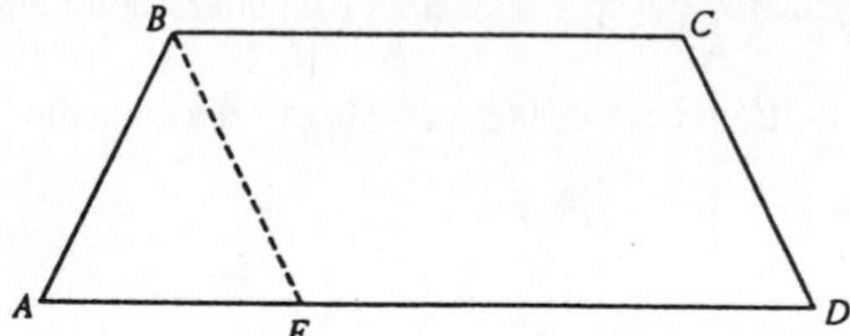

15. (a) Construct a 60° angle (equilateral triangle) and bisect it

(b) Bisect a 30° angle

(c) Add 30° and 15° angles

(d) Add 60° and 15° angles

(e) Add 90° and 15° angles

16. Make arcs of the same radius from A and B above $\overline{AB}$ and label their intersection C. Repeat the process with a new radius, labeling this intersection D. $\overleftrightarrow{CD}$ is the perpendicular bisector of $\overline{AB}$.

17. (a) Since the triangles are congruent, the acute angles formed by the hypotenuse and the ruler are congruent. Since these corresponding angles are congruent, the hypotenuses are parallel (with the ruler as the transversal.

(b) Beginning with the given line containing the hypotenuse, align the ruler along a leg of the triangle so that it passes through *P*, then slide the triangle along the ruler until the hypotenuse passes through P. Drawing the line along the hypotenuse gives the desired result.

18. Align the ruler with *l* and place the triangle with one leg on the ruler; slide the triangle until the other leg passes through P. Tracing along this leg will produce the desired line.

19. See On-going Assessment 11-1, problem 13

20. Mark off 6 points as described; connect every other point

21. Answers will vary

22. Construct two perpendicular diameters. Connect their endpoints to form a square. The diagonals bisect each other (parallelogram), are congruent (rectangle), and are perpendicular (rhombus). Combining the implications yields a square.

23. Draw any diameter. Construct its perpendicular bisector (which will be another diameter). Construct the bisectors of the right angles (giving two more diameters). These four diameters are equally spaced, giving eight equally spaced points. Connecting these gives a regular octagon.

24. Answers may vary:

```
TO ALTITUDES
 REPEAT 3 [RT 30 FD 60 RT 90 FD 110 BK 130 FD 20 LT 90 FD 60 RT 90]
END
```

25. Answers may vary:

(a)

```
TO ANGBIS :MEAS
 REPEAT 3 [FD 75 BK 75 RT :MEAS/21]
END
```

(b)

```
TO PERBIS :SIZE
 FD :SIZE/2 RT 90 FD :SIZE BK :SIZE LT 90 FD :SIZE/2 :SIZE/2
END
```

(c)

```
TO PARALLEL :SEG1 :SEG2
 FD :SEG1 PENUP RT 90
 FD 20 RT 90 PENDOWN
 FD :SEG2
END
```

On-going Assessment 11-3; Review Problems

34. $\triangle ABC \simeq \triangle DEC$ by ASA ($\overline{BC} \simeq \overline{CE}$, $\angle ACB \simeq \angle ECD$ as vertical angles, and $\angle B \simeq \angle E$ as alternate interior angles) $\Rightarrow$ $\overline{AC} \simeq \overline{DC}$ by CPCTC

35. (a) Copy the angle, then measure off each side along a side of the angle; connect

(b) Copy $\overline{AB}$; make arcs from A and B, one with radius AC and the other with radius BC; their intersection is C. Connect.

(c) Copy the side; copy the angles at opposite ends, extending their sides until they meet to form the triangle

36. (a) No.

(b) Yes.

(*i*) $\triangle LYC \simeq \triangle UCY$ by SAS (*ii*) $\triangle ULY \simeq \triangle LUC$ by SAS

(*iii*) $\triangle LOY \simeq \triangle UOC$ by ASA

37. $\overline{AB}$

38. ∠B

39. If ∠A is not the right angle, the triangles are congruent
If ∠A is the right angle, the triangles are not necessarily congruent

On-going Assessment 11-4

1. (a) Similar by AAA (all angles are 60°)

   (b) Similar (sides are proportional and angles congruent)

   (c) Not always similar (they may be proportioned differently)

   (d) Not always similar (angles may be different)

   (e) Similar (radii are proportional)

   (f) Not always similar (unless they have the same number of sides)

   (g) Similar (sides are proportional and angles congruent)

2. Make all dimensions three times as long; e.g., in (c) each side would be three diagonal units long. Possible illustrations are below:

(a)

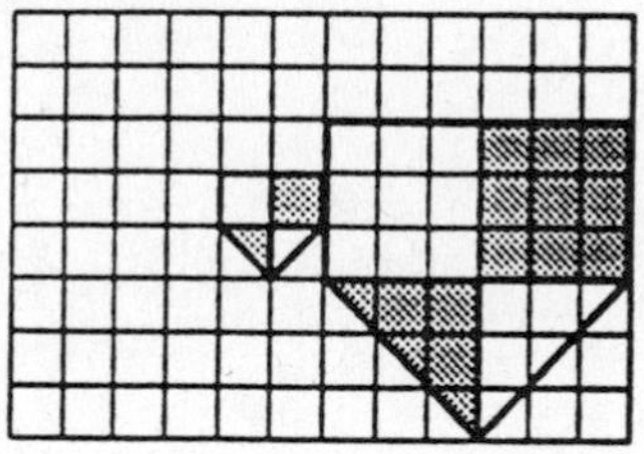

(b)

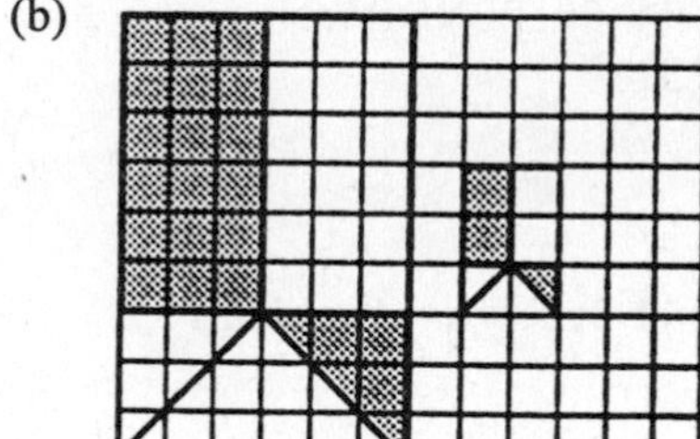

(c)

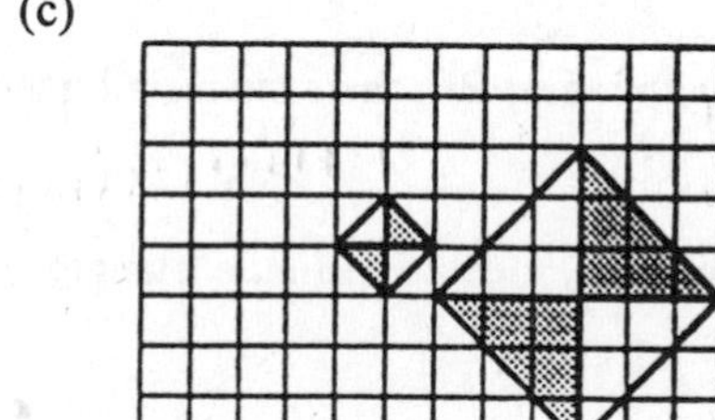

(d)

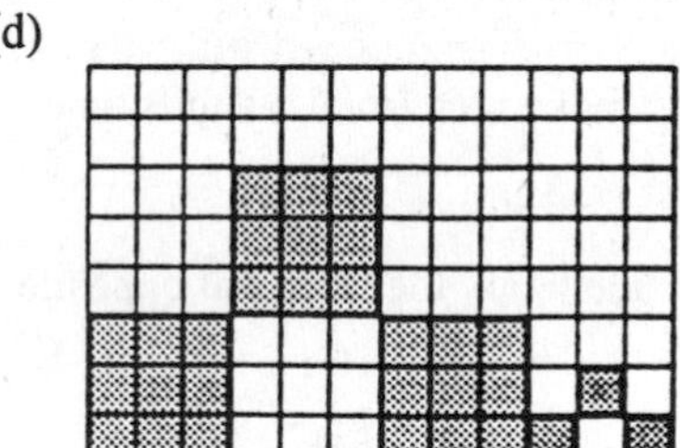

3. (a) and (b) Construct triangles as outlined (see textbook Figure 11-10 for the procedure)

   (c) The triangles are similar when corresponding sides are proportional

4. (a) and (b) Construct triangles as outlined.

4. (c) The triangles are similar if in $\triangle$ ABC and $\triangle$ DEF, $\frac{AB}{DE} = \frac{AC}{DF}$ and $\angle A \simeq \angle D$ (i.e., two proportional sides and congruent included angles)

5. Answers may vary, but possibilities are:

(a) Two rectangles, one of which is a square and the other is not

(b) Two rhombuses with the same length sides but with differing angles

6. The ratio of the perimeters is the same as the ratio of the sides.

7. (a) (*i*) $\triangle ABC \sim \triangle DEF$ by AA (*ii*) $\triangle ABC \sim \triangle EDA$ by AA

(*iii*) $\triangle ACD \sim \triangle ABE$ by AA ($\angle A$ in both triangles)

(*iv*) $\triangle ABE \sim \triangle DBC$ by AA (vertical angles)

(b) (*i*) 2:3 (*ii*) 1:2

(*iii*) 6:8 = 3:4 (*iv*) 3:4

8. (a) $\frac{\text{short side}}{\text{long side}} = \frac{5}{10} = \frac{x}{x+7} \Rightarrow 5(x+7) = 10x \Rightarrow x = 7$ (b) $\frac{3}{x} = \frac{7}{8} \Rightarrow 7x = 3 \cdot 8 \Rightarrow x = \frac{24}{7}$

(c) $\frac{x}{6} = \frac{x+4}{14} \Rightarrow 14x = 6(x+4) \Rightarrow x = 3$ (d) $\frac{x}{12-x} = \frac{8}{5} \Rightarrow 8(12 - x) = 5x \Rightarrow x = \frac{96}{13}$

9. Follow the procedure illustrated by Figure 11-43 in the textbook

10. (a) (*i*) $\triangle ABC \sim \triangle ACD$ by AA ($\angle ADC$ and $\angle ACB$ are right angles and $\angle A$ is common to both)

(*ii*) $\triangle ABC \sim \triangle CBD$ by AA ($\angle CDB$ and $\angle ACB$ are right angles and $\angle B$ is common to both)

(*iii*) $\triangle ACD \sim \triangle CBD$ by the transitive property

(b) (*i*) AC:AB = CD:CB = AD:AC (*ii*) CB:AB = CD:AC = DB:CB

(*iii*) AC:CB = AD:CD = CD:DB

11. No (the maps are similar and even though the scales may change, the actual distances do not)

12. $\triangle DCP \sim \triangle PAB \Rightarrow \frac{6}{x} = \frac{4}{10} \Rightarrow x = 15$

13. We have similar triangles with proportional sides $\Rightarrow \frac{1.5}{3} = \frac{h}{15+3}$ (where h is the height of the tree) $\Rightarrow 3h = 1.5 \cdot 18 \Rightarrow h = 9$ m (note: the girl's height was converted to m from cm)

14. (a) (*i*) 45° - 45° - 90° (bisecting a 90° angle forms two more 45° - 45° - 90° triangles)

(*ii*) 36° - 72° - 72° (bisecting a 72° angle forms another 36° - 72° - 72° triangle and a 36° - 36° - 108° triangle)

(b) (*i*) The two smaller triangles are congruent by ASA. All three triangles are similar by AA.

(*ii*) The two 36° - 72° - 72° triangles are similar. No triangles are congruent.

15. Convert all measurements to inches (3 feet = 36 inches; 7 feet = 84 inches) and use similar triangles: $\frac{36}{13} = \frac{x}{84} \Rightarrow 13x = 36 \cdot 84 \Rightarrow x \doteq 232.6$ inches $\doteq 19.38$ feet

16. $\frac{3/4}{3} = \frac{72}{x} \Rightarrow x = 288$ (i.e., the projector should be placed so that the slide is 288 – 3 inches, or 23 feet 9 inches, from the screen)

17. Slope is given by $m = \frac{y_2 - y_1}{x_2 - x_1}$; in each case let the first pair of coordinates represent point 1 and the second represent point 2:

(a) $m = \frac{0-3}{{}^-5-4} = \frac{{}^-3}{{}^-9} = \frac{1}{3}$ (b) $m = \frac{2-1}{5-{}^-4} = \frac{1}{9}$

(c) $m = \frac{2-2}{1-\sqrt{5}} = \frac{0}{1-\sqrt{5}} = 0$ (horizontal line)

(d) $m = \frac{198-81}{{}^-3-{}^-3} = \frac{117}{0} \Rightarrow$ slope undefined (vertical line)

(e) $m = \frac{10-12}{1-1.0001} = \frac{{}^-2}{{}^-0.0001} = 20{,}000$ (f) $m = \frac{b-a}{b-a} = 1 \;(a \neq b)$

18. The equation of a line with slope m through a given point (x_1, y_1) is: $y - y_1 = m(x - x_1)$
Where there are two given points, use the one which makes the arithmetic easier

(a) $y - 0 = \frac{1}{3}(x - {}^-5) \Rightarrow y = \frac{1}{3}x + \frac{5}{3}$

(b) $y - 2 = \frac{1}{9}(x - 5) \Rightarrow y - \frac{18}{9} = \frac{1}{9}x - \frac{5}{9} \Rightarrow y = \frac{1}{9}x + \frac{13}{9}$

(c) $y - 2 = 0(x - 1) \Rightarrow y - 2 = 0 \Rightarrow y = 2$

(d) Vertical line passing through (⁻3, 81) and (⁻3, 198) $\Rightarrow x = {}^-3$

(e) $y - 10 = 20{,}000(x - 1) \Rightarrow y - 10 = 20{,}000x - 20{,}000 \Rightarrow y = 20{,}000x - 19{,}990$

(f) $y - a = 1(x - a) \Rightarrow y - a = x - a \Rightarrow y = x$

19. Answers may vary

(a) The points are on the line y = 2; some others are (⁻3, 2), (5, 2), . . .

(b) The points are on the line x = ⁻1; some others are (⁻1, 7), (⁻1, ⁻5), . . .

(c) The points are on the line y = 0 (i.e., the x-axis); some others are (2, 0), (4, 0), . . .

(d) The points are on the line x = 0 (i.e., the y-axis); some others are (0, ⁻1), (0, 6), . . .

(e) The points are on the line y = x [all points are of the form (a, a)]; others are (3, 3), (2, 2), . . .

20. In each, all sides are congruent $\Rightarrow$ all corresponding sides are proportional
All interior angles are congruent $\left[\frac{(8-2)180}{180} = 135°\right]$

21. $\frac{1}{k}$ $\left(\text{All sides are in the proportion } \frac{1}{k} \Rightarrow \text{their sum must be in the same proportion}\right)$

22. All such cross-sections are circular $\Rightarrow$ they are similar

23. No [cross sections would be circular (and therefore similar) if cut parallel to the bases, but could also be rectangular or elleptical if cut perpendicularly or at an angle, respectively, to the bases]

24. Answers may vary.

(a)
```
TO RECTANGLE :LEN :WID
 REPEAT 2 [FD :LEN RT 90 FD :WID RT 90]
END

TO SIM.RECT :LEN :WID
 RECTANGLE :LEN*2 :WID*2
END
```

(b)
```
TO SIM.RECTANGLE :LEN :WID :SCALE
 RECTANGLE :LEN*:SCALE :WID*:SCALE
END
```

(c)
```
TO PARALLELOGRAM :LEN :WID :ANGLE
 REPEAT 2 [FD :LEN RT 180 – :ANGLE FD :WID RT :ANGLE]
END

TO SIM.PAR :LEN :WID :ANGLE :SCALE
 PARALLELOGRAM :LEN*:SCALE :WID*:SCALE :ANGLE
END
```

25. Answers may vary.

(a)
```
TO TRISECT :LEN
 REPEAT 3 [MARK FD :LEN/3]
END

TO MARK
 RT 90 FD 5 BK 5 LT 90
END
```

(b)
```
TO PARTITION :LEN :NUM
 REPEAT :NUM [MARK FD :LEN/:NUM]
END
```

On-going Assessment 11-4; Review Problems

32. No (the image is two-dimensional while the person is three-dimensional)

33. Copy the base and construct its perpendicular bisector. Measure the length of the altitude and mark it off on the bisector from the midpoint of the base. Connect endpoints of the base with the end of the altitude.

34. Copy the given side and construct its perpendicular bisector. Measure the given side and mark it off from one of its endpoints to locate the top vertex along the perpendicular bisector. This point and the midpoint of the given side define the altitude.

35. Answers may vary. Construct a perpendicular line at one of the endpoints of the hypotenuse, giving a 90° angle. Bisect this angle to yield a 45° angle. Copy the 45° at the other endpoint of the hypotenuse, extending until it meets the bisector which formed the other 45° angle. These will meet at a 90° angle [180° – (45° + 45°)] across from the given hypotenuse.

36. Yes (the bisector of one of a pair of vertical angles bisects the other if extended, forming two new pairs of vertical angles)

37. Answers may vary; one solution is:

```
TO TR 130 :HYPOT
  DRAW
  FD :HYPOT/2  RT  120
  FD :HYPOT  RT  120
  HOME
END
```

(In LCSI Logo, replace DRAW with CLEARSCREEN)

38. Answers may vary:

```
TO  RTISOS :HYPOT
  DRAW
  FD :HYPOT  RT  135
  CHECK
END
```

(In LCSI Logo, replace DRAW with CLEARSCREEN)

```
TO CHECK
  FORWARD  1
  SETHEADING TOWARDS  00
  IF ABS (HEADING - 225) < 2  HOME STOP
  SETHEADING - 135
  CHECK
END
```

(In LCSI Logo, replace SETHEADING TOWARDS 00 with SETHEADING TOWARDS [00] and IF ABS (HEADING - 225) < 2 HOMESTOP with IF ABS (HEADING - 225 < 2) [HOME STOP]

```
TO ABS :VALUE
IF :VALUE < 0 OUTPUT - :VALUE ELSE
OUTPUT :VALUE
END
```

(In LCSI Logo, replace IF :VALUE < 0 OUTPUT - :VALUE ELSE OUTPUT :VALUE with IF :VALUE < 0 [OUTPUT - :VALUE] [OUTPUT :VALUE])

On-going Assessment 11-5

1. (a) $\text{Sin } 41° = \frac{x}{20} \Rightarrow x = 20 \sin 41° \doteq 20 \cdot 0.656 = 13.12$ m

   (b) $\text{Sin } 35° = \frac{25}{x} \Rightarrow x \sin 35° = 25 \Rightarrow x = \frac{25}{\sin 35°} \doteq \frac{25}{0.57358} = 43.59$ m

   (c) $\text{Tan } 50° = \frac{x}{8} \Rightarrow x = 8 \tan 50° \doteq 8 \cdot 1.1918 = 9.53$ m

   (d) $\text{Tan } 37° = \frac{9}{x} \Rightarrow x \tan 37° = 9 \Rightarrow x = \frac{9}{\tan 37°} \doteq \frac{9}{0.75355} = 11.94$ m

2. $\text{Cos } 70° = \frac{x}{15} \Rightarrow x = 15 \cos 70° \doteq 15 \cdot 0.342 = 5.13$ feet

3. The diagonal of the square tile forms a 45° angle with the side $\Rightarrow$

   (*i*) $\sin 45° \doteq 0.707$ (*ii*) $\cos 45° \doteq 0.707$

   (*iii*) $\tan 45° = 1$

4. $\tan 50° = \frac{\text{height}}{7} \Rightarrow \text{height} = 7 \tan 50° \doteq 8.34$ m

5. Horizontal: $\cos 38° = \frac{h}{14} \Rightarrow h = 14 \cos 38° \doteq 11.03$ pounds
   Vertical: $\sin 38° = \frac{v}{14} \Rightarrow v = 14 \sin 38° \doteq 8.62$ pounds

6. (a) $\cos A = \frac{138}{170} \doteq 0.812 \Rightarrow A \doteq 35.7°$

   (b) Let d = distance BC: $\sin 35.7° = \frac{d}{170} \Rightarrow d = 170 \sin 35.7° \doteq 99.2$ feet across the lake

7. $\sin 28° = \frac{30}{\text{cable length}} \Rightarrow \text{cable length} = \frac{30}{\sin 28°} \doteq 63.9$ feet of wire

8. (a) $\sin 22° = \frac{v}{1500} \Rightarrow v = 1500 \sin 22° \doteq 561.9$ feet vertical rise

   (b) $\cos 22° = \frac{h}{1500} \Rightarrow h = 1500 \cos 22° \doteq 1390.8$ feet horizontally

9. $\sin 75° = \frac{40}{x} \Rightarrow x = \frac{40}{\sin 75°} \doteq 41.4 \Rightarrow$ a 42-foot ladder would be needed

10. Vertical speed is given by: $\sin 13° = \frac{V}{450 \text{ mph}} \Rightarrow V = 450 \sin 13° \doteq 101.2$ mph
    In 5 minutes: Altitude $= \frac{5}{60} \cdot 101.2 \doteq 8.4$ miles (or about 44,350 feet)

11. (a) Decimals are rounded to four places:

Angle Measure	Sine	Cosine	$\sin^2$	$\cos^2$	$\sin^2 + \cos^2$
10°	0.1736	0.9848	0.0302	0.9690	1
20°	0.3420	0.9397	0.1170	0.8830	1
30°	0.5000	0.8660	0.2500	0.7500	1
40°	0.6428	0.7660	0.4132	0.5868	1
50°	0.7660	0.6428	0.5868	0.4132	1
60°	0.8660	0.5000	0.7500	0.2500	1
70°	0.9397	0.3420	0.8830	0.1170	1
80°	0.9848	0.1736	0.9698	0.0302	1

    (b) The sum of the squares of the sine and cosine is 1 for any angle

12. $\tan 68° = \frac{x}{120} \Rightarrow x = 120 \tan 68° \doteq 297$ feet tall

13. Tangent [we measure the ratio of the opposite side (vertical rise) to the adjacent side (horizontal distance)]

14. Tangent [measure the ratio of rise (change along the y-axis) to run (change along the x-axis)]

15. (*i*) $\sin 32° = \frac{h}{120} \Rightarrow h = 120 \sin 32° \doteq 63.6$ miles horizontally (or easterly)

    (*ii*) $\cos 32° = \frac{v}{120} \Rightarrow v = 120 \cos 32° \doteq 101.8$ miles vertically (or northerly)

16. (a) Let $\angle y = x - 90° \Rightarrow \tan y = \frac{73-42}{50} = 0.62 \Rightarrow y \doteq 31.8° \Rightarrow x \doteq 121.8°$

(b) Let $\angle y = \frac{x}{2} \Rightarrow \sin y = \frac{15}{41} \doteq 0.3659 \Rightarrow y \doteq 21.46° \Rightarrow x \doteq 42.9°$

(c) $\text{Tan } 40° = \frac{x}{2} \Rightarrow x = 2 \tan 40° \doteq 2 \cdot 0.8391 = 1.68$ m

17. (a) $\text{Sin } 42° \doteq 0.669$ (b) $\text{Cos } 42° \doteq 0.743$

(c) $\text{Tan } 42° \doteq 0.900$

18. The program draws a square and one of its diagonals

Chapter 11 Review

1. (a) $\triangle ADB \simeq \triangle CDB$ by SAS (b) $\triangle GAC \simeq \triangle EDB$ by SAS

(c) $\triangle ABC \simeq \triangle EDC$ by AAS (d) $\triangle BAD \simeq \triangle EAC$ by ASA

(e) $\triangle ABD \simeq \triangle CBD$ by ASA or by SAS (f) $\triangle ABD \simeq \triangle CBD$ by SAS

(g) $\triangle ABD \simeq \triangle CBE$ by SSS (could also show $\triangle ABE \simeq \triangle CBD$ by SSS)

(h) $\triangle ABC \simeq \triangle ADC$ by SSS; using the properties of the kite,
$\triangle ABE \simeq \triangle ADE$ by SSS or SAS; $\triangle EBC \simeq \triangle EDC$ by SSS or SAS

2. Parallelogram ($\triangle EDA \simeq \triangle FBC$ by SAS $\Rightarrow \angle DAE \simeq \angle BCF$. Thus $90° - \angle EAD = 90° - \angle FCB = \angle BFC$ (i.e., $\angle EAF \simeq \angle CFB$). With these corresponding angles congruent, $\overline{AE} \parallel \overline{FC}$; $\overline{EC} \parallel \overline{AF}$ from the square. Two pairs of parallel opposite sides implies a parallelogram)

3. (a) (*i*) See Figure 11-23 in the textbook

(*ii*) Fold the angle down the middle so the sides match and the crease passes through A

(b) (*i*) See Figure 11-28 in the textbook

(*ii*) Fold the line on top of itself so that the crease passes through B

(c) (*i*) See Figure 11-26 in the textbook

(*ii*) Same as (b) (*ii*)

(d) (*i*) See Figure 11-19 or 11-20 in the textbook

(*ii*) Make line $k \perp l$ through P as in (b) and (c), then make $m \perp k$ through P as in (b). Then $m \parallel l$.

4. (a) (*i*) $\frac{x}{4} = \frac{6}{3} \Rightarrow 3x = 4 \cdot 6 \Rightarrow x = 8$ cm (*ii*) $\frac{y}{10} = \frac{3}{6} \Rightarrow 6y = 3 \cdot 10 \Rightarrow y = 5$ cm

(b) $\frac{x}{12} = \frac{2.5}{5} \Rightarrow 5x = 12 \cdot 2.5 \Rightarrow x = 6$ m

5. See Figure 11-43 in the textbook

6. $(\frac{a}{b} = \frac{c}{d})$ (in $\triangle$ ABC, $\frac{a}{b} = \frac{x}{y}$; in $\triangle$ ACD, $\frac{x}{y} = \frac{c}{d}$ $\Rightarrow$ $\frac{a}{b} = \frac{c}{d}$ by the transitive property)

7. $\overline{AB}$ must be a chord of the circle. The perpendicular bisector of a chord passes through the center, so construct this line to locate the center on *l*. Measure the radius to A or B and draw the circle with your compass.

8. (a) $\triangle$ ACB ~ $\triangle$ DEB by AA $\Rightarrow \frac{x}{3} = \frac{8}{5} \Rightarrow 5x = 3 \cdot 8 \Rightarrow x = \frac{24}{5}$ inches

   (b) $\triangle$ AED ~ $\triangle$ ACB by AA

   (*i*) $\frac{4}{6} = \frac{y+6}{11} \Rightarrow 6(y+6) = 4 \cdot 11 \Rightarrow y = \frac{4}{3}$ ft (*ii*) $\frac{6}{5} = \frac{11}{x} \Rightarrow 6x = 5 \cdot 11 \Rightarrow x = \frac{55}{6}$ ft

9. (a) False (a chord has both endpoints on the circle) (b) True

10. $\frac{\text{2 m tall}}{\text{1 m shadow}} = \frac{\text{h m high}}{\text{6 m shadow}} \Rightarrow 1h = 2 \cdot 6 \Rightarrow$ the building is 12 m high

11. (a) (*iii*) and (*iv*)

    (b) Any regular convex polygon can be inscribed in a circle

12. $\frac{h}{8} = \frac{1.5}{2} \Rightarrow 2h = 8 \cdot 1.5 \Rightarrow h = 6$ m

13. $\frac{d}{64} = \frac{16}{20} \Rightarrow 20d = 64 \cdot 16 \Rightarrow d = \frac{256}{5}$ m

14. True in some cases (if the diagonals bisect each other, then the quadrilateral is a square; if they do not bisect each other, then it is not a square)

15. (a) $m = \frac{1-{}^-3}{{}^-1-2} = \frac{4}{{}^-3} = \frac{{}^-4}{3} \Rightarrow y - {}^-3 = \frac{{}^-4}{3}(x-2) \Rightarrow y + \frac{9}{3} = \frac{{}^-4}{3}x + \frac{8}{3} \Rightarrow y = \frac{{}^-4}{3}x - \frac{1}{3}$

    (b) $m = \frac{2-0}{3-{}^-3} = \frac{2}{6} = \frac{1}{3} \Rightarrow y - 0 = \frac{1}{3}(x - {}^-3) \Rightarrow y = \frac{1}{3}x + 1$

16. If a line connects all three points, the slope between any two must be the same
But slope between (4, 2) and (0, $^-1$) = $\frac{{}^-1-2}{0-4} = \frac{3}{4}$ and slope between (0, $^-1$) and (7, $^-5$) is $\frac{{}^-5-{}^-1}{7-0} = \frac{{}^-4}{7}$
Slopes are not equal $\Rightarrow$ there is no line through the points

17. Sin 60° = $\frac{a}{6} \Rightarrow a = 6 \sin 60° \doteq 5.2 \Rightarrow$ altitude is approximately 5.2 cm

18. Sin 45° = cos 45° $\doteq$ 0.707 (opposite and adjacent sides are equal $\Rightarrow$ 45° - 45° - 90° triangle)

19. Draw an altitude from one of the other two vertices, forming a right triangle (18° - 72° - 90°). Measure the side opposite 72° and the hypotenuse; dividing the opposite side by the hypotenuse will give the 72° sin ratio.

20. There are six sides in a regular hexagon $\Rightarrow$ there are six equilateral triangles with sides 4 cm
The perpendicular to a side will form a 90° - 60° - 30° right triangle with sides *s*, 2, and 4 cm
sin 60° = $\frac{s}{4} \Rightarrow s = 4 \sin 60° \doteq 3.5$ cm

21. They are congruent (alternate interior angles)

CHAPTER 12 - MORE CONCEPTS OF MEASUREMENT

1. (a) cm^2; $in.^2$ (b) mm^2 or cm^2; $in.^2$

   (c) cm^2 or m^2; $in.^2$or yd^2 (d) m^2; yd^2

   (e) m^2; yd^2 (f) km^2; mi^2

2. Answers may vary; some possible approximate measures are:

   (a) $1.5\ m^2$ (b) $1200\ cm^2$

   (c) $2400\ cm^2$ (d) $3\ m^2$

3. In each case, note that:
   From m^2 to cm^2, move the decimal point 4 places to the right.
   From cm^2 to mm^2, move the decimal point 2 places to the right.
   From mm^2 to cm^2, move the decimal point 2 places to the left.
   From cm^2 to m^2, move the decimal point 4 places to the left.

	Item	m^2	cm^2	mm^2
(a)	Area of a sheet of paper	0.0588	588	58,800
(b)	Area of a cross section of a crayon	0.000192	1.92	192
(c)	Area of a desktop	1.5	15,000	1,500,000
(d)	Area of a dollar bill	0.01	100	10,000
(e)	Area of a postage stamp	0.0005	5	500

4. (a) $\frac{4000\text{ ft}^2}{9\text{ ft}^2\text{ per yd}^2} = 444.\bar{4}\text{ yd}^2$ (b) $\frac{10^6\text{ yd}^2}{3.0976\cdot 10^6\text{ yd}^2\text{ per mi}^2} \doteq 0.32\text{ mi}^2$

   (c) $\frac{10\text{ mi}^2}{\frac{1}{640}\text{ mi}^2\text{ per A}} = 6400\text{ A}$ (d) $\frac{3\text{ A}}{\frac{1}{43{,}560}\text{ A per ft}^2} = 130{,}680\text{ ft}^2$

5. (a) $49\text{ m}\cdot 100\text{ m} = 4900\text{ m}^2$ (b) $\frac{4900\text{ m}^2}{100\text{ m}^2\text{ per are}} = 49$ ares per field $\cdot$ 2 fields = 98 ares

   (c) $\frac{98\text{ ares}}{100\text{ ares per hectares}} = 0.98$ hectares

6. (a) Triangle with base 3 and height 2 $\Rightarrow A = \frac{1}{2}(3)(2) = 3$ units^2

   (b) Total area = (4)(3) = 12 units^2.

   Area A = $\frac{1}{2}(3)(2) = 3$ units^2.
   Area B = $\frac{1}{2}(2)(1) = 1$ unit^2.
   Area C = $\frac{1}{2}(3)(2) = 3$ units^2.
   Area D = (1)(2) = 2 units^2.

   The area of the figure is 12 − (3 + 1 + 3 + 1) = 3 units^2

   (c) Triangle with base 2 and height 2 $\Rightarrow A = \frac{1}{2}(2)(2) = 2$ units^2

6. (d)

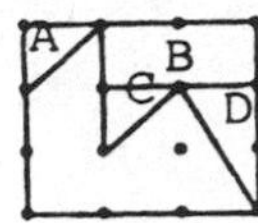

Total area = (3)(3) = 9 units^2

Area A = $\frac{1}{2}(1)(1) = \frac{1}{2}$ unit^2
Area B = (2)(1) = 2 units^2
Area C = $\frac{1}{2}(1)(1) = \frac{1}{2}$ unit^2
Area D = $\frac{1}{2}((1)(2) = 1$ unit^2

The area of the figure is $9 - (\frac{1}{2} + 2 + \frac{1}{2} + 1) = 5$ units^2

(e)

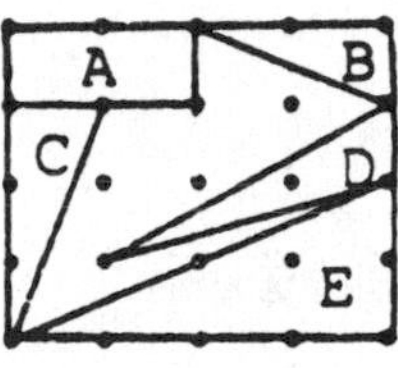

Total area = (4)(4) = 16 units^2

Area A = (2)(1) = 2 units^2
Area B = $\frac{1}{2}(2)(1) = 1$ unit^2
Area C = $\frac{1}{2}(1)(3) = 1\frac{1}{2}$ units^2
Area D = $\frac{1}{2}(1)(3) = 1\frac{1}{2}$ units^2
Area E = $\frac{1}{2}(4)(2) = 4$ units^2

The area of the figure is $16 - (2 + 1 + 1\frac{1}{2} + 1\frac{1}{2} + 4) = 6$ units^2

(f)

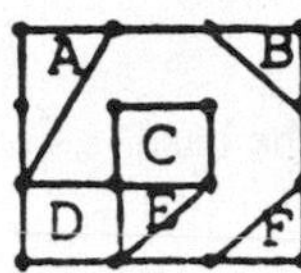

Total area = (3)(3) = 9 units^2

Area A = $\frac{1}{2}(1)(2) = 1$ unit^2
Area B = $\frac{1}{2}(1)(1) = \frac{1}{2}$ unit^2
Area C = (1)(1) = 1 unit^2
Area D = (1)(1) = 1 unit^2
Area E = $\frac{1}{2}(1)(1) = \frac{1}{2}$ unit^2
Area F = $\frac{1}{2}(1)(1) = \frac{1}{2}$ unit^2

The area of the figure is $9 - (1 + \frac{1}{2} + 1 + 1 + \frac{1}{2} + \frac{1}{2}) = 4\frac{1}{2}$ units^2

7. $I + \frac{1}{2}B - 1 = A$ checks for all these polygons:

(a) $I = 1; B = 6 \Rightarrow A = 1 + \frac{1}{2}(6) - 1 = 3$ units^2

(b) $I = 2; B = 4 \Rightarrow A = 2 + \frac{1}{2}(4) - 1 = 3$ units^2

(c) $I = 0; B = 6 \Rightarrow A = 0 + \frac{1}{2}(6) - 1 = 2$ units^2

(d) $I = 1; B = 10 \Rightarrow A = 1 + \frac{1}{2}(10) - 1 = 5$ units^2

(e) $I = 3; B = 8 \Rightarrow A = 3 + \frac{1}{2}(8) - 1 = 6$ units^2

(f) $I = 0; B = 11 \Rightarrow A = 0 + \frac{1}{2}(11) - 1 = 4\frac{1}{2}$ units^2

8. (a) $A = \frac{1}{2}bh = \frac{1}{2}(10)(4) = 20$ cm^2

(b) $A = \frac{1}{2}(6 \text{ m})(0.03 \text{ m}) = 0.09 \text{ m}^2$, or $A = \frac{1}{2}(600 \text{ cm})(3 \text{ cm}) = 900 \text{ cm}^2$

(c) $A = \frac{1}{2}(3)(5) = 7\frac{1}{2}$ m^2

(d) Place point D at the intersection of the two dashed lines. Then:
Area $\triangle$ ABD = $\frac{1}{2}(8)(6) = 24$ cm^2; area $\triangle$ CBD = $\frac{1}{2}(10)(3) = 15$ cm^2
Area $\triangle$ ABC = area $\triangle$ ABD + area $\triangle$ CBD = 24 + 15 = 39 cm^2

(e) Let $\overline{AB}$ be the base; $\overline{BC}$ be the height $\Rightarrow A = \frac{1}{2}(30)(40) = 600$ cm^2

9. (a) $A = l^2 = 3^2 = 9$ cm^2

(b) $A = l \cdot w = (8)(12) = 96$ cm^2

9. (c) Use the Pythagorean theorem:

Height of small triangle = $\sqrt{3^2 - 2^2} = \sqrt{5} \Rightarrow A_{\text{small}\,\triangle} = \frac{1}{2}(4)(\sqrt{5}) = 2\sqrt{5}$

Height of large triangle = $\sqrt{5^2 - 2^2} = \sqrt{21} \Rightarrow A_{\text{large}\,\triangle} = \frac{1}{2}(4)(\sqrt{21}) = 2\sqrt{21}$

Area of figure = $2\sqrt{21} - 2\sqrt{5} = 2(\sqrt{21} - \sqrt{5})$ cm² $\doteq 4.7$ cm²

(d) $A = b \cdot h = (5)(4) = 20$ cm²

(e) $A = \frac{1}{2}h(b_1 + b_2) = \frac{1}{2}(7)(10 + 14) = 84$ cm²

(f) $A = \frac{1}{2}(6)(27 + 8) = 105$ cm²

10. (a) (*i*) (1.3 km)(1.5 km) = 1.95 km² (*ii*) 1.95 km² = 195 ha

(b) (*i*) (1300)(1500) = 1,950,000 yd² $\doteq$ 0.6295 mi² (*ii*) $\frac{1{,}950{,}000 \text{ yd}^2}{4840 \text{ yd}^2 \text{per acre}} \doteq 402.89$ acres

(c) The metric system is easier, requiring only the movement of decimal places

11. (a) True.

(b) The area would be 60 cm² only if the parallelogram were to be a rectangle

(c) The area cannot be more than 60 cm², since the height cannot be more than 6 cm (if the base is 10 cm)

(d) Since we do not know the height, the area can only be expressed as "less than 60 cm²"

12. The diagonals of a rhombus are perpendicular. The height of $\triangle$ ABC in the diagram below is thus $\frac{b}{2}$, and $\triangle$ ABC has area $\frac{1}{2}a(\frac{b}{2}) = \frac{ab}{4}$. Since there are two such triangles, the area of the rhombus is $2 \cdot \frac{ab}{4} = \frac{ab}{2}$.

13. (a) (6.5 m)(4.5 m) = 29.25 m² $\Rightarrow$ (29.25 m²)($13.85/m²) = $405.11

(b) $\frac{15 \text{ ft} \cdot 11 \text{ft}}{9 \text{ ft}^2 \text{ per yd}^2} = 18.\overline{3}$ yd² $\Rightarrow$ (18.$\overline{3}$ yd²)($30/yd²) = $550

14. (a) $A = \pi r^2 = \pi(5^2) = 25\pi$ cm²

(b) $A = \frac{\theta}{360°} \cdot \pi r^2 = \frac{60}{360} \cdot \pi(4^2) = \frac{8}{3}\pi$ cm²

(c) $A = \frac{36}{360} \cdot \pi(6^2) = \frac{18}{5}\pi$ cm²

(d) Half-circle $\Rightarrow A = \frac{1}{2}\pi r^2 = \frac{1}{2}\pi(3^2) = \frac{9}{2}\pi$ cm²

(e) First find θ: $\frac{\theta}{360} = \frac{\text{arc length}}{2\pi r} \Rightarrow \frac{\theta}{360} = \frac{20}{2\pi(10)} \Rightarrow \theta \doteq \left(\frac{360}{\pi}\right)$ degrees

$A = \frac{\left(\frac{360}{\pi}\right)}{360} \cdot \pi(10^2) = 100$ cm²

15. Bathroom area = (300)(400) = 12,000 cm²; each tile is (10)(10) = 100 cm² $\Rightarrow \frac{12{,}000}{100} = 1200$ tiles

16. The plot is (22 m)(28 m) = 616 m² $\Rightarrow \frac{616 \text{ m}^2}{85 \text{ m}^2 \text{ per bag}} = 7.25$ bags (so 8 bags must be bought)

17. The area of a regular polygon is $\frac{1}{2}ap$, where a is the apothem (height of one of the triangle of a regular polygon) and p is the perimeter (the area of a regular triangle is $\frac{1}{2}as$, where s is the length of a side):

(a) $a = 2\sqrt{3}$; $p = 24 \Rightarrow A = \frac{1}{2}(2\sqrt{3})(24) = 24\sqrt{3} \doteq 41.57$ cm²

17. (b) $a = 3\sqrt{3}$; $s = 6 \Rightarrow A = \frac{1}{2}(6)\left(3\sqrt{3}\right) = 9\sqrt{3} \doteq 15.59 \text{ cm}^2$.

18. (*i*) Square peg inside circular hole:
Diagonal of square = 2r $\Rightarrow (2r)^2 = s^2 + s^2$ (where s is the length of a side of the square)
$\Rightarrow 4r^2 = 2s^2 \Rightarrow s^2$ = Area of square = $2r^2$
So wasted space = $\pi r^2 - 2r^2 \doteq 1.14r^2$

(*ii*) Circular peg inside square hole:
Length of side of square = 2r $\Rightarrow$ Area of square = $(2r)^2 = 4r^2$
So wasted space = $4r^2 - \pi r^2 \doteq 0.86r^2$

(*iii*) Circular peg inside square hole has less wasted space

19. (a) $C = 2\pi r \Rightarrow r = \frac{C}{2\pi} = \frac{8\pi}{2\pi} = 4$
$A = \pi r^2 \Rightarrow A = \pi(4)^2 = 16\pi \text{ cm}^2$

(b) $A_{circle} = A_{square} \Rightarrow \pi r^2 = s^2 \Rightarrow r^2 = \frac{s^2}{\pi^2} \Rightarrow r = \frac{s}{\sqrt{\pi}}$

20. (a) Radius of large circle = 2 cm $\Rightarrow$ Area = $\pi \cdot 2^2 = 4\pi \text{ cm}^2$
Each small circle has area $\pi \cdot 1^2 = \pi \text{ cm}^2$
Shaded area = $4\pi - 2\pi = 2\pi \text{ cm}^2$

(b) $A_{semicircle} = \frac{1}{2}(\pi r^2) = \frac{1}{2}\pi(1^2) = \frac{1}{2}\pi \text{ cm}^2$; $A_{triangle} = \frac{1}{2}bh = \frac{1}{2}(2)(2) = 2 \text{ cm}^2$
Shaded area = $(\frac{1}{2}\pi + 2) \text{ cm}^2$

(c) If the 1 cm radius were extended, it would be the diameter of the large circle, cutting off a small shaded semicircle the same size as the small white semicircle. The shaded area is thus equal to half the large circle, whose radius is 2 cm. The shaded area is thus $\frac{1}{2}(\pi \cdot 2^2) = 2\pi \text{ cm}^2$.

(d) Consider half the figure, as shown below. Areas A + B = Area C. Areas A + B = rectangle – semicircle = $5 \cdot 10 - \frac{1}{2}(\pi \cdot 5^2) = 50 - \frac{25}{2}\pi$. A + B + C is twice this, or $100 - 25\pi$. Considering both halves of the figure, the total unshaded area is $2(100 - 25\pi) = 200 - 50\pi$. The shaded area is that of the square less the unshaded area, or $10^2 - (200 - 50\pi) = (50\pi - 100) \text{ cm}^2$.

(e) The two shaded areas form a circle with radius $\frac{r}{2}$ $\Rightarrow$ their area = $\pi(\frac{r}{2})^2 = \frac{\pi r^2}{4}$

(f) The four shaded areas form two circles each having radius $\frac{r}{4}$ $\Rightarrow$ their area = $2\pi(\frac{r}{4})^2 = \frac{\pi r^2}{8}$

(g) The eight shaded areas form four circles each having radius $\frac{r}{8}$ $\Rightarrow$ their area = $4\pi(\frac{r}{8})^2 = \frac{\pi r^2}{16}$

21. The flower bed with its encircling sidewalk forms a circle with radius (3 + 1) = 4 m. Thus its area is $\pi(4^2)$ = $16\pi \text{ m}^2$. The flower bed by itself has an area of $\pi(3^2) = 9\pi \text{ m}^2$. The area of the sidewalk is then $16\pi - 9\pi = 7\pi \text{ m}^2$.

22. (a) $A_{square} = 144 \text{ cm}^2 \Rightarrow$ length per side = $\sqrt{144 \text{ cm}^2} = 12$ cm $\Rightarrow$ perimeter = $4 \cdot 12 = 48$ cm

(b) $\text{Perimeter}_{square} = 32$ cm $\Rightarrow$ length per side = $\frac{32 \text{ cm}}{4} = 8$ cm $\Rightarrow$ area = $(8 \text{ cm})^2 = 64 \text{ cm}^2$

23. (a) Sides of length $s \Rightarrow$ area = s^2
Sides of length $2s \Rightarrow$ area = $(2s)^2 = 4s^2$, which is quadruple the original area

23. (b) Sides of first square = 1s $\Rightarrow$ area = $(1s)^2 = 1s^2$
Sides of second square = 5s $\Rightarrow$ area = $(5s)^2 = 25s^2$ $\Rightarrow$ ratio of areas = 1:25

24. (a) Diameter doubled $\Rightarrow$ radius doubled $\Rightarrow$ $A = \pi(2r)^2 = \pi \cdot 4r^2$ $\Rightarrow$ area is quadrupled

(b) New radius is 110% of old radius = 1.1r $\Rightarrow$ $A = \pi(1.1r)^2 = \pi \cdot 1.21r^2$ $\Rightarrow$ area is increased by 21%

(c) $C = 2\pi r \Rightarrow r = \frac{C}{2\pi} \Rightarrow A = \pi \cdot \left(\frac{C}{2\pi}\right)^2$
$\Rightarrow$ if circumference is increased by a factor of 3, area will increase by a factor of $3^2 = 9$

25. $\text{Area}_{\text{rectangle}} = (64\text{ m})(25\text{ m}) = 1600\text{ m}^2 = 40^2\text{ m}^2$ $\Rightarrow$ length of square's sides = 40 m

26. First package: 3 rolls $\cdot 2\frac{1}{2}$ ft $\cdot$ 8 ft = 60 ft^2 $\Rightarrow$ $\frac{\$6.00}{60\text{ ft}^2} = 10$ ¢ per ft^2
Second package: 5 rolls $\cdot 2\frac{1}{2}$ ft $\cdot$ 6 ft = 7f ft^2 $\Rightarrow$ $\frac{\$8.00}{75\text{ ft}^2} = 10\frac{2}{3}$ ¢ per ft^2 $\Rightarrow$ first package is better buy

27. Draw diameters connecting points of tangency $\Rightarrow$ $A = (20 \cdot 16) + 2[\frac{1}{2}(\pi \cdot 8^2)] = (320 + 64\pi)\text{ m}^2$

28. Removing the same amount from all sides of the original square will form another square. Its area is given by $s^2 = 64$, so s = 8 inches. Thus 1 inch should be removed from each side (10 – 1 – 1 = 8, or 1 inch from the left and right, top and bottom). Therefore, x = 1 inch.

29. The total area of the figure is 5 units^2. Create a trapezoid by connecting a line from P to a point 2 units above P and $1\frac{1}{2}$ units to the right of P. Area of the resulting trapezoid = $\frac{1}{2}(2 + \frac{1}{2}) \cdot 2 = 2\frac{1}{2}$ units^2.

30. (a) Given $2W + 2L = 12 \Rightarrow W + L = 6 \Rightarrow W = 6 - L$

Graph:

L	0	1	2	3	4	5	6
W = 6 – L	6	5	4	3	2	1	0

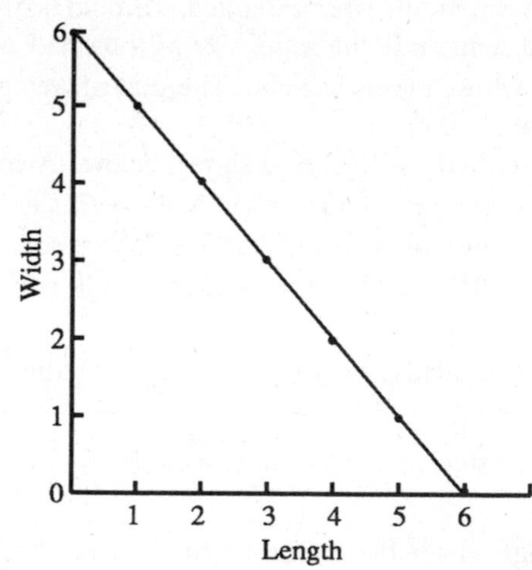

(b) Given $W \cdot L = 12 \Rightarrow W = \frac{12}{L}$

Graph:

L	1	2	3	4	6	12
$W = \frac{12}{L}$	12	6	4	3	2	1

30. (b)

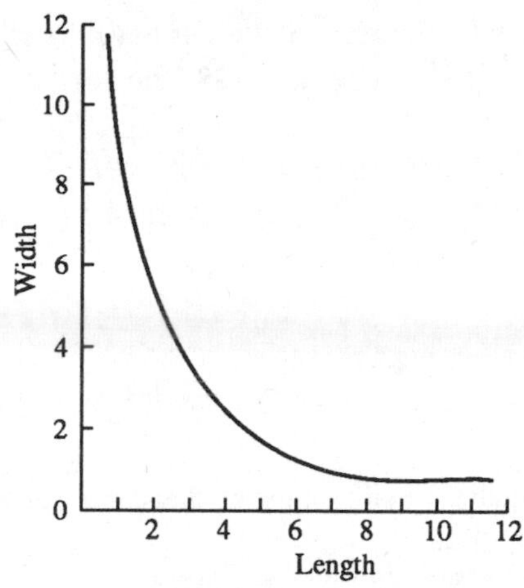

31. $A_{\text{complete target}} = \pi \cdot 5^2 = 25\pi \text{ in}^2$
$A_{\text{inside crosshatch}} = \pi \cdot 4^2 = 16\pi \text{ in}^2 \Rightarrow A_{\text{crosshatch}} = (25\pi - 16\pi) \text{ in}^2 = 9\pi \text{ in}^2$
$A_{\text{shaded region}} = \pi \cdot 3^2 = 9\pi \text{ in}^2 \Rightarrow$ areas of crosshatched and shaded regions are equal

32. (a) Area of complete rectangle = a(b + c)
Total of areas of separate rectangles = ab + ac ⇒ a(b + c) = ab + ac

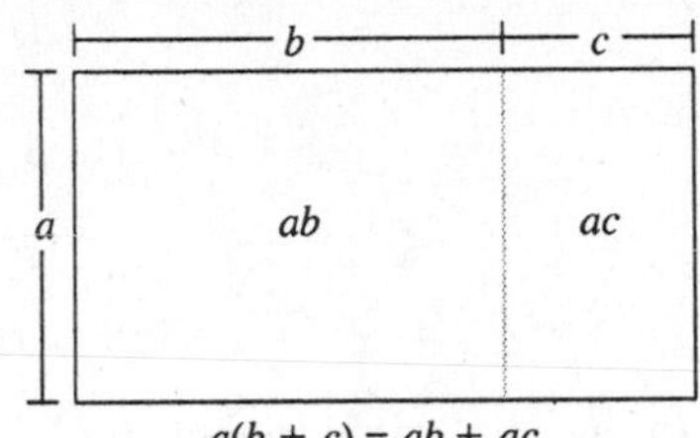

(b) Area of complete rectangle = (a + b)(c + d) = ac + ad + bc + bd
Total of areas of separate rectangles = ac + ad + bc + bd

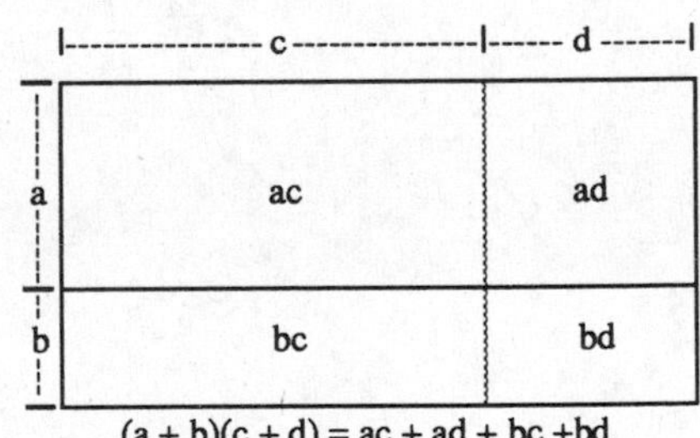

33. (a) $\frac{A_1}{A_2} = \frac{s_1^2}{s_2^2}$ and $\frac{s_1}{s_2} = \frac{2}{3} \Rightarrow \frac{A_1}{A_2} = \left(\frac{2}{3}\right)^2 = 4{:}9$

(b) By the Pythagorean theorem, $d^2 = s^2 + s^2 = 2s^2 \Rightarrow$ if $d_1{:}d_2 = 2{:}3$ then $d_1^2{:}d_2^2 = 4{:}9$
But $d_1^2{:}d_2^2 = 2s_1^2{:}2s_2^2 = s_1^2{:}s_2^2 \Rightarrow$ ratio of areas = 4:9

34. (a) 4:1

(b) The former is the square of the latter.

(c) For two triangles with corresponding sides in the ratio m:n, the bases and heights have ratios mb:nb.
The ratio of areas is then $\frac{1}{2}(mb)(mh){:}\frac{1}{2}(nb)(nh) = m^2(\frac{1}{2}bh){:}n^2(\frac{1}{2}bh) = m^2{:}n^2$.

35. (a) As developed in problems 33 and 34, the ratio of the areas of any two similar objects may be found by squaring the ratio of any corresponding lengths. So for diagonals in the ratio 20:27, areas have the ratio $20^2{:}27^2$, or 400:729. This ratio is less than that of the prices (400:600); i.e., there is less area in the smaller screen in comparison to price. The 27-inch set is a better buy.

35. (b) Let d be the diagonal of the specified set. The areas of the sets have the same ratio as that of the squared diagonals. Thus $20^2 : d^2 = 1:2$, or $\frac{400}{d^2} = \frac{1}{2} \Rightarrow d \doteq 28.3$ inches.

36. Draw altitudes $\overline{BE}$ and $\overline{DF}$ of triangles BCP and DCP, respectively. $\triangle ABE \simeq \triangle CDF$ by AAS. Thus $\overline{BE} \simeq \overline{DF}$. Because $\overline{CP}$ is a base of $\triangle BCP$ and $\triangle DCP$, and because the heights are the same, the areas must be equal.

On-going Assessment 12-2

1. (a) No (it is a 6 by 3 rectangle; to be a square the sides must be the same length and angles must be right angles)

   (b) Use the Pythagorean theorem: $y^2 = 6^2 + 3^2 = 45 \Rightarrow y = \sqrt{45} \doteq 6.7$

   (c) The new diagonal: $y_{new}^2 = 12^2 + 6^2 = 180 \Rightarrow y = \sqrt{180} \doteq 13.4$ (or double the lenth of the original diagonal)

2. . (a) $x^2 + 8^2 = 10^2 \Rightarrow x^2 + 64 = 100 \Rightarrow x^2 = 36 \Rightarrow x = 6$

   (b) $(3a)^2 + (4a)^2 = x^2 \Rightarrow 9a^2 + 16a^2 = x^2 \Rightarrow 25a^2 = x^2 \Rightarrow x = 5a$

   (c) $x^2 + 5^2 = 13^2 \Rightarrow x^2 + 25 = 169 \Rightarrow x^2 = 144 \Rightarrow x = 12$

   (d) $x^2 + (\frac{s}{2})^2 = s^2 \Rightarrow x^2 + \frac{s^2}{4} = s^2 \Rightarrow x^2 = \frac{3s^2}{4} \Rightarrow x^2 = \sqrt{\frac{3s^2}{4}} = \frac{s\sqrt{3}}{2}$

   (e) Let the base of the large right triangle be represented by a; the base of the small right triangle by b
   $8^2 + a^2 = 17^2 \Rightarrow 64 + a^2 = 289 \Rightarrow a^2 = 225 \Rightarrow a = 15$
   $8^2 + b^2 = 10^2 \Rightarrow 64 + b^2 = 100 \Rightarrow b^2 = 36 \Rightarrow b = 6$
   Thus $x = 15 - 6 = 9$

   (f) $5^2 + 12^2 = x^2 \Rightarrow 25 + 144 = x^2 \Rightarrow x^2 = 169 \Rightarrow x = 13$

   (g) $4^2 + 4^2 = (2x)^2 \Rightarrow 16 + 16 = 4x^2 \Rightarrow 32 = 4x^2 \Rightarrow x^2 = 8 \Rightarrow x = 2\sqrt{2}$

   (h) $3^2 + 6^2 = x^2 \Rightarrow 9 + 36 = x^2 \Rightarrow x^2 = 45 \Rightarrow x = \sqrt{45} = 3\sqrt{5}$

   (i) $3^2 + 3^2 = d^2 \Rightarrow 9 + 9 = d^2 \Rightarrow d^2 = 18 \Rightarrow d = \sqrt{18}$
   Then $3^2 + d^2 = x^2 \Rightarrow 9 + 18 = x^2 \Rightarrow x^2 = 27 \Rightarrow x = \sqrt{27} = 3\sqrt{3}$

   (j) $3^2 + 4^2 = y^2 \Rightarrow 9 + 16 = y^2 \Rightarrow y^2 = 25 \Rightarrow y = 5$
   Using similar triangles: $\frac{x}{5} = \frac{1}{3} \Rightarrow 3x = 5 \Rightarrow x = \frac{5}{3}$

3. $x^2 + (2x)^2 = 30^2 \Rightarrow x = 6\sqrt{5}$ and $2x = 12\sqrt{5}$

4. For the answer to be yes, the numbers must satisfy the Pythagorean theorem (with largest measure = c)

   (a) $10^2 + 16^2 \neq 24^2 \Rightarrow$ not a right triangle

   (b) $16^2 + 30^2 = 34^2 \Rightarrow$ a right triangle

   (c) $\left(\sqrt{2}\right)^2 + \left(\sqrt{2}\right)^2 = 2^2 \Rightarrow$ a right triangle

   (d) $1^2 + \left(\sqrt{3}\right)^2 = 2^2 \Rightarrow$ a right triangle

   (e) $\left(\sqrt{2}\right)^2 + \left(\sqrt{3}\right)^2 = \left(\sqrt{5}\right)^2 \Rightarrow$ a right triangle

   (f) $\left(\frac{3}{2}\right)^2 + \left(\frac{4}{2}\right)^2 = \left(\frac{5}{2}\right)^2 \Rightarrow$ a right triangle

5. Find the diagonal of a face: $9^2 + 12^2 = x^2 \Rightarrow x = 15$. The diagonal of the prism is then given by: $15^2 + 15^2 = d^2 \Rightarrow d = \sqrt{450}$. The longest segment is thus $\sqrt{450} = 15\sqrt{2}$ cm, the diagonal length of the prism.

6. The distances form the legs of a right triangle. The southbound plane travels (3.5 hr) · (376 km/hr) = 1316 km; the westbound plane travels (3.5 hr) · (648 km/hr) = 2268 km. The distance apart is given by $d^2 = (1316)^2 + (2268)^2 \Rightarrow d = \sqrt{6{,}875{,}680} \doteq 2622$ km.

7. The boat is 10 mi south and 5 mi east. Using a right triangle, the distance from A is given by: $d^2 = 10^2 + 5^2 \Rightarrow d = \sqrt{125}$ mi $\doteq 11.2$ mi.

8. If h is the height of the ladder's top: $h^2 + 3^2 = 15^2 \Rightarrow h = \sqrt{216} = 6\sqrt{6} \doteq 14.7$ feet above the ground

9. The tall pole stands 10 m above the short one. Draw a horizontal line from the top of the short pole to form a right triangle. Then $d^2 + 10^2 = 14^2 \Rightarrow d^2 = 96 \Rightarrow d = \sqrt{96} \doteq 9.8$ m.

10. (a) The altitude forms 30°-60°-90° triangles $\Rightarrow \left(\frac{s}{2}\right)^2 + h^2 = s^2 \Rightarrow$ height $= \frac{s}{2} \cdot \sqrt{3}$

$A = \frac{1}{2}bh = \frac{1}{2}(s)(\frac{s}{2} \cdot \sqrt{3}) = \frac{s^2\sqrt{3}}{4}$

(b) The triangle is isosceles with height = base = s $\Rightarrow A = \frac{1}{2}(s)(s) = \frac{s^2}{2}$

11. (a) (*i*) For the large triangle: $x^2 = 4^2 + (4\sqrt{3})^2 = 64 \Rightarrow x = 8$

(*ii*) The large triangle is a 30° - 60° - 90° triangle because:

The length of the hypotenuse (8) is twice as long as the leg opposite the 30° angle (4)

The leg opposite the 60° angle $(4\sqrt{3})$ is $\sqrt{3}$ times the shorter leg (4)

The smallest triange is thus also a 30° - 60° - 90° triangle $\Rightarrow$ the leg opposite the 30° angle = 2

Thus $y^2 = 4^2 - 2^2 = 12 \Rightarrow y = \sqrt{12} = 2\sqrt{3}$

(b) Use the special relationship for 45° - 45° - 90° right triangles: if the length of each leg is a, then the hypotenuse has length $a\sqrt{2}$

Hypotenuse $= 2\sqrt{2} \Rightarrow a = 2 \Rightarrow x = 2a = 4$

$y = \frac{1}{2}x \Rightarrow y = 2$

12. Draw radius $\overline{OK}$ forming 30°-60°-90° triangle OKC $\Rightarrow \overline{OC} = 0.65$, $\overline{CK} = \frac{0.65}{\sqrt{3}}$, $\overline{OK} = 2\left(\frac{0.65}{\sqrt{3}}\right) \doteq 0.75 = \overline{OB}$

AB = 2(0.75) = 1.5 m

13. Draw and lable the rhombus as shown:

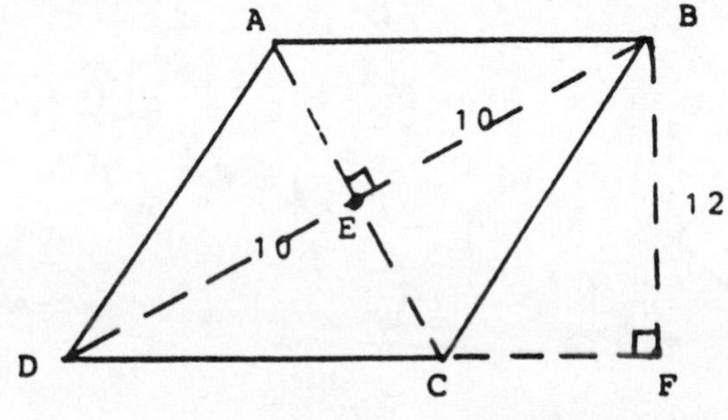

13. (*i*) Length of sides:

$AF^2 + FC^2 = AC^2 \Rightarrow 12^2 + FC^2 = 20^2 \Rightarrow FC^2 = 256 \Rightarrow FC = 16$

$DF = 16 - CD \Rightarrow (16 - CD)^2 + 12^2 = AD^2$

But $AD = CD \Rightarrow (16 - CD)^2 + 12^2 = CD^2$

$\Rightarrow 256 - 32 \cdot CD + CD^2 + 144 = CD^2 \Rightarrow 400 = 32 \cdot CD \Rightarrow CD = 12.5$

So $CD = DA = AB = BC = 12.5$ cm

(*ii*) Diagonal:

$DE^2 + AE^2 = AD^2 \Rightarrow DE^2 + 10^2 = 12.5^2$

$\Rightarrow DE^2 = 156.25 - 100 = 56.25 \Rightarrow DE = \sqrt{56.25} = 7.5$

So the length of the other diagonal $= 2 \cdot 7.5 = 15$ cm

14. $\triangle ABC$ is a right triangle with hypotenuse (diameter) $\overline{AB} \Rightarrow AB^2 = AC^2 + BC^2 \Rightarrow BC = 8$ cm

15. The brace will be a hypotenuse $\Rightarrow 3^2 + 5^2 = x^2 \Rightarrow x = \sqrt{34}$ (the diagonal distance of the bracing board)
If the board is sawed straight across, the excess length is $(8 - \sqrt{34})$ feet, or about 2.17 feet $\doteq$ 2 feet 2 inches

16. $d^2 = 90^2 + 90^2 \Rightarrow d = 90\sqrt{2} \doteq 127.28$ feet

17. Form a right triangle with a diameter, height, and length of spaghetti (the hypotenuse) that just fits.
Then $d^2 + h^2 = s^2$, or $4^2 + 10^2 = h^2 \Rightarrow h = \sqrt{116} \doteq 10.77$ inches.

18. The sides of squares made in this fashion will always be hypotenuses of right triangles [as shown in (a)]. As such, the relationship $s^2 = a^2 + b^2$ must hold, with *a* and *b* whole numbers, since they are given by spaces between dots. Only numbers representable this way can be areas of such squares (since s^2 is the area of a square).

(a) Here $1^2 + 2^2 = 5 = s^2$, so the relationship exists

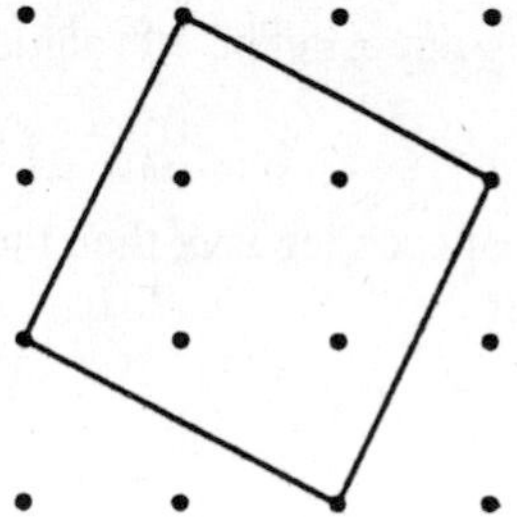

(b) Not possible.

(c) Here $2^2 + 2^2 = 8 = s^2$, so the relationship exists

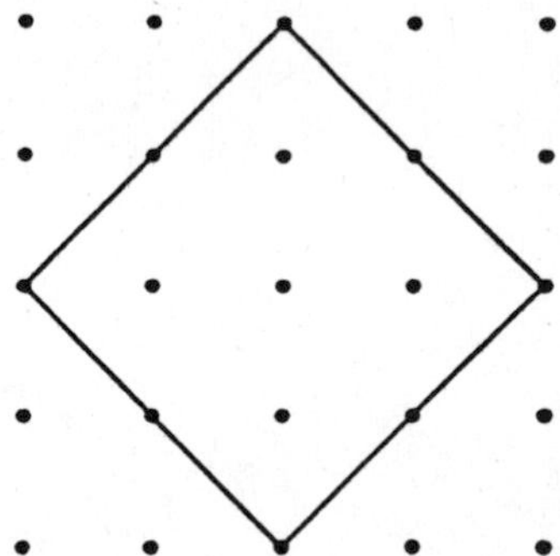

(d) Not possible.

(e) Not possible.

19. $\triangle ACD \sim \triangle ABC$; $AC/AB = AD/AC \Rightarrow b/c = x/b \Rightarrow b^2 = cx$
$\triangle BCD \simeq \triangle ABC$; $AB/CB = CB/DB \Rightarrow c/a = a/y \Rightarrow a^2 = cy$
$a^2 + b^2 = cx + cy = c(x + y) = cc = c^2$

20. $l^2 = 1^2 + 3^2 \Rightarrow l = \sqrt{10} \doteq 3.16$ m

21. Label the lower right corner D $\Rightarrow BD = CD = x$
Then $x^2 + x^2 = 12^2 \Rightarrow 2x^2 = 144 \Rightarrow x = \sqrt{72} \doteq 8.5 \Rightarrow 2x \doteq 17.0$ inches square

22. $l^2 + 150^2 = 180^2 \Rightarrow l = \sqrt{180^2 - 150^2} \doteq 99.5$ feet

23. Let x be the distance along the highway intersected by a 6.1 mile radius $\Rightarrow x^2 + 3^2 = 6.1^2$
$x = \sqrt{6.1^2 - 3^2} \doteq 5.3$ miles; the station will reach both directions $\Rightarrow 2x \doteq 10.6$ miles

24. The included angle between sides of length c is 90°. Adding the areas of the three triangles gives
$A = \frac{1}{2}ba + \frac{1}{2}ab + \frac{1}{2}cc = ab + \frac{1}{2}c^2$. Using the formula for area of a trapezoid gives
$A = \frac{1}{2}(a + b)(a + b) = \frac{1}{2}(a^2 + 2ab + b^2)$. These represent the same area, so
$ab + \frac{1}{2}c^2 = \frac{1}{2}(a^2 + 2ab + b^2) \Rightarrow 2ab + c^2 = a^2 + 2ab + b^2 \Rightarrow c^2 = a^2 + b^2$.

25. The area of the large square is equal to the sum of the areas of the smaller square and the four triangles.
Thus $(a + b)^2 = c^2 + 4(ab/2) \Rightarrow a^2 + 2ab + b^2 = c^2 + 2ab \Rightarrow a^2 + b^2 = c^2$.

26. Yes.

27. Yes. The area of an equilateral triangle with side s is $\frac{s^2}{4} \cdot \sqrt{3}$. Let the sides of the right triangle be a, b, and c, with c the hypotenuse. The areas of the equilateral triangles are thus $\frac{a^2}{4} \cdot \sqrt{3}$, $\frac{b^2}{4} \cdot \sqrt{3}$, and $\frac{c^2}{4} \cdot \sqrt{3}$.
Now answer the question, "Does $\frac{a^2}{4}\sqrt{3} + \frac{b^2}{4}\sqrt{3} = \frac{c^2}{4}\sqrt{3}$?" Multiplying both sides by $\frac{4}{\sqrt{3}}$ gives
$a^2 + b^2 = c^2$, which must be true since the triangle is right.

28. (a) $\overline{AB} = \sqrt{(0 - 0)^2 + (7 - 3)^2} = \sqrt{16} = 4$
(b) $\overline{AB} = \sqrt{(4 - 0)^2 + (0 - 3)^2} = \sqrt{25} = 5$
(c) $\overline{AB} = \sqrt{(3 - {}^-1)^2 + ({}^-4 - 2)^2} = \sqrt{52} = 2\sqrt{13}$
(d) $\overline{AB} = \sqrt{\left(\frac{1}{2} - 4\right)^2 + \left(\frac{{}^-7}{4} - {}^-5\right)^2} = \sqrt{\frac{365}{16}} \doteq 4.78$
(e) $\overline{AB} = \sqrt{(5 - 5)^2 + ({}^-2 - 3)^2} = \sqrt{25} = 5$

29. $\overline{AB} = \sqrt{({}^-4 - 0)^2 + ({}^-3 - 0)^2} = \sqrt{16 + 9} = \sqrt{25} = 5$
$\overline{AC} = \sqrt{({}^-5 - 0)^2 + (0 - 0)^2} = \sqrt{25} = 5$
$\overline{BC} = \sqrt{({}^-5 - {}^-4)^2 + (0 - {}^-3)^2} = \sqrt{({}^-1)^2 + (3)^2} = \sqrt{10}$
$\Rightarrow$ perimeter $= 5 + 5 + \sqrt{10} = 10 + \sqrt{10}$

30. Sides have lengths $\sqrt{45}$, $\sqrt{180}$, and $\sqrt{225}$; $\left(\sqrt{45}\right)^2 + \left(\sqrt{180}\right)^2 = \left(\sqrt{225}\right)^2 \Rightarrow$ the triangle is right

31. Use the distance formula: $\overline{AB} = 5$, $\overline{AC} = 7\sqrt{2}$, $\overline{BC} = 5 \Rightarrow$ since $\overline{AB} = \overline{BC}$, the triangle is isosceles

32. $\sqrt{(x - 1)^2 + (9 - 3)^2} = 10 \Rightarrow (x - 1)^2 + 6^2 = 100 \Rightarrow (x - 1)^2 = 64 \Rightarrow x - 1 = \pm 8 \Rightarrow x = \{9, {}^-7\}$

33. From the special properties of a 30° - 60° - 90° right triangle, the short leg (opposite the 30° angle) is half the hypotenuse, or $\frac{1}{2} \cdot \frac{c}{2} = \frac{c}{4}$. The longer leg (opposite 60°) is $\sqrt{3}$ times the short leg. The side opposite the 60° angle in this case is thus $\frac{c}{4} \cdot \sqrt{3}$.

On-going Assessment 12-2; Review Problems

43. 0.032 km (32 m) > 322 cm (3.22 m) > 3.2 m > 3.020 mm (0.00302 m)

44. (a) Change all measurements to mm and draw horizontal lines to form three rectangles. The rectangles will have dimensions 75 mm by 25 mm, 25 mm by 30 mm, and 35 mm by 20 mm. The areas are 1875 mm^2, 750 mm^2, and 700 mm^2, for a total of 3325 mm^2 = 33.25 cm^2.

(b) Area = $\frac{1}{2}(10)(6) = 30$ cm^2

(c) Change 600 cm to 6 m. Area = $\frac{1}{2}(6 + 10)(4) = 32$ m^2.

45.

	Radius	Diameter	Circumference	Area
(a)	5 cm	10 cm	10π cm	25π cm^2
(b)	12 cm	24 cm	24π cm	144π cm^2
(c)	$\sqrt{17}$ m	$2\sqrt{17}$ m	$2\pi\sqrt{17}$ m	17π m^2
(d)	10 cm	20 cm	20π cm	100π cm^2

46. Area has a circumference of 10 m $\Rightarrow 2\pi r = 10 \Rightarrow r = \frac{10}{2\pi} = \frac{5}{\pi}$
Area = $\pi r^2 = \pi(\frac{5}{\pi})^2 = \frac{25}{\pi}$ m^2

On-going Assessment 12-3

1. (a) SA of a cube = $6e^2$ (where e = the length of each edge) $\Rightarrow$ SA = $6(4)^2 = 96$ cm^2

(b) SA of a right circular cylinder = $2\pi r^2 + 2\pi rh$ (where r is the radius of the top and bottom circles and h is the height of the cylinder) $\Rightarrow$ SA = $2\pi(6)^2 + 2\pi(6)(12) = 72\pi + 144\pi = 216\pi$ cm^2

(c) SA of a right triangular prism = ph + 2B (where p is the perimeter, h is the height, and B is the area of the base): $p = 2l + 2w = 2(8) + 2(5) = 26$ cm; B = $lw = (8)(5) = 40$ cm^2: h = 6 cm
$\Rightarrow$ SA = (26)(6) + 2(40) = 156 + 80 = 236 cm^2

(d) SA of a sphere = $4\pi r^2$ (where r is the radius) $\Rightarrow$ SA = $4\pi(4)^2 = 64\pi$ cm^2

(e) SA of a right circular cone = $\pi r^2 + \pi rl$(where r is the radius of the base and l is the slant height from any point on the base to the vertex of the cone). To find l, use the Pythagorean theorem:
$l = \sqrt{4^2 + 3^2} = 5$ cm $\Rightarrow$ SA = $\pi(3)^2 + \pi(3)(5) = 9\pi + 15\pi = 24\pi$ cm^2

(f) SA of a right square pyramid = B + $\frac{1}{2}pl$ (where B is the area of the base, p is the perimeater of the base, and l is slant height from the base to the apex); B = b^2 (where b is the length of a face of the base) = 5^2 = 25 cm^2; p = 4b = 4(5) = 20 cm $\Rightarrow$ SA = 25 + $\frac{1}{2}(20)(6.5) = 25 + 65 = 90$ cm^2

1. (g) Hemispherical area is $\frac{1}{2}(4\pi r^2) = \frac{1}{2}(4\pi \cdot 10^2) = 200\pi$ ft^2
Base area is $\pi r^2 = \pi(10^2) = 100\pi$ ft^2
Lateral area of cylinder = $2\pi rh = 2\pi(10)(60) = 1200\pi$ ft^2
$\Rightarrow$ SA = $200\pi + 100\pi + 1200\pi = 1500\pi$ ft^2

(h) Slant height is given by: $l = \sqrt{4^2 + 8^2} = 4\sqrt{5}$ cm; conical area = $\pi rl = \pi(4)\left(4\sqrt{5}\right) = 16\sqrt{5}\pi$ cm^2
Hemispherical area = $\frac{1}{2}(4\pi r^2) = \frac{1}{2}(4)\pi(4)^2 = 32\pi$ cm^2
$\Rightarrow$ SA = $\left(32 + 16\sqrt{5}\right)\pi$ cm^2

2. Area of walls = $2(6)(25) + 2(4)(2.5) = 50$ m^2 $\Rightarrow$ paint needed = $\frac{50 \text{ m}^2}{20 \text{ m}^2 \text{ per L}} = 2.5$ L

3. Change all units to mm $\Rightarrow$ the ring then has an inner radius of 20 mm and a height of 30 mm
The outer ring has a radius of 22 mm and a height of 30 mm $\Rightarrow$ SA = $2\pi rh = 2\pi(22)(30) = 1320\pi$ mm^2
The inner ring has a radius of 20 mm and a height of 30 mm $\Rightarrow$ SA = $2\pi(20)(30) = 1200\pi$ mm^2
The area of the top and bottom rings is each the area of a circle with radius 22 mm minus the area of a circle with radius 20 mm.
There are two base rings $\Rightarrow$ SA = $2[\pi(22^2) - \pi(20^2)] = 2[484\pi - 400\pi] = 168\pi$ mm^2
The total surface area = $1320\pi + 1200\pi + 168\pi = 2688\pi$ mm^2 = 26.88π cm^2

4. SA = $4\pi(6370)^2 = 162{,}307{,}600\pi$ km^2

5. SA (large cube) = $6e^2 = 6(6)^2 = 216$ cm^2; SA (small cube) = $6(4^2) = 96$ cm^2
Ratio of surface areas = $\frac{96}{216} = \frac{4}{9} = 4{:}9$
(Note that the ratio of the surface areas is the ratio of the squares of the sides)

6. (a) Lateral surface area (first cylinder) = $2\pi rh = 2\pi(2)(6) = 24\pi$ m^2
Lateral surface area (second cylinder) = $2\pi(6)(2) = 24\pi$ m^2

(b) SA (first cylinder) = $2\pi r^2 + 2\pi rh = 2\pi(2^2) + 24\pi = 32\pi$ m^2
SA (second cylinder) = $2\pi(6^2) + 24\pi = 96\pi$ m^2
The cylinder with the larger radius (6 m) has the larger surface area

7. SA of a right pyramid = $B + \frac{1}{2}pl$, where B is the area of the base, p is the perimeter of the base, and l is the slant height from the base to the apex.
$B = \frac{1}{2}ap$, where a is the apothem. Since a hexagon is composed of equilateral triangles about the center, the distance from each vertex to the center is the same as each edge. Thus
$a = \sqrt{12^2 - 6^2} = \sqrt{108} = 6\sqrt{3}$. Then $B = \frac{1}{2}\left(6\sqrt{3}\right)(6 \cdot 12) = 216\sqrt{3}$.
Since the apothem is $6\sqrt{3}$ and the altitude is 9, $l = \sqrt{9^2 + \left(6\sqrt{3}\right)^2} = \sqrt{189} = 3\sqrt{21}$.
Finally, SA = $216\sqrt{3} + \frac{1}{2}(6 \cdot 12)\left(3\sqrt{21}\right) = \left(216\sqrt{3} + 108\sqrt{21}\right)$ m^2.

8. SA = $2\pi rh = \pi dh = \pi \cdot 2\frac{5}{8} \cdot 4 = \frac{84\pi}{8}$ in^2 $\doteq 32.97$ in^2

9. Lateral surface area = area of the paper square = $10 \cdot 10 = 100$ cm^2
Circumference of the cylinder = 10 cm $\Rightarrow$ $10 = \pi d$ $\Rightarrow$ diameter = $\frac{10}{\pi}$ cm $\Rightarrow$ radius = $\frac{5}{\pi}$
Top plus bottom areas = $2\pi\left(\frac{5}{\pi}\right)^2 = \frac{50}{\pi}$ cm^2
Total surface area = $\left(100 + \frac{50}{\pi}\right)$ cm^2 $\doteq 115.9$ cm^2

10. Slant heights are given by: $s^2 = 2.5^2 + 3^2 \Rightarrow s = \sqrt{15.25} \doteq 3.9$ ft
Area of each side = $3.9 \cdot 6 = 23.4$ ft^2 ; bottom = $5 \cdot 6 = 30$ ft^2 ; each end = $\frac{1}{2} \cdot 5 \cdot 3 = 7.5$ ft^2
Amount of material = total surface area = $2(23.4) + 30 + 2(7.5) = 91.8$ ft^2

11. Top could be $(1 \cdot 88)$ cm^2 , $(2 \cdot 44)$ cm^2 , $(4 \cdot 22)$ cm^2 , or $(8 \cdot 11)$ cm^2
End could be $(1 \cdot 32)$ cm^2 , $(2 \cdot 16)$ cm^2 , or $(4 \cdot 9)$ cm^2
Side could be $(1 \cdot 44)$ cm^2 , $(2 \cdot 22)$ cm^2 , or $(4 \cdot 11)$ cm^2
The only dimensions shared by two groups each are 4, 8, and 11 $\Rightarrow$ box is 4 cm by 8 cm by 11 cm

12. For any figure, if all dimensions have the same percentage change, the change of the area is the square of the change in a side. Thus:

(a) The surface area is quadrupled

(b) The surface area is multiplied by 9

(c) The surface area is multiplied by k^2

13. (a) Lateral surface area is proportional to slant height $\Rightarrow$ if slant height is tripled lateral surface area is tripled

(b) Lateral surface area is proportional to the radius of the base $\Rightarrow$ if radius is tripled lateral surface area is tripled

(c) Lateral surface area is proportional to the product of slant height and base radius $\Rightarrow$ when they are each tripled lateral surface area is multiplied by 9

14. (a) SA of a sphere is proportional to the square of the radius $\Rightarrow$ if radius is doubled SA is quadrupled

(b) SA is multiplied by 9

15. $SA = B + \frac{1}{2}pl$, where $B = 100$; $p = 4\sqrt{100} = 40$; $l = \sqrt{20^2 + 5^2} = 5\sqrt{17} \Rightarrow SA = (100 + \frac{1}{2} \cdot 40 \cdot 5\sqrt{17})$ cm
$= (100 + 100\sqrt{17})$ cm$^2 \doteq 512.3$ cm^2

16. (a) SA of the given structure is 40 units^2. Adding one cube could increase area by 4 units^2 (adding 5 faces but eliminating one). Maximum SA is then 44 units^2.

(b) Placing a cube in the hole eliminates 4 faces while adding only 2; minimum SA = 38 units^2

(c) Yes (arrange five cubes in a C shape; filling the hole with a sixth cube would add no surface area)

17. $l = 1.5$ m; circumference of base = $\frac{240}{360}[2\pi(1.5)] = 2\pi$ m $\Rightarrow 2\pi r = 2\pi \Rightarrow r = 1$

(a) Lateral surface area = $\pi(1)(1.5) = 1.5\pi$ m^2

(b) $SA = 1.5\pi + \pi(1^2) = 2.5\pi$ m^2

18. (a) The figure will be a cone with base radius 10 cm and height 20 cm
$SA = \pi r^2 + \pi r l = \pi(10^2) + \pi(10)\left(\sqrt{20^2 + 10^2}\right) = 100\pi + 10\pi(10\sqrt{5}) = 100\pi(1 + \sqrt{5})$ cm^2

(b) The figure will be a right circular cylinder with base radius 15 cm and height 30 cm
$SA = 2\pi r^2 + 2\pi rh = 2\pi(15^2) + 2\pi(15)(30) = 450\pi + 900\pi = 1350\pi$ cm^2

18. (c) The figure will be a truncated cone, with large end radius 25 cm and small end radius 15 cm
Extend the 35 cm line to form a right triangle and use similar triangles (where x is the hypotenuse of the extended triangle): $\frac{x-35}{15} = \frac{x}{25} \Rightarrow 25(x-35) = 15x \Rightarrow x = 87.5$
The triangle, when rotated, will form a cone with slant height 87.5 and radius 25 cm
$\Rightarrow SA = \pi r^2 + \pi r l = \pi(25^2) + \pi(25)(87.5) = 625\pi + 2187.5\pi = 2812.5\pi \text{ cm}^2$
Cutting off the top eliminates the lateral surface area $\pi r l = \pi(15)(87.5-35) = 787.5 \text{ cm}^2$
Adds circular area $\pi r^2 = \pi(15^2) = 225\pi \text{ cm}^2$
Resulting SA = $(2812.5 - 787.5 + 225)\pi = 2250\pi \text{ cm}^2$

19. (a) $SA = 6e^2 \Rightarrow e = \sqrt{\frac{10{,}648}{6}} \doteq 42$ cm

(b) Diagonal of face = $\sqrt{42^2 + 42^2} \doteq 59.4$ cm $\Rightarrow$ corner-corner diagonal = $\sqrt{59.4^2 + 42^2} \doteq 73$ cm

20. With h = height of completed cone, $\frac{h}{100} = \frac{h-40}{60}$, or h = 100. The slant height is then $100\sqrt{2}$. Slant height of the missing piece is $60\sqrt{2}$. As in problem 19(c), final surface area is
$\pi(100^2) + \pi(100)\left(100\sqrt{2}\right) - \pi(60)\left(60\sqrt{2}\right) + \pi(60^2) = (6400\sqrt{2} + 13{,}600)\pi \text{ cm}^2$.

21. The cross section is shown:

$\frac{10}{x} = \frac{40}{25} \Rightarrow x = 6.25$ (radius of the cylinder)
Lateral surface area = $2\pi r h = 2\pi(6.25)(30) = 375\pi \text{ cm}^2$

On-going Assessment 12-3; Review Problems

29. (a) $10 \text{ m}^2 = 100{,}000 \text{ cm}^2$ (b) $13{,}680 \text{ cm}^2 = 1.368 \text{ m}^2$

(c) $5 \text{ cm}^2 = 500 \text{ mm}^2$ (d) $2 \text{ km}^2 = 2{,}000{,}000 \text{ m}^2$

(e) $10^6 \text{ m}^2 = 1 \text{ km}^2$ (f) $10^{12} \text{ mm}^2 = 10^6 \text{ m}^2$

30. $d = \sqrt{10^2 + 20^2} = 10\sqrt{5}$ cm

31. $\left(\frac{1}{2}d\right)^2 + 20^2 = 30^2 \Rightarrow d = \sqrt{2000} = 20\sqrt{5}$ cm

32. (a) Change 0.6 m to 60 cm $\Rightarrow$ hypotenuse = $\sqrt{60^2 + 80^2} = 100$ cm

(*i*) Perimeter = 60 + 80 + 100 = 240 cm = 2.4 m

(*ii*) Area = $\frac{1}{2}bh = \frac{1}{2}(60)(80) = 2400 \text{ cm}^2 = 0.24 \text{ m}^2$

(b) Drawing an altitude to the end point of the top base forms a 45°-45°-90° isosceles triangle
Bottom base is 5 cm longer on each side than the top $\Rightarrow$ one leg of the isosceles triangle = 5 cm
Height is also 5 cm
Use the Pythatorean theorem: slanted segments on each side of the trapezoid are each $5\sqrt{2}$ cm

(*i*) Perimeter = $20 + 10 + 2(5\sqrt{2}) = (30 + 10\sqrt{2})$ cm

32. (b) (*ii*) Area = $\frac{1}{2}(10 + 20)(5) = 75$ cm^2

33. Use the technique of Problem Set 12-2, problem 13, to find the length of the sides to be 25 cm and the length of diagonal $\overline{AD}$ to be 30 cm

On-going Assessment 12-4

1. (a) 8000 dm^3 $[(1 \text{ m})^3 = (10 \text{ dm})^3 \Rightarrow 1 \text{ m}^3 = 1000 \text{ dm}^3]$

   (b) 0.0005 m^3 $[(1 \text{ cm})^3 = (0.01 \text{ cm})^3 \Rightarrow 1 \text{ cm}^3 = 0.000001 \text{ m}^3]$

   (c) 0.000675 km^3 $[(1 \text{ m})^3 = (0.001 \text{ km})^3 \Rightarrow 1 \text{ m}^3 = 0.000000001 \text{ km}^3]$

   (d) 3,000,000 cm^3 (1 m^3 = 1,000,000 cm^3)

   (e) 7 cm^3 (1 mm^3 = 0.001 cm^3)

   (f) 2000 cm^3 (1 m^3 = 1,000,000 cm^3)

   (g) 0.00857 yd^3 $\left(\frac{400 \text{ in}^3}{x \text{ yd}^3} = \frac{(36^3) \text{ in}^3}{1 \text{ yd}^3}\right)$

   (h) 675 ft^3 (1 yd^3 = 27 ft^3)

   (i) 345.6 in^3 (1 ft^3 = 144 in^3)

   (j) $0.69\overline{4}$ ft^3 (1 in^3 = $0.0069\overline{4}$ ft^3)

2. There are (60)(24)(30) = 43,200 minutes in a 30-day month
   There would be (15)(43,200) = 648,000 drops in 30 days
   There would be $\frac{648{,}000}{20}$ = 32,400 mL = 32.4 L of water wasted

3. (a) $V = lwh = (4)(4)(4) = 64$ cm^3

   (b) $V = lwh = (8)(5)(3) = 120$ cm^3

   (c) V = Bh (where *B* is the area of the triangle and *h* is its height)
   $B = \frac{1}{2}bh = \frac{1}{2}(6)(6) = 18$ cm^2; $h = 12 \Rightarrow V = (18)(12) = 216$ cm^3

   (d) $V = \frac{1}{3}Bh$ (where *B* is the area of the base and *h* is the height) $\Rightarrow V = \frac{1}{3}(5^2)(6) = 50$ cm^3

   (e) $V = \frac{1}{3}\pi r^2 h = \frac{1}{3}\pi(3^2)(7) = 21\pi$ cm^3

   (f) $V = \pi r^2 h = \pi(6^2)(12) = 432\pi$ cm^3

   (g) $V = \frac{4}{3}\pi r^3 = \frac{4}{3}\pi(10^3) = \frac{4000}{3}\pi$ cm^3

   (h) V of triangular prism portion = $Bh = \frac{1}{2}(30(8)(40) = 4800$ cm^3
   V of rectangular prism portion = $lwh = (30)(40)(15) = 18{,}000$ cm^3
   Total volume = 4800 + 18,000 = 22,800 ft^3

   (i) V of hemispherical portion = $\frac{1}{2}(\frac{4}{3}\pi r^3) = \frac{1}{2}(\frac{4}{3})\pi(10^3) = \frac{2000}{3}\pi$ ft^3
   V of circular cylinder = $\pi r^2 h = \pi(10^2)(60) = 6000\pi$ ft^3
   Total volume = $6000\pi + \frac{2000}{3}\pi = \frac{20{,}000}{3}\pi$ ft^3

   (j) V of triangular prism portion = $\frac{1}{2}(10)(6)(60) = 1800$ ft^3
   V of trapezoidal prism portion = $\frac{1}{2}(8)(10 + 50)(60) = 14{,}400$ ft^3
   V of rectangular prism portion = (50)(60)(20) = 60,000 ft^3
   Total volume = 1800 + 14,400 + 60,000 = 76,200 ft^3

3. (k) V of hemispherical portion = $\frac{1}{2}(\frac{4}{3}\pi \cdot 4^3) = \frac{128}{3}\pi$ cm^3
V of conical portion = $\frac{1}{3}\pi(4^3)(8) = \frac{128}{3}\pi$ cm^3
Total volume = $\frac{128}{3}\pi + \frac{128}{3}\pi = \frac{256}{3}\pi$ cm^3

4.

	(a)	(b)	(c)	(d)	(e)	(f)
cm^3	2000	500	1500	5000	750	4800
dm^3	2	0.5	1.5	5	0.750	4.8
L	2	0.5	1.5	5	0.750	4.8
mL	2000	500	1500	5000	750	4800

5. (a) 200.0 mL (b) 0.320 L

(c) 1.0 L (d) 5.00 mL

6. Convert all measurements to mm $\Rightarrow$ radius of the inner circle = 20 mm and height = 20 mm
V (outer cylinder) = $\pi r^2 h = \pi(22^2)(20) = 9680\pi$ mm^3
V (inner cylinder) = $\pi(20^2)(20) = 8000\pi$ mm^3
V (napkin ring) = $(9680 - 8000)\pi = 1680\pi$ mm^3

7. $V_1 = 4^3 = 64$; $V_2 = 6^3 = 216 \Rightarrow V_1{:}V_2 = 64{:}216 = 8{:}27$ (if all lengths of the two objects have the ratio m:n, then their volumes will have the ratio $m^3{:}n^3$)

8. Volume of a sphere is proportional to the cube of the radius $\Rightarrow$ if the radius is doubled, then volume is increased by a factor of $2^3 = 8$

9. For each right rectangular prism, $V = lwh$

	(a)	(b)	(c)	(d)
Length	20 cm	10 cm	2 cm	15 cm
Width	10 cm	2 dm	1 dm	2 dm
Height	10 cm	3 dm	2 dm	2.5
Volume (cm^3)	2000	6000	4000	7500
Volume (dm^3)	2	6	4	7.5 dm^3
Volume (L)	2	6	4L	7.5

10. $V = \pi r^2 h = \pi(6.5^2)(6) = 253.5\pi$ m^3 = 253,500π L (1m^3 = 1000 L)

11. Volume is proportional to the cube of the radius $\Rightarrow$ a sphere with 4 times the radius of another has $4^3 = 64$ times its volume $\Rightarrow$ 64:1

12. $V = lwh = (18)(18)(5) = 1620$ cm^3 = 1.62 L (1000 cm^3 = 1 L)

13. $V = lwh = (50)(25)(2) = 2500$ m^3 = 2,500,000 L (1 m^3 = 1000 L)

14. The radius of the straw is 2 mm = 0.2 cm $\Rightarrow V = \pi r^2 h = \pi(0.2^2)(25) = \pi$ cm^3 = π mL

15. (a) Volumes are multiplied by $2^3 = 8$ (b) Volumes should be multiplied by $3^3 = 27$

(c) Volumes are multiplied by n^3

16. Volume of any pyramid = $\frac{1}{3}$ · (area of base) · (height)

$$V_{\text{Great Pyramid}} = \frac{1}{3} \cdot \left[\left(\frac{930}{4}\right)^2\right] \cdot (148) = 2{,}666{,}775 \text{ m}^3$$

$$V_{\text{Transamerica Building}} = \frac{1}{3} \cdot \left[\left(\frac{140}{4}\right)^2\right] \cdot 260 = 106{,}166.\overline{6} \text{ m}^3$$

$\frac{2{,}666{,}775}{106{,}166.\overline{6}} \doteq 25 \Rightarrow$ the Great Pyramid has about 25 times the volume of the Transamerica Building

17. (a) $V_{\text{Great Pyramid}} = \frac{1}{3} \cdot (756)^2 \cdot 481 = 91{,}636{,}272 \text{ ft}^3$

(b) $V_{\text{each apartment}} = 35 \cdot 20 \cdot 8 = 5600 \text{ ft}^3 \Rightarrow \frac{91{,}636{,}272}{5600} \doteq 16{,}363.6 \Rightarrow$ about 16,364 apartments equivalent volume

18. Partition the pool into two solids, where the volume of each is B (area of base) · h (height):
A right rectangular prism measuring 25 m by 10 m by 2 m
A right triangular prisim with base legs 2 m by 10 m and height 10 m
$V_{\text{rectangular prism}} = 25 \cdot 10 \cdot 2 = 500$ m; $V_{\text{triangular prism}} = \frac{1}{2} \cdot 2 \cdot 10 \cdot 10 = 100 \text{ m}^3$
$V_{\text{pool}} = V_{\text{rectangular prism}} + V_{\text{triangular prism}} = 500 + 100 = 600 \text{ m}^3$

19. $V = \pi r^2 h = \pi \cdot (1.5 \text{ cm})^2 \cdot (5000 \text{ cm}) = 11{,}250\pi \text{ cm}^3 = 11.25\pi \text{ L} \doteq 35.3$ L of water

20. No (the larger marble has three dimensions each 4 times those of the small marbles $\Rightarrow$ it has $4^3 = 64$ times the volume $\Rightarrow$ it would take 64 one-cm marbles to give enough steel for 1 four-cm marble)

21. A cross-section of the cone shows two 30° - 60° - 90° triangles $\Rightarrow$ the radius at a height of 4 in. is 2 in. $\Rightarrow$ each of the cup's dimensions are halved $\Rightarrow \frac{1}{2} \cdot \frac{1}{2} \cdot \frac{1}{2} = \frac{1}{8}$ the volume of the full cup when it is filled to half its height

22. 100% + 30% = 130% = 1.3 $\Rightarrow$ volume = 1.3 · 1.3 · 1.3 = 2.197 = 219.7%
$\Rightarrow$ volume is increased by 219.7% – 100% = 119.7% $\doteq$ 120%

23. $V = \frac{4}{3}\pi r^3 = \frac{4}{3}\pi\left[\left(\frac{7927}{2}\right)^3\right] = 260{,}810{,}575{,}168$ cubic miles $\doteq 2.6 \cdot 10^{11}$ cubic miles

24. $V_{\text{first freezer}} = 1.5 \cdot 1.5 \cdot 5 = 11.25 \text{ ft}^3 \Rightarrow \frac{11.25 \text{ ft}^3}{\$350} = \$31.11$ per ft³
$V_{\text{second freezer}} = 2 \cdot 2 \cdot 4 = 16 \text{ ft}^3 \Rightarrow \frac{16 \text{ ft}^3}{\$400} = \$25.00$ per ft³ $\Rightarrow$ The larger freezer is a better buy

25. $V_{\text{can}} = \pi r^2 h = \pi \cdot (3.5)^2 \cdot (2 \cdot 3.5 \cdot 3) = 257.25\pi \text{ cm}^3$
$V_{\text{tennis balls}} = 3 \cdot \left(\frac{4}{3}\pi r^3\right) = 3 \cdot \frac{4}{3} \cdot \pi \cdot (3.5)^3 = 171.5\pi \text{ cm}^3$
$V_{\text{air}} = 257.25\pi - 171.5\pi = 85.75\pi \text{ cm}^3 \Rightarrow \frac{85.75\pi \text{ cm}^3}{257.25\pi \text{ cm}^3} = \frac{1}{3} = 33\frac{1}{3}\%$ of the can occupied by air

26. Let r be the radius of each of the cans and h be the height of the box and the cans; the dimensions of the base of the box are 6r by 4r
$V_{box} = (6r)(4r)(h) = 24r^2h$; $V_{6\ cans} = 6\pi r^2 h$; $V_{wasted} = 24r^2h - 6\pi r^2 h = 6r^2h(4 - \pi)$
The portion wasted is $\frac{6r^2h(1-\pi)}{24r^2h} = \frac{4-\pi}{4} \doteq 21.5\%$

27. Perimeter = 16 $\Rightarrow$ each side = 4 m $\Rightarrow V = \frac{1}{3}Bh = \frac{1}{3}(4^2)(3) = 16 \text{ m}^3$

28. $V_{prism} = AB \cdot BC \cdot AP$
$V_{pyramid} = \frac{1}{3}(AB \cdot BC \cdot AX) = \frac{1}{3}(AB \cdot BC \cdot 3AP) = AB \cdot BC \cdot AP \Rightarrow$ the volumes are equal

29. $1 \text{ L} = 1000 \text{ cm}^3$; $V = \pi r^2 h \Rightarrow 1000 = \pi(12^2)h \Rightarrow h = \frac{1000}{144\pi} \doteq 2.2$ cm

30. No (the volume of a pyramid is $\frac{1}{3}$Bh, compared to Bh for the box $\Rightarrow$ the pyramid provides only $\frac{1}{3}$ the popcorn for $\frac{1}{2}$ the price)

31. $V_{\text{5-cm grapefruit}} = \frac{4}{3}\pi(5^3) \doteq 523.6 \text{ cm}^3 \Rightarrow \frac{523.6 \text{ cm}^3}{22¢} \doteq 23.8 \text{ cm}^3$ per cent
$V_{\text{6-cm grapefruit}} = \frac{4}{3}\pi(6^3) \doteq 904.8 \text{ cm}^3 \Rightarrow \frac{904.8 \text{ cm}^3}{31¢} \doteq 29.2 \text{ cm}^3$ per cent $\Rightarrow$ the larger fruit is a better buy

32. Circumference of a circle = $2\pi r \Rightarrow r = \frac{C}{2\pi}$
Radius of larger melon = $\frac{60}{2\pi}$; radius of smaller melon = $\frac{50}{2\pi}$
Ratio of radii = $\frac{\left(\frac{60}{2\pi}\right)}{\left(\frac{50}{2\pi}\right)} = 1.2$
Volume of sphere is proportional to cube of radius $\Rightarrow V_{\text{larger melon}} = 1.2^3 \doteq 1.7$ times $V_{\text{smaller melon}}$
The larger melon is a better buy (volume is 1.7 times that of the smaller but price is only 1.5 times as much)

33. (a) Answers may vary, but one design would be a square base with sides 5 m and height 12 m

(b) There are infinitely many factors s and h such that $\frac{1}{3}s^2h = 100 \Rightarrow$ there are infinitely many pyramids

34. Assume a regular pyramid; then let s = length of a side = height $\Rightarrow$ slant height of the pyramid is the hypotenuse of the right triangle with height s and base $\frac{s}{2}$, or
$$\sqrt{s^2 + \left(\frac{s}{2}\right)^2} = \sqrt{s^2 + \left(\frac{s^2}{4}\right)} = \sqrt{\frac{5s^2}{4}} = \frac{\sqrt{5}s}{2}$$
Area of each of the four triangles in the lateral surface of the pyramid = $\frac{1}{2}bh = \frac{1}{2} \cdot s \cdot \frac{\sqrt{5}s}{2} = \frac{\sqrt{5}s^2}{4}$
There are four sides $\Rightarrow$ lateral surface area = $4 \cdot \frac{\sqrt{5}s^2}{4} = \sqrt{5}s^2$
Lateral surface area = 2 m² $\Rightarrow \sqrt{5}s^2 = 2 \Rightarrow s = \sqrt{\frac{2}{\sqrt{5}}}$
Finally, $V = \frac{1}{3}Bh = \frac{1}{3} \cdot s^2 \cdot s = \frac{1}{3}s^3 = \frac{1}{3}\left(\sqrt{\frac{2}{\sqrt{5}}}\right)^3 \doteq 0.28 \text{ m}^3$

35. (a) Dimensions are 160 cm by 160 cm by 20 cm $\Rightarrow$ volume = 512,000 cm³

(b) $l = w = y - 2x;\ h = x \Rightarrow V = x(y - 2x)^2$

36. $h_{stack} = 20 \cdot \frac{1}{16}$ in = 1.25 inch; outer radius = 3.5 inch; inner radius = 0.75 inch
$V_{\text{outer radius cylinder}} = \pi r^2 h = \pi(3.5^2)(1.25) \doteq 15.3\pi \text{ in}^3$
$V_{\text{inner radius cylinder}} = \pi(0.75^2)(1.25) \doteq 0.7\pi \text{ in}^3$
$V_{\text{record stack}} = (15.3 - 0.7)\pi = 14.6\pi \doteq 45.9 \text{ in}^3$

37. For the ice cream: $r = 5 \Rightarrow V = \frac{4}{3}\pi(5^3) = \frac{500}{3}\pi \text{ cm}^3$
For the cone: $r = 5;\ h = 10 \Rightarrow V = \frac{1}{3}\pi(5^2)(10) = \frac{250}{3}\pi \text{ cm}^3$
The cone needs twice its present volume to hold the ice cream (volume is proportional to height $\Rightarrow$ it would need to be 20 cm high)

38. Volume is proportional to the cube of the radius $\Rightarrow$ radius is proportional to the cube root of volume
Volume is halved $\Rightarrow$ radius is decreased by a factor of $\sqrt[3]{0.5} \doteq 0.794$

On-going Assessment 12-4; Review Problems

47. (a) $2B + ph = 2(\frac{1}{2})(30)(40) + (120)(120) = 15{,}600 \text{ cm}^2$

47. (b) $B + \frac{1}{2}pl = 10^2 + \frac{1}{2}(40)(10\sqrt{2}) = (100 + 200\sqrt{2})\text{ cm}^2$

(c) $2B + ph = 2\left(9 \cdot 8 + \frac{9^2 \cdot \sqrt{3}}{4}\right) + (43)(35) = \left(1649 + \frac{81}{2}\sqrt{3}\right)\text{ m}^3 \doteq 1719\text{ m}^2$

48. (a) Change 1.3 m to 130 cm. Then the other side of the rectangle is given by $w^2 = 130^2 - 120^2$ $\Rightarrow$ w = 50 cm. $P = 2w + 2l = 2(120) + 2(50) = 340$ cm.

(b) $A = lw = (120)(50) = 6000\text{ cm}^2$

49. Let b = 2; $h = \sqrt{3^2 - 1^2} = 2\sqrt{2} \Rightarrow A = \frac{1}{2}(2)(2\sqrt{2}) = 2\sqrt{2}\text{ m}^2$

50. Height of printed material = 74 – (12 + 12) = 50 cm
Width of printed material = w – (6 + 6) = (w – 12) cm
Area of printed material = 50(w – 12) = 2500 $\Rightarrow$ w = 62 cm

On-going Assessment 12-5

1. (a) A car would weigh in thousands of pounds $\Rightarrow$ kilograms or metric tons

(b) A woman could weigh 130 pounds $\Rightarrow$ kilograms

(c) Juice would weigh in ounces $\Rightarrow$ grams

(d) Metric tons

(e) Grams

(f) Grams

(g) Metric tons

(h) Grams or kilograms

(i) Grams or kilograms

2. (a) Milligrams

(b) Kilograms

(c) Milligrams

(d) Grams

(e) Grams

(f) Milligrams

3. (a) 15,000 g = 15 kg

(b) 8000 kg = 8 t

(c) 0.036 kg = 36 g

(d) 72 g = 0.072 kg

(e) 4230 mg = 4.230 g

(f) 3 g 7 mg = 3.007 g

(g) 5 kg 750 g = 5750 g

(h) 5 kg 750 g = 5.750 kg

(i) 0.03 t = 30 kg

(j) 2.6 lbs = $2.6 \cdot 16 = 41.6$ oz

(k) 25 oz = $25 \cdot \frac{1}{16} = 1\frac{9}{16}$ lb

(l) 50 oz = $50 \cdot \frac{1}{16} = 3\frac{1}{8}$ lb

(m) 3.8 lbs = $3.8 \cdot 16 = 60.8$ oz

4. (a) No (1,000,000 g = 1000 kg)

(b) Possible (100,000 g = 100 kg)

(c) Yes (10,000 g = 10 kg)

(d) Yes (1000 g = 1 kg)

4. (e) Yes

5. $V = lwh = (40)(20)(20) = 16{,}000 \text{ cm}^3$. $1 \text{ cm}^3 = 1$ g of water $\Rightarrow$ $16{,}000 \text{ cm}^3 = 16{,}000 \text{ g} = 16$ kg.

6. $400 \text{ g} = 0.04 \text{ kg} \Rightarrow \text{cost} = (0.04)(5.80) = \$2.32$

7. $1 \text{ g} = 0.001 \text{ kg} \Rightarrow \text{cost} = (0.001)(20) = \$0.02 = 2¢$ per g

8. Abel: $\frac{\$9.00}{1 \text{ kg}} = \$9.00$ per kg; Babel: $\frac{\$4.60}{0.4 \text{ kg}} = \$11.50$ per kg $\Rightarrow$ Abel made the better buy

9. (a) $C = \frac{5}{9}(F - 32) = \frac{5}{9}(10 - 32) = \frac{5}{9}({}^{-}22) \doteq {}^{-}12°$ C
   (b) $C = \frac{5}{9}(0 - 32) \doteq {}^{-}18°$ C
   (c) $C = \frac{5}{9}(30 - 32) \doteq {}^{-}1°$ C
   (d) $C = \frac{5}{9}(100 - 32) \doteq 38°$ C
   (e) $C = \frac{5}{9}(212 - 32) = 100°$ C
   (f) $C = \frac{5}{9}({}^{-}40 - 32) = {}^{-}40°$ C (this is the only temperature at which F and C have the same value)

10. (a) Probably not (68° F)
    (b) No (79° F)
    (c) No (37° C = 98.6° F)
    (d) Probably (39° C = 102.2° F)
    (e) No (104° F)
    (f) Yes (95° F)
    (g) Yes (⁻50° F)
    (h) Chilly (61° F)
    (i) Comfortably hot (86° F)

11. (a) $F = \frac{9}{5}C + 32 = \frac{9}{5}(10) + 32 = 50°$ F
    (b) $F = \frac{9}{5}(0) + 32 = 32°$ F
    (c) $F = \frac{9}{5}(30) + 32 = 86°$ F
    (d) $F = \frac{9}{5}(100) + 32 = 212°$ F
    (e) $F = \frac{9}{5}(212) + 32 \doteq 414°$ F
    (f) $F = \frac{9}{5}({}^{-}40) + 32 = {}^{-}40°$ F

12. Answers may vary; assume pulse of 72 beats per minute:
    60 mL · 72 beats per minute · 60 minutes per hour · 24 hours per day · 7 days = 43,545,600 mL $\doteq$ 43,546 L per week

13. (a) $1 \text{ ha} = 10{,}000 \text{ m}^2 = 100{,}000{,}000 \text{ cm}^2 \Rightarrow 2 \text{ cm} \cdot 100{,}000{,}000 \text{ cm}^2 = 200{,}000{,}000 \text{ cm}^3 = 200{,}000$ L fell
    (b) 1 L water weighs 1 kg $\Rightarrow$ 200,000 L water = 200,000 kg = 200 t

14. $V = 25 \cdot 18 \cdot 9 = 4050 \text{ in}^3 \Rightarrow \frac{4050 \text{ in}^3}{231 \text{ in}^3 \text{ per gallon}} \doteq 17.532$ gallons $\Rightarrow$ 17.532 gallons · 8.3 lb per gallon = 145.52 lbs

On-going Assessment 12-5; Review Problems

21. (a) (*i*) Perimeter $= \frac{1}{2}(2\pi \cdot 6) + 2\left(\sqrt{6^2 + 8^2}\right) = (6\pi + 20)$ cm
    (*ii*) Area $= \frac{1}{2}(\pi \cdot 6^2) + \frac{1}{2} \cdot 12 \cdot 8 = (18\pi + 48) \text{ cm}^2$
    (b) (*i*) Perimeter $= \frac{1}{2}(2\pi \cdot 20) + 2[\frac{1}{2}(2\pi \cdot 10)] = 40\pi$ cm

21. (b) (*ii*) Area = $\frac{1}{2}(\pi \cdot 20^2) - 2[\frac{1}{2}(\pi \cdot 10^2)] = 100\pi$ cm^2

(c) (*i*) Perimeter $= 3 + 10 + 11 + 3 + \left(\sqrt{3^2 + 4^2} = 5\right) + (11 - 4 = 7) + 6 + \left(\sqrt{3^2 + 4^2} = 5\right) = 50$ m

(*ii*) Area $= 2[\frac{1}{2}(3)(4)] + (4)(7) + (4)(10) = 80$ m^2

22. (a) 35 cm (b) 0.16 m^2

(c) 400,000 mm^2 (d) 5,200,000 cm^3

(e) 5200 L (f) 0.0035 m^3

23. (a) Yes $\left[1^2 + \left(\sqrt{2}\right)^2 = \left(\sqrt{3}\right)^2\right]$ (b) No $(3^2 + 2^2 \neq 5^2)$

(c) Yes $(1.2^2 + 0.5^2 = 1.3^2)$

(d) No $\left[\text{Sides are: } \left(\sqrt{4^2 + 1^2} = \sqrt{17}\right); \left(\sqrt{3^2 + 1^2} = \sqrt{10}\right); \left(\sqrt{3^2 + 4^2} = 5\right); \text{ and } \left(\sqrt{17}\right)^2 + \left(\sqrt{10}\right)^2 \neq 5^2\right]$

24. The person has walked a total of 6km north and 5 km east, forming the legs of a right triangle $\Rightarrow d = \sqrt{6^2 + 5^2} = \sqrt{61}$ km

25. (a) (*i*) Volume $= \frac{1}{3}\pi(30^2)(40) = 12{,}000\pi$ cm^3 (*ii*) SA $= \pi(30^2) + \pi(30)(50) = 2400\pi$ cm^2

(b) (*i*) Volume $= \frac{1}{2}(65)(33)(40) = 42{,}900$ cm^3

(*ii*) SA $= 2\left[\frac{1}{2}(65)(33)\right] + \left(33 + 65 + \sqrt{5314}\right)(40) = \left(6065 + 40\sqrt{5314}\right)$ cm^2

Chapter 12 Review

1. $A = \frac{1}{2}(4)(11) - \frac{1}{2}(4)(3k) = 16$ units^2

2. Using Pick's theorem (Problem Set 12-1, problem 7), $A = I + \frac{1}{2}B - 1$

(a) $I = 7, B = 5 \Rightarrow A = 7 + \frac{1}{2}(5) - 1 = 8\frac{1}{2}$ cm^2 (b) $I = 5, B = 5 \Rightarrow A = 5 + \frac{1}{2}(5) - 1 = 6\frac{1}{2}$ cm^2

(c) $I = 2, B = 12 \Rightarrow A = 2 + \frac{1}{2}(12) - 1 = 7$ cm^2

3. Sum the areas of the four triangles: $A = 2\left(\frac{1}{2} \cdot 5 \cdot 12\right) + 2\left(\frac{1}{2} \cdot 12 \cdot \sqrt{20^2 - 12^2}\right) = 252$ cm^2

4. Rearranging as shown gives a rectangle with width $\frac{h}{2}$ and length $\overline{A'B'} = b_2 + b_1 \Rightarrow$ $A = lw = \frac{h}{2}(b_1 + b_2)$ which must be the area of the initial trapezoid

5. (a) $A = \frac{1}{2}ap$ (where $a = 3\sqrt{3}$ and $p = 6 \cdot 6 = 36$) $\Rightarrow A = \frac{1}{2}(3\sqrt{3})(36) = 54\sqrt{3}$ cm^2

(b) $A = \pi r^2$ (where $r = 6$) $\Rightarrow A = \pi(6^2) = 36\pi$ cm^2

6. (a) $A = \pi(4^2) - \pi(2^2) = 12\pi$ cm^2

(b) $A_{\text{semicircle}} = \frac{1}{2}(\pi \cdot 3^2) = 4.5\pi$ cm^2; $A_{\text{triangle}} = \frac{1}{2}(6)(4) = 12$ cm^2 $\Rightarrow A_{\text{shaded region}} = (4.5\pi + 12)$ cm^2

6. (c) $A = (6)(4) = 24 \text{ cm}^2$

(d) $A = \frac{1}{2}(2)(3) + (12)(3) + (3)(7) + \frac{1}{2}(3)(3) = 64.5 \text{ cm}^2$

(e) $A = (8)(18) + \frac{1}{2}(3)(18 + 5) = 178.5 \text{ cm}^2$ (f) $A = \frac{40}{360}(\pi \cdot 6^2) = 4\pi \text{ cm}^2$

7. (a) Yes $(5^2 + 12^2 = 13^2)$

(b) No $(40 + 60 < 104 \Rightarrow$ measures cannot represent any triangle)

8. (a) (*i*) $SA = B + \frac{1}{2}pl \left(\text{where } l = \sqrt{4^2 + 6^2} = 2\sqrt{13}\right) \Rightarrow SA = 8^2 + \frac{1}{2}(32)(2\sqrt{13}) = (64 + 2\sqrt{13}) \text{ cm}^2$

(*ii*) $V = \frac{1}{3}Bh = \frac{1}{3}(8^2)(6) = 128 \text{ cm}^3$

(b) (*i*) $SA = \pi r^2 + \pi r l$ (where $l = \sqrt{6^2 + 8^2} = 10) \Rightarrow SA = \pi(6^2) + \pi(6)(10) = 96\pi \text{ cm}^2$

(*ii*) $V = \frac{1}{3}\pi r^2 h = \frac{1}{3}\pi(6^2)(8) = 96\pi \text{ cm}^3$

(c) (*i*) $SA = 4\pi r^2 = 4\pi(5^2) = 100\pi \text{ m}^2$ (*ii*) $V = \frac{4}{3}\pi r^3 = \frac{4}{3}\pi(5^3) = \frac{500}{3}\pi \text{ m}^3$

(d) (*i*) $SA = 2\pi r^2 + 2\pi rh = 2\pi(3^2) + 2\pi(3)(6) = 54\pi \text{ cm}^2$

(*ii*) $V = \pi r^2 h = \pi(3^2)(6) = 54\pi \text{ cm}^3$

(e) (*i*) $SA = sB + ph = 2(4)(10) + (28)(8) = 304 \text{ m}^2$ (*ii*) $V = lwh = (10)(4)(8) = 320 \text{ m}^3$

9. $l = \sqrt{12^2 + 5^2} = 13 \Rightarrow$ Lateral area $= \pi r l = \pi(5)(13) = 65\pi \text{ m}^2$

10. The graph really shows an eight-fold growth (with both lengths changed, volume is proportional to the cube of length, so if lengths are doubled volume is increased by a factor of 8)

11. (a) Metric tons (b) 1 cm^3

(c) 1 gram (d) $1 \text{ L} = 1 \text{ dm}^3$

(e) 25 L (f) 2000 a

(g) $51{,}800 \text{ cm}^3$ (h) $10{,}000{,}000 \text{ m}^2$

(i) 50,000 mL (j) 5.830 L

(k) $25{,}000 \text{ dm}^2$ (l) 75,000 mL

(m) 52.813 kg (n) 4.8 t

12. $h_1^3 : h_2^3 = V_1 : V_2$

13. (a) $V = (1)(2)(3) = 6 \text{ m}^3 = 6{,}000{,}000 \text{ cm}^3 \Rightarrow 6{,}000{,}000 \text{ g} = 6{,}000 \text{ kg}$

(b) $V_{sphere} = \frac{4}{3}\pi(30^3) = 36{,}000\pi \doteq 113{,}097 \text{ cm}^3$. Consider the height increase from the sphere, changing length and width to cm: $V = 113{,}097 = (100)(200)h \Rightarrow h = 5.65$ cm (rise from the sphere). The tank was half full (i.e., h = 1.5 m); with a rise of 5.65 cm = 0.0565 m the new height is 1.5565 m.

14. (a) liters (b) kilograms

(c) grams (d) grams

(e) kilograms (f) metric tons

(g) milliliters

15. (a) Unlikely (15° C = 59° F) (b) Likely (26° C = 79° F)

(c) Unlikely (0° C is the freezing point of water) (d) Unlikely (100° C is the boiling point of water)

(e) Unlikely (water will not freeze until its temperature lowers to 0° C)

16. (a) 2000 g (2 dc^3 = 2000 cm^3) (b) 1000 g

(c) 3 g (d) 0.0042 kg

(e) 0.0002 m^3

CHAPTER 13 - MOTION GEOMETRY AND TESSELLATIONS

1. (a) Each corner of the trapezoid moves two dots to the right:

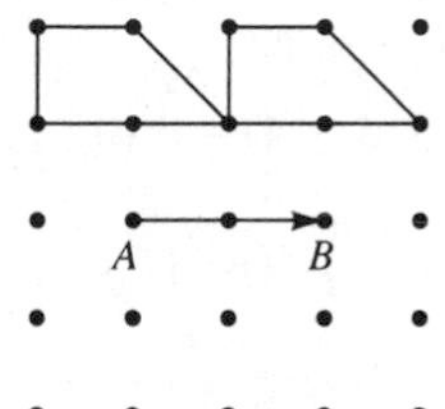

(b) Each corner of the trapezoid moves two dots down diagonally:

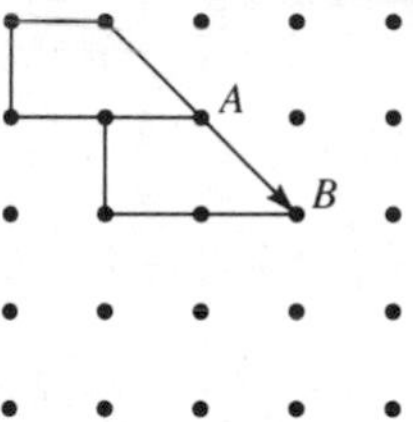

2. Reverse the translation so that the image completes a slide from X′ to X (to what is called its pre-image). Then check by carrying out the given motion in the "forward" direction; i.e., see if $\overline{AB}$ goes to $\overline{A'B'}$.

(a)

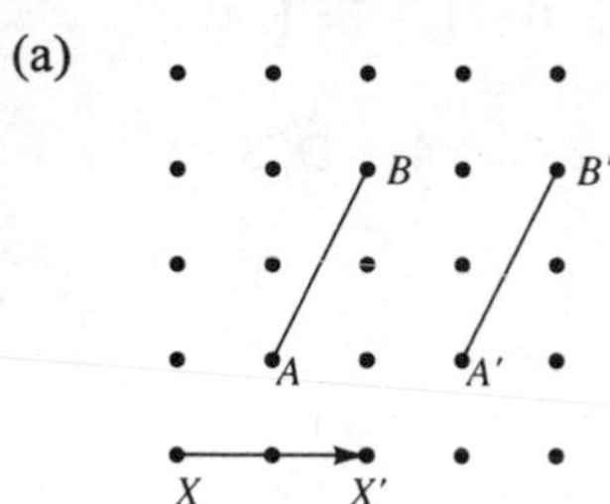

(b)

3. 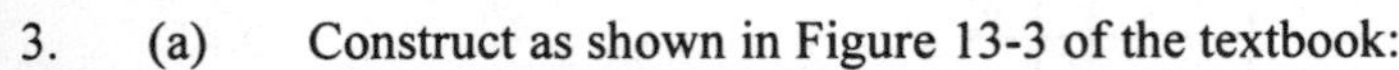
(a) Construct as shown in Figure 13-3 of the textbook:

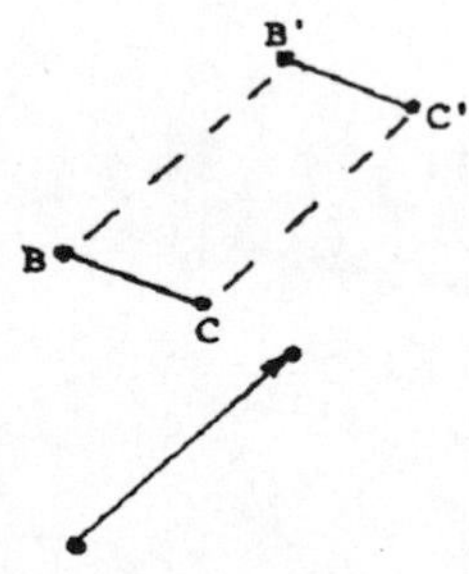

(b) Move the original figure along the slide line as shown:

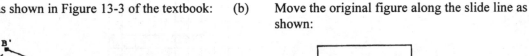

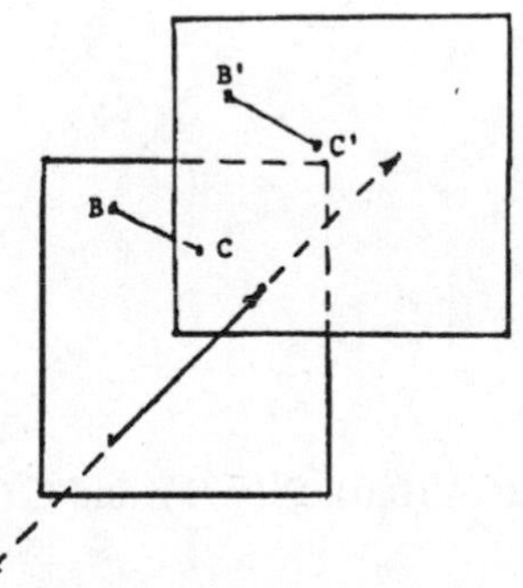

4. (a) $(0, 0) \to (0 + 3, 0 - 4) = (3, {}^-4)$ (b) $({}^-3, 4) \to ({}^-3 + 3, 4 - 4) = (0, 0)$

(c) $({}^-6, {}^-9) \to ({}^-6 + 3, {}^-9 - 4) = ({}^-3, {}^-13)$ (d) $(7, 14) \to (7 + 3, 14 - 4) = (10, 10)$

5. To go from an image to the coordinates of the original points, reverse the signs of the translations: [that is, $(x', y') \to (x' + 3, y' - 4) = (x, y)$]

(a) $(0, 0) \to (0 + 3, 0 - 4) = (3, {}^-4)$ (b) $({}^-3, 4) \to ({}^-3 + 3, 4 - 4) = (0, 0)$

(c) $({}^-6, {}^-9) \to ({}^-6 + 3, {}^-9 - 4) = ({}^-3, {}^-13)$ (d) $(7, 14) \to (7 + 3, 14 - 4) = (10, 10)$

6. (a) (*i*) $A({}^-4, 2) \to ({}^-4 + 3, 2 - 4) = A'({}^-1, {}^-2)$ (*ii*) $B({}^-2, 2) \to ({}^-2 + 3, 2 - 4) = B'(1, {}^-2)$

(*iii*) $C(0, 0) \to (0 + 3, 0 - 4) = C'(3, {}^-4)$ (*iv*) $D({}^-2, 0) \to ({}^-2 + 3, 0 - 4) = D'(1, {}^-4)$

6. (b) (*i*) $A(^-1, 1) \rightarrow (^-1 + 3, 1 - 4) = A'(2, ^-3)$ (*ii*) $B(1, 4) \rightarrow (1 + 3, 4 - 4) = B'(4, 0)$

(*iii*) $C(3, ^-1) \rightarrow (3 + 3, ^-1 - 4) = C'(6, ^-5)$

(c) (*i*) $A(^-2, 3) \rightarrow (^-2 + 3, 3 - 4) = A'(1, ^-1)$ (*ii*) $B(^-2, 1) \rightarrow (^-2 + 3, 1 - 4) = B'(1, ^-3)$

(*iii*) $C(^-2, ^-1) \rightarrow (^-2 + 3, ^-1 - 4) = C'(1, ^-5)$

(d) (*i*) $A(^-4, ^-1) \rightarrow (^-4 + 3, ^-1 - 4) = A'(^-1, ^-5)$ (*ii*) $B(^-3, 3) \rightarrow (^-3 + 3, 3 - 4) = B'(0, ^-1)$

(*iii*) $C(2, 2) \rightarrow (2 + 3, 2 - 4) = C'(5, ^-2)$ (*iv*) $D(1, ^-1) \rightarrow (1 + 3, ^-1 - 4) = D'(4, ^-5)$

7. In each case, $(x', y') \rightarrow (x' - 3, y' + 4) = (x, y)$

(a) Label points $A'(^-1, 0)$, $B'(2, 0)$, $C'(3, ^-3)$, and $D'(0, ^-3)$ $\Rightarrow$

(*i*) $A'(^-1, 0) \rightarrow (^-1 - 3, 0 + 4) = A(^-4, 4)$ (*ii*) $B'(2, 0) \rightarrow (2 - 3, 0 + 4) = B(^-1, 4)$

(*iii*) $C'(3, ^-3) \rightarrow (3 - 3, ^-3 + 4) = C(0, 1)$ (*iv*) $D'(0, ^-3) \rightarrow (0 - 3, ^-3 + 4) = D(^-3, 1)$

The figure whose image was shown is:

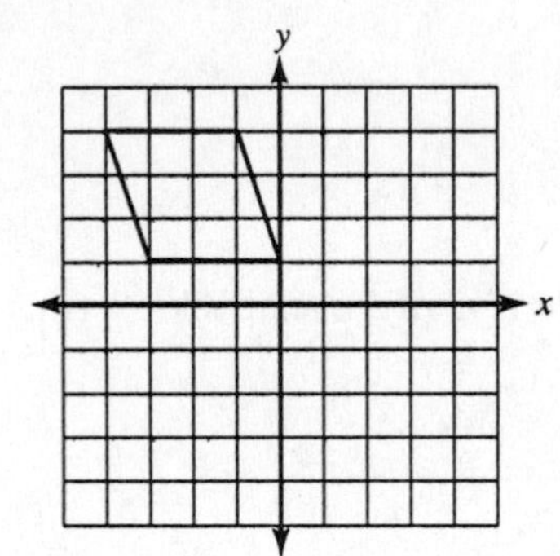

(b) Label points $A'(0,0)$, $B'(5, 1)$, and $C'(3, ^-3)$ $\Rightarrow$

(*i*) $A'(0, 0) \rightarrow (0 - 3, 0 + 4) = A(^-3, 4)$ (*ii*) $B'(5, 1) \rightarrow (5 - 3, 1 + 4) = B(2, 5)$

(*iii*) $C'(3, ^-3) \rightarrow (3 - 3, ^-3 + 4) = C(0, 1)$

The figure whose image was shown is:

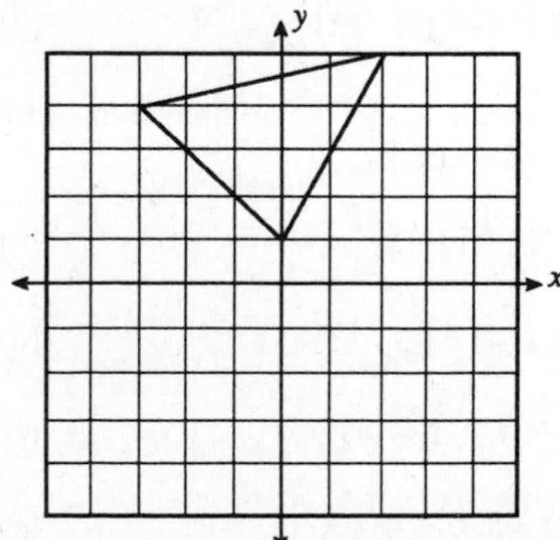

8. Use the technique demonstrated in Example 13-3 of the textbook to obtain:

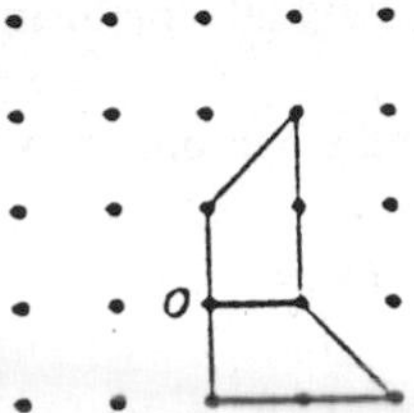

9. See Figure 13-12: Draw circles with center O and radii to each corner of the figures to be rotated; then move clockwise $\alpha°$ to locate the images:

(a)

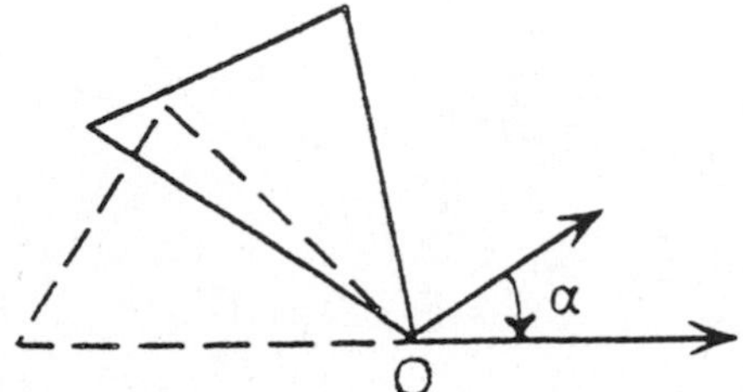

(b)

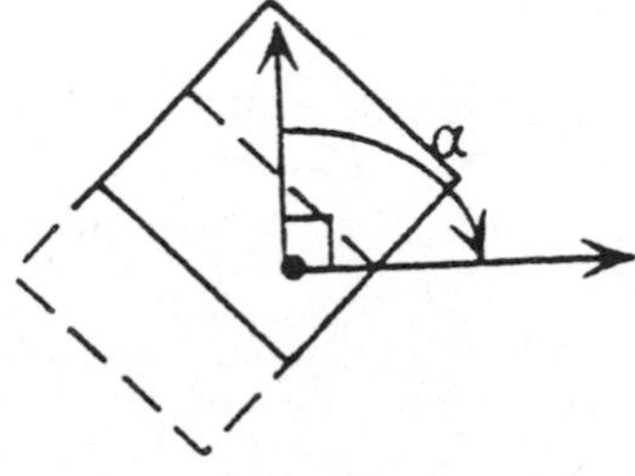

10. Reverse the rotation (to the counterclockwise direction) to locate $\overline{AB}$; i.e., the pre-image:

(a)

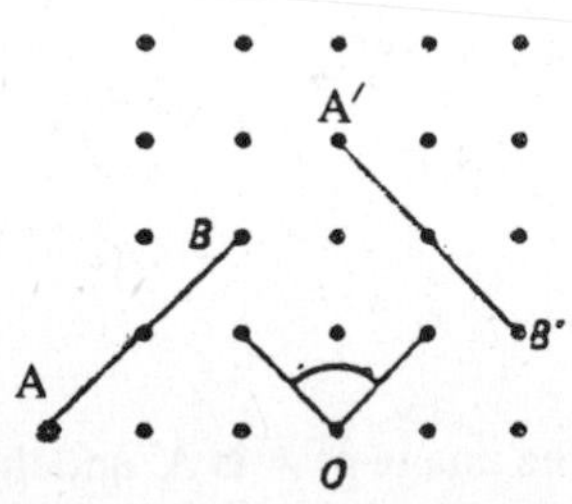

(b)

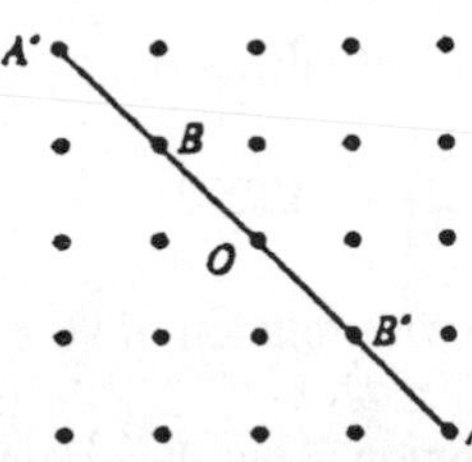

11. (a) Answers may vary, but H, I, N, O, S, X, or Z could appear in such rotational words. Examples include SOS. Variations could use M and W in rotational images; e.g., MOW.

(b) Answers may vary; typewritten numbers 1, 8, 11, 69, 88, 96, 101, 111, 181, 609, 619, 689, 808, 818, 888, 906, 916, 986, 1001, 1111, 1691, 1881, 1961, 6009, 6119, 6699, 6889, 6969, 8008, 8118, 8698, 8888, 8968, 9006, 9116, 9696, 9886, and 9966 demonstrate this property. Digitally displayed numbers such as 2, 5, 22, 55, 121, 151, etc., also may be considered.

12. (a) When the figure is creased and folded along the perpendicular to $\overline{PP'}$, the point P falls on P′ which shows that the perpendicular also bisects $\overline{PP'}$. Alternatively, by the definition of rotation, $\overline{PO} = \overline{PO'}$ which implies that O is equidistant from P and P′ and so is on the perpendicular bisector of $\overline{PP'}$.

(b) From part (a), O is on the perpendicular bisector of $\overline{AA'}$ and $\overline{BB'}$, as well as $\overline{CC'}$. O can therefore be found by determining the point where any two of the perpendicular bisectors intersect. $\angle AOA'$ is the angle of rotation.

13. (a) and (b) Construct a perpendicular to $\overline{OP}$ through O (see Figure 11-28). Measure $\overline{DP}$ and mark it off from O along the perpendicular [to the left for (a); right for (b)]. This locates P′.

(c) Bisect the angle used for (a) (see Figure 11-23), then mark off $\overline{OP}$ along the bisector from O to locate P′.

(d) Make arcs of radius OP from both O and P so that they intersect clockwise from P. The intersection is P′. (This is the construction for an equilateral triangle $\Rightarrow$ 60° angles)

13. (e) Perform (d) in the opposite direction; bisect the angle as in (c).

14. Signs of the x and y coordinates will be reversed under a half-turn about the origin:

(a) $(4, 0) \rightarrow ({}^-4, 0)$

(b) $(0, 3) \rightarrow (0, {}^-3)$

(c) $(2, 4) \rightarrow ({}^-2, {}^-4)$

(d) $({}^-2, 5) \rightarrow (2, {}^-5)$

(e) $({}^-2, {}^-4) \rightarrow (2, 4)$

(f) $(a, b) \rightarrow ({}^-a, {}^-b)$

15. Use a straight-edge and compass, and follow the procedure of Example 13-4. See below:

(a)

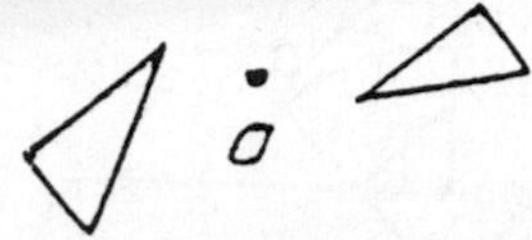

(b)

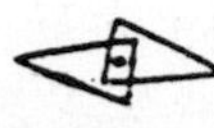

16. (a) $l' = l$

(b) $l' \parallel l$

(c) $l' \perp l$

(d) l′ and l intersect at a 60° angle

17. (a) (*i*) $A(3, 2) \rightarrow A'({}^-2, 3)$

(*ii*) $A({}^-2, 3) \rightarrow A'({}^-3, {}^-2)$

(*iii*) $A(3, {}^-2) \rightarrow A'(2. 3)$

(b) Counterclockwise rotation of 90°: $(a, b) \rightarrow ({}^-b, a)$

(c) Under the rotation about the origin counterclockwise by a right angle, the image of A is A′ and the image of B is B′, as shown below. $A'B' = AB$ and $\overline{OB'} = \overline{OB} \Rightarrow \overline{OB'} = a$ and $\overline{A'B'} = b$. A is in the first quadrant $\Rightarrow$ A′ is in the second quadrant $\Rightarrow$ the coordinates of A′ are $({}^-b, a)$. A similar argument holds if A is in any quadrant.

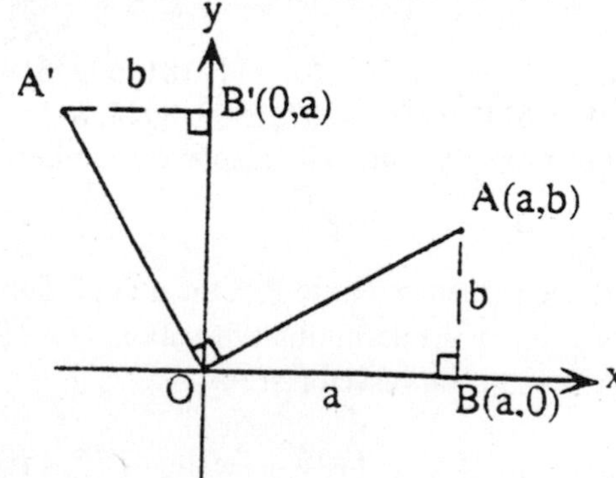

18. (a) Complete as indicated

(b) A rotation in the direction of the larger of α and β, having their difference as magnitude

(c) No

(d) Yes, as in (b)

19. Perform a half-turn of m about P (place points x and y on m; draw $\overrightarrow{xP}$ and $\overrightarrow{yP}$, then locate x′ and y′ with x′P = xP and y′P = yP) to locate m′. The intersection of m' and l locates A. Draw $\overrightarrow{AP}$ to locate B on m.

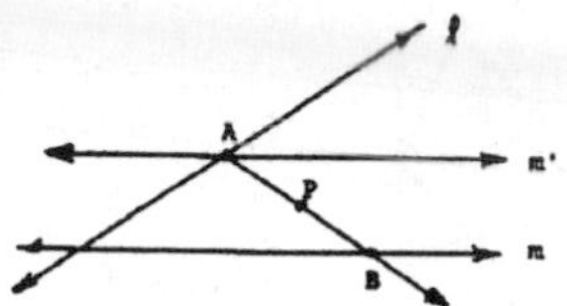

20. Answers may vary. One method is to draw a segment from the top of Rainbow Park to some point B on Shady Lane. Bisect this and perform a half-turn about the midpoint of the bottom of Rainbow Park, calling it the image A. $\overline{AB}$ is a road of proper direction and length which must be moved so that it meets Sunny Street. Locate the proper position by constructing a parallel to Shady Lane through A. Call the point at which it intersects Sunny Street A'. Then translate $\overline{AB} \rightarrow \overline{A'B'}$; this is the desired location.

21. (a) Execute the program

(b)
```
TO SLIDE :DIRECTION :DISTANCE :SIDE
  EQUILATERAL :SIDE
  SETHEADING :DIRECTION
  FORWARD :DISTANCE
  PENDOWN
  SETHEADING 0
  EQUILATERAL :SIDE
END

TO EQUILATERAL :SIDE
  REPEAT 3 [FORWARD :SIDE RIGHT 120]
END
```

22.
```
TO ROTATE :A :SIDE
  SQUARE :SIDE
  RIGHT :A
  SQUARE :SIDE
END

TO SQUARE :SIDE
  REPEAT 4 [FORWARD :SIDE RIGHT 90]
END
```

23. (a)
```
TO TURN.CIRCLE :A
  CIRCLE
  LEFT :A
  CIRCLE
END

TO CIRCLE
  REPEAT 360 [FORWARD 1 RT 1]
END
```

To produce the desired transformation, execute TURN.CIRCLE 180

(b) To produce the desired transformation, execute TURN.CIRCLE 90

1. Locate the image of vertices directly across (perpendicular to) *l* on the geoboard:

(a)

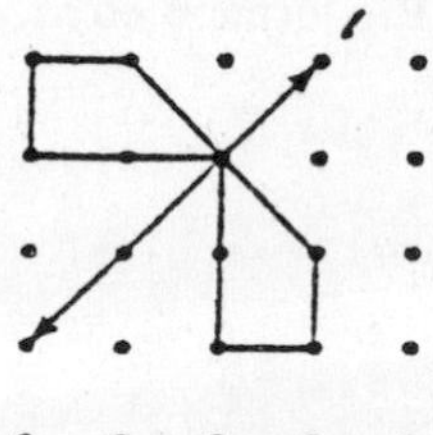

(b)

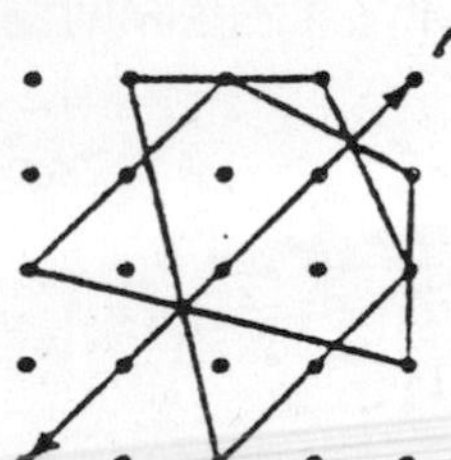

2. Methods will vary; the image should be:

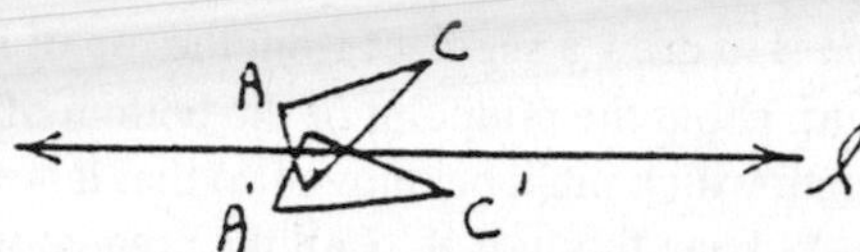

3. Find the image of the center of the circle; measure the radius of the given circle and use it to construct the image circle.

4. Reflecting lines are described for each:

(a) All diameters (infinitely many)

(b) Perpendicular bisector and line containing the segment

(c) Line containing the ray

(d) Perpendicular bisectors of sides and lines containing diagonals

(e) Perpendicular bisectors of pairs of parallel sides

(f) None

(g) Perpendicular bisector of the side that is not congruent to the other two

(h) Perpendicular bisectors of each of the sides

(i) None

(j) Perpendicular bisector of parallel sides

(k) Perpendicular bisector of the chord connecting the endpoints of the arc

(l) The diagonal determined by vertices of the noncongruent angles

(m) The diagonals

(n) Perpendicular bisectors of parallel sides and diameters (three) determined by vertices on circumscribed circle

(o) Same as (n) for even n; for odd n the perpendicular bisectors of all sides (in either case, there will be n reflecting lines in all)

5. The original figure is reflected back upon itself

6. (a) The final images will be congruent but in different locations

6. (b) A translation determined by a slide arrow from P to R. (Let P be any point on l and Q on m such that PQ $\perp$ l. Point R is on $\overline{PQ}$ such that $\overline{PQ} = \overline{QR}$.)

7. (a)

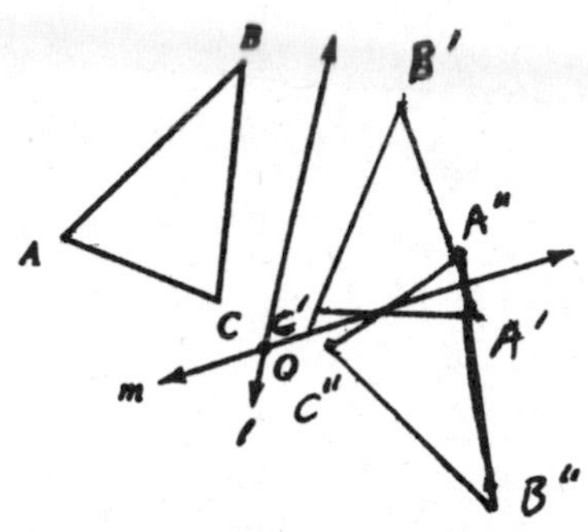

(b) A rotation about O through an angle 2α, where α is the measure of the angle between l and m in the direction from l to m as shown (confirmed by using tracing paper)

(c) A half-turn about O

8. Construct as suggested (results will be unchanged)

9. (a) Examples may vary but include MOM, WOW, TOOT, HAH

(b) (*i*) Examples include BOX, HIKE, CODE, OBOE, etc

(*ii*) The letters B, C, D, E, H, I, K (depending on construction), O, and X may be used

(c) 1, 8, 11, 88, 101, 181, 808, 818, 888, 1001, 1111, 1881

10. (a) For glide reflections with the translation parallel to the reflection line, the images are the same regardless of order

(b) Reflections and translations are commutative only for the conditions described in (a)

11. None of the images has a reverse orientation, so there are no reflections or glide reflections involved. Thus:
1 to 2 is a counterclockwise rotation.
1 to 3 is a clockwise rotation.
1 to 4 is a translation down.
1 to 5 is a rotation (with an exterior point as the center of rotation).
1 to 6 is a translation (sides are parallel to 1).
1 to 7 is a translation (sides are parallel).

12. Reflect A about road 1 to locate A′, and B about road 2 to locate B′. Align A′ and B′ to locate P and Q. (An extension of the problem illustrated in Figure 13-33.) Reflecting A and B creates the straight-line (i.e., shortest) path $\overline{A'B'}$, which by construction is equal to the distance (AP + PQ + QB) for the actual roads.

13. Reflect B over the x-axis to obtain B′ $\Rightarrow$ the line $\overline{AB'}$ is the shortest distance between the two points and so is the same distance as AC + CB

(a) $B' = (10, {}^-1)$; from $(0, 4)$ to $(10, {}^-1)$ $\Rightarrow$ $d = \sqrt{(10-0)^2 + ({}^-1-4)^2} = \sqrt{125} = 5\sqrt{5} \doteq 11.2$

(b) $B' = (5, {}^-2)$; from $({}^-2, 6)$ to $(5, {}^-2)$ $\Rightarrow$ $d = \sqrt{(5-{}^-2)^2 + ({}^-2-6)^2} = \sqrt{113} \doteq 10.6$

14. (a) When reflecting across the x-axis, $P(x, y) \to P'(x, {}^-y)$

(*i*) $A(3, 4) \to A'(3, {}^-4)$ (*ii*) $B(2, {}^-6) \to B'(2, 6)$

(*iii*) $C({}^-2, 5) \to C'({}^-2, {}^-5)$

(b) When reflecting across the y-axis, $P(x, y) \to P'({}^-x, y)$

(*i*) $A(3, 4) \to A'({}^-3, 4)$ (*ii*) $B(2, {}^-6) \to B'({}^-2, {}^-6)$

(*iii*) $C({}^-2, 5) \to C'(2, 5)$

(c) When reflecting across the line $y = x$, $P(x, y) \to P'(y, x)$

(*i*) $A(3, 4) \to A'(4, 3)$. (*ii*) $B(2, {}^-6) \to B'({}^-6, 2)$

(*iii*) $C({}^-2, 5) \to C'(5, {}^-2)$

(d) When reflecting across the line $y = {}^-x$, $P(x, y) \to P'({}^-y, {}^-x)$

(*i*) $A(3, 4) \to A'({}^-4, {}^-3)$ (*ii*) $B(2, {}^-6) \to B'(6, {}^-2)$

(*iii*) $C({}^-2, 5) \to C'({}^-5, 2)$

15. (a) (*i*) $(x, y) \to (x, {}^-y)$ under reflection in the x-axis (*ii*) $(x, y) \to ({}^-x, y)$ under reflection in the y-axis

(*iii*) $(x, y) \to (y, x)$ under reflection in the line $y = x$

(*iv*) $(x, y) \to ({}^-y, {}^-x)$ under reflection in the line $y = {}^-x$

(b) $({}^-x, {}^-y)$ [the first reflection yields $(x, y) \to (x, {}^-y)$; the next gives $(x, {}^-y) \to ({}^-x, {}^-y) = P''$]
This result is a half-turn about the origin

On-going Assessment 13-2; Review Problems

25. (*i*) 360° rotation ⇒ all letters

(*ii*) 180° rotation ⇒ H, I, N, O, S, Z (no other rotations result in the original letter)

26. H, I, N, O, S, Z

27. A half-turn about the center of the letter O

28. (a) A rotation of any angle about the center of the circle will transform the circle into itself

(b) Reflections about lines containing diameters

29. (a) Rectangle (b) Area = area of $\triangle ABC$

(c) (*i*) A half-turn preserves angle measure ⇒ right angles at P′ and Q′ ⇒ PP′Q′Q is a rectangle

29. (c) (*ii*) $\triangle$ABC and rectangle PP′Q′Q both contain pentagon MANQP
$\triangle$CMP $\simeq$ $\triangle$AMP′ and $\triangle$AQ′N $\simeq$ $\triangle$BQN $\Rightarrow$ each triangle has the same area
Area $\triangle$ABC = Area ($\triangle$CMP + $\triangle$AQ′N + pentagon MANQP)

(*iii*) So the areas are equal

30. Construct $\overline{BE} \perp \overline{AD}$; translate $\triangle$ABE horizontally the length BC (its image is $\triangle$DCE′) $\Rightarrow$ the rectangle BEE′C will be created; its area is equal to that of parallelogram ABCD

On-going Assessment 13-3

1. (a) Slide the small triangle down three units (translation), then complete a size transformation with scale factor 2 (since the larger triangle has sides twice as long) using the top right vertex as the center

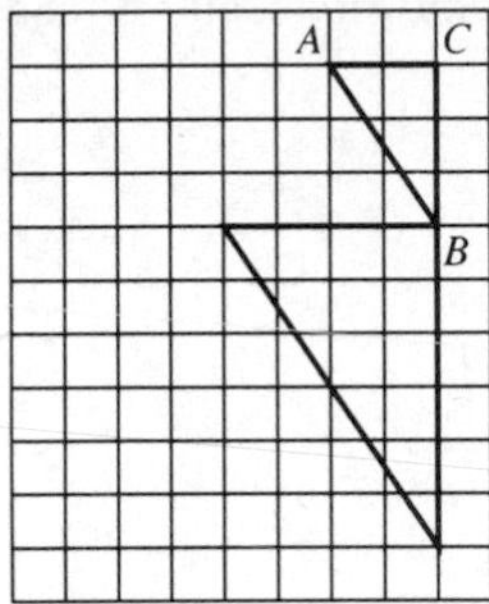

(b) Slide right 5, up 1, then complete the size transformation as in (a)

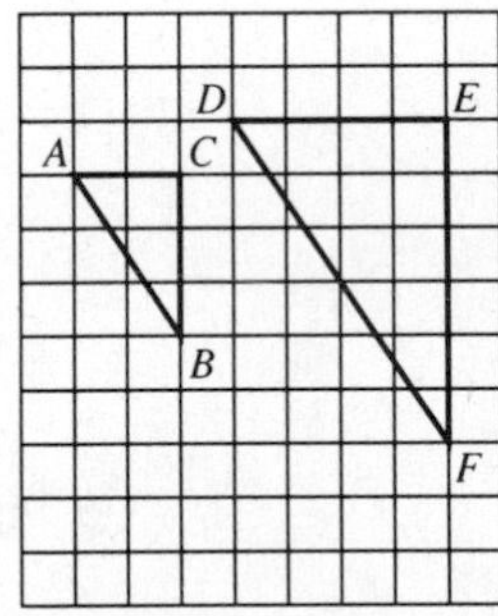

(c) Rotate 90° counterclockwise with the lower right vertex of the small triangle as the center of rotation. Then size transformation with scale factor 2 using the same point as center.

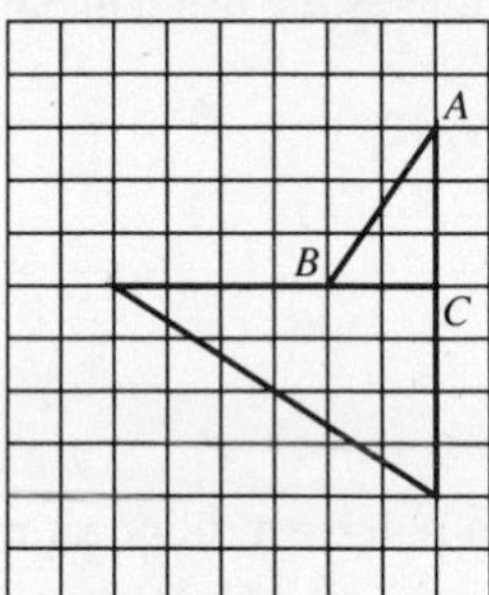

2. Vertices A′, B′, and C′ will be half the distance from O as vertices A, B, and C, respectively:

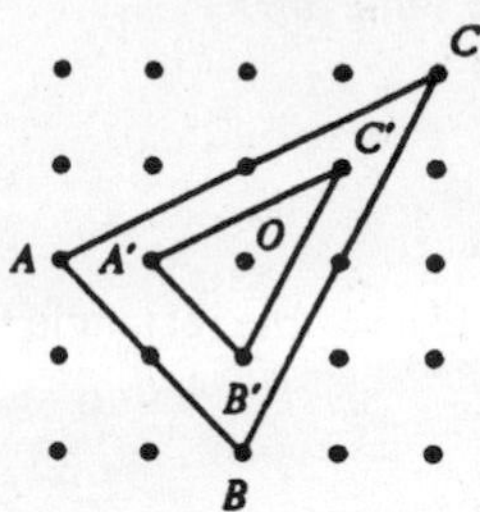

3. (a) Translation taking B to B′ followed by a size transformation with center B′ (and scale factor 2)

(b) Rotate 90° counterclockwise using center B, translate to take B to B′, then a size translation with scale factor $\frac{1}{2}$

(c) Half-turn with the midpoint of $\overline{AA'}$ as center, followed by a size transformation with center A′ and scale factor $\frac{1}{2}$

(d) Half-turn about C followed by a size transformation with center C and scale factor $\frac{3}{2}$

4. (a) Scale factor $= \frac{4}{10} = \frac{2}{5} \Rightarrow x = \frac{2}{5}(15) = 6;\ y = \frac{2}{5}(13) = 5\frac{1}{5}$

(b) Scale factor $= \frac{7}{15} \Rightarrow x = \frac{7}{15}(14) = \frac{98}{15} = 6\frac{8}{15}$; $y = 6 \div \frac{7}{15} = \frac{90}{7} = 12\frac{6}{7}$

5. (a) The triangles are similar

(b) The triangles have a scale factor of $\frac{60\text{ mm}}{7\text{ m}} = \frac{60\text{ mm}}{700\text{ mm}} = \frac{3}{350}$

Object $\times \frac{3}{350} = 35$ mm $\Rightarrow$ Object $= 35 \div \left(\frac{3}{350}\right) = 4083$ mm $= 4.083$ m

(c) Scale factor would be $\frac{35\text{ mm}}{14{,}000\text{ mm}} = \frac{1}{400}$

Focal length must be $\frac{1}{400} \cdot 7000$ mm $= 17.5$ mm

6. (a) Scale factor $= \frac{9}{3} = 3 \Rightarrow x = 3 \cdot 4 = 12;\ y = 3 \cdot 5 - 5 = 10$

(b) Scale factor $= \frac{10}{3} \Rightarrow x + 5 = \frac{10}{3}x \Rightarrow x = \frac{15}{7}; y + 4 = \frac{10}{3}y \Rightarrow y = \frac{12}{7}$

7. (a) Each image must be three times as far horizontally and vertically from the origin as the original points:

(*i*) A(2, 3) → A′(6, 9) (*ii*) B(3, 4) → B′(9, 12)

(*iii*) C($^-2$, 3) → C′($^-6$, 9)

(b) (x, y) → (rx, ry)

8. Size transformation with center O and scale factor $= \frac{1}{r}$ (equivalent to using division to reverse multiplication)

17. (a) A translation determined by slide arrow NM (N to M)

(b) A counter-clockwise rotation of 75° about O

(c) A clockwise rotation of 45° about A

(d) A reflection about m and translation $\overrightarrow{BA}$ (if the translation is not parallel to the reflection line, the translation from B to A and reflection about m must be performed in the opposite order from the original)

(e) A second reflection in line n

18. (a) (4, 3) reflects about m to (4, 1); (4, 1) reflects about n to (2, 1)

(b) (0, 1) → (0, 3) → (6, 3)

(c) (⁻1, 0) → (⁻1, 4) → (7, 4)

(d) (0, 0) → (0, 4) → (6, 4)

On-going Assessment 13-4

1. (a) (*i*) Yes (A geometrical figure has line symmetry if it is its own image under a reflection in some line. A line may be drawn through the center circle, either horizontally or vertically, about which the figure is its own image. The line may also be drawn through any of the sets of arrows.)

(*ii*) Yes (the figure will match the original figure after rotations of 90°, 180°, or 270°)

(*iii*) Yes (any figure having 180° rotational symmetry has point symmetry about the turn center)

(b) (*i*) Yes (a vertical line through the middle of the bulb is a line of symmetry)

(*ii*) No (the figure will not match the original under rotations of less than 360 °)

(*iii*) No (the figure does not have 180° rotational symmetry)

(c) (*i*) Yes (a vertical line through the stem is a line of symmetry)

(*ii*) No

(*iii*) No

(d) (*i*) Yes (a horizontal line through the middle of the plane is a line of symmetry)

(*ii*) No

(*iii*) No

2. Answers may vary, but some possibilites are:

(a) The Yellow Pages symbol (see 6b)

(b) A regular pentagon (Chrysler symbol)

(c) The letter N

3. Reflect the given portions about l:

(a)

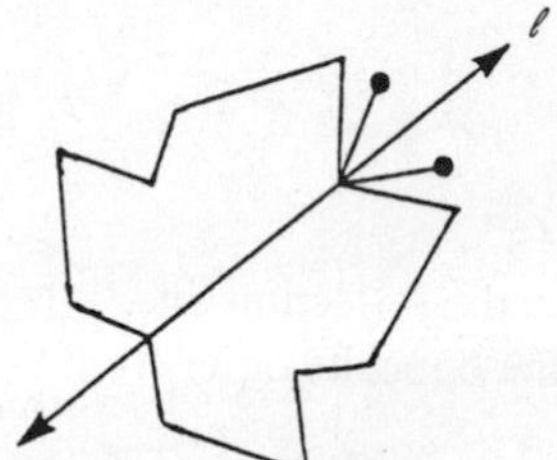

(b)

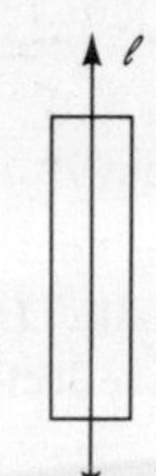

4. (a) (*i*) Switzerland has four lines of symmetry (the diagonals and horizontal or vertical lines through the center)

(*ii*) South Korea has no lines of symmetry

(*iii*) Israel has two lines of symmetry (horizontally and vertically through the center)

(*iv*) Barbados has one line of symmetry (vertically through the center)

(b) (*i*)

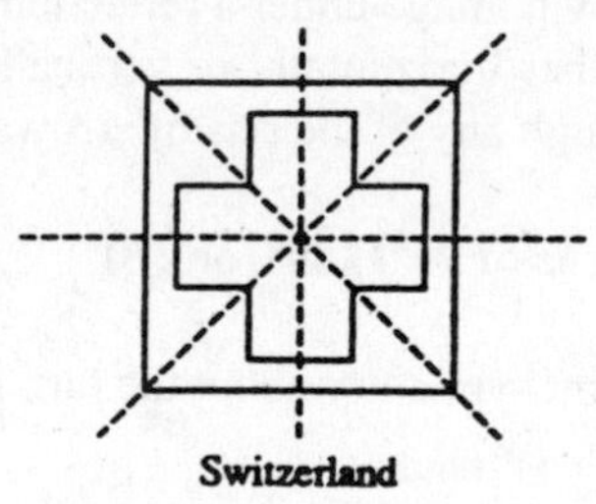

Switzerland

(*iii*)

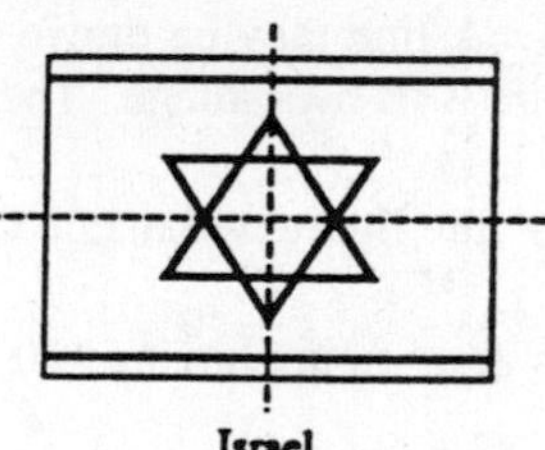

Israel

(*iv*)

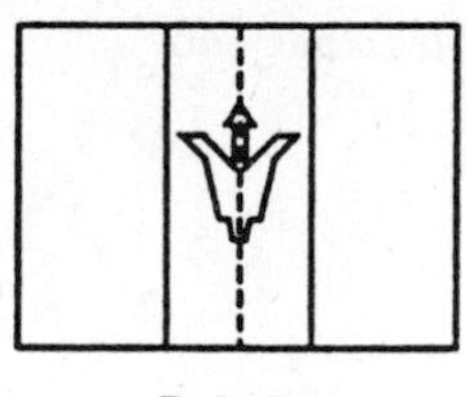

Barbados

5. (a) 6 (three through the vertices; three midway between vertices)

(b) Yes (60° symmetry about the center)

6. (a) One line of symmetry (vertically through the center)

(b) One (vertically through the center)

(c) None

(d) Five (one through each vertex and its opposite face)

7. (a) A half turn will yield point symmetry

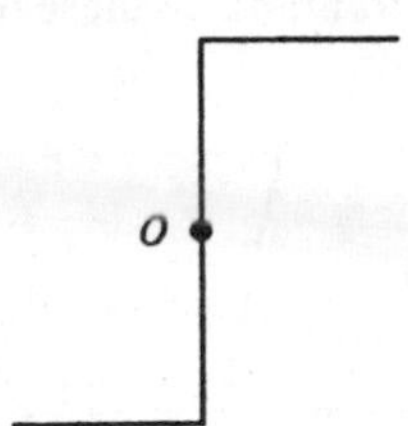

(b) The shape must be the same each 60°

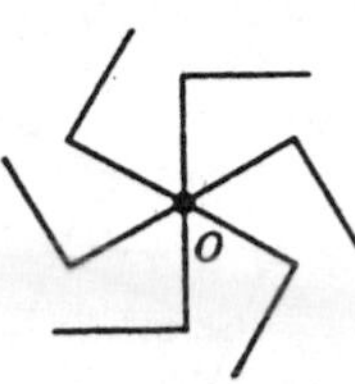

8. (a) Seven (three through the "peaks", three through the "valleys", and one perpendicular to the others through the width of the figure)

   (b) Two (one through the middle "peak" and one through the width)

   (c) Seven (three through the vertices, three through the faces, and one perpendicular to the others through the width of the figure)

   (d) 33 (16 through the peaks, 16 through the valleys, and one through the width)

9.
```
TO TURN.SYM :S :N :A
 REPEAT :N [SQUARE :S RIGHT :A]
END

TO SQUARE :S
 REPEAT 4 [FORWARD :S RIGHT 90]
END
```

   (a) Execute TURN.SYM 50 6 60

   (b) Execute TURN.SYM 50 3 120

   (c) Execute TURN.SYM 50 2 180

   (d) Execute TURN.SYM 50 3 240

   (e) Execute TURN.SYM 50 6 300

10.
```
TO TURN.SY :S :N :A
 REPEAT :N [EQTRI :S RIGHT :A]
END

TO EQUITRI :S
 REPEAT 3 [FORWARD :S RIGHT 120]
END
```

   (a) Execute TURN.SY 50 6 60

   (b) Execute TURN.SY 50 3 120

   (c) Execute TURN.SY 50 3 240

   (d) Execute TURN.SY 50 6 300

On-going Assessment 13-4; Review Problems

18. (a), (b), and (c): One method is to trace over the figure heavily, then fold at *l* and trace along the figure (as seen through the paper), copying the image with a "carbon paper" process

19. (a), (b), and (c): Map the vertices perpendicularly across *l* and then connect them (i.e., construct a perpendicular to *l* through each vertex and locate the image of the vertex along this line)

1. (a) Forming rectangles will tessellate the plane:

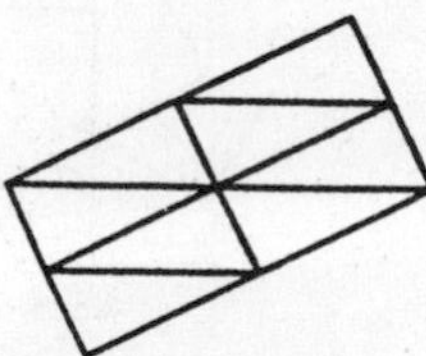

(b) Rotate the trapezoid 180° and place to form a parallelogram; place these together to cover the plane:

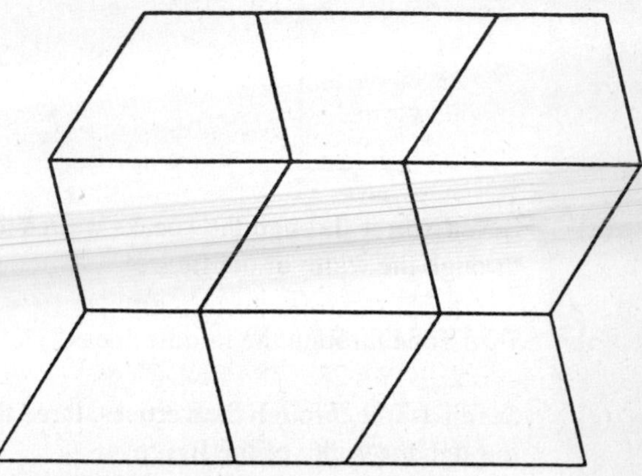

2. (a) Perform half-turns about the midpoints of all sides

(b) Yes (If a polygon tessellates the plane, the sum of the angles around every vertex must be 360°. Successive 180° turns of a quadrilateral about the midpoints of its sides will produce four congruent quadrilaterals around a common vertex, with each of the quadrilateral's angles being represented at each vertex. These angles must add to 360°, as do angles of any quadrilateral.)

3. Experimentation by cutting shapes out and moving them about is one way to learn about these types of problems.

(a)

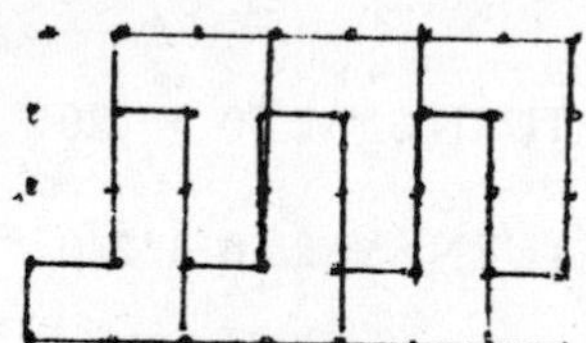

(b) Cannot be tessellated

(c)

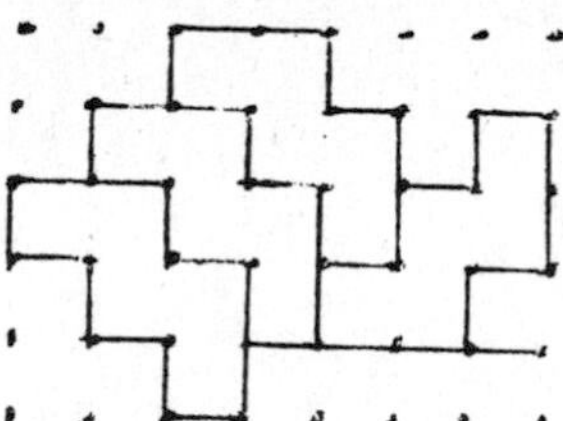

(d) Tessellate as in (a)

4. Answers may vary

(a) Use hexagons and triangles sized as in the figure, and squares with sides equal to the sum of the hexagon and triangle side. Shapes can be mixed, or a row of squares can be placed between hexagon/triangle rows.

(b) Place a square on every other side of an octogon; nest octogons in the gaps

5. (a) The dual is another tessellation of squares (congruent to those given)

(b) A tessellation of equilateral triangles

(c) The tessellation of equilateral triangles illustrated in the statement of the problem

6. (a)
```
TO TESSELSQUARE
 PENUP BACK 70 PENDOWN
 REPEAT 9 [SQUARE 20 FORWARD 20]
 PENUP BACK 180 RIGHT 90
 FORWARD 20 LEFT 90 PENDOWN
 REPEAT 9 [SQUARE 20 FORWARD 20]
END

TO SQUARE :SIDE
 REPEAT 4 [FORWARD :SIDE RIGHT 90]
END
```

(b)
```
TO TESSELTRI
 PENUP BACK 70 PENDOWN
 REPEAT 9 [TRIANGLE 20 FORWARD 20]
 PENUP BACK 180 RIGHT 60
 FORWARD 20 LEFT 60 PENDOWN
 REPEAT 9 [TRIANGLE 20 FORWARD 20]
END

TO TRIANGLE :SIDE
 REPEAT 3 [FORWARD :SIDE RIGHT 120]
END
```

(c)
```
TO TESSELHEX
 PENUP BACK 70 LEFT 90 PENDOWN
 REPEAT 4 [HEXAGON 20 RIGHT 120 FORWARD 20 LEFT 60 HEXAGON 20
  FORWARD 20 LEFT 60]
END

TO HEXAGON :SIDE
 REPEAT 6 [FORWARD :SIDE RIGHT 60]
END
```

7.
```
TO TILESTRIP :S
 REPEAT 4 [TILE :S PENUP RIGHT 180 FORWARD 3*:S PENDOWN]
END

TO TILE :S
 RIGHT 180
 REPEAT 3 [REPEAT 4 [FORWARD :S LEFT 60] RIGHT 120]
END
```

1. (a)

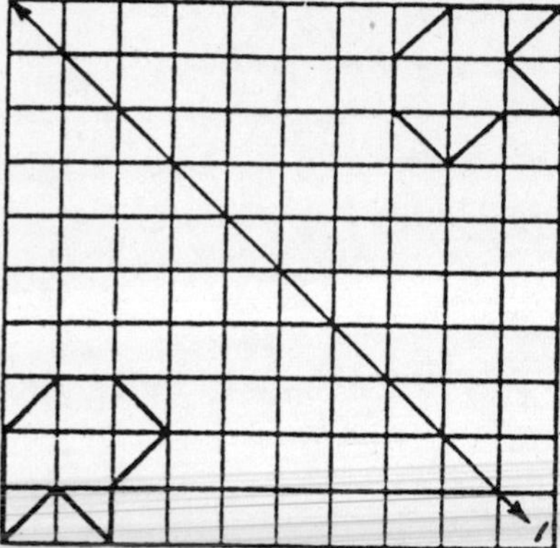

(b)

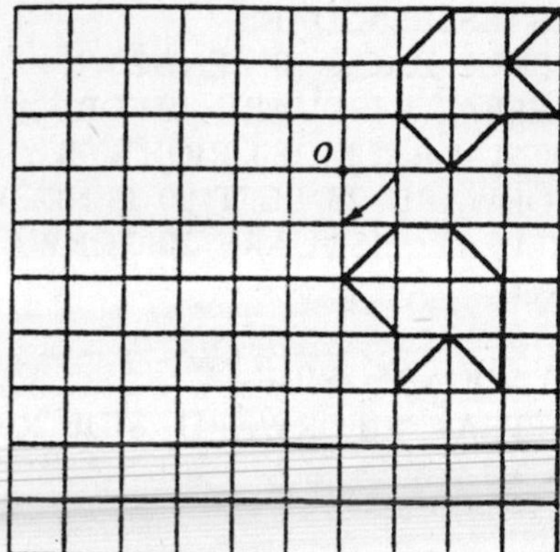

(c)

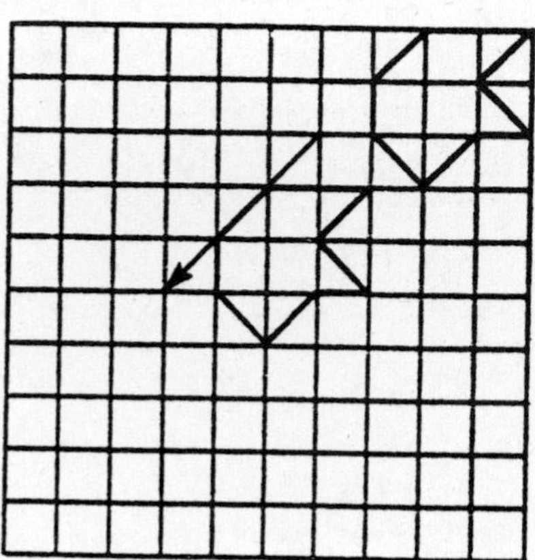

2. Construct as specified:

(a)

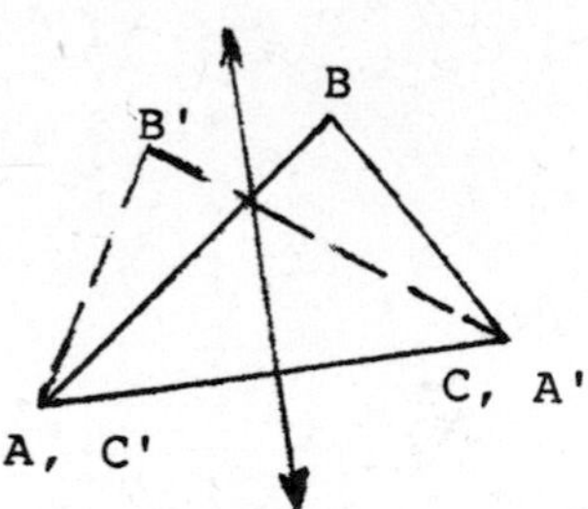

(b)

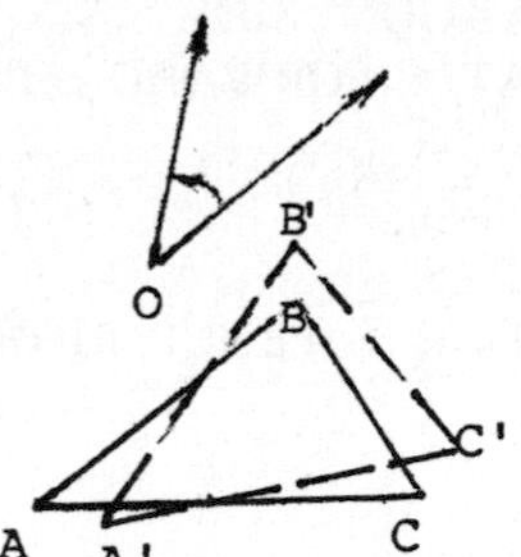

(c)

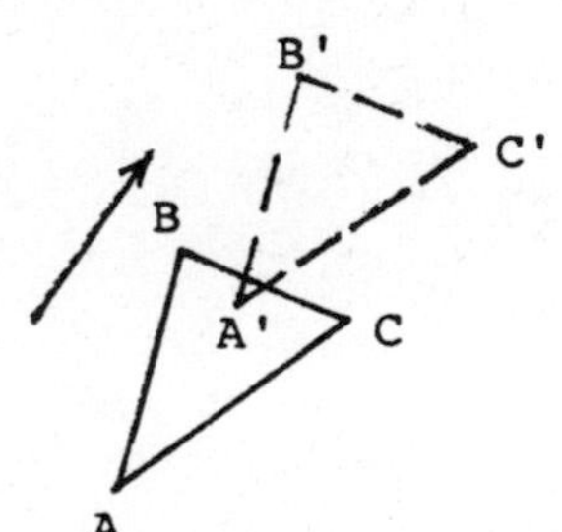

3. (a) Four (two diagonals, one horizontal and one vertical)

(b) One (the diameter bisecting the central angle)

(c) One (the bisector of the point angle)

(d) None